SCHAUM'S OUTLINE OF

MODERN ELEMENTARY ALGEBRA

•

by

BARNETT RICH, Ph.D.

SCHAUM'S OUTLINE SERIES

McGRAW-HILL BOOK COMPANY

New York, St. Louis, San Francisco, Düsseldorf, Johannesburg, Kuala Lumpur, London, Mexico, Montreal, New Delhi, Panama, Rio de Janeiro, Singapore, Sydney, and Toronto

Copyright © 1973 by McGraw-Hill, Inc. All rights reserved. Printed in the
United States of America. No part of this publication may be reproduced,
stored in a retrieval system, or transmitted, in any form or by any means,
electronic, mechanical, photocopying, recording, or otherwise, without the
prior written permission of the publisher.

07-052247-2

13 14 15 SH SH 8 7 6 5 4 3 2 1

Preface

Modern Elementary Algebra presents a modern course in elementary algebra including a review of arithmetic. Each unit of work included in the text is fully in accord with first courses in algebra throughout the United States. Emphasis is upon broad, basic, and unifying algebraic concepts and principles: sets of numbers, the precise use of language, the laws and structure of algebra, and the justification of its operations and procedures. A major objective of the text is to show how teaching algebra from a modern point of view requires the combining of the "how" and the "why." In today's world, topics such as sets, coordinates, number systems, graphs of one and two dimensions, equations, inequalities, and absolute values have acquired special importance. Because of their significance, the reader will find these topics are treated in depth.

Above all else, this book is intended *to provide maximum help for students and maximum service for teachers.*

PROVIDING HELP FOR STUDENTS

The learning of algebra is of crucial importance. Without a solid foundation in algebra, all subsequent work in mathematics is seriously impaired. This book has been designed to improve the learning of algebra far beyond the typical and traditional book in the subject. Those who need help in algebra will find this text most useful for these reasons:

(1) **Learning Each Rule, Formula, and Principle.** Each important rule, formula, and principle is stated in simple language, is made to stand out in distinctive bold type, and is applied to one or more sets of solved problems.

(2) **Learning Each Procedure.** Each algebraic procedure is developed step-by-step, with each step immediately applied to problems alongside of the procedure.

(3) **Learning Each Set of Solved Problems.** Each set of solved problems is used to clarify and illustrate a rule or principle. The particular character of each such set is indicated by a title. *There are more than* **3000** *carefully selected and fully solved problems.*

(4) **Learning Each Set of Supplementary Problems.** Each set of supplementary problems provides further application of a rule or principle. A guide number with each such set refers a student needing help to the related set of solved problems. *There are over* **3500** *supplementary problems.* Each of these contains its required answer and, where needed, further aids to solution.

(5) **Understanding Each Chapter.** Understanding is emphasized throughout the book. Introductory units in each chapter are used for this purpose. These units clarify the underlying ideas of the chapter which are essential for such understanding.

(6) **Enriching the Learning of Algebra.** The work of students can be considerably enriched by the challenging materials and problems contained in this text. These enrichment materials look ahead to the 10th and 11th years of mathematics and substantially enlarge the scope of the standard traditional course of study in algebra.

(7) **Accelerating the Learning of Algebra.** A willing, capable student will be enabled to accelerate the algebra course and, through the use of this text, accomplish the work of the standard course of study in much less time.

PROVIDING SERVICE FOR TEACHERS

Teachers of algebra will find this text most useful for these reasons:

(1) Teaching Each Chapter. Each chapter has a central unifying theme. Each chapter is divided into two to fifteen major units which support the central theme of the chapter. In turn, these units or chapter divisions are arranged in a graded sequence for greater teaching effectiveness.

(2) Teaching Each Unit. Each of the chapter divisions is a master lesson. Each such unit contains the materials needed for the full teaching development of those principles and procedures which are related to the unit.

(3) Teaching Sets of Solved Problems. Using this text, the teacher and the class can completely cover many more solved problems. In so doing, the class will gain greater understanding of the way in which each principle applies in many varied situations. In order that lesson development may proceed from the simple to the more difficult, the solved problems have been carefully graded from one set to another and also within sets. Furthermore, the text seeks to present the best solution or solutions of each problem. Where more than one method of solution is equally valuable, each such method is included. These methods have been selected on the basis of the author's extensive practical classroom experience.

(4) Preparing Homework Assignments. The preparation of homework assignments is facilitated because the supplementary problems are related to the sets of solved problems. It is suggested that in class the underlying principle and the major steps used in solving problems be given greatest attention. At home, students can complete the solved problems and then proceed to do those supplementary problems which are related to the solved ones.

OTHERS WHO WILL FIND THIS TEXT ADVANTAGEOUS

The text can be used most profitably by many others besides students and teachers. In this group are included (1) the parents of algebra students who wish to refer their children to the wealth of self-study materials available in the text, or who may wish to refresh their own memory of algebra in order to help their children directly; (2) the supervisor who seeks to accelerate select groups or to provide enrichment materials to supplement an algebra course of study; (3) the person who seeks to review algebra quickly and effectively; and (4) the person who seeks to learn algebra through independent study.

The author acknowledges his deep gratitude to Mr. Henry Hayden for the artistry, arrangement, and typographical design of each page of the book. These have added immeasurably to the effective presentation of its content.

BARNETT RICH

New York City
February 1973

CONTENTS

CONTENTS

CONTENTS

Chapter 1

From Arithmetic to Algebra

1. SIMPLE RELATIONS AMONG NUMBERS, SETS, OPERATIONS, AND VARIABLES

Fundamental Operations on Numbers

In this chapter, we are going to lead you from arithmetic to algebra. Underlying algebra as well as arithmetic are the four fundamental operations:

1. ADDITION (sum)
2. SUBTRACTION (difference)
3. MULTIPLICATION (product)
4. DIVISION (quotient)

The answer for each operation is the word enclosed in parentheses. The answer in subtraction may also be called the remainder.

Using Numerals to Name Numbers

A numeral is a number-name. Thus, 5, V, and /X/ are names of the number 5 in the same way that the word "pen" is the name of the actual writing instrument. A number is an idea while the numeral that stands for the number is only the name of the idea. The following eight sentences are assertions about numbers but what you see in the sentences are the numerals that name the numbers.

Sentences and Statements

The following two columns contain eight sentences or assertions; four of them are true and the other four false. A sentence that is definitely true is a true statement while a sentence that is definitely false is a false statement.

True Statements	False Statements
1. The sum of 5 and 3 is 8.	1. The sum of 5 and 3 is 10.
2. The product of 4 and 5 is 20.	2. The product of 4 and 5 is 25.
3. If 6 is subtracted from 10, the difference is 4.	3. If 6 is subtracted from 10, the difference is 2.
4. If 24 is divided by 3, the quotient is 8.	4. If 24 is divided by 3, the quotient is 6.

An **open sentence** is a sentence that is neither a true statement nor a false statement.

Thus, "The sum of a number and 4 is 10" is an open sentence which cannot be characterized either as a true statement or as a false statement.

Numerical Expressions

A **numerical expression** may be formed to name a number by combining numerals and symbols of operation. The number named is the **value** of the numerical expression.

Thus, $8 + 4$, $15 - 3$, 6×2, and $\dfrac{25 - 1}{2}$ are numerical expressions whose value is 12.

To **evaluate** an expression is to find the value of the expression.

Thus, to evaluate $\dfrac{20 + 4}{3}$, we find its value, which is 8.

Equal expressions are those having the same value while **unequal expressions** do not have the same value. The symbol of equality is "$=$" while the symbol of inequality is "$\neq$".

Thus, "$8 + 4 = 10 + 2$" and "$6 + 4 \neq 10 + 3$" are true statements. However, "$8 + 4 \neq 10 + 2$" and "$6 + 4 = 10 + 5$" are false statements.

Substitution Principle: In any process, a numerical expression may be substituted for any equal numerical expression.

Thus, by applying the substitution principle to $n = \frac{20 + 4}{3 - 1}$, we first obtain $n = \frac{24}{2}$; then we obtain $n = 12$.

Conjunctions and Disjunctions

A **conjunction** of statements is formed when statements are joined using the word **and** while a **disjunction** of statements is formed when the word **or** joins the statements.

A conjunction is true only if **each** of the joined statements is true.

Thus, the conjunction "2 + 1 = 3 and 5 − 4 = 1" is true since "2 + 1 = 3" is true and "5 − 4 = 1" is also true.

A disjunction is true if **at least one** of the joined statements is true.

Thus, the disjunction "2 + 1 = 3 or 5 − 4 = 9" is a true statement since "2 + 1 = 3" is true even though "5 − 4 = 9" is false.

Specifying Sets of Numbers: Finite Sets and the Empty Set

A **set of numbers** can be specified if its **members** or **elements** can be identified. If the numbers in a set are identified as 1, 3, 5, 7 and 9, the set can be specified by listing the numerals for the numbers within braces, { }, and using a capital letter to represent the set, thus: $A = \{1, 3, 5, 7, 9\}$. Such a listing is called a **roster**.

The symbol ε means "is a member of" or "belongs to" while the symbol $\notin$ means "is **not a** member of" or "does **not** belong to".

Thus, if $B = \{1, 2, 3, 4, 5\}$, then $3 \varepsilon B$ and $8 \notin B$.

A set may also be specified by using a **description** or **rule**.

Thus, $B = \{$ first five counting numbers $\}$ describes the set $\{1, 2, 3, 4, 5\}$.

Sets A and B specified previously are **finite sets** having a limited number of members. A finite set may have only one member and mathematicians find it helpful to speak of a set that has no members, such as the set of counting numbers between 2 and 3. A set having no members is called the **empty set** or the **null set**. There can be but one empty set and the symbol $\emptyset$ is used to denote it.

Hence, $\emptyset = \{$counting numbers between 2 and 3$\} = \{\ \}$

A finite set which has large number of members may be specified by roster using three dots, ... Thus, if C is the set of three-digit counting numbers, then

$$C = \{100, 101, 102, \ldots, 997, 998, 999\}$$

Read the three dots, "and so on through". It is understood that the missing numerals follow the same pattern as the ones that are shown.

A set may also be specified using **set-builder notation**. For example, if $B = \{1, 2, 3, 4, 5\}$, then B may be specified in set-builder notation as $B = \{x: x < 6,\ x$ is a counting number$\}$, read, "B is the set of all x such that x is less than 6 and x is a counting number". The colon is read, "such that". Instead of a colon, a vertical bar may be used.

Thus, the set $\{2, 4, 6, 8\}$ may be written in set-builder notation as

$$\{x \mid x \text{ is a single-digit even counting number}\}.$$

Sets of Natural Numbers and Whole Numbers: Infinite Sets

Originally, number meant one of the counting numbers: 1, 2, 3, 4, 5, ... The three dots are read, "and so on". In this case, the pattern continues without end. Another name for a counting number is **natural number** due to the fact that counting was done by people on fingers given to them by nature.

Since there is no last natural number, the set of natural numbers is an **infinite set**.

Using N to represent the set of natural numbers:

$N = \{1, 2, 3, 4, \ldots\}$ or $N = \{\text{natural numbers}\}$ or $N = \{x: x \text{ is a natural number}\}$.

The set of **whole numbers** includes the natural numbers and also zero, 0. Zero is not a natural number. The set of whole numbers is an infinite set since there is no last whole number.

Using W to represent the set of whole numbers:

$W = \{0, 1, 2, 3, \ldots\}$ or $W = \{\text{whole numbers}\}$ or $W = \{x: x \text{ is a whole number}\}$.

The set of whole numbers may be divided or partitioned into two subsets, the set of odd whole numbers and the set of even whole numbers:

1. The set of odd whole numbers $= \{1, 3, 5, 7, \ldots\}$
2. The set of even whole numbers $= \{0, 2, 4, 6, \ldots\}$

Note that each even whole number is divisible by 2 while each odd whole number is not.

The **successor** of a whole number is the next greater whole number.

Thus, the successor of 145 is 146. The successor of an odd whole number must be an even whole number while the successor of an even whole number must be an odd whole number.

A **digit** of a whole number is any one of the numerals in the number.

Thus, the number 145 has three digits, 1, 4, and 5.

Equivalent and Equal Sets: One-to-One Correspondence Between Sets

Equivalent sets are sets having the same number of members while **equal sets** are sets having exactly the same members. The members of a set may be arranged in any order.

Thus, $\{1, 2, 3\}$ and $\{3, 1, 2\}$ are equal sets but $\{1, 2, 3\}$ and $\{10, 11, 12\}$ are equivalent sets. We may write $\{1, 2, 3 = \{3, 1, 2\}$.

A **one-to-one correspondence** between two equivalent sets is a pairing of their elements so that **one and only one** member of one of the sets is assigned to each member of the other set.

Thus, a one-to-one correspondence may be set up by pairing the fingers of the left hand with the fingers of the right hand. Fig. (a) shows how a one-to-one correspondence may be set up between the set of sides of a triangle and the set of the first three natural numbers.

The following pairing shows how a one-to-one correspondence can be set up between the members of two infinite sets:

Fig. (a)

$$\{\text{doubles of natural numbers}\} = \{2 \quad 4 \quad 6 \quad 8 \quad 10 \quad \ldots\}$$
$$\updownarrow \quad \updownarrow \quad \updownarrow \quad \updownarrow \quad \updownarrow$$
$$\{\text{natural numbers}\} \qquad = \{1 \quad 2 \quad 3 \quad 4 \quad 5 \quad \ldots\}$$

A one-to-one correspondence of the greatest importance in mathematics is the correspondence that exists between the set of points on a line and the set of real numbers — to be discussed in a later chapter.

Variables and Constants

A **variable** is a letter or other symbol which may represent any number in a specified set of numbers. The set represented by the variable is called the **replacement set** or the **domain** of the variable.

Thus, if x represents 1, 10, or any other whole number, then x is a variable and the set of whole numbers is the replacement set or domain of x. Numbers such as 1 and 10 that may be replaced are the **values** of the variable.

A **constant** is a letter or other symbol that represents only one number. For example, 5 and π are constants. If a variable represents a set having a single member such as $\{5\}$, then the variable may be regarded as a constant.

A **variable expression** is an expression that contains a variable. A variable expression is also called a **variable phrase**, an **open expression**, or an **open phrase**.

Thus, if n is a variable, then $7n$, $n + 7$, $\frac{1}{2}n - 5$, and $\frac{3n + 1}{5n + 1}$ are variable expressions.

In the following set of verbal statements and algebraic equations, note how variable expressions may be used to replace lengthy verbal statements:

Verbal Statements	Algebraic Equations
1. Seven times a number reduced by the same number equals six times the number.	*1.* $7n - n = 6n$
2. The sum of twice a number and three times the same number equals five times that number.	*2.* $2n + 3n = 5n$
3. The perimeter of a square equals four times the length of one of its sides.	*3.* $p = 4s$

In the first example, "$7n$" is used to replace "seven times a number". When multiplying a variable by a constant, the multiplication sign may be omitted. Multiplication may also be indicated by using a multiplication sign, a raised dot, or parentheses.

Thus, "seven times a number" may be shown by $7 \times n$, $7 \cdot n$, $7(n)$, or simply $7n$.

Omitting the multiplication sign, as in $7n$, is the preferred method of indicating multiplication. However, the multiplication sign may not be omitted when showing the multiplication of two numbers.

Thus, "seven times four" may be written as 7×4, $7 \cdot 4$, or $7(4)$, but never as 74.

To **evaluate** a variable expression is to find its value for given values of the variable.

Thus, using the replacement set $\{1, 2, 5, 10\}$ as the set of given values of x, the set of values of the expression $2x + 1$ is $\{3, 5, 11, 21\}$. Note the one-to-one correspondence of the two sets:

$$\{1 \quad\quad 2 \quad\quad 5 \quad\quad 10\}$$
$$\downarrow \quad\quad\quad \downarrow \quad\quad\quad \downarrow \quad\quad\quad \downarrow$$
$$\{3 \quad\quad 5 \quad\quad 11 \quad\quad 21\}$$

A **formula** is an equation in which a variable is expressed in terms of other variables.

Thus, $p = 4s$ is a formula in which the variable p is expressed in terms of the variable s.

The **truth set** or **solution set** of an open sentence is the set of values in the replacement set of the variable for which the open sentence is true.

Thus, the truth set or solution set of $y + 2 = 5$ is $\{3\}$ if the replacement set of y is the set of natural numbers.

Properties of 0 and 1: Additive Identity and Multiplicative Identity

If the domain of the variable n is the set of whole numbers, then each of the following important properties of 0 and 1 are true statements. In later work, these properties will be extended to apply to any "real number".

Properties of 0 and 1

Verbal Statements	Algebraic Statements
1. **Multiplicative Property of Zero** If any number is multiplied by 0, the product is 0. Thus, $1357 \times 0 = 0$.	*1.* $n \cdot 0 = 0$
2. **Additive Property of Zero** If 0 is added to any number, the sum is the number. Thus, $1357 + 0 = 1357$. Because identically the same number remains when 0 is added to it, 0 is called the **additive identity**.	*2.* $n + 0 = n$
3. **Multiplicative Property of One** If any number is multiplied by 1, the product is the number. Thus, $1357 \times 1 = 1357$. Because identically the same number remains when it is multiplied by 1, 1 is called the **multiplicative identity**.	*3.* $n \cdot 1 = n$

1.1 Numerals and Numbers

In each, state whether the sentence refers to numerals or to numbers:

a) The digits of 23 are 2 and 3,   *c*) 23 is less than 32,   *e*) 32 is 2 more
b) 23 is the sum of 20 and 3,   *d*) Both 23 and 32 combine 2 and 3,   than 30.

Ans. Sentences *a*) and *d*) refer to numerals. Sentences *b*), *c*) and *e*) refer to the numbers named by the numerals.

1.2 Open Sentences, True and False Statements

State whether each is a true statement, a false statement, or an open sentence:

a) $1 + 1 = 2 \times 1$ *Ans.* true statement since $2 = 2$.
b) $10 \times 1 \neq 10 + 1$ *Ans.* true statement since 10 does not equal 11.
c) $25 + 0 = 25 \times 1$ *Ans.* true statement since 25 equals 25.
d) $15 + 5 = 5 + 15$ *Ans.* true statement since $20 = 20$.
e) The sum of 150 and 0 is 150   *Ans.* true statement since $150 = 150$.
f) The sum of a whole number and 0 is the number   *Ans.* true statement since it applies the additive property of 0.
g) The sum of a whole number and 4 is 4   *Ans.* open sentence, true for 0 but false for any other whole number.
h) The product of 150 and 1 is 151   *Ans.* false statement since 150 does not equal 151.
i) If 3 is subtracted from 20, the difference is the same as when 20 is subtracted from 3
  Ans. false statement since 17 is the first difference and -17 is the second difference. If only natural numbers are permitted, then 20 cannot be subtracted from 3.
j) The product of 8 and 4 is the same as the product of 4 and 8   *Ans.* true statement since $32 = 32$.
k) If 8 is divided by 4, the quotient is the same as when 4 is divided by 8.   *Ans.* false statement since the first quotient is 2 and the second quotient is $\frac{1}{2}$.

1.3 Listing Sets by Roster

List each set by roster:

a) the set of natural numbers less than 4   *Ans.* {1, 2, 3}
b) the set of odd whole numbers greater than 1 and less than 10   *Ans.* {3, 5, 7, 9}
c) the set of successors of the members of {4, 5, 6}   *Ans.* {5, 6, 7}
d) the set of whole numbers represented by $2n$ if n represents the set {1, 3, 5}   *Ans.* {2, 6, 10}
e) the set of natural numbers represented by $x - 5$ if x represents the set {5, 10, 15}
  Ans. {5, 10} (Do not include 0 since 0 is not a natural number.)
f) the set of successors of x if $x + 3$ represents the set {10, 20, 30}   *Ans.* {8, 18, 28}
  (The set represented by x is {7, 17, 27}.)
g) the set of missing numbers in the set {1, 3, 5, ..., 17, 19, 21}   *Ans.* {7, 9, 11, 13, 15}
h) the set of missing numbers in the set {1, 2, 3, ..., 47, 48, 49}
  Ans. {4, 5, 6, ..., 44, 45, 46}

1.4 Members of the Sets of Whole Numbers and Natural Numbers

Write each number using digits:

a) the least natural number having two digits
b) the greatest natural number having three digits
c) the greatest of all whole numbers
d) the successor of one thousand
e) one thousand ten
f) one million one hundred
g) one billion, one thousand, one
h) one trillion one hundred

Ans. a) 10
  b) 999
  c) there is no greatest whole number
  d) 1001
  e) 1010
  f) 1,000,100
  g) 1,000,001,001
  h) 1,000,000,000,100

1.5 Relating Sets and Members of Sets

State whether each statement is true or false with reference to the indicated sets:

$A = \{1, 3, 5, 7\}, \quad B = \{2, 4, 6\}, \quad C = \{0\}, \quad D = \emptyset, \quad E = \{6, 2, 4\}, \quad F = \{\frac{1}{4}, \frac{1}{2}, 1\}$

a) A and B are equal sets.   e) $6 \in B$ i) $\frac{1}{4} \in F$ or $\frac{1}{2} \in E$

b) B and E are equal sets.   f) $\frac{1}{2} \notin F$ j) A and F can be put into a

c) B and F are equal sets.   g) $1 \in A$ and $0 \in C$ one-to-one correspondence.

d) C is the empty set.   h) $\frac{1}{4} \in F$ and $\frac{1}{2} \in E$ k) E and F can be put into a
         one-to-one correspondence.

Ans.

a) False since A and B do not have the same number of members.

b) True since B and E have exactly the same members.

c) False, B and F are equivalent but not equal.

d) False, since C has one member, 0. (The empty set is D.)

e) True since 6 belongs to B.

f) False since $\frac{1}{2}$ does belong to F.

g) True since both of the joined statements of the conjunction are true.

h) False since only one of the joined statements of the conjunction is true.

i) True since a disjunction is true if at least one of the joined statements is true.

j) False since three members of one set cannot be paired separately with four members of the other.

k) True. Note the following one-to-one correspondence.

$$E = \{6 \quad 2 \quad 4\}$$
$$F = \{\tfrac{1}{4} \quad \tfrac{1}{2} \quad 1\}$$

1.6 Simplifying a Variable Expression Involving Multiplication

State each product without multiplication signs:

a) $7 \times y$ Ans. $7y$ d) $10 \times r \times s$ Ans. $10rs$ g) $\frac{1}{2} \times 8 \times n$ Ans. $4n$

b) $3 \times 5 \times a$ Ans. $15a$ e) $b \times c \times d$ Ans. bcd h) $.07 \times p \times q \times t$ Ans. $.07pqt$

c) $l \times w$ Ans. lw f) $7 \times 11 \times h \times k$ Ans. $77hk$

1.7 Replacing a Verbal Statement by an Algebraic Equation

Using variable expressions, replace each verbal statement by an algebraic equation:

a) If six times a number is reduced by the same number, the result must be five times the number.

b) The sum of twice a number, three times the same number and four times the same number is equivalent to nine times the number.

c) Increasing a number by itself and 20 is the same as doubling the number and adding 20.

Ans. a) $6n - n = 5n$ b) $2n + 3n + 4n = 9n$ c) $n + n + 20 = 2n + 20$.

1.8 Replacing a Verbal Rule by a Formula

Using the initial letters of words as variables, replace each verbal rule by a formula:

a) The perimeter of a square is four times a side.

b) The perimeter of a rectangle is twice the length added to twice the width.

c) The area of a rectangle is the product of its length and width.

d) The selling price of an article is the sum of its cost and its profit.

Ans. a) $p = 4s$,   b) $p = 2l + 2w$,   c) $A = lw$,   d) $s = c + p$

1.9 Replacement Set or the Domain of a Variable

If $A = \{1, 2, 3, 4, 5, 6, 7, 8, 9\}$ is the replacement set of the variable n, state the truth or solution set of each sentence:

a) $n + 3 = 10$ e) $n + 10 = 10 + n$ i) $2n = n + 5$

b) n is greater than 7.   f) $n - 8 = 8 - n$ j) $2n \neq n + 5$

c) n is an even number.   g) $0 \cdot n = n$ k) $\{n : n \text{ is at least } 7\}$

d) $n \cdot n = 25$ h) $0 \cdot n = 0$ l) $\{n : n \text{ is no more than } 4\}$

Ans. a) $\{7\}$, b) $\{8, 9\}$, c) $\{2, 4, 6, 8\}$, d) $\{5\}$, e) A (true for all members of set A), f) 8, g) $\emptyset$
     since 0 is not in A, h) A (true for all members of set A), i) $\{5\}$, j) $\{1, 2, 3, 4, 6, 7, 8, 9\}$
     Note that 5 is not a member of the solution set, k) $\{7, 8, 9\}$, l) $\{1, 2, 3, 4\}$

1.10 Properties of 0 and 1

Evaluate each numerical expression and state the property of 0 or 1 that applies:

a) $123,000 \times 0$ d) $1 + 0$ g) $3 \times 4 \times 0$

b) $123,000 \times 1$ e) 1×0 h) $3 \times 4 \times 1$

c) $123,000 + 0$ f) 1×1

Ans. a) 0   d) 1   g) 0

b) 123,000   e) 0   h) 12

c) 123,000   f) 1

The multiplicative property of 0 applies to (a), (e), and (g); the additive property of 0 applies to (c), and (d); the multiplicative property of 1 applies to (b), (e), (f), and (h).

2. INTERCHANGING NUMBERS IN ADDITION: COMMUTATIVE LAW OF ADDITION

Addends are numbers being added. Their sum is the answer obtained.

Thus, in $5 + 3 = 8$, the addends are 5 and 3. Their sum is 8.

Numerical addends are numbers used as addends.

Thus, in $3 + 4 + 6 = 13$; 3, 4 and 6 are numerical addends.

Literal addends are variables which represent numbers being added.

Thus, in $a + b = 8$, a and b are literal addends.

Commutative Law of Addition: Interchanging addends does not change their sum.

Thus, $2 + 3 = 3 + 2$ and $3 + 4 + 6 = 4 + 6 + 3$.

In general, $a + b = b + a$ and $b + c + a = a + b + c$.

Interchanging addends may be used

(*1*) **to simplify addition.**

Thus, $25 + 82 + 75$ by interchanging becomes $25 + 75 + 82$.

The sum is $100 + 82 = 182$.

(*2*) **to check addition.**

Thus, numbers may be added downwards and checked upwards:

```
   add down        check up
       148            148  ↑
       357            357  |
       762            762  |
      ----           ----
      1267           1267
```

(*3*) **to rearrange addends in a preferred order.**

Thus, $b + c + a$ becomes $a + b + c$ if the literal addends are to be arranged alphabetically. Also, $3 + x$ becomes $x + 3$ if the literal addend is to precede the numerical addend.

2.1 Applying Commutative Law of Addition: Interchanging Addends to Simplify Addition

Simplify each addition by interchanging addends:

a) $20 + 73 + 280$ c) $\frac{3}{4} + 2\frac{1}{2} + 1\frac{1}{4}$ e) $1.95 + 2.65 + .05 + .35$

b) $42 + 113 + 58$ d) $1\frac{1}{2} + 2\frac{2}{7} + \frac{1}{2} + \frac{1}{7}$ f) $9.4 + 18.7 + 1.3 + .6$

Ans. a) $20 + 280 + 73$ c) $\frac{3}{4} + 1\frac{1}{4} + 2\frac{1}{2}$ e) $1.95 + .05 + 2.65 + .35$

$300 + 73 = 373$ $2 + 2\frac{1}{2} = 4\frac{1}{2}$ $2 + 3 = 5$

b) $42 + 58 + 113$ d) $1\frac{1}{2} + \frac{1}{2} + 2\frac{2}{7} + \frac{1}{7}$ f) $9.4 + .6 + 18.7 + 1.3$

$100 + 113 = 213$ $2 + 2\frac{3}{7} = 4\frac{3}{7}$ $10 + 20 = 30$

2.2 Applying Commutative Law of Addition: Rearranging Addends to Obtain a Preferred Order

Rearrange the addends so that literal addends are arranged alphabetically and precede numerical addends:

$a)\ 3 + b$	$c)\ d + 10 + e$	$e)\ 15 + x + 10$	$g)\ w + y + x$
$b)\ c + a$	$d)\ c + 12 + b$	$f)\ 20 + s + r$	$h)\ b + 8 + c + a$

Ans. $a)\ b + 3$	$c)\ d + e + 10$	$e)\ x + 25$	$g)\ w + x + y$
$b)\ a + c$	$d)\ b + c + 12$	$f)\ r + s + 20$	$h)\ a + b + c + 8$

3. INTERCHANGING NUMBERS IN MULTIPLICATION: COMMUTATIVE LAW OF MULTIPLICATION

Factors are numbers being multiplied. Their product is the answer obtained.

Thus, in $5 \times 3 = 15$, the factors are 5 and 3. Their product is 15.

Numerical factors are numbers used as factors.

Thus, in $2 \times 3 \times 5 = 30$; 2, 3 and 5 are numerical factors.

Literal factors are variables which represent numbers being multiplied.

Thus, in $ab = 20$, a and b are literal factors.

Commutative Law of Multiplication: **Interchanging factors does not change their product.**

Thus, $2 \times 5 = 5 \times 2$ and $2 \times 4 \times 5 = 2 \times 5 \times 4$.

In general, $ab = ba$ and $cba = abc$.

Interchanging factors may be used

(1) **to simplify multiplication.**

Thus, $4 \times 13 \times 25$ by interchanging becomes $4 \times 25 \times 13$.

The product is $100 \times 13 = 1300$.

(2) **to check multiplication.**

Thus, since $24 \times 75 = 75 \times 24$,

24	check: 75
× 75	× 24
120	300
168	150
1800	1800

(3) **to rearrange factors in a preferred order.**

Thus, bca becomes abc if the literal factors are arranged alphabetically. Also, $x3$ becomes $3x$ if the numerical factor is to precede the literal factor.

3.1 Applying Commutative Law of Multiplication: Interchanging Factors to Simplify Multiplication

Simplify each multiplication by interchanging factors:

$a)\ 2 \times 17 \times 5$	$c)\ 7\frac{1}{2} \times 7 \times 4$	$e)\ 1.25 \times 4.4 \times 4 \times 5$
$b)\ 25 \times 19 \times 4 \times 2$	$d)\ 33\frac{1}{3} \times 23 \times 3$	$f)\ .33 \times 225 \times 3\frac{1}{3} \times 4$

Ans. $a)\ 2 \times 5 \times 17$	$c)\ 7\frac{1}{2} \times 4 \times 7$	$e)\ 1.25 \times 4 \times 4.4 \times 5$
$10 \times 17 = 170$	$30 \times 7 = 210$	$5 \times 22 = 110$
$b)\ 25 \times 4 \times 19 \times 2$	$d)\ 33\frac{1}{3} \times 3 \times 23$	$f)\ .33 \times 3\frac{1}{3} \times 225 \times 4$
$100 \times 38 = 3800$	$100 \times 23 = 2300$	$1.1 \times 900 = 990$

3.2 Applying Commutative Law of Multiplication: Rearranging Factors to Obtain a Preferred Order

Rearrange the factors so that literal factors are arranged alphabetically and follow numerical factors:

$a)\ b\,3$ $b)\ c\,a$ $c)\ d\,10\,e$ $d)\ c\,12\,b$ $e)\ 15\,x\,10$ $f)\ 20\,s\,r$ $g)\ w\,y\,x$ $h)\ b\,35\,c\,a$

$Ans.\ a)\ 3\,b$ $b)\ ac$ $c)\ 10\,de$ $d)\ 12\,bc$ $e)\ 150\,x$ $f)\ 20\,rs$ $g)\ wxy$ $h)\ 35\,abc$

4. SYMBOLIZING THE OPERATIONS IN ALGEBRA

The symbols for the fundamental operations are as follows:

1. ADDITION: $+$
2. SUBTRACTION: $-$
3. MULTIPLICATION: $\times$, $(\ )$, $\cdot$, no sign
4. DIVISION: $\div$, $:$, fraction bar

Thus, $n+4$ means "add n and 4". $4\times n$, $4(n)$, $4\cdot n$, $4n$ mean "multiply n and 4".

$n-4$ means "subtract 4 from n". $n\div 4$, $n:4$, $\frac{n}{4}$ mean "divide n by 4".

> **RULE: Division by zero is an impossible operation.**

Thus, $4\div 0$ or $x\div 0$ is impossible.

Hence, $\frac{4}{0}$ or $\frac{x}{0}$ is meaningless.

Also, $\frac{4}{n}$ is meaningless if $n=0$.

Note. When dividing a number a by a number b, we say, "$a\div b$ or $\frac{a}{b}$ cannot be defined if $b=0$."

4.1 Symbols for Multiplication

Symbolize each using multiplication signs:

$a)$ 8 times 11 $c)$ b times c $e)$ 5 multiplied by a and the result divided by b
$b)$ 8 times x $d)$ 8 divided by x $f)$ d divided by the product of 7 and e

$Ans.\ a)$ 8×11, $8\cdot 11$, $8(11)$ or $(8)(11)$ $c)$ $b\cdot c$ or bc (avoid $b\times c$) $e)$ $\frac{5a}{b}$

$b)$ $8\cdot x$ or $8x$ (avoid $8\times x$) $d)$ $\frac{8}{x}$ or $8\div x$ ($\frac{8}{x}$ is preferred) $f)$ $\frac{d}{7e}$

4.2 Division by Zero: Fractions Whose Denominator Has a Single Variable

When is each division impossible? Give a reason for your answer.

$a)\ \frac{5}{a}$ $b)\ \frac{7}{2b}$ $c)\ \frac{2}{c-6}$ $d)\ \frac{10}{3d-9}$ $e)\ \frac{3x}{35-7e}$

$Ans.$ Each answer is underlined. To obtain an impossible division, the denominator must be 0.

$a)$ $\underline{a=0}$.
$b)$ $\underline{b=0}$. Applying the multiplicative property of 0, if $b=0$, then $2b=0$.
$c)$ $\underline{c=6}$. Applying the substitution principle, if $c=6$, then $c-6=6-6=0$.
$d)$ $\underline{d=3}$. Applying the substitution principle, if $d=3$, then $3d-9=3(3)-9=9-9=0$.
$e)$ $\underline{e=5}$. Applying the substitution principle, if $e=5$, then $35-7e=35-7(5)=35-35=0$.

4.3 Division by Zero: Fractions Whose Denominator Has More Than One Variable

When is each division impossible? Give a reason for your answer.

$a)\ \frac{a}{xy}$ $b)\ \frac{3x}{2ab}$ $c)\ \frac{10}{x-y}$ $d)\ \frac{x}{y-2z}$

$Ans.$ Each answer is underlined. To obtain an impossible division, the denominator must be 0.

$a)$ $\underline{x=0\text{ or }y=0}$. Applying the multiplicative property of 0, if $x=0$ or $y=0$, then $xy=0$.
$b)$ $\underline{a=0\text{ or }b=0}$. Applying the multiplicative property of 0, if $a=0$ or $b=0$, then $2ab=0$.
$c)$ $\underline{x=y}$. Applying the substitution principle, if $x=y$, then $x-y=x-x=0$.
$d)$ $\underline{y=2z}$. Applying the substitution principle, if $y=2z$, then $y-2z=y-y=0$.

5. EXPRESSING ADDITION AND SUBTRACTION ALGEBRAICALLY

In algebra, changing verbal expressions into algebraic expressions is of major importance. The operations of addition and subtraction are denoted by words such as the following:

WORDS DENOTING ADDITION		WORDS DENOTING SUBTRACTION	
sum	more than	difference	less than
plus	greater than	minus	smaller than
gain	larger than	lose	fewer than
increase	enlarge	decrease	shorten
rise	grow	drop	depreciate
expand	augment	lower	diminish

The Commutative Law applies to addition but does not apply to subtraction. If one number is subtracted from another number, the numbers may not be interchanged. For example, $a - 3$ equals $3 - a$ only when $a = 3$. In general, $a - b = b - a$ is true only when $a = b$. Hence, we have the following rules:

In adding two numbers, the numbers (addends) may be interchanged.

Thus, "the sum of n and 20" may be represented by $n + 20$ or $20 + n$.

But in subtracting one number from another, the numbers may not be interchanged.

Thus, "a number less 20" may be represented by $n - 20$ but **not** by $20 - n$.

Also, "20 minus a number" may be represented by $20 - n$ but **not** by $n - 20$.

5.1 Expressing Addition Algebraically

If n represents a number, express algebraically:

a) the sum of the number and 7   c) the number increased by 9   e) 20 enlarged by the number
b) the number plus 8   d) 15 plus the number   f) 25 augmented by the number

Ans. a) $n + 7$ or $7 + n$ c) $n + 9$ or $9 + n$ e) $20 + n$ or $n + 20$
b) $n + 8$ or $8 + n$ d) $15 + n$ or $n + 15$ f) $25 + n$ or $n + 25$

5.2 Expressing Subtraction Algebraically

If n represents a number, express algebraically:

a) the difference if the number is
subtracted from 15   Ans. $15 - n$
b) the number diminished by 20   Ans. $n - 20$
c) 25 less than the number   Ans. $n - 25$
d) 25 less the number   Ans. $25 - n$

e) the difference if 15 is subtracted
from the number   Ans. $n - 15$
f) 50 subtracted from the number   Ans. $n - 50$
g) the number subtracted from 50   Ans. $50 - n$
h) the number reduced by 75   Ans. $n - 75$

5.3 Changing Verbal Expressions into Algebraic Expressions

Express algebraically: Ans.

a) the no. of lb of a weight that is 10 lb heavier than w lb   a) $w + 10$
b) the no. of mi in a distance that is 40 mi farther than d mi   b) $d + 40$
c) the no. of degrees in a temperature $50°$ hotter than t degrees   c) $t + 50$
d) the no. of dollars in a price $60 cheaper than p dollars   d) $p - 60$
e) the no. of mph (miles per hour) in a speed 30 mph faster than r mph   e) $r + 30$
f) the no. of ft in a length of l ft expanded 6 ft   f) $l + 6$
g) the no. of oz in a weight that is 10 oz lighter than w oz   g) $w - 10$
h) the no. of yd in a distance that is 120 ft shorter than d yd   h) $d - 40$

6. EXPRESSING MULTIPLICATION AND DIVISION ALGEBRAICALLY

<u>WORDS DENOTING MULTIPLICATION</u>   <u>WORDS DENOTING DIVISION</u>

multiplied by	double	divided by	ratio
times	triple or treble	quotient	half
product	quadruple		
twice	quintuple		

The Commutative Law applies to multiplication but does not apply to division. If one number is divided by another number, the numbers may not be interchanged. For example, $\frac{b}{5} = \frac{5}{b}$ is true only when $b = 5$. In general, $\frac{a}{b} = \frac{b}{a}$ is true only when $a = b$. Hence, we have the following rules:

In multiplying two numbers, the numbers (factors) may be interchanged.

Thus, "the product of n and 10" may be represented by $n10$ or $10n$. The latter is preferred.

But in dividing one number by another, the numbers may not be interchanged.

Thus, "a number divided by 20" may be represented by $\frac{n}{20}$ but not by $\frac{20}{n}$.

Also, "20 divided by a number" may be represented by $\frac{20}{n}$ but not by $\frac{n}{20}$.

6.1 Representing Multiplication or Division

State verbal expressions that may be represented by each of the following:

a) $5x$ b) $\frac{y}{5}$ c) $\frac{5w}{7}$

Ans. a) 1. 5 multiplied by x | b) 1. y divided by 5 | c) 1. five-sevenths of w
     2. 5 times x | 2. quotient of y and 5 | 2. $5w$ divided by 7
     3. product of 5 and x | 3. ratio of y to 5 | 3. quotient of $5w$ and 7
      | 4. one-fifth of y | 4. ratio of $5w$ to 7

6.2 Expressing Division Algebraically

If n represents a number, express algebraically in the form of a fraction:

a) the quotient of the number and 10   c) twice the number divided by 7
b) the ratio of 10 to the number   d) 20 divided by the product of the number and 3

Ans.   a) $\frac{n}{10}$ b) $\frac{10}{n}$ c) $\frac{2n}{7}$ d) $\frac{20}{3n}$

7. EXPRESSING ALGEBRAICALLY EXPRESSIONS INVOLVING TWO OR MORE OPERATIONS

Parentheses ( ) are used to treat an expression as a single number.
Thus, to double the sum of 4 and x, write $2(4+x)$.

7.1 Expressing Algebraically Expressions Involving Two Operations

Express algebraically: *Ans.*
    a) a increased by twice b a) $a + 2b$
    b) twice the sum of a and b b) $2(a+b)$
    c) 30 decreased by three times c c) $30 - 3c$
    d) three times the difference of 30 and c d) $3(30-c)$
    e) 50 minus the product of 10 and p e) $50 - 10p$
    f) the product of 50 and the sum of p and 10 f) $50(p+10)$
    g) 100 increased by the quotient of x and y g) $100 + \frac{x}{y}$
    h) the quotient of x and the sum of y and 100 h) $\frac{x}{y+100}$
    i) the average of s and 20   i) $\frac{s+20}{2}$ or $\frac{1}{2}(s+20)$

7.2 Expressing Algebraically More Difficult Expressions

Express algebraically: *Ans.*

a) half of a, increased by the product of 25 and b a) $\dfrac{a}{2} + 25b$

b) four times c, decreased by one-fifth of d b) $4c - \dfrac{d}{5}$

c) half the sum of m and twice n c) $\dfrac{m + 2n}{2}$ or $\frac{1}{2}(m + 2n)$

d) the average of m, r and 80   d) $\dfrac{m + r + 80}{3}$ or $\frac{1}{3}(m + r + 80)$

e) 60 diminished by one-third the product of 7 and x e) $60 - \dfrac{7x}{3}$

f) twice the sum of e and 30, diminished by 40   f) $2(e + 30) - 40$

g) two-thirds the sum of n and three-sevenths of p g) $\dfrac{2}{3}(n + \dfrac{3p}{7})$

h) the product of a and b, decreased by twice the
difference of c and d h) $ab - 2(c - d)$

i) the quotient of x and 10, minus four times their sum   i) $\dfrac{x}{10} - 4(x + 10)$

7.3 Changing Verbal Expressions into Algebraic Expressions

Express algebraically: *Ans.*

a) a speed in mph that is 30 mph faster than twice another of r mph   a) $2r + 30$

b) a weight in lb that is 20 lb lighter than 3 times another of w lb   b) $3w - 20$

c) a temperature in degrees that is 15° colder than two-thirds another of $t°$ c) $\dfrac{2t}{3} - 15$

d) a price in cents that is 25¢ cheaper than another of D dollars   d) $100D - 25$

e) a length in inches that is 8 in. longer than another of f ft.   e) $12f + 8$

8. ASSOCIATIVE LAWS OF ADDITION AND MULTIPLICATION

Associative Law of Addition
The way in which numbers are added in groups of two does not change their sum.

Thus, the sum, $2 + 3 + 5$, may be found by obtaining **partial sums** in two ways:

(1) Add 2 and 3 to obtain a partial sum of 5, then add 5 and 5;
$$2 + 3 + 5 = (2 + 3) + 5 = 5 + 5 = 10$$

(2) Add 3 and 5 to obtain a partial sum of 8, then add 2 and 8:
$$2 + 3 + 5 = 2 + (3 + 5) = 2 + 8 = 10.$$

Hence, $2 + 3 + 5 = (2 + 3) + 5 = 2 + (3 + 5)$.

In general, $a + b + c = (a + b) + c = a + (b + c)$

Associative Law of Multiplication
The way in which numbers are multiplied in groups of two does not change their product.

Thus, the product, $2 \cdot 3 \cdot 5$, may be found by obtaining **partial products** in two ways:

(1) Multiply 2 and 3 to obtain a partial product of 6, then multiply 6 and 5:
$$2 \cdot 3 \cdot 5 = (2 \cdot 3) \cdot 5 = 6 \cdot 5 = 30$$

(2) Multiply 3 and 5 to obtain a partial product of 15, then multiply 2 and 15:
$$2 \cdot 3 \cdot 5 = 2 \cdot (3 \cdot 5) = 2 \cdot 15 = 30.$$

Hence, $2 \cdot 3 \cdot 5 = (2 \cdot 3) \cdot 5 = 2 \cdot (3 \cdot 5)$

In general, $abc = (ab)c = a(bc)$

As in the following case, a sum may be simplified by using both the Commutative and Associative Laws of Addition:

$$25 + (467 + 175) = 25 + (175 + 467) \text{ (Commutative Law of Addition)}$$
$$= (25 + 175) + 467 \text{ (Associative Law of Addition)}$$
$$= 200 + 467 = 667 \ Ans.$$

As in the following case, a product may be simplified by using both the Commutative and Associative Laws of Multiplication:

$$(\tfrac{1}{4} \times 35) \times 400 = (35 \times \tfrac{1}{4}) \times 400 \text{ (Commutative Law of Multiplication)}$$
$$= 35 \times (\tfrac{1}{4} \times 400) \text{ (Associative Law of Multiplication)}$$
$$= 35 \times 100 = 3500 \ Ans.$$

8.1 Applying the Associative and Commutative Laws

State the Law that applies to each numbered step:

(Other steps are preceded by (S), which indicates the use of the substitution principle.)

a) (1) $13 + (87 + 62) = (13 + 87) + 62$

   (S) $\qquad\qquad = 100 + 162 = 162$

b) (1) $(40 \times \tfrac{1}{3}) \times 66 = 40 \times (\tfrac{1}{3} \times 66)$

   (S) $\qquad\qquad\quad = 40 \times 22 = 880$

c) (1) $7\tfrac{1}{2} + (30 + x) = (7\tfrac{1}{2} + 30) + x$

   (S) $\qquad\qquad\quad = 37\tfrac{1}{2} + x$

   (2) $\qquad\qquad\quad = x + 37\tfrac{1}{2}$

d) (1) $(y \cdot 2\tfrac{1}{2}) \cdot 10 = y \cdot (2\tfrac{1}{2} \cdot 10)$

   (S) $\qquad\qquad\quad = y \cdot 25$

   (2) $\qquad\qquad\quad = 25 \cdot y \text{ or } 25y$

Ans. a) (1) Associative Law of Addition

    b) (1) Associative Law of Multiplication

c) (1) Associative Law of Addition

   (2) Commutative Law of Addition

d) (1) Associative Law of Multiplication

   (2) Commutative Law of Multiplication

8.2 Verifying the Associative Laws When Finding the Sum or Product of Three Numbers

If $a = 2$, $b = 3$, $c = 5$, and $d = 10$, show that

a) $(a + b) + c = a + (b + c)$
b) $(a + c) + d = a + (c + d)$
c) $(d + b) + c = d + (b + c)$

d) $(ab)c = a(bc)$
e) $(ac)d = a(cd)$
f) $(db)c = d(bc)$

Ans. a) $(5) + 5 = 2 + (8)$ and $10 = 10$

    b) $(7) + 10 = 2 + (15)$ and $17 = 17$

    c) $(13) + 5 = 10 + (8)$ and $18 = 18$

d) $(6)5 = 2(15)$ and $30 = 30$

e) $(10)10 = 2(50)$ and $100 = 100$

f) $(30)5 = 10(15)$ and $150 = 150$

8.3 Verifying the Associative Laws When Finding the Sum or Product of Four Numbers

If $a = 1$, $b = 5$, $c = 10$, $d = 20$, and $e = 100$, show that

a) $(a + b + c) + d = a + (b + c + d)$
b) $(b + c) + (d + e) = b + (c + d + e)$
c) $(d + a + c) + e = (d + a) + (c + e)$

d) $(abc)d = a(bcd)$
e) $(bc)(de) = b(cde)$
f) $(dac)e = (da)(ce)$

Ans.

a) $(16) + 20 = 1 + (35)$ and $36 = 36$
b) $(15) + (120) = 5 + (130)$ and $135 = 135$
c) $(31) + 100 = (21) + (110)$ and $131 = 131$

d) $(50)20 = 1(1000)$ and $1000 = 1000$
e) $(50)(2000) = 5(20,000)$ and $100,000 = 100,000$
g) $(200)100 = (20)(1000)$ and $20,000 = 20,000$

9. ORDER IN WHICH FUNDAMENTAL OPERATIONS ARE PERFORMED

In evaluating a numerical expression not containing parentheses, the operations involved must be performed in a certain order. Note in the following, how **multiplication and division must precede addition and subtraction!**

To Evaluate a Numerical Expression Not Containing Parentheses

Evaluate: $a)\ 3 + 4 \times 2$ $b)\ 5 \times 4 - 18 \div 6$

Procedure: **Solution:**

1) Do **multiplications and divisions (M & D)** in order from left to right: 1) $3 + 4 \times 2$ 1) $5 \times 4 - 18 \div 6$

                                               $3 + 8$ $20 - 3$

2) Do remaining **additions and subtractions (A & S)** in order from left to right: 2) 11 *Ans.*   2) 17 *Ans.*

To Evaluate an Algebraic Expression Not Containing Parentheses

Evaluate $x + 2y - \dfrac{z}{5}$ when $x = 5,\ y = 3,\ z = 20$.

Procedure: **Solution:**

1) **Substitute** the value given for each variable: 1) $x + 2y - \dfrac{z}{5}$

                                          $5 + 2(3) - \dfrac{20}{5}$

2) Do **multiplications and divisions (M & D)** in order from left to right: 2) $5 + 6 - 4$

3) Do remaining **additions and subtractions (A & S)** in order from left to right: 3) 7 *Ans.*

9.1 Evaluating Numerical Expressions

Evaluate:

Procedure:	$a)\ 24 \div 4 + 8$	$b)\ 24 + 8 \div 4$	$c)\ 8 \times 6 - 10 \div 5 + 12$
1) Do M & D:	$6 + 8$	$24 + 2$	$48 - 2 + 12$
2) Do A & S:	14 *Ans.*	26 *Ans.*	58 *Ans.*

9.2 Evaluating Algebraic Expressions

Evaluate if $a = 8,\ b = 10,\ x = 3$:

Procedure:	$a)\quad 4b - \dfrac{a}{4}$	$b)\quad 12x + ab$	$c)\quad \dfrac{3a}{4} + \dfrac{4b}{5} - \dfrac{2x}{3}$
1) Substitute:	$4 \times 10 - \dfrac{8}{4}$	$12 \times 3 + 8 \times 10$	$\dfrac{3}{4} \times 8 + \dfrac{4}{5} \times 10 - \dfrac{2}{3} \times 3$
2) Do M & D:	$40 - 2$	$36 + 80$	$6 + 8 - 2$
3) Do A & S:	38 *Ans.*	116 *Ans.*	12 *Ans.*

9.3 Evaluating When the Value of One of the Variables Is Zero

Evaluate if $w = 4,\ x = 2,$ and $y = 0$:

	$a)\ wx + y$	$b)\ w + xy$	$c)\ \dfrac{w+y}{x}$	$d)\ \dfrac{xy}{w}$	$e)\ \dfrac{x}{w+y}$	$f)\ \dfrac{wx}{y}$
Solutions:	$4 \times 2 + 0$	$4 + 2 \times 0$	$\dfrac{4+0}{2}$	$\dfrac{2 \times 0}{4}$	$\dfrac{2}{4+0}$	$\dfrac{4 \times 2}{0}$
	$8 + 0$	$4 + 0$	$\dfrac{4}{2}$	$\dfrac{0}{4}$	$\dfrac{2}{4}$	$\dfrac{8}{0}$
	8 *Ans.*	4 *Ans.*	2 *Ans.*	0 *Ans.*	$\dfrac{1}{2}$ *Ans.*	meaning-less *Ans.*

Note: In (a), (c), and (e), the additive property of zero is applied, while in (b) and (d), the multiplicative property of zero is applied. In (f), division by zero is impossible.

10. THE USES OF PARENTHESES: CHANGING THE ORDER OF OPERATIONS

Parentheses may be used

(1) **to treat an expression as a single number.**

Thus, $2(x+y)$ represents twice the sum of x and y.

(2) **to replace the multiplication sign.**

Thus, $4(5)$ represents the product of 4 and 5.

(3) **to change the order of operations in evaluating.**

Thus, to evaluate $2(4+3)$, **add** 4 and 3 in the parentheses **before multiplying;**
that is, $2(4+3) = 2 \cdot 7 = 14$. Compare this
with $2 \cdot 4 + 3 = 8+3 = 11$.

To Evaluate an Algebraic Expression Containing Parentheses

Evaluate: $2(a+b) + 3a - \dfrac{b}{2}$ if $a = 7$, $b = 2$.

Procedure:	Solution:
1) **Substitute** the value given for each variable:	1) $2(7+2) + 3 \cdot 7 - \dfrac{2}{2}$
2) **Evaluate inside parentheses:**	2) $2 \cdot 9 + 3 \cdot 7 - \dfrac{2}{2}$
3) Do **multiplications and divisions (M & D)** in order from left to right:	3) $18 + 21 - 1$
4) Do remaining **additions and subtractions (A & S)** in order from left to right:	4) 38 *Ans.*

10.1 Evaluating Numerical Expressions Containing Parentheses

Evaluate:

Procedure:	a) $3(4-2) + 12$	b) $7 - \frac{1}{2}(14-6)$	c) $8 + \frac{1}{3}(4+2)$	d) $20 - 5(4-1)$
1) Do ( ):	$3 \cdot 2 + 12$	$7 - \frac{1}{2} \cdot 8$	$8 + \frac{1}{3} \cdot 6$	$20 - 5 \cdot 3$
2) Do **M & D**:	$6 + 12$	$7 - 4$	$8 + 2$	$20 - 15$
3) Do **A & S**:	18 *Ans.*	3 *Ans.*	10 *Ans.*	5 *Ans.*

10.2 Evaluating Algebraic Expressions Containing Parentheses

Evaluate if $a = 10$, $b = 2$, and $x = 12$:

Procedure:	a) $3(x+2b) - 30$	b) $8 + 2(\frac{a}{b} + x)$	c) $3x - \frac{1}{2}(a+b)$
1) **Substitute**:	$3(12 + 2 \cdot 2) - 30$	$8 + 2(\frac{10}{2} + 12)$	$3 \cdot 12 - \frac{1}{2}(10+2)$
2) Do ( ):	$3 \cdot 16 - 30$	$8 + 2 \cdot 17$	$36 - \frac{1}{2} \cdot 12$
3) Do **M & D**:	$48 - 30$	$8 + 34$	$36 - 6$
4) Do **A & S**:	18 *Ans.*	42 *Ans.*	30 *Ans.*

10.3 Evaluating When the Value of a Variable Is Zero

Evaluate if $w = 1$, $y = 4$, and $x = 0$:

	a) $x(2w + 3y)$	b) $y(wx + 5)$	c) $\frac{1}{2}(y + \frac{x}{w}) + 5$	d) $\dfrac{y}{w+x} - w(y+x)$
Solutions:	$0(2 \cdot 1 + 3 \cdot 4)$	$4(1 \cdot 0 + 5)$	$\frac{1}{2}(4 + \frac{0}{1}) + 5$	$\dfrac{4}{1+0} - 1(4+0)$
	$0 \cdot 14$	$4 \cdot 5$	$\frac{1}{2} \cdot 4 + 5$	$4 - 4$
	0 *Ans.*	20 *Ans.*	7 *Ans.*	0 *Ans.*

Note: In (a) and (b), the multiplicative property of zero is applied, while in (c) and (d) the additive property of 0 is applied.

11. MULTIPLYING FACTORS IN TERMS: NUMERICAL AND LITERAL COEFFICIENT

A **term** is a number, a variable, or the product or quotient of numbers and variables.

Thus, $5, 8y, cd, 3wx$ and $\frac{2}{3}rst$ are terms.

Also, the expression $8y + 5$ consists of two terms $8y$ and 5.

A **factor of a term** is each of the numbers or variables multiplied to form the term.

Thus, 8 and y are factors of the term $8y$; $3, w$ and x are factors of the term $3wx$.

Also, 5 and $(a + b)$ are the factors of the term $5(a + b)$.

Any factor or group of factors of a term is a **coefficient** of the product of the remaining factors.

Thus, in $3abc$, 3 is the **numerical coefficient** of abc while abc is the **literal coefficient** of 3. Note that the literal coefficient is the product of the variable factors.

The following table contains further examples:

	Term	Numerical Coefficient	Literal Coefficient
(1)	xy	1	xy
(2)	$\frac{3y}{7}$	$\frac{3}{7}$	y
(3)	$\frac{3ab}{5c}$	$\frac{3}{5}$	$\frac{ab}{c}$

An **expression** consists of one or more terms connected by plus or minus signs.

Thus, $2x$, $3ab + 2$ and $5a - 2b - 7$ are expressions.

11.1 Expressions Containing Terms

State the number of terms and the terms in each expression.

a) $8abc$ *Ans.* 1 term : $8abc$
b) $8 + a + bc$ *Ans.* 3 terms: 8, a and bc
c) $8a + bc$ *Ans.* 2 terms: $8a$ and bc
d) $3b + c + d$ *Ans.* 3 terms: $3b$, c and d
e) $3 + bcd$ *Ans.* 2 terms: 3 and bcd
f) $3(b + c) + d$ *Ans.* 2 terms: $3(b + c)$ and d

11.2 Factors of Terms

State the factors of the following, disregarding 1 and the product itself:

a) 21   *Ans.* 3 and 7   e) $\frac{1}{3}m$ *Ans.* $\frac{1}{3}$ and m
b) 121   *Ans.* 11 and 11   f) $\frac{n}{5}$ *Ans.* $\frac{1}{5}$ and n
c) rs *Ans.* r and s g) $\frac{n+3}{5}$ *Ans.* $\frac{1}{5}$ and $(n + 3)$
d) $5cd$ *Ans.* 5, c and d h) $3(x + 2)$ *Ans.* 3 and $(x + 2)$

11.3 Numerical and Literal Coefficient:

State each numerical and literal coefficient:

	a) y	b) $\frac{4x}{5}$	c) $\frac{w}{7}$	d) $.7abc$	e) $8(a + b)$
Numerical Coefficient:	1	$\frac{4}{5}$	$\frac{1}{7}$	.7	8
Literal Coefficient:	y	x	w	abc	$(a + b)$

12. REPEATED MULTIPLYING OF A FACTOR: BASE, EXPONENT AND POWER

$$\text{BASE}^{EXPONENT} = \text{POWER}$$

In $2\cdot2\cdot2\cdot2\cdot2$, the factor 2 is being multiplied repeatedly. This may be written in a shorter form as 2^5 where the repeated factor 2 is the **base** while the small 5 written above and to the right of 2 is the **exponent**. The answer 32 is called the fifth **power** of 2.

An **exponent** is a number which indicates how many times another number, the **base**, is being used as a repeated factor. The **power** is the answer thus obtained. Thus, since $3\cdot3\cdot3\cdot3$ or $3^4 = 81$, 3 is the base, 4 is the exponent and 81 is the fourth power of 3.

TABLE OF POWERS

The table of powers contains the first five powers of the most frequently used numerical bases 1, 2, 3, 4, 5 and 10. It will be very useful to learn these.

| | EXPONENT | | | | |
	1	2	3	4	5
BASE 1	1	1	1	1	1
2	2	4	8	16	32
3	3	9	27	81	243
4	4	16	64	256	1024
5	5	25	125	625	3125
10	10	100	1,000	10,000	100,000

Variable Bases: Squares and Cubes

The area of a square with a side s, is found by multiplying s by s. This may be written as $A = s^2$ and read "Area equals s-square". Here, A is the second power of s. See Fig. (a).

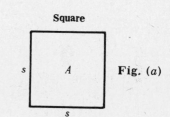

Square

Fig. (a)

The volume of a cube with a side s, is found by multiplying s three times; that is, $s\cdot s\cdot s$. This may be written as $V = s^3$ and read, "Volume equals s-cube". Here, V is the third power of s. See Fig. (b).

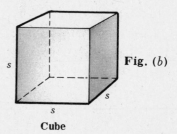

Fig. (b)

Cube

Reading Powers

"b^2" is read as "b-square", "b to the second power", "b-second" or "b to the second".

"x^3" is read as "x-cube", "x to the third power", "x-third" or "x to the third".

12.1 Writing as Bases and Exponents

Write each, using bases and exponents:

a) $5\cdot5\cdot5$ c) $2\cdot8\cdot8\cdot8\cdot8$ e) $bbccc$ g) $(3y)(3y)(3y)$ i) $7rr(s-8)$ k) $\dfrac{7w}{xx}$

b) $3\cdot3\cdot7\cdot7$ d) $bbbbb$ f) $12bccd$ h) $2(a+b)(a+b)$ j) $\dfrac{yy}{x}$ l) $\dfrac{2ttt}{5vvvv}$

Ans. a) 5^3 c) $2\cdot8^4$ e) b^2c^3 g) $(3y)^3$ i) $7r^2(s-8)$ k) $\dfrac{7w}{x^2}$

b) $3^2 7^2$ d) b^5 f) $12bc^2d$ h) $2(a+b)^2$ j) $\dfrac{y^2}{x}$ l) $\dfrac{2t^3}{5v^4}$

12.2 Writing Without Exponents:

Write each without exponents:

a) 2^6

b) $3 \cdot 4^2$

c) $5 \cdot 7^3 \cdot 8$

d) x^5

e) $10y^4z^2$

f) $8rs^2t^3$

g) $(2x)^3$

h) $6(5y)^2$

i) $4(a-b)^2$

j) $\dfrac{a^5}{b^2}$

k) $\dfrac{2(a+b)^2}{c^5}$

l) $\dfrac{a^2+b^2}{c^3-d^3}$

Ans. a) $2 \cdot 2 \cdot 2 \cdot 2 \cdot 2 \cdot 2$

b) $3 \cdot 4 \cdot 4$

c) $5 \cdot 7 \cdot 7 \cdot 7 \cdot 8$

d) $xxxxx$

e) $10yyyyzz$

f) $8rssttt$

g) $(2x)(2x)(2x)$

h) $6(5y)(5y)$

i) $4(a-b)(a-b)$

j) $\dfrac{aaaaa}{bb}$

k) $\dfrac{2(a+b)(a+b)}{ccccc}$

l) $\dfrac{aa+bb}{ccc-ddd}$

12.3 Evaluating Powers

Evaluate (the table of powers may be used to check values):

a) 3^5

b) 5^4

c) 10^3

d) 2^2+3^2

e) 2^3+3^3

f) 10^4-4^4

g) $1^2 \cdot 1^3 \cdot 1^4$

h) $2^3 5^2$

i) $\frac{1}{2} \cdot 2^4 \cdot 3^2$

j) $10+3 \cdot 2^2$

k) $8 \cdot 10^2-3^3$

l) $\frac{1}{2} \cdot 4^2 - \frac{1}{3} \cdot 3^2$

m) $(3+4^2)(3^3-5^2)$

n) $\dfrac{4^4}{2^5}$

o) $\dfrac{3^3+2^5}{10^2}$

Ans. a) 243

b) 625

c) 1,000

d) $4+9=13$

e) $8+27=35$

f) $10,000-256$
$=9,744$

g) $1 \cdot 1 \cdot 1 = 1$

h) $8 \cdot 25 = 200$

i) $\frac{1}{2} \cdot 16 \cdot 9 = 72$

j) $10+3 \cdot 4 = 22$

k) $8 \cdot 100 - 27 = 773$

l) $\frac{1}{2} \cdot 16 - \frac{1}{3} \cdot 9 = 5$

m) $19 \cdot 2 = 38$

n) $\dfrac{256}{32} = 8$

o) $\dfrac{27+32}{100} = \dfrac{59}{100}$

12.4 Evaluating Powers of Fractions and Decimals

Evaluate:

a) $.2^4$

b) $.5^2$

c) $.01^3$

d) $1000(.2^3)$

e) $\frac{1}{3}(.3^2)$

f) $200(.4^4)$

g) $(\frac{1}{2})^3$

h) $(\frac{2}{3})^2$

i) $(\frac{5}{3})^4$

j) $100(\frac{1}{5})^2$

k) $32(\frac{3}{2})^3$

l) $80(\frac{5}{2})^3$

Ans. a) .0016

b) .25

c) .000001

d) $1000(.008) = 8$

e) $\frac{1}{3}(.09) = .03$

f) $200(.0256) = 5.12$

g) $\frac{1}{2} \cdot \frac{1}{2} \cdot \frac{1}{2} = \frac{1}{8}$

h) $\frac{2}{3} \cdot \frac{2}{3} = \frac{4}{9}$

i) $\frac{5}{3} \cdot \frac{5}{3} \cdot \frac{5}{3} \cdot \frac{5}{3} = \frac{625}{81}$

j) $100(\frac{1}{25}) = 4$

k) $32(\frac{27}{8}) = 108$

l) $80(\frac{125}{8}) = 1250$

12.5 Evaluating Powers of Variable Bases

Evaluate if $a=5$, $b=1$ and $c=10$:

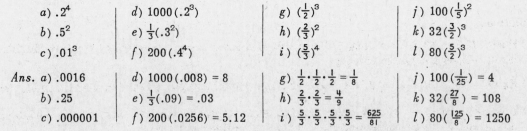

a) a^3

b) b^4

c) c^2

d) $2a^2$

e) $(2a)^2$

f) $(a+2)^2$

g) $(\frac{1}{2}c)^2$

h) $(\frac{b}{3})^2$

i) $\frac{4a^2}{c}$

j) a^2+c^2

k) $(c+3b)^2$

l) $5(a^2-b^2)$

m) $c^2(a+b)$

n) $c(a-b^2)$

o) $3b(a^3-c^2)$

Ans. a) $5 \cdot 5 \cdot 5 = 125$

b) $1 \cdot 1 \cdot 1 \cdot 1 = 1$

c) $10 \cdot 10 = 100$

d) $2 \cdot 25 = 50$

e) $10^2 = 100$

f) $7^2 = 49$

g) $5^2 = 25$

h) $(\frac{1}{3})^2 = \frac{1}{9}$

i) $\frac{100}{10} = 10$

j) $25+100 = 125$

k) $13^2 = 169$

l) $5 \cdot 24 = 120$

m) $100 \cdot 6 = 600$

n) $10 \cdot 4 = 40$

o) $3 \cdot 25 = 75$

13. LAW OF CLOSURE

If the whole numbers 5 and 3 are added, the result is 8, which is a whole number. If 5 and 3 are multiplied, the result is 15, which is a whole number. We need not restrict ourselves to 5 and 3 because the sum of any two whole numbers is a whole number. Also the product of any two whole numbers is a whole number. Hence, we say that the set of whole numbers is **closed under addition and multiplication** in accordance with the following definition:

> **Law of Closure**: A set is closed under an operation if, when the operation is applied to any two members of the set, the result of the operation is a unique member of the set.

Closure under an operation depends on the set of numbers involved and the operation that is applied to the set. Suppose we consider the set {0,1} and apply the operations of addition and multiplication to that set. Note in the multiplication table, Fig. 1, that the set is closed under multiplication. However, the addition table, Fig. 2, shows that the set is **not** closed under addition since 2 is not a member of the set {0,1}.

×	0	1
0	0	0
1	0	1

Multiplication

Fig. 1

+	0	1
0	0	1
1	1	2

Addition

Fig. 2

Keep in mind that a set is not closed under an operation if there is any member or members of the set to which the operation does not apply.

Thus since $1 \div 0$ is impossible, the set {0,1} is not closed under division.

13.1 Law of Closure

State whether each statement is true or false:

a) The set of whole numbers and the set of natural numbers are closed under subtraction
b) The set of natural numbers is closed under division
c) The set {1, 2} is not closed under either addition or multiplication
d) The set of odd natural numbers is closed under multiplication but not under addition
e) The set of powers of 2 is closed under multiplication
f) The set of natural numbers is closed under the operation of averaging two numbers

Solutions:

a) False. If 5 is subtracted from 3, the result is neither a whole number nor a natural number. The result, −2, is a negative integer.

b) False. If 5 is divided by 3, the result is not a natural number. The result $\frac{5}{3}$ is a rational number.

c) True. The set is not closed under addition since 3 and 4 do not belong to the set, and the set is not closed under multiplication since 4 does not belong to the set.

d) True. The product of any two odd natural numbers is an odd natural number but the sum of any two odd natural numbers is an even natural number. Test for 5 and 3.

e) True. The product of any two powers of 2 is a power of 2.

f) False. If 3 and 4 are averaged, the average, $3\frac{1}{2}$ is not a natural number.

SUPPLEMENTARY PROBLEMS

The numbers in the parentheses at the right of each set of problems indicate where to find the same type of example in this chapter. For example, (1.1) indicates that set 1.1 in this chapter involves problems of the same type. If help is needed, a student should review the set to which reference is made.

1. In each, state whether the sentence refers to numerals or to members: **(1.1)**

  a) In 43, 3 comes after 4   *d*) 3 combined with 4 is 43 or 34

  b) In counting, 3 comes before 4   *e*) 43 consists of 4 and 3

  c) 3 added to 4 is 7   *f*) 34 is the sum of 3 tens and 4

  Ans. a) numerals *b*) numbers *c*) numbers *d*) numerals *e*) numerals *f*) numbers

2. State whether each sentence is true, false, or an open sentence: **(1.2)**

  a) $37 \times 25 = 25 \times 37$ *Ans.* true

  b) $257 + 681 = 681 + 257$ *Ans.* true

  c) $1000 \times 0 \neq 1 \times 0$ *Ans.* false since $0 = 0$

  d) The sum of 0 and any whole number equals the product of the number and 1. *Ans.* true

  e) The product of a whole number and itself is greater than 1. *Ans.* open sentence, false when the whole number is 0 or 1 but true for any other whole number.

  f) 24 decreased by 3 equals 24 subtracted from 45. *Ans.* true

  g) A whole number multiplied by itself is equal to its double. *Ans.* open sentence, true for 0 and 2 but false for any other whole number.

  h) If a natural number is increased by a second natural number and the resulting sum is then decreased by the second number, the final result is the first number. *Ans.* true

3. List each set by roster: **(1.3)**

  a) The set of natural numbers between 3 and 9. *Ans.* {4, 5, 6, 7, 8}

  b) The set of whole numbers less than 4. *Ans.* {0, 1, 2, 3}

  c) The set of successors of the odd whole numbers between 4 and 10. *Ans.* {6, 8, 10}

  d) The set of natural numbers represented by $3n$ if n represents the set {2, 5, 8}.
   Ans. {6, 15, 24}

  e) The set of numbers that differ from 10 by 3. *Ans.* {7, 13}

  f) The set of fractions less than 1 whose numerators and denominators are members of the set {1, 2, 3}. *Ans.* $\{\frac{1}{2}, \frac{1}{3}, \frac{2}{3}\}$

  g) The set of natural numbers that differ from 3 by no more than 3. *Ans.* {1, 2, 3, 4, 5, 6}

  h) The set of natural numbers represented by $n \cdot n$ if n represents the set whole numbers between 4 and 8. *Ans.* {25, 36, 49}.

4. Write each number using digits: **(1.4)**

  a) The least natural number having three digits. *Ans.* 100

  b) The whole number which is the successor of the greatest natural number having six digits. *Ans.* 1,000,000

  c) The greatest of the natural numbers. *Ans.* there is no greatest natural number.

  d) One thousand, one hundred, one. *Ans.* 1,101

  e) One million, ten thousand, ten. *Ans.* 1,010,010

5. State whether each statement is true or false with reference to the indicated sets: **(1.5)**

  $A = \{2, 4, 6, 8, 10\}, \quad B = \{1, 3, 5, 7\}, \quad C = \emptyset, \quad D = \{\frac{1}{2}, \frac{1}{4}, \frac{1}{6}, \frac{1}{8}\}, \quad E = \{10, 6, 2, 8, 4\}$

  a) A and D are equivalent sets. *Ans.* false

  b) B and D are equivalent sets. *Ans.* true

  c) A and E are equal sets. *Ans.* true

  d) C is the null or empty set. *Ans.* true

  e) $0 \in C$ *Ans.* false

  f) A and D can be put into a one-to-one correspondence. *Ans.* false

  g) $2 \in D$ *Ans.* false

  h) $1 \in B$ and $1 \notin D$ *Ans.* true

  i) $\frac{1}{4} \in D$ or $\frac{1}{2} \in A$ *Ans.* true since either statement may be true in a true disjunction.

6. State each product without multiplication signs: **(1.6)**

   a) $8 \times w$ c) $b \times c \times d$ e) $.5 \times y \times z$ g) $2\frac{1}{3} \times g \times h \times n$

   b) $2 \times 8 \times a$ d) $10 \times l \times m$ f) $\frac{2}{3} \times 12 \times t$ h) $.15 \times 100 \times q \times r$

   Ans. a) $8w$ b) $16a$ c) bcd d) $10lm$ e) $.5yz$ f) $8t$ g) $2\frac{1}{3}ghn$ h) $15qr$

7. Using letters and symbols, replace each verbal statement by an algebraic equation: **(1.7)**

   a) Three times a number added to eight times the same number is equivalent to eleven times the number.

   b) The difference between ten times a number and one-half of the same number is exactly the same as nine and one-half times the number.

   c) The perimeter of an equilateral triangle is equal to three times the length of one of the sides.

   d) The area of a square is found by multiplying the length of a side by itself.

   Ans. a) $3n + 8n = 11n$, b) $10n - \frac{1}{2}n = 9\frac{1}{2}n$, c) $p = 3s$ $A = ss$

8. Using the initial letters of words as variables, replace each verbal rule by a formula: **(1.8)**

   a) The perimeter of a regular hexagon is six times a side.

   b) The area of a triangle is one-half the product of the base and height.

   c) The profit made on an article is the difference between the selling price and the cost.

   d) The semiperimeter of a rectangle is the sum of the length and width.

   e) The volume of a rectangular box is the product of the length, the width and the height.

   Ans. a) $p = 6s$, b) $A = \frac{1}{2}bh$, c) $p = s - c$, d) $s = l + w$, e) $V = lwh$

9. If $S = \{1, 3, 5, 7, 9, 11\}$ is the replacement set of the variable n, state the truth or **(1.9)**
   solution set of each sentence:

   a) n is less than 8.   *Ans.* $\{1, 3, 5, 7\}$

   b) n is greater than $3\frac{1}{2}$.   *Ans.* $\{5, 7, 9, 11\}$

   c) n is between 2 and 9.   *Ans.* $\{3, 5, 7\}$

   d) $n + 5$ is less than or equal to 12.   *Ans.* $\{1, 3, 5, 7\}$

   e) $3n = 30$.   *Ans.* $\emptyset$

   f) $n - 7 = 7 - n$.   *Ans.* $\{7\}$

   g) $n + 5 \neq 5 + n$.   *Ans.* $\emptyset$

   h) n is at least 6.   *Ans.* $\{7, 9, 11\}$

   i) The maximum value of n is 5.   *Ans.* $\{1, 3, 5\}$

   j) $11n = 11$.   *Ans.* $\{1\}$

   k) $4n - 4$ is less than $3n$.   *Ans.* $\{1, 3\}$

   l) n is less than one-half of the greatest member in S.   *Ans.* $\{1, 3, 5\}$

   m) n is more than twice the least member of S.   *Ans.* $\{3, 5, 7, 9, 11\}$

   n) $\{n : n$ differs from 5 by at least $3\}$ *Ans.* $\{1, 9, 11\}$

   o) $\{n : 3 + n + 20 = 20 + n + 3\}$ *Ans.* $\{1, 3, 5, 7, 9, 11\}$

10. Evaluate each numerical expression and state the property of 0 or 1 that applies: **(1.10)**

   a) $1,000 + 0$ *Ans.* 1,000, additive property of 0.

   b) $1,000 \times 1$ *Ans.* 1,000, multiplicative property of 1

   c) $1,000 \times 0$ *Ans.* 0, multiplicative property of 0

   d) $50 \times 40 \times 0$ *Ans.* 0, multiplicative property of 0

   e) $50 \times 40 \times 1$ *Ans.* 2,000, multiplicative property of 1

   f) 0×1 *Ans.* 0, multiplicative properties of 0 and 1

   g) $0 + 1$ *Ans.* 1, additive property of 0

   h) $10 \times 0 + 10$ *Ans.* 10, both the multiplicative and additive properties of 0

   i) $20 \times 1 + 0$ *Ans.* 20, multiplicative property of 1 and additive property of 0

11. Simplify each addition by interchanging addends: (2.1)

$a)$ $64 + 138 + 36$ $c)$ $1\frac{1}{3} + \frac{3}{5} + 6\frac{2}{3}$ $e)$ $12\frac{1}{2}\% + 46\% + 87\frac{1}{2}\%$

$b)$ $15 + 78 + 15 + 170$ $d)$ $2\frac{1}{8} + \frac{13}{16} + \frac{3}{16} + \frac{3}{8}$ $f)$ $5.991 + 1.79 + .21 + .009$

Ans. $a)$ $64 + 36 + 138$ $c)$ $1\frac{1}{3} + 6\frac{2}{3} + \frac{3}{5}$ $e)$ $12\frac{1}{2}\% + 87\frac{1}{2}\% + 46\%$

　　　　$100 + 138 = 238$ $8 + \frac{3}{5} = 8\frac{3}{5}$ $100\% + 46\% = 146\%$

　　$b)$ $15 + 15 + 170 + 78$ $d)$ $2\frac{1}{8} + \frac{3}{8} + \frac{13}{16} + \frac{3}{16}$ $f)$ $5.991 + .009 + 1.79 + .21$

　　　　$200 + 78 = 278$ $2\frac{1}{2} + 1 = 3\frac{1}{2}$ $6 + 2 = 8$

12. Rearrange the addends so that *literal addends are arranged alphabetically and precede numerical addends:*   (2.2)

$a)$ $10 + d$ $c)$ $15 + g + f$ $e)$ $d + b + e + a$ $g)$ $5 + m + 4 + j + 11$

$b)$ $y + x$ $d)$ $17 + r + q + 13$ $f)$ $s + 12 + p + 48$ $h)$ $v + w + 16 + t + 50$

Ans. $a)$ $d + 10$ $c)$ $f + g + 15$ $e)$ $a + b + d + e$ $g)$ $j + m + 20$

　　$b)$ $x + y$ $d)$ $q + r + 30$ $f)$ $p + s + 60$ $h)$ $t + v + w + 66$

13. Simplify each multiplication by interchanging factors: (3.1)

$a)$ $5 \times 26 \times 40$ $c)$ $10\frac{1}{2} \times 7 \times 2$ $e)$ $3.75 \times .15 \times 20 \times 4$

$b)$ $17 \times 12 \times 6$ $d)$ $303 \times 8 \times 1\frac{2}{3}$ $f)$ $66\frac{2}{3}\% \times 50 \times 27$

Ans. $a)$ $5 \times 40 \times 26$ $c)$ $10\frac{1}{2} \times 2 \times 7$ $e)$ $3.75 \times 4 \times .15 \times 20$

　　　　$200 \times 26 = 5200$ $21 \times 7 = 147$ $15 \times 3 = 45$

　　$b)$ $17 \times 6 \times 12$ $d)$ $303 \times 1\frac{2}{3} \times 8$ $f)$ $66\frac{2}{3}\% \times 27 \times 50$

　　　　$102 \times 12 = 1224$ $505 \times 8 = 4040$ $\frac{2}{3} \times 27 \times 50 = 18 \times 50 = 900$

14. Rearrange the factors so that *literal factors are arranged alphabetically and follow* (3.2) *numerical factors:*

$a)$ $r\,8$ $b)$ cab $c)$ $qp\,7$ $d)$ $4v\,3t$ $e)$ $x\,5y\,7w$ $f)$ $def\,13c$ $g)$ $2h\,5k\,10$ $h)$ $r\,11sm\,4$ $i)$ $cd\,13ab$

Ans. $a)$ $8r$ $b)$ abc $c)$ $7pq$ $d)$ $12tv$ $e)$ $35wxy$ $f)$ $13cdef$ $g)$ $100hk$ $h)$ $44mrs$ $i)$ $13abcd$

15. Express each using symbols of operation: $e)$ f divided by 7   *Ans.* $\frac{f}{7}$ (4.1)

$a)$ the product of 8, m and n *Ans.* $8mn$

$b)$ 5 times p times q *Ans.* $5pq$ $f)$ 25 divided by x *Ans.* $\frac{25}{x}$

$c)$ two-thirds of c *Ans.* $\frac{2}{3}c$

$d)$ one-half of b multiplied by h *Ans.* $\frac{1}{2}bh$ $g)$ the product of u and v divided by 9.
　　　　　　　　　　　　　　　　　　　　　　Ans. $\frac{uv}{9}$

16. When is each division impossible?   (4.2, 4.3)

$a)$ $\frac{7}{d}$ $b)$ $\frac{r}{t}$ $c)$ $\frac{3}{4x}$ $d)$ $\frac{5}{a-8}$ $e)$ $\frac{b}{7-c}$ $f)$ $\frac{10}{2x-4}$ $g)$ $\frac{50}{w-y}$ $h)$ $\frac{100}{pq}$ $i)$ $\frac{45}{x-2y}$

Ans. $a)$ if $d = 0$ $c)$ if $x = 0$ $e)$ if $c = 7$ $g)$ if $w = y$ $i)$ if $x = 2y$

　　$b)$ if $t = 0$ $d)$ if $a = 8$ $f)$ if $x = 2$ $h)$ if $p = 0$ or $q = 0$

17. If n represents a number, express algebraically: (5.1, 5.2)

$a)$ 25 more than the number $g)$ 30 less than the number

$b)$ 30 greater than the number $h)$ 35 fewer than the number

$c)$ the sum of the number and 35 $i)$ 40 less the number

$d)$ the number increased by 40 $j)$ 45 decreased by the number

$e)$ 45 plus the number $k)$ 50 minus the number

$f)$ 50 added to the number $l)$ 55 subtracted from the number.

Ans. $a)$ $n+25$ or $25+n$ $d)$ $n+40$ or $40+n$ $g)$ $n-30$ $j)$ $45-n$

　　$b)$ $n+30$ or $30+n$ $e)$ $n+45$ or $45+n$ $h)$ $n-35$ $k)$ $50-n$

　　$c)$ $n+35$ or $35+n$ $f)$ $n+50$ or $50+n$ $i)$ $40-n$ $l)$ $n-55$

18. Express algebraically: (5.3)

    a) the no. of tons of a weight that is 15 tons lighter than *w* tons.   *Ans.* $w-15$

    b) the no. of ft in a length that is 50 ft shorter than *l* ft. $l-50$

    c) the no. of sec in a time interval that is 1 minute less than *t* sec. $t-60$

    d) the no. of cents in a price that is $1 more than *p* cents. $p+100$

    e) the no. of ft per sec (fps) in a speed that is 20 fps slower than *r* fps. $r-20$

    f) the no. of ft in a distance that is 10 yd farther than *d* ft. $d+30$

    g) the no. of sq ft in an area that is 30 sq ft greater than *A* sq ft. $A+30$

    h) the no. of degrees in a temperature that is 40° colder than *t*°. $t-40$

    i) the no. of floors in a building that is 8 floors higher than *f* floors. $f+8$

    j) the no. of yr in an age 5 yr younger than *a* yr. $a-5$

19. Express algebraically: (6.1, 6.2)

    a) *x* times 3   *c*) product of 12 and *y*   *e*) 10 divided by *y*

    b) one-eighth of *b*   *d*) three-eighths of *r*   *f*) quotient of *y* and 10

Ans. *a*) $3x$ *b*) $\frac{b}{8}$ or $\frac{1}{8}b$ *c*) $12y$ *d*) $\frac{3}{8}r$ or $\frac{3r}{8}$ *e*) $\frac{10}{y}$ *f*) $\frac{y}{10}$

20. Express algebraically: (7.1 and 7.2)

    a) *b* decreased by one-half *c*   *f*) twice *d*, less 25

    b) one-third of *g*, decreased by 5   *g*) 8 more than the product of 5 and *x*

    c) four times *r*, divided by 9   *h*) four times the sum of *r* and 9

    d) the average of *m* and 60   *i*) the average of 60, *m*, *p* and *q*

    e) three-quarters of *x*, less *y*   *j*) the ratio of *b* to three times *c*

Ans. *a*) $b-\frac{c}{2}$ *c*) $\frac{4r}{9}$ *e*) $\frac{3x}{4}-y$ *f*) $2d-25$ *h*) $4(r+9)$ *j*) $\frac{b}{3c}$

       b) $\frac{g}{3}-5$ *d*) $\frac{m+60}{2}$ *g*) $5x+8$ *i*) $\frac{m+p+q+60}{4}$

21. Express algebraically: (7.3)

    a) a distance in yd that is 25 yd shorter than three times another of *d* yd.   *Ans.* $3d-25$

    b) a weight in oz that is 5 oz more than twice another of *w* oz. $2w+5$

    c) a temperature in degrees that is 8° warmer than five times another of *T*°. $5T+8$

    d) a price in dollars that is $50 dearer than one-half another of *p* dollars. $\frac{p}{2}+50$

    e) a price in cents that is 50¢ cheaper than one-third another of *p* cents. $\frac{p}{3}-50$

    f) a length in ft that is 2 ft longer than *y* yd. $3y+2$

22. State the law that applies to each numbered step: (8.1)

(Other steps are preceded by (S) which indicates the use of the substitution principle.)

    a) (1) $(w\cdot\frac{1}{7})\cdot 35 = w\cdot(\frac{1}{7}\cdot 35)$ *c*) (1) $\frac{1}{2}+(x+9\frac{1}{2}) = \frac{1}{2}+(9\frac{1}{2}+x)$

        (S) $= w\cdot 5$ (2) $= (\frac{1}{2}+9\frac{1}{2})+x$

        (2) $= 5\cdot w$ or $5w$ (S) $= 10+x$

                                                (3) $= x+10$

    b) (1) $25+(46+175) = 25+(175+46)$

        (2) $= (25+175)+46$

        (S) $= 200+46 = 246$

Ans. *a*) (1) Associative Law of Multiplication, (2) Commutative Law of Multiplication

       b) (1) Commutative Law of Addition, (2) Associative Law of Addition

       c) (1) Commutative Law of Addition, (2) Associative Law of Addition

           (3) Commutative Law of Addition

23. If $a = 2,$ $b = 5,$ $c = 10,$ $d = 100,$ and $e = 1,000,$ show that   **(8.2, 8.3)**

a) $(a+b) + c = (b+c)$ d) $(a+c+e) + (d+b) = (a+c) + (e+d) + b$ g) $(bd)(ae) = b(dae)$

b) $(a+b) + (c+d) = (a+b+c) + d$ e) $(ab)c = a(bc)$

c) $(b+d) + (a+e) = b + (d+a+e)$ f) $(ab)(cd) = (abc)d$

Ans. a) $(7) + 10 = 2 + (15)$ and $17 = 17$ e) $(10)10 = 2(50)$ and $100 = 100$

     b) $(7) + (110) = (17) + 100$ and $117 = 117$ f) $(10)(1,000) = (100)100$ and

     c) $(105) + (1,002) = 5 + (1,102)$ and $1,107 = 1,107$ $10,000 = 10,000$

     d) $(1,012) + (105) = (12) + (1,100) + 5$ and   g) $(500)(2,000) = 5(200,000)$ and

        $1,117 = 1,117$ $1,000,000 = 1,000,000$

24. Evaluate: **(9.1)**

a) $40 - 2 \times 5$ c) $40 \div 2 + 5$ e) $16 \div 2 - \frac{1}{2} \cdot 10$ g) $40 \times 2 - 40 \div 2$

b) $3 \times 8 - 2 \times 5$ d) $3 + 8 - 2 \times 5$ f) $3 + 8 \times 2 \times 5$ h) $3 + 8 \times 2 - 5 \div 10$

Ans. a) 30   b) 14   c) 25   d) 1   e) 3   f) 83   g) 60   h) $18\frac{1}{2}$

25. Evaluate if $a=5$, $b=6$ and $c=10$:   **(9.2)**

a) $a + b - c$ *Ans.* 1   f) $3 + \frac{c}{a}$ *Ans.* 5   k) $5a + 4b - 2c$ *Ans.* 29

b) $a + 2b$ *Ans.* 17   g) $\frac{4}{5}c$ or $\frac{4c}{5}$ *Ans.* 8   l) $6c - 2ab$ *Ans.* 0

c) $a + \frac{b}{2}$ *Ans.* 8   h) $\frac{2}{3}b + \frac{3}{2}c$ *Ans.* 19   m) $a + \frac{c-b}{2}$ *Ans.* 7

d) $\frac{a+b}{2}$ *Ans.* $5\frac{1}{2}$ i) $\frac{a+b}{c-9}$ *Ans.* 11   n) $a + c - \frac{b}{2}$ *Ans.* 12

e) $\frac{3c}{a}$ *Ans.* 6   j) $\frac{ab}{c}$ *Ans.* 3   o) $\frac{a+c-b}{3}$ *Ans.* 3

26. Evaluate if $x=3$, $y=2$ and $z=0$:   **(9.3)**

a) $x + y + z$ *Ans.* 5   f) $\frac{z}{x}$ *Ans.* 0   k) $xz + yz$ *Ans.* 0

b) $x - y - z$ *Ans.* 1   g) $\frac{x}{z}$ *Ans.* meaningless   l) $\frac{z}{x+y}$ *Ans.* 0

c) $x(y+z)$ *Ans.* 6   h) xyz *Ans.* 0   m) $\frac{x}{y+z}$ *Ans.* $1\frac{1}{2}$

d) $z(x+y)$ *Ans.* 0   i) $xy + z$ *Ans.* 6   n) $x + \frac{z}{y}$ *Ans.* 3

e) $y(x+z)$ *Ans.* 6   j) $x + yz$ *Ans.* 3   o) $\frac{y+z}{x}$ *Ans.* $\frac{2}{3}$

27. Evaluate: **(10.1)**

a) $5(8+2)$ *Ans.* 50   e) $8 \cdot 2(5-3)$ *Ans.* 32   i) $4(4 \cdot 4 - 4)$ *Ans.* 48

b) $5(8-2)$ *Ans.* 30   f) $3(6+2 \cdot 5)$ *Ans.* 48   j) $(4+4)4 - 4$ *Ans.* 28

c) $8 + 2(5-3)$ *Ans.* 12   g) $(3 \cdot 6 + 2)5$ *Ans.* 100   k) $(4+4)(4-4)$ *Ans.* 0

d) $8(2 \cdot 5 - 3)$ *Ans.* 56   h) $3(6+2)5$ *Ans.* 120   l) $4 + 4(4-4)$ *Ans.* 4

28. Evaluate if $a=4$, $b=3$ and $c=5$:   **(10.2)**

a) $a(b+c)$ *Ans.* 32   e) $\frac{1}{2}(a+b) + c$ *Ans.* $8\frac{1}{2}$ i) $3a + 2(c-b)$ *Ans.* 16

b) $b(c-a)$ *Ans.* 3   f) $3(b+2c)$ *Ans.* 39   j) $3(a+2c) - b$ *Ans.* 39

c) $c(a-b)$ *Ans.* 5   g) $3(b+2)c$ *Ans.* 75   k) $3(a+2c-b)$ *Ans.* 33

d) $\frac{1}{2}(a+b+c)$ *Ans.* 6   h) $(3b+2)c$ *Ans.* 55   l) $3(a+2)(c-b)$ *Ans.* 36

29. Evaluate if $x=6$, $y=4$, $w=2$ and $z=0$:   **(10.3)**

a) $x(y+w)$ *Ans.* 36   d) $wx(y+z)$ *Ans.* 48   g) $z \div (x+w)$ *Ans.* 0

b) $z(w+x)$ *Ans.* 0   e) $x + y(w+z)$ *Ans.* 14   h) $wy \div (z+x)$ *Ans.* $\frac{4}{3}$

c) $w(x-y)$ *Ans.* 4   f) $x + z(y-w)$ *Ans.* 6   i) $(w+x)(y-z)$ *Ans.* 32

30. State the number of terms and the terms in each expression: **(11.1)**

a) $5xyz$ *Ans.* 1 term: $5xyz$ d) $3a + bc$ *Ans.* 2 terms: $3a$ and bc

b) $5 + xyz$ *Ans.* 2 terms: 5 and xyz e) $3ab + c$ *Ans.* 2 terms: $3ab$ and c

c) $5 + x + y + z$ *Ans.* 4 terms: 5, x, y and z f) $3a(b+c)$ *Ans.* 1 term: $3a(b+c)$

31. State the factors of the following, disregarding 1 and the product itself: **(11.2)**

         a) 77 b) 25 c) pq d) $\frac{3}{4}x$ e) $\frac{w}{10}$ f) $8(x-5)$ g) $\frac{y-2}{4}$

Ans. a) 7 and 11, b) 5 and 5, c) p and q, d) $\frac{3}{4}$ and x, e) $\frac{1}{10}$ and w, f) 8 and $(x-5)$, g) $\frac{1}{4}, (y-2)$

32. State each numerical and literal coefficient: **(11.3)**

         a) w b) $\frac{1}{8}x$ c) $\frac{n}{10}$ d) $.03\,ab$ e) $\frac{3y}{10}$ f) $\frac{2a}{3b}$ g) $\frac{3}{5}(a-b)$

Ans.

	(a)	(b)	(c)	(d)	(e)	(f)	(g)
NUMERICAL COEFFICIENT:	1	$\frac{1}{8}$	$\frac{1}{10}$	.03	$\frac{3}{10}$	$\frac{2}{3}$	$\frac{3}{5}$
LITERAL COEFFICIENT:	w	x	n	ab	y	$\frac{a}{b}$	$a-b$

33. Write each, using bases and exponents: **(12.1)**

         a) $7\cdot3\cdot3$ b) $7xyyy$ c) $\frac{7x}{yyy}$ d) $(7x)(7x)$ e) $(a+5)(a+5)$ f) $\frac{2rrw}{5stvv}$

Ans. a) $7\cdot3^2$ b) $7xy^3$ c) $\frac{7x}{y^3}$ d) $(7x)^2$ e) $(a+5)^2$ f) $\frac{2r^2w}{5stv^2}$

34. Write each without exponents: **(12.2)**

         a) $4\cdot7^2$ b) $\frac{1}{2}y^4$ c) $\frac{5a}{b^4}$ d) $(ab)^3$ e) $(x+2)^2$ f) $\frac{a^2-b^3}{c+d^2}$

Ans. a) $4\cdot7\cdot7$ b) $\frac{1}{2}yyyy$ c) $\frac{5a}{bbbb}$ d) $(ab)(ab)(ab)$ e) $(x+2)(x+2)$ f) $\frac{aa-bbb}{c+dd}$

35. Evaluate (the table of powers may be used to check values): **(12.3)**

     a) 3^3-2^3 c) 10^3+5^4 e) $1^2+2^2+3^2$ g) $1^5+1^4+1^3+1^2$ i) $5\cdot1^3-3\cdot1^5$

     b) $5^2\cdot2^5$ d) $10^2\div2$ f) $5^3\div5$ h) $2^5-4\cdot2^2$ j) $\frac{1}{2}\cdot2^2+\frac{1}{3}\cdot3^3$

Ans. a) 19, b) 800   c) 1625, d) 50   e) 14, f) 25   g) 4, h) 16   i) 2, j) 11

36. Evaluate: **(12.4)**

     a) $.1^2\cdot9^2$ b) $.3\cdot4^2$ c) $3^2\,4^2$ d) $40(\frac{1}{2})^3$ e) $(\frac{2}{5})^3$ f) $\frac{2^3}{5^2}$ g) $\frac{10}{.1^2}$

Ans. a) $.81$ b) 4.8 c) 144 d) 5 e) $\frac{8}{125}$ f) $\frac{8}{25}$ g) 1000

37. Evaluate if $a=3$ and $b=2$: **(12.5)**

a) a^2b	*Ans.* 18	e) $(a+b)^2$	*Ans.* 25	i) a^3-b^3	*Ans.* 19
b) ab^2	*Ans.* 12	f) a^2+b^2	*Ans.* 13	j) $(a-b)^3$	*Ans.* 1
c) $(ab)^2$	*Ans.* 36	g) a^3b	*Ans.* 54	k) a^2b^3	*Ans.* 72
d) $a+b^2$	*Ans.* 7	h) $(ab)^3$	*Ans.* 216	l) a^3b^2	*Ans.* 108

38. Evaluate if $w=1$, $x=3$, $y=4$: **(12.5)**

a) $2w^2$ *Ans.* 2	d) y^2+x^2 *Ans.* 25	g) $(y-x)^2$ *Ans.* 1	j) y^3x *Ans.* 192
b) $(2w)^2$ *Ans.* 4	e) $(y+x)^2$ *Ans.* 49	h) $(w+x+y)^2$ *Ans.* 64	k) yx^3 *Ans.* 108
c) $(x+2)^2$ *Ans.* 25	f) y^2-x^2 *Ans.* 7	i) $w^2+x^2+y^2$ *Ans.* 26	l) $(yx)^3$ *Ans.* 1728

39. State whether each statement is true or false: **(13.1)**

   a) The set of whole numbers is closed under division,   *Ans.* false
      except for the division by zero.

   b) The set of even natural numbers is closed under ad-   *Ans.* true
      dition and multiplication.

   c) The set of $\{0, \frac{1}{2}, 1\}$ is closed under multiplication.   *Ans.* false since $\frac{1}{2}(\frac{1}{2})=\frac{1}{4}$

   d) The set of powers of 2 is closed under multiplication   *Ans.* true
      but not under addition.

   e) The set of natural numbers is closed under the opera-   *Ans.* true
      tion of squaring (multiplying a number by itself).

   f) The set of whole numbers is closed under operation of   *Ans.* false since $\frac{1}{2}(1+2)=1\frac{1}{2}$
      averaging two numbers.

Chapter 2

Simple Equations and Their Solution

1. UNDERSTANDING SIMPLE EQUATIONS AND THEIR SOLUTION

In elementary school, you studied fractions whose numerator and denominator are natural numbers. Such fractions were in use in ancient times. Since the fractions in use today are far more advanced than the fractions involved in elementary school arithmetic, we shall refer to arithmetic fractions according to the following definition:

An **arithmetic fraction** is a number expressible as a fraction whose numerator and denominator are natural numbers. A natural number is an arithmetic fraction since it may be expressed with a denominator of 1. A decimal is also an arithmetic fraction since its denominator is a power of 10.

Thus, $\frac{5}{1}$ or 5, $\frac{5}{7}$, $\frac{5}{3}$ or $1\frac{2}{3}$, and $\frac{21}{10}$ or 2.1 are arithmetic fractions.

An **equation** is a sentence stating that two expressions are equal or have the same value.

Thus, $2n = 8$, $8x = 4$, $5x - x = 4x$, and $x + 2y = 5$ are equations.

In this chapter, we shall consider only simple equations in one variable. Unless otherwise stated, assume that the replacement set of the variable in any equation in this chapter is the set of arithmetic fractions and 0.

In an equation, the expression to the left of the equals sign is called the **left member** or **left side** of the equation while the expression to the right is the **right member** or **right side** of the equation.

Thus, in the equation $6n = 3n - 9$, $6n$ is the left member or left side while $3n - 9$ is the right member or right side.

An **equation is a true statement** if both members are equal in value; a false statement if both members are not equal in value; and an open sentence if the truth or falsity of its members cannot be determined.

Thus, in $8x = 4$, if x is replaced by $\frac{1}{2}$, the result, $8(\frac{1}{2}) = 4$ is a true statement; while if n is replaced by any number other than $\frac{1}{2}$, such as $\frac{1}{4}$ or 5, the result is a false statement.

Identities and Equivalent Expressions

An **identity** is an equation which is true for all members in the replacement set while a **conditional equation** is not true for all such members. For the sake of simplicity, we shall refer to a conditional equation as an equation, as is customarily done.

Thus, $5x - x = 4x$ is an identity while $5x - x = 4$ is a conditional equation, or simply an equation.

Equivalent expressions in one variable are expressions that have the same value for every replacement of the variable by a member of the replacement set. In an identity, the sides of the identity are equivalent expressions.

Thus, in the identity $5x - x = 4x$, the two sides, $5x - x$ and $4x$ are equivalent expressions.

Substitution Principle for Equivalent Expressions

In any process, an expression may be substituted for an equivalent expression.

By using the substitution principle for equivalent expressions, $4x$ may be substituted for $5x - x$ in the equation $5x - x = 4$ to obtain $4x = 4$, which is a simpler equation. Also, an expression such as $5x + 2x - x + 5$ may be simplified by replacing $5x + 2x - x$ by its equivalent $6x$ to obtain a simpler expression $6x + 5$.

Properties of Equality

One of the properties of equality is the **symmetric property**, by means of which we can interchange the members or sides of an equation. In general, if $a = b$, then $b = a$.

Thus, using the symmetric property of equality, the equation $6n = 3n - 9$ may be changed into the equation $3n - 9 = 6n$.

Another property of equality is the **transitive property**, by means of which we can equate two expressions that are equivalent to a third expression. In general, if $a = b$ and $b = c$, then $a = c$.

Thus, if $y = 2x$ and $2x = 8$, then $y = 8$.

According to the third property of equality, a number or expression is equal to itself. This property is called the **reflexive property** of equality and its general statement is $a = a$.

A **root of an equation** is any member of the replacement set of the variable which when substituted for the variable makes the equation a true statement. A root of an equation is said to **satisfy the equation.**

Thus $\frac{1}{2}$ is a root of the equation $8x = 4$ since $8(\frac{1}{2}) = 4$ is a true statement. However, $\frac{1}{4}$ is not a root since $8(\frac{1}{4}) = 4$ is false. The root $\frac{1}{2}$ satisfies $8x = 4$.

The **solution set**, or **truth set**, of an equation is the set of its roots.

Thus, the solution set of $8x = 4$ is $\{\frac{1}{2}\}$.

Solving an equation is the process of finding its solution set.

Thus, the equation $8x = 4$ is solved when the solution set is found to be $\{\frac{1}{2}\}$. Also the equation $2x + 3 = 11$ is solved when the solution set is found to be $\{4\}$.

Checking or **verifying** an equation is the process of determining whether a given number is a root of the equation.

Thus, check in $2x + 3 = 11$ for $x = 4$ and $x = 5$ as follows:

$$
\begin{array}{ll|l}
2x + 3 = 11 & 2x + 3 = 11 & \textbf{Note.} \\
2(4) + 3 \overset{?}{=} 11 & 2(5) + 3 \overset{?}{=} 11 & (1) \text{ The symbol } \overset{?}{=} \text{ is read "should equal".} \\
8 + 3 \overset{?}{=} 11 & 10 + 3 \overset{?}{=} 11 & (2) \text{ The symbol } \neq \text{ is read "does not equal".} \\
11 = 11 & 13 \neq 11 &
\end{array}
$$

Hence, 4 is a root of $2x + 3 = 11$ since it satisfies the equation.

1.1 Checking an Equation to Determine a Root

By checking, determine which is a root of the equation:

a) Check $2n + 3n = 25$ for $n = 5$ and $n = 6$

Check: $n = 5$	$n = 6$
$2n + 3n = 25$	$2n + 3n = 25$
$2(5) + 3(5) \overset{?}{=} 25$	$2(6) + 3(6) \overset{?}{=} 25$
$10 + 15 \overset{?}{=} 25$	$12 + 18 \overset{?}{=} 25$
$25 = 25$	$30 \neq 25$

Ans. 5 is a root of $2n + 3n = 25$

b) Check $8x - 14 = 6x$ for $x = 6$ and $x = 7$

Check: $x = 6$	$x = 7$
$8x - 14 = 6x$	$8x - 14 = 6x$
$8(6) - 14 \overset{?}{=} 6(6)$	$8(7) - 14 \overset{?}{=} 6(7)$
$48 - 14 \overset{?}{=} 36$	$56 - 14 \overset{?}{=} 42$
$34 \neq 36$	$42 = 42$

Ans. 7 is a root of $8x - 14 = 6x$

1.2 Checking an Identity to Show That Any Given Value Is a Root

By checking the identity $4(x + 2) = 4x + 8$, show that x may have any of the following values:

a) $x = 10$ b) $x = 6$ c) $x = 4\frac{1}{2}$ d) $x = 3.2$

Check:

a)	b)	c)	d)
$4(x + 2) = 4x + 8$	$4(x + 2) = 4x + 8$	$4(x + 2) = 4x + 8$	$4(x + 2) = 4x + 8$
$4(10 + 2) \overset{?}{=} 4(10) + 8$	$4(6 + 2) \overset{?}{=} 4(6) + 8$	$4(4\frac{1}{2} + 2) \overset{?}{=} 4(4\frac{1}{2}) + 8$	$4(3.2 + 2) \overset{?}{=} 4(3.2) + 8$
$4(12) \overset{?}{=} 40 + 8$	$4(8) \overset{?}{=} 24 + 8$	$4(6\frac{1}{2}) \overset{?}{=} 18 + 8$	$4(5.2) \overset{?}{=} 12.8 + 8$
$48 = 48$	$32 = 32$	$26 = 26$	$20.8 = 20.8$

2. TRANSLATING IN VERBAL PROBLEMS TO OBTAIN EQUATIONS

In algebra, a simple verbal problem having one unknown is solved when the unknown is found. In the process, it is necessary to "translate" a verbal sentence into an equation. The first step in problems of this type is to let the unknown be represented by a variable.

Thus, if n represents the unknown in "Twice what number equals 12?", we obtain "$2n = 12$".

2.1 Translating into Equations

Translate into an equation, letting n represent the unknown number:
(You need not find the value of the unknown.)

a) 4 less than what number equals 8 ?   *Ans.* a) $n - 4 = 8$

b) One-half of what number equals 10 ?   b) $\frac{n}{2} = 10$

c) Ten times what number equals 20 ?   c) $10n = 20$

d) What number increased by 12 equals 17 ?   d) $n + 12 = 17$

e) Twice what number added to 8 is 16 ?   e) $2n + 8 = 16$

f) 15 less than three times what number is 27?   f) $3n - 15 = 27$

g) The sum of what number and twice the same number is 18 ?   g) $n + 2n = 18$

h) What number and 4 more equals five times the number ?   h) $n + 4 = 5n$

i) Twice the sum of a certain number and five is 24. What is the number ?   i) $2(n+5) = 24$

2.2 Matching Sentences and Equations

Match a sentence in Column 1 with an equation in Column 2:

Column 1

1. The product of 8 and a number is 40.
2. A number increased by 8 is 40.
3. 8 less than a number equals 40.
4. Eight times a number less 8 is 40.
5. Eight times the sum of a number and 8 is 40.
6. One-eighth of a number is 40.

Column 2

a) $n - 8 = 40$
b) $8(n+8) = 40$
c) $8n = 40$
d) $\frac{n}{8} = 40$
e) $8n - 8 = 40$
f) $n + 8 = 40$

Ans. *1* and *c*, *2* and *f*, *3* and *a*, *4* and *e*, *5* and *b*, *6* and *d*.

2.3 Representing Unknowns

Represent the unknown by a variable and obtain an equation for each problem:
(You need not solve each equation.)

a) A man worked for 5 hours and earned $8.75. What was his hourly wage ?

Ans. a) Let w = his hourly wage in dollars.
Then, $5w = 8.75$

b) How old is Henry now, if ten years ago, he was 23 years old ?

b) Let H = Henry's age now.
Then, $H - 10 = 23$

c) After gaining 12 lb , Mary weighed 120 lb. What was her previous weight ?

c) Let M = Mary's previous weight in lb.
Then, $M + 12 = 120$

d) A baseball team won four times as many games as it lost. How many games did it lose, if it played a total of 100 games ?

d) Let n = no. of games lost and
$4n$ = no. of games won.
Then, $n + 4n = 100$

3. SOLVING SIMPLE EQUATIONS USING INVERSE OPERATIONS

In mathematics, you may think of inverse operations as operations that undo each other. To understand the functions of inverse operations, think how often you do something and then you undo it. You earn money, then you spend it; you get up, then you lie down; you open a door, then you close it; you go out, then you go in. Of course, not everything that you do can be undone. Consider putting an egg together after you have fried it.

Addition and subtraction are inverse operations.   Also, **multiplication and division are inverse operations.** Figure (*a*) illustrates how addition undoes subtraction, and how subtraction undoes addition. Figure (*b*) illustrates how multiplication undoes division, and how division undoes multiplication.

1. Addition and subtraction are shown to be inverse operations since adding 5 to 10, then subtracting 5 from the result leads back to 10; or, subtracting 5 from 15, then adding 5 to the result leads back to 10.

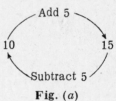

Fig. (*a*)

Suppose that in addition to having $10 you earn $5, making a total of $15. If now you spend $5, you will have the original amount of $10.

2. Multiplication and division are shown to be inverse operations since multiplying 10 by 5, then dividing the result by 5 leads back to 10; or, dividing 50 by 5, then multiplying the result by 5 leads back to 50.

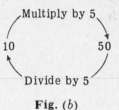

Fig. (*b*)

Suppose that the number of persons in a group of 10 is multiplied by 5, making a new group of 50 persons. If now the number is divided by 5, we will find that the number of persons is the original number 10.

An understanding of inverse operations helps us understand the solution of equations. To solve an equation, think of it as asking a question such as in each of the following equations:

Equation	Question Asked By Equation	Finding Root Of Equation
1. $n + 4 = 12$	What number plus 4 equals 12 ?	$n = 12 - 4 = 8$
2. $n - 4 = 12$	What number minus 4 equals 12 ?	$n = 12 + 4 = 16$
3. $4n = 12$	What number multiplied by 4 equals 12 ?	$n = 12 \div 4 = 3$
4. $\frac{n}{4} = 12$	What number divided by 4 equals 12 ?	$n = 12 \cdot 4 = 48$

Note the two operations involved in each of the above cases:
1. The equation, $n + 4 = 12$, involving **addition** is solved by **subtracting** 4 from 12.
2. The equation, $n - 4 = 12$, involving **subtraction** is solved by **adding** 4 to 12.
3. The equation, $4n = 12$, involving **multiplication** is solved by **dividing** 4 into 12.
4. The equation, $\frac{n}{4} = 12$, involving **division** is solved by **multiplying** 4 by 12.

Note in equations *1* and *2* the roles played by the inverse operations of addition and subtraction, one operation in the original equation on the left and the other in the related equation on the right. Similarly, note in equation *3* and *4*, the roles played by the inverse operations of multiplication and division.

Rule 1.   Addition and subtraction are inverse operations.
   Thus, in $n + 6 = 10$, n and 6 are **added**. To find n, **subtract** 6 from 10.
   In $n - 3 = 9$, 3 is **subtracted** from n. To find n, **add** 3 to 9.

Rule 2.   Multiplication and division are inverse operations.
   Thus, in $7n = 35$, n and 7 are **multiplied**. To find n, **divide** 7 into 35.
   In $\frac{n}{11} = 4$, n is **divided** by 11. To find n, **multiply** 11 by 4.

3.1 Rule 1: Addition and Subtraction are Inverse Operations

Solve each equation:

Equations Involving Addition of Unknown	Solutions Requiring Subtraction *Ans.*	Equations Involving Subtraction from Unknown	Solutions Requiring Addition *Ans.*
a) $x + 3 = 8$	a) $x = 8 - 3$ or 5	e) $x - 10 = 2$	e) $x = 2 + 10$ or 12
b) $5 + y = 13$	b) $y = 13 - 5$ or 8	f) $w - 20 = 12$	f) $w = 12 + 20$ or 32
c) $15 = a + 10$	c) $a = 15 - 10$ or 5	g) $18 = a - 13$	g) $a = 18 + 13$ or 31
d) $28 = 20 + b$	d) $b = 28 - 20$ or 8	h) $21 = b - 2$	h) $b = 21 + 2$ or 23

3.2 Rule 2: Multiplication and Division are Inverse Operations

Solve each equation:

Equations Involving Multiplication of Unknown	Solutions Requiring Division *Ans.*	Equations Involving Division of Unknown	Solutions Requiring Multiplication *Ans.*
a) $3x = 12$	a) $x = \frac{12}{3}$ or 4	e) $\frac{x}{3} = 12$	e) $x = 12 \cdot 3$ or 36
b) $12y = 3$	b) $y = \frac{3}{12}$ or $\frac{1}{4}$	f) $\frac{y}{12} = 3$	f) $y = 3 \cdot 12$ or 36
c) $35 = 7a$	c) $a = \frac{35}{7}$ or 5	g) $4 = \frac{a}{7}$	g) $a = 4 \cdot 7$ or 28
d) $7 = 35b$	d) $b = \frac{7}{35}$ or $\frac{1}{5}$	h) $7 = \frac{b}{4}$	h) $b = 7 \cdot 4$ or 28

3.3 Solving by Using Inverse Operations

Solve each equation, showing operation used to solve:

	Ans.		*Ans.*
a) $x + 5 = 20$	a) $x = 20 - 5$ or 15	i) $14 = a - 7$	i) $a = 14 + 7$ or 21
b) $x - 5 = 20$	b) $x = 20 + 5$ or 25	j) $14 = 7a$	j) $a = \frac{14}{7}$ or 2
c) $5x = 20$	c) $x = \frac{20}{5}$ or 4	k) $14 = \frac{a}{7}$	k) $a = 14(7)$ or 98
d) $\frac{x}{5} = 20$	d) $x = 20(5)$ or 100	l) $b - 8 = 2$	l) $b = 2 + 8$ or 10
e) $10 + y = 30$	e) $y = 30 - 10$ or 20	m) $8b = 2$	m) $b = \frac{2}{8}$ or $\frac{1}{4}$
f) $10y = 30$	f) $y = \frac{30}{10}$ or 3	n) $\frac{b}{8} = 2$	n) $b = 2(8)$ or 16
g) $\frac{y}{10} = 30$	g) $y = 30(10)$ or 300	o) $24 = 6 + c$	o) $c = 24 - 6$ or 18
h) $14 = a + 7$	h) $a = 14 - 7$ or 7	p) $6 = 24c$	p) $c = \frac{6}{24}$ or $\frac{1}{4}$

4. RULES FOR SOLVING EQUATIONS

Equivalent equations are equations having the same solution set; that is, the same root or or roots. In the previous section, equations were solved by changing, or transforming, them into equivalent equations using inverse operations.

Thus, $n + 4 = 12$ and $n = 12 - 4$ are equivalent equations.

Rules of Equality for Solving Equations

1. Addition Rule of Equality

To change an equation into an equivalent equation, the same number may be **added to** both sides.

2. Subtraction Rule of Equality

To change an equation into an equivalent equation, the same number may be **subtracted from** both sides.

3. Multiplication Rule of Equality

To change an equation into an equivalent equation, both sides may be **multiplied by** the same number.

4. Division Rule of Equality

To change an equation into an equivalent equation, both sides may be **divided by** the same number, except division by zero.

These four rules of equality may be summed up in one rule:

The Rule of Equality for Fundamental Operations

To change an equation into an equivalent equation, perform the same fundamental operation on both sides using the same number, except division by zero.

To understand these **Rules of Equality**, think of an **equality** as a **scale in balance**.

If only one side of a balanced scale is changed, the scale becomes unbalanced. To balance the scale, exactly the same change must be made on the other side. Similarly, if only one side of an equation is changed, the result need not be an equivalent equation. To obtain an equivalent equation, the same fundamental operation should be performed on both sides using the same number.

Balanced Scales

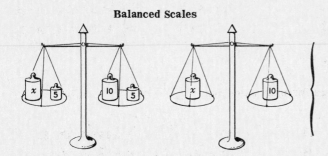

Thus, if 5 is subtracted from both sides of a balanced scale, the scale is still in balance.

EQUALITIES

$$x + 5 = 15$$
$$\underline{ - 5 = - 5}$$
$$x = 10$$

If 5 is subtracted from both sides of an equation, the result is an equivalent equation.

4.1 Using Rules of Equality

State the equality rule used to solve each equation:

a) $x + 15 = 21$ b) $40 = r - 8$ c) $25 = 5m$ d) $\frac{n}{8} = 3$ e) $24x = 8$

$\underline{-15 = -15}$ $\underline{+8 = +8}$ $\frac{25}{5} = \frac{5m}{5}$ $8 \cdot \frac{n}{8} = 8 \cdot 3$ $\frac{24x}{24} = \frac{8}{24}$

$x = 6$ $48 = r$ $5 = m$ $n = 24$ $x = \frac{1}{3}$

Ans. a) subtraction rule, *b)* addition rule, *c)* division rule, *d)* multiplication rule, *e)* division rule.

5. USING DIVISION TO SOLVE AN EQUATION

Division Rule of Equality
To change an equation into an equivalent equation,
both sides may be divided by the same number, except division by zero.

To Solve an Equation Using the Division Rule of Equality

Solve: $a)$ $2n = 16$ | $b)$ $16n = 2$

Procedure: Solutions:

1) **Divide both sides of the equation by the coefficient or multiplier of the variable:**

$$D_2 \quad \frac{2n}{2} = \frac{16}{2} \qquad\qquad D_{16} \quad \frac{16n}{16} = \frac{2}{16}$$

$$Ans. \ n = 8 \qquad\qquad Ans. \ n = \frac{1}{8}$$

2) **Check** the original equation:

$$
\begin{array}{c|c}
\text{Check:} \quad 2n = 16 & 16n = 2 \\
2(8) \overset{?}{=} 16 & 16(\tfrac{1}{8}) \overset{?}{=} 2 \\
16 = 16 & 2 = 2
\end{array}
$$

Note 1. "D" is a convenient symbol for "dividing both sides".
"D_2" means "divide both sides by 2".

Note 2. A common factor may be eliminated in $\dfrac{\overset{1}{2}n}{\underset{}{2}}$ and $\dfrac{\overset{1}{16}n}{\underset{}{16}}$.

5.1 Solving Equations with Natural Number Coefficients

Solve each equation:

$a)$ $\quad 7x = 35$ | $b)$ $\quad 35y = 7$ | $c)$ $\quad 33 = 11z$ | $d)$ $\quad 11 = 33w$

$$D_7 \quad \frac{7x}{7} = \frac{35}{7} \qquad D_{35} \quad \frac{35y}{35} = \frac{7}{35} \qquad D_{11} \quad \frac{33}{11} = \frac{11z}{11} \qquad D_{33} \quad \frac{11}{33} = \frac{33w}{33}$$

$$Ans. \quad x = 5 \qquad\qquad Ans. \quad y = \frac{1}{5} \qquad\qquad Ans. \ 3 = z \qquad\qquad Ans. \ \frac{1}{3} = w$$

Check: **Check:**   **Check:**   **Check:**

$$
\begin{array}{c|c|c|c}
7x = 35 & 35y = 7 & 33 = 11z & 11 = 33w \\
7(5) \overset{?}{=} 35 & 35(\tfrac{1}{5}) \overset{?}{=} 7 & 33 \overset{?}{=} 11(3) & 11 \overset{?}{=} 33(\tfrac{1}{3}) \\
35 = 35 & 7 = 7 & 33 = 33 & 11 = 11
\end{array}
$$

5.2 Division in Equations with Decimal Coefficients

Find each solution set:

$a)$ $\quad .3a = 9$ | $b)$ $\quad 1.2b = 48$ | $c)$ $\quad 15 = .05c$

$$D_{.3} \quad \frac{.3a}{.3} = \frac{9}{.3} \qquad D_{1.2} \quad \frac{1.2b}{1.2} = \frac{48}{1.2} \qquad D_{.05} \quad \frac{15}{.05} = \frac{.05c}{.05}$$

$$a = 30 \qquad\qquad b = 40 \qquad\qquad 300 = c$$

$Ans.$ $\{30\}$ $Ans.$ $\{40\}$ $Ans.$ $\{300\}$

Check: **Check:**   **Check:**

$$
\begin{array}{c|c|c}
.3a = 9 & 1.2b = 48 & 15 = .05c \\
.3(30) \overset{?}{=} 9 & 1.2(40) \overset{?}{=} 48 & 15 \overset{?}{=} .05(300) \\
9 = 9 & 48 = 48 & 15 = 15
\end{array}
$$

5.3 Solving Equations with Percents as Coefficients

Solve each equation. (*Hint: First, replace each percent by a decimal.*)

a) $22\% s = 88$

Since $22\% = .22$,

$\mathbf{D}_{.22}$ $\dfrac{.22s}{.22} = \dfrac{88}{.22}$

Ans. $s = 400$

Check:

$$22\% s = 88$$
$$(.22)(400) \overset{?}{=} 88$$
$$88 = 88$$

b) $75\% t = 18$

Since $75\% = .75$,

$\mathbf{D}_{.75}$ $\dfrac{.75t}{.75} = \dfrac{18}{.75}$

Ans. $t = 24$

Check:

$$75\% t = 18$$
$$(.75)(24) \overset{?}{=} 18$$
$$18 = 18$$

c) $72 = 2\% n$

Since $2\% = .02$,

$\mathbf{D}_{.02}$ $\dfrac{72}{.02} = \dfrac{.02n}{.02}$

Ans. $3600 = n$

Check:

$$72 = 2\% n$$
$$72 \overset{?}{=} (.02)(3600)$$
$$72 = 72$$

5.4 Solving Equations with Like Terms on One Side

Solve each equation. (*Hint: First, collect like terms.*)

a) $60 = 7x - x$
       $60 = 6x$

$\mathbf{D}_6$ $\dfrac{60}{6} = \dfrac{6x}{6}$

Ans. $10 = x$

Check:

$$60 = 7x - x$$
$$60 \overset{?}{=} 70 - 10$$
$$60 = 60$$

b) $3x + 5x = 48$
       $8x = 48$

$\mathbf{D}_8$ $\dfrac{8x}{8} = \dfrac{48}{8}$

Ans. $x = 6$

Check:

$$3x + 5x = 48$$
$$18 + 30 \overset{?}{=} 48$$
$$48 = 48$$

c) $7x - 2x = 55$
       $5x = 55$

$\mathbf{D}_5$ $\dfrac{5x}{5} = \dfrac{55}{5}$

Ans. $x = 11$

Check:

$$7x - 2x = 55$$
$$77 - 22 \overset{?}{=} 55$$
$$55 = 55$$

5.5 Division Rule in a Wage Problem

John worked 7 hr. and earned $8.54. What was his hourly wage?

Solution: Let h = his hourly wage in $.

Then, $7h = 8.54$

$\mathbf{D}_7$ $\dfrac{7h}{7} = \dfrac{8.54}{7}$

      $h = 1.22$

Ans. John's hourly wage was $1.22.

Check (the problem):

In 7 hr., John should earn $8.54.

Hence,

$$7(\$1.22) \overset{?}{=} \$8.54$$
$$\$8.54 = \$8.54$$

5.6 Division Rule in a Commission Problem

Mr. Black's commission rate was 3%. If he earned $66 in commission, how much did he sell?

Solution: Let s = Mr. Black's sales in $.

Then, $3\% s$ or $.03s = 66$

$\mathbf{D}_{.03}$ $\dfrac{.03s}{.03} = \dfrac{66}{.03}$

      $s = 2200$

Ans. Mr. Black's sales were $2200.

Check (the problem):

At 3%, Mr. Black's commission should be $66. Hence,

$$3\% \text{ of } \$2200 \overset{?}{=} \$66$$
$$(.03)(\$2200) \overset{?}{=} \$66$$
$$\$66 = \$66$$

6. USING MULTIPLICATION TO SOLVE AN EQUATION: RECIPROCALS AND MULTIPLICATIVE INVERSES

Multiplication Rule of Equality
To change an equation into an equivalent equation, both sides may be multiplied by the same number.

To Solve an Equation Using the Multiplication Rule of Equality

Solve: $a)\ \dfrac{w}{3} = 5$ | $b)\quad 10 = \dfrac{x}{7}$

Procedure:

Solutions:

1. **Multiply both sides of the equation by the divisor of the variable:**

$M_3 \qquad 3\cdot\dfrac{w}{3} = 5\cdot 3$ | $M_7 \quad 7\cdot 10 = \dfrac{x}{7}\cdot 7$

Ans. $\qquad w = 15$ | *Ans.* $70 = x$

2. **Check** the original equation:

Check: $\qquad \dfrac{w}{3} = 5$ | Check: $10 = \dfrac{x}{7}$

$\qquad \dfrac{15}{3} \overset{?}{=} 5$ | $10 \overset{?}{=} \dfrac{70}{7}$

$\qquad 5 = 5$ | $10 = 10$

Note 1. "M" is a convenient symbol for "multiplying both sides".
"M_3" means "multiply both sides by 3".

Note 2. A common factor may be eliminated in $\overset{1}{\cancel{3}}\cdot\dfrac{w}{\cancel{3}}$ and $\dfrac{x}{\cancel{7}}\cdot\dfrac{1}{\cancel{7}}$

Reciprocals or Multiplicative Inverses

The **reciprocal of a number** is 1 divided by the number except when the number is 0.

Thus, the reciprocal of 5 is $\dfrac{1}{5}$, and the reciprocal of $\dfrac{2}{3}$ is $1 \div \dfrac{2}{3}$, which is $\dfrac{3}{2}$.

In general, $\dfrac{1}{n}$ is the reciprocal of n when $n \neq 0$.

The **reciprocal of a number is also its multiplicative inverse** according to the following definition:

Multiplicative inverses are two numbers whose product is 1.

Thus, the product of $\dfrac{2}{3}$ and $\dfrac{3}{2}$, which is $\dfrac{2}{3}(\dfrac{3}{2}) = 1$. Also, the product, $5(\dfrac{1}{5}) = 1$. Hence, the same numbers are multiplicative inverses as well as reciprocals.

We may think of the reciprocal or multiplicative inverse of a fraction as the fraction obtained when its numerator and denominator are interchanged or "**inverted**". The idea of "inverting a fraction" is part of the following rule:

Dividing by a Fraction

To **divide by a fraction**, invert the fraction and multiply. Thus, $8 \div \dfrac{2}{3} = 8 \times \dfrac{3}{2}$ or 12. Hence, multiplying by $\dfrac{3}{2}$ is equivalent to dividing by $\dfrac{2}{3}$.

To Solve an Equation Whose Variable has a Fractional Coefficient

Solve: $a)\ \dfrac{2}{3}x = 8$ | $b)\quad \dfrac{5}{3}y = 25$

Procedure:

Solutions:

1. **Multiply both sides of the equation by the fractional coefficient inverted:**
(*instead of dividing by the fractional coefficient*)

$M_{3/2} \qquad \dfrac{3}{2}\cdot\dfrac{2}{3}x = 8\cdot\dfrac{3}{2}$ | $M_{3/5} \quad \dfrac{3}{5}\cdot\dfrac{5}{3}y = 25\cdot\dfrac{3}{5}$

Ans. $\qquad x = 12$ | *Ans.* $\quad y = 15$

2. **Check** the original equation:

Check: $\qquad \dfrac{2}{3}x = 8$ | Check: $\dfrac{5}{3}y = 25$

$\qquad \dfrac{2}{3}\cdot 12 \overset{?}{=} 8$ | $\dfrac{5}{3}\cdot 15 \overset{?}{=} 25$

$\qquad 8 = 8$ | $25 = 25$

Note. The "fractional coefficient inverted" is the reciprocal or multiplicative inverse of the coefficient.

6.1 Solving Equations with Natural Number Divisors

Solve each equation:

a)	b)	c)	d)
$\frac{x}{8} = 4$	$\frac{1}{3}y = 12$	$20 = \frac{z}{10}$	$.2 = \frac{w}{40}$
$M_8 \quad 8 \cdot \frac{x}{8} = 4 \cdot 8$	$M_3 \quad 3 \cdot \frac{1}{3}y = 12 \cdot 3$	$M_{10} \quad 10 \cdot 20 = \frac{z}{10} \cdot 10$	$M_{40} \quad 40(.2) = \frac{w}{40} \cdot 40$
Ans. $\quad x = 32$	*Ans.* $\quad y = 36$	*Ans.* $\quad 200 = z$	*Ans.* $\quad 8 = w$
Check:	**Check:**	**Check:**	**Check:**
$\frac{x}{8} = 4$	$\frac{1}{3}y = 12$	$20 = \frac{z}{10}$	$.2 = \frac{w}{40}$
$\frac{32}{8} \overset{?}{=} 4$	$\frac{1}{3}(36) \overset{?}{=} 12$	$20 \overset{?}{=} \frac{200}{10}$	$.2 \overset{?}{=} \frac{8}{40}$
$4 = 4$	$12 = 12$	$20 = 20$	$.2 = .2$

6.2 Solving Equations with Decimal Divisors

Find each solution set:

a)	b)	c)
$\frac{a}{.5} = 4$	$\frac{b}{.08} = 400$	$1.5 = \frac{c}{1.2}$
$M_{.5} \quad .5\left(\frac{a}{.5}\right) = 4(.5)$	$M_{.08} \quad .08\left(\frac{b}{.08}\right) = 400(.08)$	$M_{1.2} \quad 1.2(1.5) = \left(\frac{c}{1.2}\right)1.2$
$a = 2$	$b = 32$	$1.8 = c$
Ans. {2}	*Ans.* {32}	*Ans.* {1.8}

(*Check your answers.*)

6.3 Solving Equations with Fractional Coefficients

Solve each equation.
(*Hint: Multiply by the fractional coefficient inverted.*)

a)	b)	c)
$\frac{2}{5}x = 10$	$1\frac{1}{3}w = 30$	$c - \frac{1}{4}c = 24$
Solutions:	$\frac{4}{3}w = 30$	$\frac{3}{4}c = 24$
$M_{5/2} \quad \frac{5}{2} \cdot \frac{2}{5}x = 10\left(\frac{5}{2}\right)$	$M_{3/4} \quad \frac{3}{4} \cdot \frac{4}{3}w = 30\left(\frac{3}{4}\right)$	$M_{4/3} \quad \frac{4}{3} \cdot \frac{3}{4}c = 24\left(\frac{4}{3}\right)$
Ans. $\quad x = 25$	*Ans.* $\quad w = 22\frac{1}{2}$	*Ans.* $\quad c = 32$

(*Check your answers.*)

6.4 Solving Equations with Percents as Coefficients

Solve each equation.
(*Hint. Replace a percent by a fraction if the percent equals an easy fraction.*)

a)	b)	c)
$66\frac{2}{3}\% s = 22$	$87\frac{1}{2}\% t = 35$	$120\% w = 72$
Solutions:		
$\frac{2}{3}s = 22$	$\frac{7}{8}t = 35$	$\frac{6}{5}w = 72$
$M_{3/2} \quad \frac{3}{2} \cdot \frac{2}{3}s = 22\left(\frac{3}{2}\right)$	$M_{8/7} \quad \frac{8}{7} \cdot \frac{7}{8}t = 35\left(\frac{8}{7}\right)$	$M_{5/6} \quad \frac{5}{6} \cdot \frac{6}{5}w = 72\left(\frac{5}{6}\right)$
Ans. $\quad s = 33$	*Ans.* $\quad t = 40$	*Ans.* $\quad w = 60$

(*Check your answers.*)

6.5 Multiplication Rule in Investment Problem

Mr. White receives 5% on a stock investment. If his interest at the end of one year was $140, how large was his investment?

Solution:

Let s = the sum invested in $.

then, $5\% s$ or $\dfrac{s}{20} = 140$

$M_{20} \qquad 20 \cdot \dfrac{s}{20} = 140\,(20)$

$\qquad\qquad\qquad s = 2800$

Ans. The investment was $2800.

Check (the problem):

5% of the investment should be $140.

Hence,

$5\%\,(\$2800) \overset{?}{=} \$140$

$\$140 = \$140$

7. USING SUBTRACTION TO SOLVE AN EQUATION

> **Subtraction Rule of Equality**
> To change an equation into an equivalent equation, the same number may be subtracted from both sides.

To Solve an Equation Using the Subtraction Rule of Equality

Solve : a) $w + 12 = 19$ b) $28 = 11 + x$

Procedure:

1. Subtract from both sides the number added to the variable:

2. Check the original equation:

Solutions :

$\qquad w + 12 = 19$

$S_{12} \qquad -12 = -12$

Ans. $w \quad = \quad 7$

$\qquad\qquad 28 = 11 + x$

$S_{11} \qquad -11 = -11$

Ans. $17 = \quad x$

Check:

$w + 12 = 19$

$7 + 12 \overset{?}{=} 19$

$19 = 19$

$28 = 11 + x$

$28 \overset{?}{=} 11 + 17$

$28 = 28$

Note. "S" is a convenient symbol for "subtracting from both sides".
"S_{11}" means "subtract 11 from both sides".

7.1 Subtraction Rule in Equations Containing Natural Numbers

Find each solution set:

a) $\quad r + 8 = 13$

$S_8 \qquad -8 = -8$

Ans. {5} $\quad r \quad = 5$

Check:

$r + 8 = 13$

$5 + 8 \overset{?}{=} 13$

$13 = 13$

b) $\quad 15 + t = 60$

$S_{15} \quad -15 \quad = -15$

Ans. {45} $\qquad t = 45$

Check:

$15 + t = 60$

$15 + 45 \overset{?}{=} 60$

$60 = 60$

c) $\quad 110 = s + 20$

$S_{20} \quad -20 = -20$

Ans. {90} $\quad 90 = s$

Check:

$110 = s + 20$

$110 \overset{?}{=} 90 + 20$

$110 = 110$

7.2 Subtraction Rule in Equations Containing Fractions or Decimals

Solve each equation:

a) $\quad b + \dfrac{1}{3} = 3\dfrac{2}{3}$

$S_{\frac{1}{3}} \qquad -\dfrac{1}{3} = -\dfrac{1}{3}$

Ans. $b \quad = 3\dfrac{1}{3}$

Check:

$b + \dfrac{1}{3} = 3\dfrac{2}{3}$

$3\dfrac{1}{3} + \dfrac{1}{3} \overset{?}{=} 3\dfrac{2}{3}$

$3\dfrac{2}{3} = 3\dfrac{2}{3}$

b) $\quad 2\dfrac{3}{4} + c = 8\dfrac{1}{2}$

$S_{2\frac{3}{4}} \quad -2\dfrac{3}{4} \quad = -2\dfrac{3}{4}$

Ans. $\qquad c = 5\dfrac{3}{4}$

Check:

$2\dfrac{3}{4} + c = 8\dfrac{1}{2}$

$2\dfrac{3}{4} + 5\dfrac{3}{4} \overset{?}{=} 8\dfrac{1}{2}$

$8\dfrac{1}{2} = 8\dfrac{1}{2}$

c) $\quad 20.8 = d + 6.9$

$S_{6.9} \quad -6.9 = -6.9$

Ans. $\quad 13.9 = d$

Check:

$20.8 = d + 6.9$

$20.8 \overset{?}{=} 13.9 + 6.9$

$20.8 = 20.8$

7.3 Subtraction Rule in Problem Solving

After an increase of 22¢, the price of grade A eggs rose to 81¢. What was the original price?

Solution:

Let p = original price in ¢.

Then, $p + 22 = 81$

S_{22} $\underline{-22 = -22}$

$\phantom{S_{22}}$ $p = 59$

Ans. The original price was 59¢.

Check (the problem):

After increasing 22¢, the new price should be 81¢.

Hence,

$$59¢ + 22¢ \overset{?}{=} 81¢$$
$$81¢ = 81¢$$

7.4 Subtraction Rule in Problem Solving

Harold's height is 5 ft. 3 in. If he is 9 in. taller than John, how tall is John?

Solution:

Let J = John's height in ft.

Then, $J + \frac{3}{4} = 5\frac{1}{4}$ (9 in. = $\frac{3}{4}$ ft.)

$S_{3/4}$ $\underline{-\frac{3}{4} = -\frac{3}{4}}$

$\phantom{S_{3/4}}$ $J \phantom{+\frac{3}{4}} = 4\frac{1}{2}$

Ans. John is $4\frac{1}{2}$ ft. or 4 ft. 6 in. tall.

Check (the problem):

9 in. more than John's height should equal 5 ft. 3 in.

$$4\frac{1}{2} \text{ ft.} + \frac{3}{4} \text{ ft.} \overset{?}{=} 5\frac{1}{4} \text{ ft.}$$
$$5\frac{1}{4} \text{ ft.} = 5\frac{1}{4} \text{ ft.}$$

8. USING ADDITION TO SOLVE AN EQUATION

Addition Rule of Equality

To change an equation into an equivalent equation, the same number may be added to both sides.

To Solve an Equation Using the Addition Rule of Equality

Solve: *a*) $n - 19 = 21$ *b*) $17 = m - 8$

Procedure:

Solutions:

1. Add to both sides the number subtracted from the variable:

 $n - 19 = 21$ $\qquad$ $17 = m - 8$

A_{19} $\quad \underline{+19 = +19}$ $\qquad$ A_8 $\quad \underline{+8 = +8}$

Ans. $\quad n = 40$ $\qquad$ *Ans.* $\quad 25 = m$

2. Check the original equation:

Check: $\quad n - 19 = 21$ $\qquad$ **Check:** $17 = m - 8$

 $40 - 19 \overset{?}{=} 21$ $\qquad$ $17 \overset{?}{=} 25 - 8$

 $21 = 21$ $\qquad\qquad$ $17 = 17$

Note. "A" is a convenient symbol for "adding to both sides".

 "A_{19}" means "add 19 to both sides".

8.1 Addition Rule in Equations Containing Natural Numbers

Find each solution set:

a) $w - 10 = 19$
A_{10} $\quad \underline{+10 = +10}$
$\phantom{A_{10}}$ $w = 29$
Ans. {29}
Check:
 $w - 10 = 19$
 $29 - 10 \overset{?}{=} 19$
 $19 = 19$

b) $x - 19 = 10$
A_{19} $\quad \underline{+19 = +19}$
$\phantom{A_{19}}$ $x = 29$
Ans. {29}
Check:
 $x - 19 = 10$
 $29 - 19 \overset{?}{=} 10$
 $10 = 10$

c) $7 = y - 82$
A_{82} $\quad \underline{+82 = +82}$
$\phantom{A_{82}}$ $89 = y$
Ans. {89}
Check:
 $7 = y - 82$
 $7 \overset{?}{=} 89 - 82$
 $7 = 7$

d) $82 = z - 7$
A_7 $\quad \underline{+ 7 = + 7}$
 $89 = z$
Ans. {89}
Check:
 $82 = z - 7$
 $82 \overset{?}{=} 89 - 7$
 $82 = 82$

8.2 Addition Rule in Equations Containing Fractions or Decimals

Solve each equation:

a) $h - \frac{3}{8} = 5\frac{1}{4}$

$\mathbf{A}_{3/8} \quad + \frac{3}{8} = \frac{3}{8}$

$Ans. \quad h \quad = 5\frac{5}{8}$

(*Check your answers.*)

b) $j - 20\frac{7}{12} = 1\frac{1}{12}$

$\mathbf{A}_{20\frac{7}{12}} \quad + 20\frac{7}{12} = 20\frac{7}{12}$

$Ans. \quad j \quad = 21\frac{2}{3}$

c) $12.5 = m - 2.9$

$\mathbf{A}_{2.9} \quad + 2.9 = + 2.9$

$Ans. \quad 15.4 = m$

8.3 Addition Rule in Problem Solving

A drop of $8°$ brought the temperature to $64°$. What was the original temperature?

Solution:

Let t = original temperature in $°$.

Then, $t - 8 = 64$

$\mathbf{A}_8 \qquad + 8 = + 8$

$\qquad t \quad = 72$

Ans. The original temperature was $72°$.

Check (the problem):

The original temperature, dropped $8°$, should become $64°$.

Hence,

$72° - 8° \overset{?}{=} 64°$

$64° = 64°$

8.4 Addition Rule in Problem Solving

After giving 15 marbles to Sam, Joe has 43 left. How many did Joe have originally?

Solution:

Let m = the original no. of marbles.

Then, $m - 15 = 43$

$\mathbf{A}_{15} \qquad + 15 = + 15$

$\qquad m \quad = 58$

Ans. Sam had 58 marbles at first.

Check (the problem):

The original number of marbles, less 15, should be 43.

Hence,

$58 \text{ marbles} - 15 \text{ marbles} \overset{?}{=} 43 \text{ marbles}$

$43 \text{ marbles} = 43 \text{ marbles}$

9. USING TWO OR MORE OPERATIONS TO SOLVE AN EQUATION

In equations where two operations are performed upon the variable, two inverse operations may be needed to solve the equation.

Thus, in $2x + 7 = 19$, the two operations upon the variable are **multiplication and addition.** To solve, use **division and subtraction**, performing subtraction first.

Also, in $\frac{x}{3} - 5 = 2$, the two operations upon the variable are **division and subtraction.** To solve, use **multiplication and addition**, performing addition first.

To Solve Equations Using Two Inverse Operations

Procedure:

Solve: a) $2x + 7 = 19$

Solutions:

b) $\frac{x}{3} - 5 = 2$

1. Perform **addition** to undo subtraction, or **subtraction** to undo addition:

a) $2x + 7 = 19$

$\mathbf{S}_7 \qquad -7 = -7$

$\qquad 2x \quad = 12$

b) $\frac{x}{3} - 5 = 2$

$\mathbf{A}_5 \qquad + 5 = +5$

$\qquad \frac{x}{3} \quad = 7$

2. Perform **multiplication** to undo division, or **division** to undo **multiplication**:

$\mathbf{D}_2 \qquad \frac{2x}{2} = \frac{12}{2}$

Ans. $\qquad x = 6$

$\mathbf{M}_3 \qquad 3 \cdot \frac{x}{3} = 3 \cdot 7$

Ans. $\qquad x = 21$

3. **Check** in the original equation:

Check: $2x + 7 = 19$

$2(6) + 7 \overset{?}{=} 19$

$19 = 19$

Check: $\frac{x}{3} - 5 = 2$

$\frac{21}{3} - 5 \overset{?}{=} 2$

$2 = 2$

9.1 Using Two Inverse Operations to Solve an Equation

Solve each equation:

a)

$2x + 7 = 11$

S_7 $\quad -7 = -7$

$\quad 2x \quad = 4$

D_2 $\quad \dfrac{2x}{2} = \dfrac{4}{2}$

Ans. $\quad x = 2$

Check:

$2x + 7 = 11$

$2(2) + 7 \overset{?}{=} 11$

$4 + 7 \overset{?}{=} 11$

$11 = 11$

b)

$3x - 5 = 7$

A_5 $\quad +5 = +5$

$\quad 3x \quad = 12$

D_3 $\quad \dfrac{3x}{3} = \dfrac{12}{3}$

Ans. $\quad x = 4$

Check:

$3x - 5 = 7$

$3(4) - 5 \overset{?}{=} 7$

$12 - 5 \overset{?}{=} 7$

$7 = 7$

c)

$\dfrac{x}{3} + 5 = 7$

S_5 $\quad -5 = -5$

$\quad \dfrac{x}{3} \quad = 2$

M_3 $\quad 3 \cdot \dfrac{x}{3} = 3 \cdot 2$

Ans. $\quad x = 6$

Check:

$\dfrac{x}{3} + 5 = 7$

$\dfrac{6}{3} + 5 \overset{?}{=} 7$

$2 + 5 \overset{?}{=} 7$

$7 = 7$

d)

$\dfrac{x}{5} - 3 = 7$

A_3 $\quad +3 = 3$

$\quad \dfrac{x}{5} \quad = 10$

M_5 $\quad 5 \cdot \dfrac{x}{5} = 5 \cdot 10$

Ans. $\quad x = 50$

Check:

$\dfrac{x}{5} - 3 = 7$

$\dfrac{50}{5} - 3 \overset{?}{=} 7$

$10 - 3 \overset{?}{=} 7$

$7 = 7$

9.2 Solving Equations with Like Terms on the Same Side

Solve each equation. (*Hint: Combine like terms first.*)

a)

$8n + 4n - 3 = 9$

$\quad 12n - 3 = 9$

A_3 $\quad +3 = 3$

$\quad 12n \quad = 12$

D_{12} $\quad \dfrac{12n}{12} = \dfrac{12}{12}$

Ans. $\quad n = 1$

b)

$13n + 4 + n = 39$

$\quad 14n + 4 = 39$

S_4 $\quad -4 = -4$

$\quad 14n \quad = 35$

D_{14} $\quad \dfrac{14n}{14} = \dfrac{35}{14}$

Ans. $\quad n = 2\tfrac{1}{2}$

c)

$10 = 7 + n - \dfrac{n}{2}$

$10 = 7 + \dfrac{n}{2}$

S_7 $\quad -7 = -7$

$\quad 3 = \dfrac{n}{2}$

M_2 $\quad 2 \cdot 3 = (\dfrac{n}{2}) 2$

Ans. $\quad 6 = n$

(*Check your answers.*)

9.3 Solving Equations with Like Terms on Both Sides

Find each solution set. (*Hint: First, add or subtract to collect like terms on the same side.*)

a)

$\quad 5n = 40 - 3n$

A_{3n} $\quad +3n = +3n$

$\quad 8n = 40$

D_8 $\quad \dfrac{8n}{8} = \dfrac{40}{8}$

$\quad n = 5$

Ans. {5}

(*Check your answers.*)

b)

$\quad 4u + 5 = 5u - 30$

A_{30} $\quad +30 = +30$

$\quad 4u + 35 = 5u$

S_{4u} $\quad -4u = -4u$

$\quad 35 = u$

Ans. {35}

c)

$\quad 3r + 10 = 2r + 20$

S_{10} $\quad -10 = -10$

$\quad 3r = 2r + 10$

S_{2r} $\quad -2r = -2r$

$\quad r = 10$

Ans. {10}

9.4 Solving Equations in Which the Variable is a Divisor

Solve each equation. (*Hint: First, multiply both sides by the variable.*)

a)

$\quad \dfrac{8}{x} = 2$

M_x $\quad x(\dfrac{8}{x}) = 2x$

$\quad 8 = 2x$

D_2 $\quad \dfrac{8}{2} = \dfrac{2x}{2}$

Ans. $\quad 4 = x$

b)

$\quad 12 = \dfrac{3}{y}$

M_y $\quad 12y = (\dfrac{3}{y})y$

$\quad 12y = 3$

D_{12} $\quad \dfrac{12y}{12} = \dfrac{3}{12}$

Ans. $\quad y = \tfrac{1}{4}$

c)

$\quad \dfrac{7}{x} = \dfrac{1}{5}$

M_x $\quad x \cdot \dfrac{7}{x} = \dfrac{1}{5}x$

$\quad 7 = \dfrac{x}{5}$

M_5 $\quad 5 \cdot 7 = (\dfrac{x}{5})5$

Ans. $\quad 35 = x$

d)

$\quad \dfrac{1}{7} = \dfrac{3}{x}$

M_x $\quad \dfrac{1}{7}x = \dfrac{3}{x} \cdot x$

$\quad \dfrac{x}{7} = 3$

M_7 $\quad 7 \cdot \dfrac{x}{7} = 3(7)$

Ans. $\quad x = 21$

(*Check your answers.*)

9.5 Solving Equations whose Variable has a Fractional Coefficient

a) Solve: $\frac{3}{8}x = 9$

Solutions:

Using One Operation	Using Two Operations
a) $\frac{3}{8}x = 9$	*a*) $\frac{3}{8}x = 9$
$M_{8/3}$ $\frac{8}{3} \cdot \frac{3}{8}x = \frac{8}{3} \cdot 9$	M_8 $8 \cdot \frac{3}{8}x = 8 \cdot 9$
Ans. $x = 24$	$3x = 72$
	D_3 $\frac{3x}{3} = \frac{72}{3}$
	Ans. $x = 24$

b) Solve: $25 = \frac{5}{4}x$

Solutions:

Using One Operation	Using Two Operations
b) $25 = \frac{5}{4}x$	*b*) $25 = \frac{5}{4}x$
$M_{4/5}$ $\frac{4}{5} \cdot 25 = \frac{4}{5} \cdot \frac{5}{4}x$	M_4 $4(25) = 4 \cdot \frac{5}{4}x$
Ans. $20 = x$	$100 = 5x$
	D_5 $\frac{100}{5} = \frac{5x}{5}$
	Ans. $20 = x$

(*Check your answers.*)

9.6 Solving More Difficult Equations

a) $\frac{3}{4}y - 5 = 7$

A_5 $\underline{+5 = +5}$

       $\frac{3}{4}y = 12$

$M_{4/3}$ $\frac{4}{3} \cdot \frac{3}{4}y = \frac{4}{3} \cdot 12$

Ans. $y = 16$

b) $8 + \frac{2}{7}b = 20$

S_8 $\underline{-8 \qquad = -8}$

       $\frac{2}{7}b = 12$

$M_{7/2}$ $\frac{7}{2} \cdot \frac{2}{7}b = \frac{7}{2} \cdot 12$

Ans. $b = 42$

c) $48 - \frac{5}{3}w = 23$

$A_{\frac{5}{3}w}$ $\underline{+\frac{5}{3}w = +\frac{5}{3}w}$

      $48 = \frac{5}{3}w + 23$

S_{23} $\underline{-23 \qquad = \qquad -23}$

      $25 = \frac{5}{3}w$

$M_{3/5}$ $\frac{3}{5} \cdot 25 = \frac{3}{5} \cdot \frac{5}{3}w$

Ans. $15 = w$

(*Check your answers.*)

9.7 Using Two Operations in Problem Solving

a) How many boys are there in a class of 36 pupils if the number of girls is 6 more?

Solution:

a)   Let b = the number of boys

     Then $b + 6$ = the number of girls

         $b + b + 6 = 36$

S_6 $2b + 6 = 36$

D_2 $2b = 30$

         $b = 15$

Ans. There are 15 boys.

(*Check your answers.*)

b) How many boys are there in a class of 36 pupils if the number of girls is three times as many?

Solution:

b)   Let b = the number of boys

     Then $3b$ = the number of girls

         $b + 3b = 36$

D_4 $4b = 36$

         $b = 9$

Ans. There are 9 boys.

9.8 Using Two Operations in Problem Solving

Paul has $2.60 in his bank. By adding equal deposits each week for 20 weeks, he hopes to have $7.80. How much should each weekly deposit be?

Solution:

     Let d = no. of cents in each deposit

Then $20d + 260 = 780$

S_{260} $\underline{-260 = -260}$

D_{20} $20d = 520$

         $d = 26$

Ans. He must deposit 26¢ a week.

Check (the problem):

20 deposits and $2.60 should equal the total of $7.80.

Hence,

$20(\$.26) + \$2.60 \overset{?}{=} \$7.80$

$\$5.20 + \$2.60 \overset{?}{=} \$7.80$

$\$7.80 = \$7.80$

9.9 Using Two Operations in Problem Solving

Mr. Richards sold his house for $9000. His loss amounted to two-fifths of his cost. What did the house cost him?

Solution:

Let c = the cost in $

Then $9000 = c - \frac{2}{5}c$

$9000 = \frac{3}{5}c$

$M_{5/3}$ $\frac{5}{3} \cdot 9000 = \frac{5}{3} \cdot \frac{3}{5}c$

$15,000 = c$

Ans. The cost was $15,000.

Check (the problem):

If $15,000 is the cost, the loss is $\frac{2}{5} \cdot \$15,000$ or $6000. The selling price of $9000 should be the cost minus the loss. Hence,

$\$9000 \overset{?}{=} \$15,000 - \$6000$

$\$9000 = \$9000$

SUPPLEMENTARY PROBLEMS

1. By checking, determine which value is a root of the equation: **(1.1)**
   a) $3x + 4x = 42$ for $x = 4, 6$ and 8 *Ans.* $x = 6$
   b) $3n + 14 = 47$ for $n = 9, 10$ and 11 *Ans.* $n = 11$
   c) $6y - 48 = 2y$ for $y = 8, 10$ and 12 *Ans.* $y = 12$

2. By checking, show that x may have any of the following values in the identity $2(x - 3) = 2x - 6$:
   a) $x = 10$, b) $x = 6$, c) $x = 4\frac{1}{2}$, d) $x = 3.1$ **(1.2)**

3. Translate into an equation, letting n represent the number: **(2.1)**
   (*You need not find the value of the unknown.*)
   a) What number diminished by 8 equals 13?   *Ans.* $n - 8 = 13$
   b) Two-thirds of what number equals 10?   *Ans.* $\frac{2}{3}n = 10$
   c) Three times the sum of a number and six is 33. What is the number? *Ans.* $3(n + 6) = 33$
   d) What number increased by 20 equals three times the same number? *Ans.* $n + 20 = 3n$
   e) What number increased by 5 equals twice the same number decreased by 4? *Ans.* $n + 5 = 2n - 4$

4. Match the statement in *Column 1* with the equations in *Column 2*: **(2.2)**

Column 1	*Column 2*
1. The sum of 8 and twice a number is 18.	a) $\frac{n}{8} + 2 = 18$
2. Twice a number less 8 is 18.	b) $8(n - 2) = 18$
3. Twice the sum of a number and 8 is 18.	c) $\frac{1}{2}(8 - n) = 18$
4. Eight times the difference of a number and 2 is 18.	d) $2(n + 8) = 18$
5. One-half the difference of 8 and a number is 18.	e) $2n + 8 = 18$
6. 2 more than one-eighth of a number is 18.	f) $\frac{n}{2} - 8 = 18$
7. 8 less than half a number is 18.	g) $2n - 8 = 18$

Ans. *1* and *e*, *2* and *g*, *3* and *d*, *4* and *b*, *5* and *c*, *6* and *a*, *7* and *f*.

5. Letting n represent the number of games lost, obtain an equation for each problem: **(2.3)**
   (*You need not solve each equation.*)
   a) A team won three times as many games as it lost.
      It played a total of 52 games.   *Ans. a)* $n + 3n = 52$
   b) A team won 20 games more than it lost.
      It played a total of 84 games.   *Ans. b)* $n + n + 20 = 84$
   c) A team won 15 games less than twice the number lost.
      It played a total of 78 games.   *Ans. c)* $n + 2n - 15 = 78$

6. Solve each equation: (3.1)

a) $a+5=9$ $Ans.\ a=4$ e) $x+11=21+8$ $Ans.\ x=18$ i) $45=m-13$ $Ans.\ m=58$

b) $7+b=15$ $Ans.\ b=8$ f) $27+13=18+y$ $Ans.\ y=22$ j) $22=n-50$ $Ans.\ n=72$

c) $20=c+12$ $Ans.\ c=8$ g) $h-6=14$ $Ans.\ h=20$ k) $x-42=80-75$ $Ans.\ x=47$

d) $75=55+d$ $Ans.\ d=20$ h) $k-14=6$ $Ans.\ k=20$ l) $100-31=y-84$ $Ans.\ y=153$

7. Solve each equation: (3.2)

a) $4p=48$ d) $4n=2$ g) $\frac{t}{5}=6$ j) $\frac{y}{12}=\frac{3}{2}$

b) $10r=160$ e) $12w=4$ h) $\frac{u}{65}=1$ k) $\frac{a}{10}=\frac{2}{5}$

c) $25s=35$ f) $24x=21$ i) $\frac{x}{15}=4$ l) $\frac{1}{3}b=\frac{5}{6}$

$Ans.$ a) $p=12$ d) $n=\frac{1}{2}$ g) $t=30$ j) $y=18$

b) $r=16$ e) $w=\frac{1}{3}$ h) $u=65$ k) $a=4$

c) $s=\frac{7}{5}$ or $1\frac{2}{5}$ f) $x=\frac{7}{8}$ i) $x=60$ l) $b=\frac{5}{2}$ or $2\frac{1}{2}$

8. Solve each equation: (3.3)

a) $n+8=24$ e) $3+y=15$ i) $16=y-20$ m) $x+\frac{1}{3}=9$

b) $n-8=24$ f) $15=y-3$ j) $16=\frac{y}{20}$ n) $x-\frac{1}{3}=9$

c) $8n=24$ g) $15=3y$ k) $\frac{y}{20}=16$ o) $\frac{1}{3}x=9$

d) $\frac{n}{8}=24$ h) $15=\frac{y}{3}$ l) $16+y=20$ p) $\frac{x}{9}=\frac{1}{3}$

$Ans.$ a) $n=16$ c) $n=3$ e) $y=12$ g) $y=5$ i) $y=36$ k) $y=320$ m) $x=8\frac{2}{3}$ o) $x=27$

b) $n=32$ d) $n=192$ f) $y=18$ h) $y=45$ j) $y=320$ l) $y=4$ n) $x=9\frac{1}{3}$ p) $x=3$

9. Solve each equation: (3.3)

a) $x+11=14$ f) $h-3=7\frac{1}{2}$ k) $11r=55$ p) $6\frac{1}{2}=\frac{l}{2}$

b) $11+y=24$ g) $35=m-20\frac{1}{3}$ l) $44s=44$ q) $1.7=\frac{n}{3}$

c) $22=13+a$ h) $17\frac{3}{4}=n-2\frac{1}{4}$ m) $10t=5$ r) $100=\frac{h}{.7}$

d) $45=b+33$ i) $x+1.2=5.7$ n) $8x=3$ s) $24=\frac{t}{.5}$

e) $z-9=3$ j) $10.8=y-3.2$ o) $3y=0$ t) $.009=\frac{x}{1000}$

$Ans.$ a) $x=3$ d) $b=12$ g) $m=55\frac{1}{3}$ j) $y=14$ m) $t=\frac{1}{2}$ p) $l=13$ s) $t=12$

b) $y=13$ e) $z=12$ h) $n=20$ k) $r=5$ n) $x=\frac{3}{8}$ q) $n=5.1$ t) $x=9$

c) $a=9$ f) $h=10\frac{1}{2}$ i) $x=4.5$ l) $s=1$ o) $y=0$ r) $h=70$

10. State the equality rule used in each: (4.1)

a) $6r=30$ c) $30=\frac{r}{6}$ e) $100x=5$

    $\frac{6r}{6}=\frac{30}{6}$ $6(30)=6\cdot\frac{r}{6}$ $\frac{100x}{100}=\frac{5}{100}$

    $r=5$ $180=r$ $x=\frac{1}{20}$

b) $30=r-6$ d) $30=6+r$ f) $100=\frac{y}{5}$

    $\underline{+\ 6=\ +6}$ $\underline{-\ 6=-6}$ $5(100)=5(\frac{y}{5})$

    $36=r$ $24=r$ $500=y$

$Ans.$ addition rule in (b), subtraction rule in (d), multiplication rule in (c) and (f), division rule in (a) and (e).

11. Solve each equation: (5.1)

a) $12x=60$ b) $60y=12$ c) $24=2z$ d) $2=24w$ e) $6r=9$ f) $9s=6$ g) $10=4t$ h) $4=10u$

$Ans.$ a) $x=5$ b) $y=\frac{1}{5}$ c) $12=z$ d) $\frac{1}{12}=w$ e) $r=\frac{3}{2}$ f) $s=\frac{2}{3}$ g) $\frac{5}{2}=t$ h) $\frac{2}{5}=u$

12. Find each solution set: (5.2)

$a)\ .7a = 21$ $\qquad$ $c)\ 24 = .06c$ $\qquad$ $e)\ .1h = 100$ $\qquad$ $g)\ 25.2 = .12k$

$b)\ 1.1b = 55$ $\qquad$ $d)\ 18 = .009d$ $\qquad$ $f)\ .6j = .96$ $\qquad$ $h)\ 7.5 = .015m$

Ans. $a)\ \{30\}$ $\qquad$ $c)\ \{400\}$ $\qquad$ $e)\ \{1000\}$ $\qquad$ $g)\ \{210\}$

$b)\ \{50\}$ $\qquad$ $d)\ \{2000\}$ $\qquad$ $f)\ \{1.6\}$ $\qquad$ $h)\ \{500\}$

13. Solve each equation: (5.3)

$a)\ 10\%s = 7$ $\qquad$ $c)\ 18 = 3\%n$ $\qquad$ $e)\ 5\%m = 13$ $\qquad$ $g)\ .23 = 1\%y$

$b)\ 25\%t = 3$ $\qquad$ $d)\ 14 = 70\%w$ $\qquad$ $f)\ 17\%x = 6.8$ $\qquad$ $h)\ 3.69 = 90\%z$

Ans. $a)\ s = 70$ $\qquad$ $c)\ 600 = n$ $\qquad$ $e)\ m = 260$ $\qquad$ $g)\ 23 = y$

$b)\ t = 12$ $\qquad$ $d)\ 20 = w$ $\qquad$ $f)\ x = 40$ $\qquad$ $h)\ 4.1 = z$

14. Solve each equation: (5.4)

$a)\ 14 = 3x - x$ $\qquad$ $c)\ 8z - 3z = 45$ $\qquad$ $e)\ 24 = 4\frac{1}{2}x - \frac{x}{2}$ $\qquad$ $g)\ 7\frac{1}{2}z - 7z = 28$

$b)\ 7y + 3y = 50$ $\qquad$ $d)\ 132 = 10w + 3w - w$ $\qquad$ $f)\ 4y + 15y = 57$ $\qquad$ $h)\ 15w - 3w - 2w = 85$

Ans. $a)\ 7 = x$ $\qquad$ $c)\ z = 9$ $\qquad$ $e)\ 6 = x$ $\qquad$ $g)\ z = 56$

$b)\ y = 5$ $\qquad$ $d)\ 11 = w$ $\qquad$ $f)\ y = 3$ $\qquad$ $h)\ w = 8\frac{1}{2}$

15. Harry earned \$9.63. What was his hourly wage if he worked $a)$ 3 hr., $b)$ 9 hr., $c)$ $\frac{1}{2}$ hr.?   (5.5)
Ans. $a)$ \$3.21, $b)$ \$1.07, $c)$ \$19.26

16. Mr. Brown's commission rate is 5%. How much did he sell if his commissions were   (5.6)
$a)$ \$85, $b)$ \$750, $c)$ \$6.20 ?   *Ans.* $a)$ \$1700, $b)$ \$15,000, $c)$ \$124

17. Solve each equation: (6.1)

$a)\ \frac{x}{3} = 2$ $\quad$ $b)\ \frac{1}{7}y = 12$ $\quad$ $c)\ 16 = \frac{z}{5}$ $\quad$ $d)\ 3 = \frac{1}{50}w$ $\quad$ $e)\ \frac{a}{2} = 3$ $\quad$ $f)\ \frac{1}{30}b = 20$ $\quad$ $g)\ .6 = \frac{c}{10}$

Ans. $a)\ x = 6$ $\quad$ $b)\ y = 84$ $\quad$ $c)\ 80 = z$ $\quad$ $d)\ 150 = w$ $\quad$ $e)\ a = 6$ $\quad$ $f)\ b = 600$ $\quad$ $g)\ 6 = c$

18. Find each solution set: (6.2)

$a)\ \frac{a}{.7} = 10$ $\quad$ $b)\ \frac{b}{.02} = 600$ $\quad$ $c)\ 30 = \frac{c}{2.4}$ $\quad$ $d)\ 11 = \frac{d}{.05}$ $\quad$ $e)\ \frac{m}{.4} = 220$ $\quad$ $f)\ \frac{n}{.01} = 3$

Ans. $a)\ \{7\}$ $\quad$ $b)\ \{12\}$ $\quad$ $c)\ \{72\}$ $\quad$ $d)\ \{.55\}$ $\quad$ $e)\ \{88\}$ $\quad$ $f)\ \{.03\}$

19. Solve each equation: (6.3)

$a)\ \frac{3}{4}x = 21$ $\quad$ $b)\ \frac{4}{3}y = 32$ $\quad$ $c)\ \frac{3x}{2} = 9$ $\quad$ $d)\ 45 = \frac{5}{9}y$ $\quad$ $e)\ 2\frac{1}{5}z = 55$ $\quad$ $f)\ 2c + \frac{1}{2}c = 10$

Ans. $a)\ x = 28$ $\quad$ $b)\ y = 24$ $\quad$ $c)\ x = 6$ $\quad$ $d)\ y = 81$ $\quad$ $e)\ z = 25$ $\quad$ $f)\ c = 4$

20. Solve each equation: (6.4)

$a)\ 37\frac{1}{2}\%s = 15$ $\quad$ $b)\ 60\%t = 60$ $\quad$ $c)\ 16\frac{2}{3}\%n = 14$ $\quad$ $d)\ 150\%r = 15$ $\quad$ $e)\ 83\frac{1}{3}\%w = 35$

Hint: $37\frac{1}{2}\% = \frac{3}{8}$ $\qquad$ $60\% = \frac{3}{5}$ $\qquad$ $16\frac{2}{3}\% = \frac{1}{6}$ $\qquad$ $150\% = 1\frac{1}{2}$ or $\frac{3}{2}$ $\qquad$ $83\frac{1}{3}\% = \frac{5}{6}$

Ans. $a)\ s = 40$ $\quad$ $b)\ t = 100$ $\quad$ $c)\ n = 84$ $\quad$ $d)\ r = 10$ $\quad$ $e)\ w = 42$

21. On a trip, John covered a distance of 35 mi. What was the total distance of the trip if the distance traveled was $a)\ \frac{5}{6}$ of the total distance, $b)$ 70% of the total distance?   (6.5)
Ans. $a)$ 42 mi., $b)$ 50 mi.

22. Mr. Reynolds receives 7% per year on a stock investment. How large is his investment if, at the end of one year, his interest is $a)$ \$28, $b)$ \$350, $c)$ \$4.27?   *Ans.* $a)$ \$400, $b)$ \$5000, $c)$ \$61   (6.5)

23. Find each solution set: (7.1)

$a)\ r + 25 = 70$	$c)\ 18 = s + 3$	$e)\ x + 130 = 754$	$g)\ 259 = s + 237$
$b)\ 31 + t = 140$	$d)\ 842 = 720 + u$	$f)\ 116 + y = 807$	$h)\ 901 = 857 + w$

Ans. $a)\ \{45\}$ $c)\ \{15\}$ $e)\ \{624\}$ $g)\ \{22\}$
     $b)\ \{109\}$ $d)\ \{122\}$ $f)\ \{691\}$ $h)\ \{44\}$

24. Solve each equation: (7.2)

$a)\ b + \frac{2}{3} = 7\frac{2}{3}$	$c)\ 35.4 = d + 23.2$	$e)\ f + \frac{5}{8} = 3\frac{1}{2}$	$g)\ 7.28 = m + .79$
$b)\ 1\frac{1}{2} + c = 8\frac{3}{4}$	$d)\ 87.4 = 80.6 + e$	$f)\ 8\frac{1}{6} + g = 10\frac{5}{6}$	$h)\ 15.87 = 6.41 + n$

Ans. $a)\ b = 7$ $c)\ 12.2 = d$ $e)\ f = 2\frac{7}{8}$ $g)\ 6.49 = m$
     $b)\ c = 7\frac{1}{4}$ $d)\ 6.8 = e$ $f)\ c = 2\frac{2}{3}$ $h)\ 9.46 = n$

25. The price of eggs rose 29¢. What was the original price if the new price is $a)$ 70¢, $b)$ \$1.05 ?
Ans. $a)$ 41¢, $b)$ 76¢   (7.3)

26. Will is 8 in. taller than George. How tall is George if Will's height is $a)$ 5 ft. 2 in., $b)$ 4 ft. 3 in. ?
Ans. $a)$ 4 ft. 6 in., $b)$ 3 ft. 7 in.   (7.4)

27. Find each solution set: (8.1)

$a)\ w - 8 = 22$	$c)\ 40 = y - 3$	$e)\ m - 140 = 25$	$g)\ 158 = p - 317$
$b)\ x - 22 = 8$	$d)\ 3 = z - 40$	$f)\ n - 200 = 41$	$h)\ 256 = r - 781$

Ans. $a)\ \{30\}$ $c)\ \{43\}$ $e)\ \{165\}$ $g)\ \{475\}$
     $b)\ \{30\}$ $d)\ \{43\}$ $f)\ \{241\}$ $h)\ \{1037\}$

28. Solve each equation: (8.2)

$a)\ h - \frac{7}{8} = 8\frac{3}{4}$	$c)\ 28.4 = m - 13.9$	$e)\ p - 1\frac{5}{12} = 1\frac{7}{12}$	$g)\ .03 = s - 2.07$
$b)\ j - 34\frac{1}{2} = 65$	$d)\ .37 = n - 8.96$	$f)\ r - 14\frac{2}{3} = 5\frac{1}{3}$	$h)\ 5.84 = t - 3.06$

Ans. $a)\ h = 9\frac{5}{8}$ $c)\ 42.3 = m$ $e)\ p = 3$ $g)\ 2.10 = s$
     $b)\ j = 99\frac{1}{2}$ $d)\ 9.33 = n$ $f)\ r = 20$ $h)\ 8.90 = t$

29. What was the original temperature if a drop of $12°$ brought the temperature to   (8.3)
$a)\ 75°$, $b)\ 14\frac{1}{2}°$, $c)\ 6\frac{1}{4}°$?   Ans. $a)\ 87°$, $b)\ 26\frac{1}{2}°$, $c)\ 18\frac{1}{4}°$

30. How many marbles did Sam have originally if after giving 35 marbles to Jim, he found that the number of marbles he had left was
$a)\ 5$, $b)\ 12$, $c)\ 15$, $d)\ 35$, $e)\ 75$?   Ans. $a)\ 40$, $b)\ 47$, $c)\ 50$, $d)\ 70$, $e)\ 110$ (8.4)

31. Solve each equation: (9.1)

$a)\ 2x + 5 = 9$	$e)\ 2x - 5 = 9$	$i)\ \frac{x}{4} + 3 = 7$	$m)\ \frac{x}{4} - 3 = 7$
$b)\ 4x + 11 = 21$	$f)\ 4x - 11 = 21$	$j)\ \frac{x}{5} + 2 = 10$	$n)\ \frac{x}{5} - 2 = 10$
$c)\ 20 = 3x + 8$	$g)\ 60 = 10x - 20$	$k)\ 17 = \frac{x}{2} + 15$	$o)\ 3 = \frac{x}{12} - 7\frac{1}{4}$
$d)\ 13 = 6 + 7x$	$h)\ 11 = 6x - 16$	$l)\ 25 = \frac{x}{10} + 2$	$p)\ 5\frac{1}{2} = \frac{x}{8} - 4$

Ans. $a)\ x = 2$ $e)\ x = 7$ $i)\ x = 16$ $m)\ x = 40$
     $b)\ x = 2\frac{1}{2}$ $f)\ x = 8$ $j)\ x = 40$ $n)\ x = 60$
     $c)\ x = 4$ $g)\ x = 8$ $k)\ x = 4$ $o)\ x = 123$
     $d)\ x = 1$ $h)\ x = 4\frac{1}{2}$ $l)\ x = 230$ $p)\ x = 76$

32. Solve each equation: (9.2)

a) $10n + 5n - 6 = 9$ c) $25 = 19 + 20n - 18n$ e) $19n - 10 + n = 80$ g) $40 = 25t + 22 - 13t$

b) $7m + 10 - 2m = 45$ d) $35 = 6p + 8 + 3p$ f) $3\frac{1}{2}r + r + 2 = 20$ h) $145 = 10 + 7.6s - 3.1s$

Ans. a) $n = 1$ b) $m = 7$ c) $n = 3$ d) $p = 3$ e) $n = 4\frac{1}{2}$ f) $r = 4$ g) $t = \frac{3}{2}$ or $1\frac{1}{2}$ h) $s = 30$

33. Find each solution set: (9.3)

a) $5r = 2r + 27$ c) $10r - 11 = 8r$ e) $13b = 15 + 3b$ g) $9u = 16u - 105$

b) $2r = 90 - 7r$ d) $18 - 5a = a$ f) $100 + 3\frac{1}{2}t = 23\frac{1}{2}t$ h) $5x + 3 - 2x = x + 8$

Ans. a) $\{9\}$ b) $\{10\}$ c) $\{5\frac{1}{2}\}$ d) $\{3\}$ e) $\{1\frac{1}{2}\}$ f) $\{5\}$ g) $\{15\}$ h) $\{2\frac{1}{2}\}$

34. Solve each equation: (9.4)

a) $\frac{40}{x} = 5$ c) $14 = \frac{28}{y}$ e) $\frac{32}{n} = 8$ g) $4 = \frac{15}{w}$

b) $\frac{5}{x} = 40$ d) $28 = \frac{14}{y}$ f) $\frac{3}{n} = 2$ h) $15 = \frac{90}{w}$

Ans. a) $x = 8$ b) $x = \frac{1}{8}$ c) $y = 2$ d) $y = \frac{1}{2}$ e) $n = 4$ f) $n = 1\frac{1}{2}$ g) $w = 3\frac{3}{4}$ h) $w = 6$

35. Find each solution set: (9.5, 9.6)

a) $\frac{7}{8}x = 21$ d) $1\frac{1}{2}w = 15$ g) $\frac{4}{5}n + 6 = 22$ j) $10 = \frac{2}{9}r + 8$

b) $\frac{3}{4}x = 39$ e) $2\frac{1}{3}b = 35$ h) $10 + \frac{6}{5}m = 52$ k) $6 = 16 - \frac{5t}{3}$

c) $\frac{5}{4}y = 15$ f) $2c + 2\frac{1}{2}c = 54$ i) $30 - \frac{3}{2}p = 24$ l) $3s + \frac{s}{3} - 7 = 5$

Ans. a) $\{24\}$ d) $\{10\}$ g) $\{20\}$ j) $\{9\}$

b) $\{52\}$ e) $\{15\}$ h) $\{35\}$ k) $\{6\}$

c) $\{12\}$ f) $\{12\}$ i) $\{4\}$ l) $\{3.6\}$

36. Find each solution set.   (9.1 to 9.6)

a) $20 = 3x - 10$ Ans. a) $\{10\}$ k) $\frac{x}{2} + 27 = 30$ Ans. k) $\{6\}$

b) $20 = \frac{x}{3} - 10$ b) $\{90\}$ l) $8x + 3 = 43$ l) $\{5\}$

c) $15 = \frac{3}{4}y$ c) $\{20\}$ m) $21 = \frac{7}{5}w$ m) $\{15\}$

d) $17 = 24 - z$ d) $\{7\}$ n) $60 = 66 - 12w$ n) $\{\frac{1}{2}\}$

e) $3 = \frac{39}{x}$ e) $\{13\}$ o) $10b - 3b = 49$ o) $\{7\}$

f) $\frac{15}{x} = \frac{5}{4}$ f) $\{12\}$ p) $12b - 5 = .28 + b$ p) $\{.48\}$

g) $5c = 2c + 4.5$ g) $\{1.5\}$ q) $6d - .8 = 2d$ q) $\{.2\}$

h) $.30 - g = .13$ h) $\{.17\}$ r) $40 - .5h = 5$ r) $\{70\}$

i) $\frac{3}{4}n + 11\frac{1}{2} = 20\frac{1}{2}$ i) $\{12\}$ s) $40 - \frac{3}{5}m = 37$ s) $\{5\}$

j) $6w + 5w - 8 = 8w$ j) $\{2\frac{2}{3}\}$ t) $12t - 2t + 10 = 9t + 12$ t) $\{2\}$

37. How many girls are there in a class of 30 pupils if a) the number of boys is 10 less,   (9.7)
b) the number of boys is four times as many?   Ans. a) 20 girls b) 6 girls

38. Charles has \$3.70 in his bank and hopes to increase this to \$10 by making equal deposits each week. How much should he deposit if he deposits money for a) 14 wk., b) 5 wk.?   (9.8)
Ans. a) 45¢ b) \$1.26

39. Mr. Barr sold his house for \$12,000. How much did the house cost him if his loss was   (9.9)
a) $\frac{1}{3}$ of the cost, b) 20% of the cost?   Ans. a) \$18,000 b) \$15,000

Chapter 3

Real Numbers

1. UNDERSTANDING REAL NUMBERS AND THE REAL NUMBER LINE

The temperatures listed in Fig. (a) are the Fahrenheit temperatures for five cities on a winter's day. Note how these temperatures are shown on a **number line** or a **number scale**. On this number line, plus and minus signs are used to distinguish between temperatures above zero and those below zero. Such numbers are **positive** or **negative numbers**. Together with zero, positive and negative numbers are called **real numbers**. Since positive numbers have plus signs and negative numbers have negative signs, they are called signed numbers. Zero, 0, is an unsigned number since 0 is neither positive nor negative.

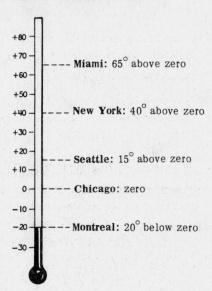

Fig. (a)

In mathematics, positive and negative numbers are used to represent quantities that are opposites of each other.

Thus, if +40; read "positive 40", represents 40° above zero, then −40, read "negative 40", represents 40° below zero.

A negative number can be indicated only by means of the minus sign, (−). However, a positive number may be shown by using a plus sign, (+), or by no sign at all.

Thus, 35° above zero may be indicated either by +35 or by 35.

The following table illustrates pairs of opposites which may be represented by +25 and −25.

+ 25	− 25
$25 deposited	$25 withdrawn
25 mph faster	25 mph slower
25 lb. gained	25 lb. lost
25 mi. to the north	25 mi. to the south

Absolute Value of a Real Number

In any pair of opposites, the positive of the pair is the absolute value of each of the numbers. The absolute value of a real number a is written $|a|$.

Thus, 40 is the absolute value of each of the opposites, 40 and −40. Hence, using the absolute value symbol, we write $40 = |+40|$ and $40 = |-40|$.

The absolute value of 0 is defined as 0; that is $|0| = 0$

In general, for every nonzero real number, a, the absolute value of a is defined as the positive number in the pair of real numbers, a and $-a$.

Thus, $3.45 = |+3.45| = |-3.45|$.

Note that the absolute value of each of a pair of opposites may be written by simply removing the sign of either number.

Understanding the Number Line

> **The number line is the graph of the set of real numbers.**

The graph of the set of real numbers is the entire number line. The number line is referred to as the real number line, Fig. (b).

THE REAL NUMBER LINE

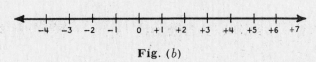

Fig. (b)

When graphing the set of real numbers, the number line, Fig. (b), is heavily shaded and the arrowheads at either end of the line are made heavy.

Constructing the Number Line

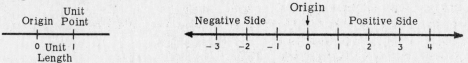

Procedure to Construct the Number Line

1. Draw a line and choose any point of the line as the origin with 0 associated with it. The number 0 is the coordinate of the point chosen as the origin, and the origin is the graph of 0.

2. Choose a point to the right of the origin and associate this point with the number 1. The distance from the origin to the unit point is the **unit length**. The unit point is the graph of 1, and 1 is the coordinate of the unit point.

3. Using the unit length, mark off successive points to the right and label these points, +1, +2, +3, +4, . . .

4. Using the unit length, mark off successive points to the left and label these points −1, −2, −3, −4, . . .

Relating a Point on the Number Line with a Real Number

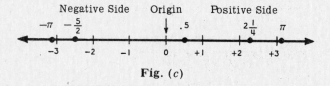

Fig. (c)

On the horizontal number line, Fig. (c), real numbers such as .5, 1, $2\frac{1}{4}$, π, $-\frac{5}{2}$, and $-\pi$ are associated with points. Note on both the horizontal and vertical number lines how positive and negative numbers are placed on opposite sides of 0. On the horizontal number line, each of the points to the right of 0 is paired with a positive number while each of the points to the left is paired with a negative number. Similarly, on the vertical number line, Fig. (d), each of the points above 0 is paired with a positive number while each of the points below 0 is paired with a negative number. In each case, the positive numbers are on the positive side of the line and the negative numbers are on the negative side of the line.

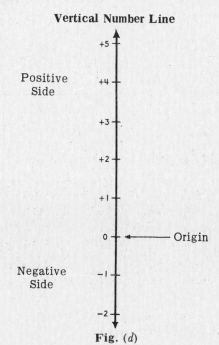

Fig. (d)

The arrowheads at either end of the number line indicate that the number line continues without end in either direction. The point paired with a number is called the **graph** of the number and this number is the **coordinate** of the point.

In graphing real numbers on a number line, we assume two important principles:

1. To any given real number, there corresponds one and only one point on the number line.
2. To any given point on the number line, there corresponds one and only one real number.

The two important principles which relate a point on the number line with a real number are combined into the following single principle:

> **There is a one-to-one correspondence between the set of points on the number line and the set of real numbers.**

1.1 Words Opposite in Meaning

State the words that are opposite in meaning to the following:

a) gain   *e*) north   *i*) deposit   *m*) A.D.
b) rise   *f*) east   *j*) asset   *n*) expand
c) above   *g*) right   *k*) earnings   *o*) accelerate
d) up   *h*) forward   *l*) receipt   *p*) clockwise

Ans. *a*) loss   *e*) south   *i*) withdrawal   *m*) B.C.
b) fall   *f*) west   *j*) liability   *n*) contract
c) below   *g*) left   *k*) spendings   *o*) decelerate
d) down   *h*) backward   *l*) payment   *p*) counterclockwise

1.2 Expressing Quantities as Signed Numbers

State the quantity represented by each signed number:

a) By -10, if $+10$ means 10 yd. gained   *e*) By -100, if $+100$ means 100 ft. east
b) By -5, if $+5$ means \$5 earned   *f*) By -3, if $+3$ means 3 steps right
c) By $+15$, if -15 means 15 mi. south   *g*) By 20, if -20 means 20 oz. underweight
d) By $+8$, if -8 means 8 hr. earlier   *h*) By 5, if -5 means 5 flights down.

Ans. *a*) 10 yd. lost   *c*) 15 mi. north   *e*) 100 ft. west   *g*) 20 oz. overweight
b) \$5 spent   *d*) 8 hr. later   *f*) 3 steps left   *h*) 5 flights up

1.3 Absolute Value of a Real Number

Evaluate:

(*a*) $|25| + |-25|$ *Ans.* $25 + 25 = 50$

(*b*) $|36| - |-36|$ *Ans.* $36 - 36 = 0$

(*c*) $|\frac{1}{2}| + |-\frac{1}{2}| + |\frac{1}{4}| - |-\frac{1}{4}|$ *Ans.* $\frac{1}{2} + \frac{1}{2} + \frac{1}{4} - \frac{1}{4} = 1$

(*d*) $2|-3.5| - 4|-.25|$ *Ans.* $2(3.5) - 4(.25) = 7 - 1 = 6$

(*e*) $(3|-1|)(5|-2|)$ *Ans.* $(3 \cdot 1)(5 \cdot 2) = 3(10) = 30$

(*f*) $\frac{10|+5|}{10|-5|}$ *Ans.* $\frac{10(5)}{10(5)} = 1$

(*g*) $(|-10|)^2$ *Ans.* $(10)^2 = 100$

1.4 Points on a Number Line and Their Coordinates

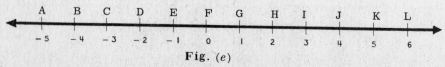

Fig. (*e*)

Using the number line, Fig. (*e*) with reference to the graphs and coordinates shown, name

a) the coordinates of points A, D, and the origin   *Ans.* $-5, -2, 0$
b) the graphs of the natural numbers   *Ans.* G, H, I, J, K, L

(*c*) the coordinates of points midway between (1) A and C, (2) C and G, (3) A and G
   Ans. (1) −4, (2) −1, (3) −2

(*d*) the graphs of coordinates that are greater than −5 and less than or equal to 0
   Ans. B, C, D, E, F

(*e*) the graphs of coordinates whose absolute value is less than 3   *Ans.* D, E, F, G, H

2. USING THE REAL NUMBER LINE

The number line has many important uses. In this section, we shall study the following purposes which may be served by the number line:

A. To Understand the Meanings of Real Numbers
B. To Compare Real Numbers
C. To Solve Verbal Problems
D. To Graph Sets of Natural Numbers, Whole Numbers, or Integers
E. To Graph Sets of Real Numbers

A. USING A NUMBER LINE TO UNDERSTAND THE MEANINGS OF REAL NUMBERS

A real number may refer to (1) **a position**, or (2) **a change in position**.

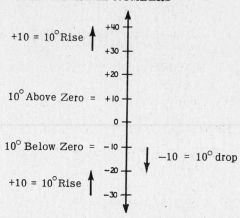

Thus, +10 may refer to the position on the temperature number scale of the graph of 10° above zero. Furthermore, +10 may indicate a 10° rise in temperature. The rise of 10° may begin with any temperature. Note on the vertical scale the use of arrows to show the size of the change and its direction. A negative number such as −10 could be used to refer to 10° below zero or to a drop of 10° in temperature. With reference to temperature, zero, 0, may mean **0° or no change in temperature**.

2.1 Two Meanings of Real Numbers

On a temperature scale, state two meanings of *a*) + 25, *b*) − 25, *c*) 0.

Ans. *a*) + 25 means (*1*) 25° above zero or (*2*) a rise of 25° from any temperature.
   b) −25 means (*1*) 25° below zero or (*2*) a drop of 25° from any temperature.
   c) 0 means (*1*) zero degrees or (*2*) no change in temperature.

Note. As a number in arithmetic, 0 means "nothing". Do not confuse this meaning of zero with the other two.

2.2 Indicating Position or Change of Position

With reference to a temperature scale, what real number indicates

(*a*) 15° below zero   *Ans.* −15
(*b*) a rise of 15° in temperature   *Ans.* +15 or 15
(*c*) zero degrees   *Ans.* 0
(*d*) no change in temperature   *Ans.* 0
(*e*) a rise of 10° followed by   *Ans.* (+10) + (−15). The combined effect of the two changes
   a drop of 15°   is −5, indicating that the result is a drop of 5°.

B. USING A NUMBER LINE AND INEQUALITY SYMBOLS TO COMPARE REAL NUMBERS

Increase To Right

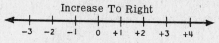

Horizontal Number Line

On a horizontal number line, real numbers increase to the right; on a vertical number line, the increase is upwards. Hence, on a horizontal number line, the graph of the greater of two numbers is to the right of the graph of the smaller; whereas on a vertical number line, the graph of the greater is above the graph of the smaller. Because of the positions of the graphs of −2 and 1, we conclude that −2 is less than 1. Using the inequality symbol, <, which is read "**is less than**", we write −2 < 1. Using the inequality symbol, >, which is read "**is greater than**", we write 1 > −2.

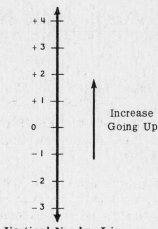

Vertical Number Line

The inequality symbols, > and <, need not be confused if you remember each symbol as an arrowhead pointing toward the smaller number (in a true statement). From the graph, note that 0 is *between* −1 and 2. It follows that −1 is less than 0 and 0 is less than 2; that is, −1 < 0 and 0 < 2. In compact form, these facts may be combined into −1 < 0 < 2, read "−1 is less than 0, which is less than 2".

RULES FOR COMPARING REAL NUMBERS

Rule 1. Any positive number is greater than 0.

Thus, +5 > 0. Note on the number line, that each positive number is to the right of 0; to the right signifying, "greater than".

Rule 2. Any negative number is less than 0.

Thus, −5 < 0. Note on the number line, that each negative number is to the left of 0; to the left signifying, "less than".

Rule 3. Any positive number is greater than any negative number.

Thus, $+\frac{1}{4} > -1,000$. Note on the number line, that each positive number is to the right of each negative number.

Rule 4. The greater of two positive numbers has the greater absolute value.

Thus, since +10 > +5, then $|+10| > |+5|$. This is true because the absolute value of a positive number is the positive number.

Rule 5. The greater of two negative numbers has the smaller absolute value.

Thus, since −5 > −10, then $|-5| < |-10|$. This is true since $|-5| = 5$ while $|-10| = 10$.

Note: In rules 1, 2, and 3, the number line referred to is the horizontal number line.

2.3 Comparing Real Numbers

Which is greater?

    a) $+\frac{1}{4}$ or 0   *b*) +50 or +30   *c*) − 30 or 0   *d*) − 30 or −10   *e*) +10 or −100

    (*Refer to the rules for comparing real numbers.*)

Ans. a) $+\frac{1}{4}$ *b*) +50   *c*) 0   *d*) −10   *e*) +10

    (Rule 1)   **(Rule 4)**   **(Rule 2)**   **(Rule 5)**   **(Rule 3)**

2.4 Determining the Correct Equality or Inequality Symbol

In each, obtain a true statement by replacing the question mark with either =, <, or >:

a) −2 ? 0   *Ans.* <   *d*) −5 × 1 ? −5   *Ans.* =   *g*) 25 × 1 ? 25 + 1   *Ans.* <

b) 0 ? −25   *Ans.* >   *e*) $\frac{1}{2}$? $\frac{1}{4}$ *Ans.* >   *h*) $|-25|$? $|25|$ *Ans.* =

c) 20 × 0 ? 0   *Ans.* =   *f*) $\frac{1}{2} \times \frac{1}{2}$? $\frac{1}{4}$ *Ans.* =   *i*) $|-5|$? $|-10|$ *Ans.* <

2.5 Using Inequality Symbols

Express each symbol verbally and state whether each statement is true or false:

a) −3 > − 20   *Ans.* −3 is greater than −20. True.

b) 2 < 6 < 8   *Ans.* 2 is less than 6, which is less than 8. True.

c) $-10 < -\frac{1}{2} < 0$ *Ans.* −10 is less than $-\frac{1}{2}$, which is less than 0. True.

d) $5 > 0 > -5$ *Ans.* 5 is greater than 0, which is greater than −5. True.

e) $-2 < 0 < -3$ *Ans.* −2 is less than 0, which is less than −3. False since 0 is greater than −3

f) $2 + 2 \neq 2 \times 2$ *Ans.* 2 plus 2 is not equal to 2 times 2. False since 4 = 4.

g) $|-25| \neq |+25|$ *Ans.* Absolute value of −25 does not equal the absolute value of +25. False since 25 = 25.

C. USING NUMBER LINES TO SOLVE VERBAL PROBLEMS

The following four verbal problems show how number lines may be used to solve such problems:

2.6 Beginning with the main floor, an elevator went up 4 floors, then up two more and then down 8. Find its location after making these changes.

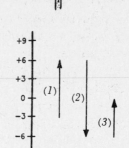

Solution: Each interval is one floor. The origin, 0, indicates the main floor. The three changes are shown by arrows:

    (*1*) 4 floors up, (*2*) 2 floors up, (*3*) 8 floors down
The final location is − 2.

Ans. 2 floors below the main floor.

2.7 Beginning with 3° below zero, the temperature changed by rising 9°, then dropping 12° and finally rising 6°. Find the final temperature.

Solution: Each interval is 3°. The temperature began at 3° below zero, −3 on the scale. Arrows show the temperature changes:

    (*1*) 9° rise, (*2*) 12° drop, (*3*) 6° rise
The final temperature reading is 0.

Ans. zero degrees

2.8 A plane started from a point 150 mi. west of its base and flew directly east, reaching a point 150 mi. east of the base. How far did it travel?

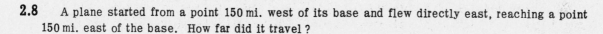
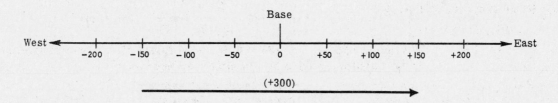

Solution: Each interval is 50 mi. The origin indicates the base. The arrow begins at −150 and ends at +150. It has a length of 300 and points eastward.

Ans. 300 mi. eastward

D. USING NUMBER LINES TO GRAPH SETS OF NATURAL NUMBERS, WHOLE NUMBERS, AND INTEGERS

Figure (*f*) indicates how the set $\{-3, -1, 1, 3, 5\}$ can be graphed using a number line. Note that each number in the set is the coordinate of a heavy dot on the

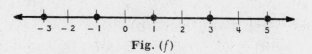

Fig. (*f*)

number line. The set of these heavy dots is the graph of the given set.

Rule. **The graph of a set of numbers is the set of points which are the graphs of the numbers.**

The Set of Integers: Positive Integers, Zero, and Negative Integers

The set of integers may be divided into three sets, as follows:

1. The set of positive integers: $\{+1, +2, +3, +4, +5, \ldots\}$
2. The set of zero: $\{0\}$
3. The set of negative integers: $\{-1, -2, -3, -4, -5, \ldots\}$

Using capital I to represent the set of integers, we list the set as follows:

$$I = \{\ldots, -5, -4, -3, -2, -1, 0, 1, 2, 3, 4, 5, \ldots\}$$

Figure (g) indicates how the set of integers can be graphed using the number line. Heavy arrowheads at each of the ends of the line are used to indicate that the set continues without end both to the left and to the right. Each heavy dot is the graph of an integer.

Graph of the Set of Integers

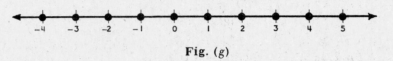

Fig. (g)

2.9 Graphing Sets of Natural Numbers, Whole Numbers, and Integers

List the numbers described in each set and graph the set:

a) The set of natural numbers between 3 and 8.
b) The set of negative even integers.
c) The set of positive odd integers.
d) The set of whole numbers represented by $2n$ if n represents the set $\{0, 1, 2, 3\}$.
e) The set of natural numbers represented by $2x - 1$ if x represents the set $\{-1, 0, 1, 2, 3, 4\}$
f) The set of integers whose absolute values are 0, 1, and 2.

Solutions:

a) The natural numbers between 3 and 8 are those greater than 3 and smaller than 8.
$A = \{4, 5, 6, 7\}$

b) The set of negative even integers is an infinite set of those integers that are negative and divisible by 2. $B = \{\ldots, -10, -8, -6, -4, -2\}$

c) The set of positive odd integers is an infinite set of those positive integers that end in 1, 3, 5, 7, or 9. $C = \{1, 3, 5, 7, 9, \ldots\}$

d) The required set consists of numbers that are the doubles of 0, 1, 2 and 3. $D = \{0, 2, 4, 6\}$

e) If $-1, 0, 1, 2,$ and 3 are substituted for x in the expression $2x - 1$, we obtain the values $-3, -1, 1, 3, 5$ and 7. However, -3 and -1 are not natural numbers. $E = \{1, 3, 5, 7\}$

f) 0 is the absolute value of 0, 1 is the absolute value of 1 and -1, and 2 is the absolute value of 2 and -2 $F = \{-2, -1, 0, 1, 2\}$

E. USING NUMBER LINES TO GRAPH SETS OF REAL NUMBERS AND SET-BUILDER NOTATION TO DESCRIBE THE SETS

Figure (a) indicates how the set of real numbers between −4 and 3 can be graphed using a number line. The part of the number line that is heavily shaded from A to B contains all the points that are the graphs of the real numbers in the given set. The open endpoint dots show that −4 and 3 are not in the given set of numbers.

Set-builder notation, which was discussed earlier, can be used to describe the given set:

$$\{x : -4 < x < 3, x \text{ is a real number}\}$$

Read this notation as "the set of **all** real numbers x such that −4 is less than x, which is less than 3". (Think of the colon as the symbol for "such that".)

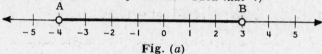

Fig. (a)

2.10 Graphing Sets of Real Numbers: Set-Builder Notation

Graph each set and write the set, using set-builder notation:

a) The set of real numbers greater than or equal to −4,
b) The set of real numbers whose absolute value is less than 3,
c) The set of real numbers whose absolute value is greater than 1.

Solutions:

a) In set-builder notation, the given set can be stated as

$$\{x : x \geq -4, x \text{ is a real number}\}$$

Read this as "The set of all real numbers x such that x is greater than or equal to −4". (Think of this sentence as a disjunction which combines two sentences: (1) x is greater than −4 **or** (2) x is equal to −4.)

The graph of this set, Fig. (b) is the line that is heavily shaded, the set of all the points that are the graph of the real numbers in the given set. The closed endpoint dot shows that −4 is in the given set of numbers.

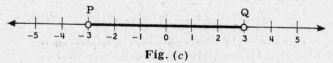

Fig. (b)

b) In set-builder notation, the given set can be stated as

$$\{x : |x| < 3, x \text{ is a real number}\}$$

Read this as "The set of all real numbers x such that the absolute value of x is less than 3".

The graph of this set, Fig. (c), is the part of the number line that is heavily shaded from P to Q. In this part are all the points that are the graphs of the real numbers in the given set. Think of these points as the points whose distance from the origin is less than 3. Note that the endpoint dots are open to show that −3 and 3 are not numbers in the given set.

P   Q
–5 –4 –3 –2 –1 0   1   2   3   4   5

Fig. (c)

c) In set-builder notation, the given set can be stated as

$$\{x : |x| > 1, x \text{ is a real number}\}$$

Read this as "The set of all real numbers x such that the absolute value of x is greater than 1."

The graph of this set, Fig. (d) is the pair of lines that are heavily shaded, the set of all the points that are the graphs or the real numbers in the given set. Note that the endpoint dots are open to show that −1 and 1 are not in the given set of numbers. Think of the points in the graph as those points whose distance from the origin is greater than 1.

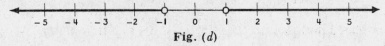

Fig. (d)

3. ADDING SIGNED NUMBERS: OPPOSITES AND ADDITIVE INVERSES

In algebra, **adding signed numbers** means **combining them** to obtain a single number which represents the total or combined effect.

Thus, if Mary first gains 10 lb. and then loses 15 lb., the total effect of the two changes is a loss of 5 lb. This is shown by adding signed numbers: $(+10) + (−15) = −5$.

Uses of the symbol "+": The symbol "+", when used in adding two signed numbers, has two meanings: (1) "+" may mean "add" or (2) "+" may mean "positive number".

Thus $(−8) + (+15)$ means **add positive** 15 to negative 8.

Rules For Adding Signed Numbers

Rule 1. To add two signed numbers with like signs, add their absolute values. The sign of the sum is the common sign of the numbers.

Thus, to add $(+7)$ and $(+3)$ or to add $(−7)$ and $(−3)$, add the absolute values 7 and 3. The sign of the sum is the common sign.

Hence, $(+7) + (+3) = +10$ and $(−7) + (−3) = −10$.

Rule 2. To add two signed numbers with unlike signs, subtract the smaller absolute value from the other. The sign of the sum is the sign of the number having the greater absolute value.

Thus, to add $(+7)$ and $(−3)$ or $(−7)$ and $(+3)$, subtract the absolute value 3 from the absolute value 7. The sign of the sum is the sign of the number having the larger absolute value. Hence, $(+7) + (−3) = +4$ and $(−7) + (+3) = −4$.

THINK!
IN ADDING TWO SIGNED NUMBERS:
Add Absolute Values for Like Signs, Subtract for Unlike.

Rule 3. Zero is the sum of two signed numbers with unlike signs and the same absolute value. Such numbers are opposites or additive inverses of each other.

Thus, $(+27) + (−27) = 0$. The numbers, +27 and −27, are opposites or additive inverses of each other, according to the following definition:

Additive inverses are two real numbers whose sum is 0.

To understand the meaning of opposites, note in Fig. (a) that the graphs of opposites are on opposite sides of the origin and at the same distance from it. Opposites include such pairs of numbers as −1 and 1, −20 and 20, and −1.4 and 1.4. Keep in mind that the sum of two opposites is zero, Rule 3.

Number Line

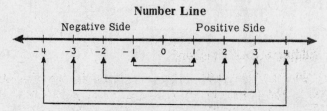

Fig. (a) Opposites On A Number Line

3.1 Combining by Means of Signed Numbers

Using signed numbers, find each sum:

a) 10 yd. gained plus 5 yd. lost.

b) 8 steps right plus 10 steps left.

c) $5 earned plus $5 spent.

d) 80 mi. south plus 100 mi. south.

Solutions:

a) 10 yd. gained plus 5 yd. lost
$$(+10) + (-5)$$
Ans. +5 or 5 yd. gained

b) 8 steps right plus 10 steps left
$$(+8) + (-10)$$
Ans. −2 or 2 steps left

c) $5 earned plus $5 spent
$$(+5) + (-5)$$
Ans. 0 or no change

d) 80 mi. south plus 100 mi. south
$$(-80) + (-100)$$
Ans. −180 or 180 mi. south

3.2 Rule 1. Adding Signed Numbers with Like Signs

Add: a) (+8), (+2)   b) (−8), (−2)   c) (−30), $(-14\frac{1}{2})$

Procedure: Solutions:

	a) (+8) + (+2)	b) (−8) + (−2)	c) $(-30) + (-14\frac{1}{2})$
1. Add absolute values:	8 + 2 = 10	8 + 2 = 10	$30 + 14\frac{1}{2} = 44\frac{1}{2}$
2. Use the common sign:	**Ans.** +10	**Ans.** −10	**Ans.** $-44\frac{1}{2}$

3.3 Rule 2. Adding Signed Numbers with Unlike Signs

Add: a) (+7), (−5)   b) (−17), (+10)

Procedure: Solutions:

	a) (+7) + (−5)	b) (−17) + (+10)
1. Subtract absolute values:	7 − 5 = 2	17 − 10 = 7
2. Use the sign of number having greater absolute value:	Sign of +7 is +. **Ans.** +2	Sign of −17 is −. **Ans.** −7

3.4 Rule 3. Adding Signed Numbers which are Opposites of Each Other

Add: a) (−18), (+18)   b) $(+30\frac{1}{2})$, $(-30\frac{1}{2})$ c) (−1.75), (+1.75)

Procedure: Solutions:

	a) (−18) + (+18)	b) $(+30\frac{1}{2}) + (-30\frac{1}{2})$	c) (−1.75) + (+1.75)
Sum is always zero:	**Ans.** 0	**Ans.** 0	**Ans.** 0

3.5 Rules 1, 2 and 3. Adding Signed Numbers

Add +25 to a) +30, b) −30, c) −25 .

Ans. a) (+30) + (+25) = +55   **(Rule 1)**
b) (−30) + (+25) = −5   **(Rule 2)**
c) (−25) + (+25) = 0   **(Rule 3)**

To −20, add d) −30, e) +10, f) +20

Ans. d) (−20) + (−30) = −50   **(Rule 1)**
e) (−20) + (+10) = −10   **(Rule 2)**
f) (−20) + (+20) = 0   **(Rule 3)**

56

REAL NUMBERS

4. SIMPLIFYING THE ADDITION OF SIGNED NUMBERS

To simplify the writing used in adding signed numbers:
(1) Parentheses may be omitted.
(2) The symbol "+" may be omitted when it means "add".
(3) If the first signed number is positive, its + sign may be omitted.
Thus, $8 + 9 - 10$ may be written instead of $(+8) + (+9) + (-10)$.

To Simplify Adding Signed Numbers

Add: $(+23), (-12), (-8), (+10)$

Procedure:

Solution:

1. Add all the positive numbers:
(*Their sum is positive.*)

1. Add +'s: 23
              10
              ――
              33

2. Add all the negative numbers:
(*Their sum is negative.*)

2. Add −'s: −12
             − 8
             ――――
             −20

3. Add the resulting sums:

3. Add sums: $33 - 20$
Ans. 13

4.1 Simplifying the Addition of Signed Numbers

Express in simplified form, horizontally and vertically; then add:

a) $(+27) + (-15) + (+3) + (-5)$, b) $(-8) + (+13) + (-20) + (+9)$, c) $(+11.2) + (+13.5) + (-6.7) + (+20.9)$

Simplified Horizontal Forms:

a) $27 - 15 + 3 - 5$ | b) $-8 + 13 - 20 + 9$ | c) $11.2 + 13.5 - 6.7 + 20.9$

Simplified Vertical Forms:

27	− 8	11.2
−15	13	13.5
3	−20	− 6.7
− 5	9	20.9
Ans. 10	*Ans.* − 6	*Ans.* 38.9

4.2 Adding Positive and Negatives Separately

Add: a) $(+27), (-15), (+3), (-5)$ | b) $(-8), (+13), (-20), (+9)$ | c) $(+11.2), (+13.5), (-6.7), (+20.9), (-3.1)$

Solutions:

a) Simplify:
$27 - 15 + 3 - 5$

Add +'s	Add −'s
27	−15
3	− 5
30	−20

Add results: $30 - 20$
Ans. 10

b) Simplify:
$-8 + 13 - 20 + 9$

Add +'s	Add −'s
13	− 8
9	−20
22	−28

Add results: $22 - 28$
Ans. −6

c) Simplify:
$11.2 + 13.5 - 6.7 + 20.9 - 3.1$

Add +'s	Add −'s
11.2	−6.7
13.5	−3.1
20.9	−9.8
45.6	

Add results: $45.6 - 9.8$
Ans. 35.8

4.3 Using Signed Numbers and Number Scales to Solve Problems

In May, Tom added deposits of $30 and $20. Later, he withdrew $40 and $30. Find the change in his balance due to these changes using a) signed numbers and b) number line:

a) Signed Number Solution

Add	Add +'s	Add −'s
+30	30	−40
+20	20	−30
−40	50	−70
−30		

$$50 - 70 = -20$$

Ans. $20 less

b) Number Line Solution

The last of the 4 arrows ends at −20. This means $20 less than the original balance.

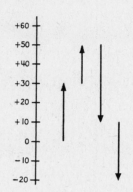

5. SUBTRACTING SIGNED NUMBERS

The symbol "−", used in subtracting signed numbers, has two meanings:
(1) "−" may mean "subtract" or
(2) "−" may mean "negative number".

Thus, $(+8) - (-15)$ means **subtract negative** 15 from positive 8.

Using Subtraction to Find the Change From One Position to Another

Subtraction may be used to find the change from one position to another. (See **5.6** to **5.8**.)

Thus, to find a temperature change from 10° below zero to 20° above zero, subtract (−10) from (+20). The result is +30, meaning a rise of 30°.

Rule for Subtracting Signed Numbers

Rule 1. **To subtract** a positive number, **add** its opposite which is negative.

Thus, to subtract (+10), add (−10). For example, $(+18) - (\mathbf{+10})$
$$= (+18) + (\mathbf{-10}). \quad Ans. \ +8$$

Rule 2. **To subtract** a negative number, **add** its opposite which is positive.

Thus, to subtract (−10), add (+10). For example, $(+30) - (\mathbf{-10})$
$$= (+30) + (\mathbf{+10}). \quad Ans. \ +40$$

T H I N K !

To Subtract a Signed Number, Add Its Opposite.

5.1 Rule 1. Subtracting a Positive Number

Subtract: a) (+8) from (+29) b) (+80) from (+80) c) (+18) from (−40)

Procedure: Solutions:

To **subtract** a positive,
add its opposite negative:

a) $(+29) - (+8)$
$(+29) + (-8)$
Ans. 21

b) $(+80) - (\mathbf{+80})$
$(+80) + (\mathbf{-80})$
Ans. 0

c) $(-40) - (\mathbf{+18})$
$(-40) + (\mathbf{-18})$
Ans. −58

5.2 Rule 2. Subtracting a Negative Number

Subtract: a) (−7) from (+20) b) (−67) from (−67) c) (−27) from (−87)

Procedure: Solutions:

To **subtract** a negative,
add its opposite positive:

a) $(+20) - (-7)$
$(+20) + (+7)$
Ans. 27

b) $(-67) - (\mathbf{-67})$
$(-67) + (\mathbf{+67})$
Ans. 0

c) $(-87) - (\mathbf{-27})$
$(-87) + (\mathbf{+27})$
Ans. −60

5.3 Subtracting Vertically

Subtract the lower number from the upper:

a)	+40	b)	+40	c)	−40
	+10		+55		−75

Solutions: (To subtract a signed number, add its opposite.)

a) $\quad$ +40 $\qquad$ +40
$\quad$ −(+10) → +(−10)
Ans. $\qquad\qquad$ +30

b) $\quad$ +40 $\qquad$ +40
$\quad$ −(+55) → +(−55)
Ans. $\qquad\qquad$ − 15

c) $\quad$ −40 $\qquad$ −40
$\quad$ −(−75) → +(+75)
Ans. $\qquad\qquad$ +35

5.4 Rules 1 and 2. Subtracting Signed Numbers

Subtract +3 from a) +11, b) −15 . $\qquad$ From −8, subtract c) −15, d) −5 .

Solutions:

a) (+11) − (+3)
$\quad$ (+11) + (−3)
$\quad\quad$ 11 − 3
Ans. 8

b) (−15) − (+3)
$\quad$ (−15) + (−3)
$\quad$ −15 − 3
Ans. − 18

c) (−8) − (−15)
$\quad$ (−8) + (+15)
$\quad$ −8 + 15
Ans. +7

d) (−8) − (−5)
$\quad$ (−8) + (+5)
$\quad$ −8 + 5
Ans. −3

5.5 Combining Addition and Subtraction of Signed Numbers

Combine:

a) (+10) + (+6) − (−2)
$\quad$ (+10) + (+6) + (+2)
$\quad\quad$ 10 + 6 + 2
Ans. 18

b) (+8) − (−12) − (+5) + (−3)
$\quad$ (+8) + (+12) + (−5) + (−3)
$\quad\quad$ 8 + 12 − 5 − 3
Ans. 12

c) (−11) − (+5) + (−7)
$\quad$ (−11) + (−5) + (−7)
$\quad$ −11 − 5 − 7
Ans. −23

5.6 Finding the Change Between Two Signed Numbers

Find the change from +20 to −60, using a) number line and b) signed numbers:

a) **Number Line Solution**

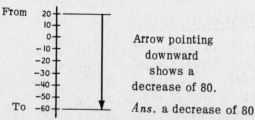

Arrow pointing
downward
shows a
decrease of 80.

Ans. a decrease of 80

b) **Signed Number Solution**

Subtract 20 from − 60,

$\quad$ −60 − (+20)
$\quad$ −60 + (−20)
$\qquad$ −80

5.7 Finding the Distance Between Two Levels

Using (1) a number line and (2) signed numbers, find the distance from 300 ft. below sea level to a) 800 ft. below sea level, b) sea level, c) 100 ft. above sea level.

Number Line Solution

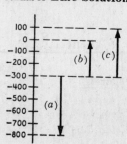

Signed Number Solution

a) −800 − (−300)
$\quad$ −800 + (+300)
$\qquad$ −500
Ans. 500 ft. down

b) 0 − (−300)
$\quad$ 0 + (+300)
$\qquad$ +300
Ans. 300 ft. up

c) 100 − (−300)
$\quad$ 100 + (+300)
$\qquad$ +400
Ans. 400 ft. up

(*Show how each arrow indicates an answer.*)

5.8 Finding a Temperature Change

On Monday, the temperature changed from $-10°$ to $20°$. On Tuesday, the change was from $20°$ to $-20°$. Find each change, using *a*) number line and *b*) signed numbers.

Number Line Solution

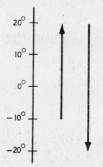

Signed Number Solution

MONDAY CHANGE	TUESDAY CHANGE
$20 - (-10)$	$-20 - (+20)$
$20 + (+10)$	$-20 + (-20)$
$+30$	-40
Ans. Rise of $30°$	*Ans.* Drop of $40°$

(*Show how each arrow indicates an answer.*)

6. MULTIPLYING SIGNED NUMBERS

Rules for Multiplying Two Signed Numbers

Rule 1. To multiply two signed numbers with like signs, multiply their absolute values. The required product is positive.

Thus, $(+5)(+4) = +20$ and $(-5)(-4) = +20$.

Rule 2. To multiply two signed numbers with unlike signs, multiply their absolute values. The required product is negative.

Thus, $(-7)(+2) = -14$ and $(+7)(-2) = -14$.

T H I N K !

> IN MULTIPLYING TWO SIGNED NUMBERS:
> **Like Signs Result in Positive Product, Unlike Signs in Negative.**

Rule 3. Zero times any signed number equals zero. (Multiplicative Property of Zero.)

Thus, $0(-8\frac{1}{2}) = 0$ and $(44.7)(0) = 0$.

Rules for Multiplying More Than Two Signed Numbers

Rule 4. **The product is positive** if all the signed numbers are positive or if there is an even number of negatives.

Thus, $(+10)(+4)(-3)(-5) = +600$.

Rule 5. **The product is negative** if there is an odd number of negatives.

Thus, $(+10)(-4)(-3)(-5) = -600$.

Rule 6. **The product is zero** if any number is zero.

Thus, $(-5)(+82)(0)(316\frac{1}{2}) = 0$.

6.1 Rule 1. Multiplying Signed Numbers with Like Signs

	Multiply: *a*) $(+5)(+9)$	*b*) $(-5)(-11)$	*c*) $(-3)(-2.4)$
Procedure:	**Solutions:**		
	a) $(+5)(+9)$	*b*) $(-5)(-11)$	*c*) $(-3)(-2.4)$
1. Multiply absolute values:	$5(9) = 45$	$5(11) = 55$	$3(2.4) = 7.2$
2. The product is positive:	*Ans.* $+45$	*Ans.* $+55$	*Ans.* $+7.2$

6.2 Rule 2. Multiplying Signed Numbers with Unlike Signs

Multiply: *a*) $(+8)(-9)$ *b*) $(-20)(+5)$ *c*) $(+3\frac{1}{2})(-10)$

Procedure: **Solutions:**

	a) $(+8)(-9)$	*b*) $(-20)(+5)$	*c*) $(+3\frac{1}{2})(-10)$
1. Multiply absolute values:	$8(9) = 72$	$20(5) = 100$	$3\frac{1}{2}(10) = 35$
2. The product is negative:	**Ans.** -72	**Ans.** -100	**Ans.** -35

6.3 Rules 1 to 3. Multiplying Signed Numbers

Multiply $+10$ by *a*) $+18$, *b*) 0, *c*) -13 Multiply -20 by *d*) $+2.5$, *e*) 0, *f*) $-2\frac{1}{4}$

Ans. *a*) $(+10)(+18) = +180$ **(Rule 1)**   *d*) $(-20)(+2.5) = -50$ **(Rule 2)**

   b) $(+10)(0) = 0$ **(Rule 3)**   *e*) $(-20)\,0 = 0$ **(Rule 3)**

   c) $(+10)(-13) = -130$ **(Rule 2)**   *f*) $(-20)(-2\frac{1}{4}) = +45$ **(Rule 1)**

6.4 Rules 4 to 6. Multiplying More Than Two Signed Numbers

Multiply:

a) $(+2)(+3)(+4)$ *Ans.* $+24$ **(Rule 4)**   *f*) $(-1)(-2)(-5)(-10)$ *Ans.* $+100$ **(Rule 4)**

b) $(+2)(+3)(-4)$ *Ans.* -24 **(Rule 5)**   *g*) $(-1)(-2)(+5)(+10)$ *Ans.* $+100$ **(Rule 4)**

c) $(+2)(-3)(-4)$ *Ans.* $+24$ **(Rule 4)**   *h*) $(-1)(+2)(+5)(+10)$ *Ans.* -100 **(Rule 5)**

d) $(-2)(-3)(-4)$ *Ans.* -24 **(Rule 5)**   *i*) $(-1)(-2)(-5)(+10)$ *Ans.* -100 **(Rule 5)**

e) $(+2)(+3)(-4)(0)$ *Ans.* 0 **(Rule 6)**   *j*) $(-1)(-2)(+5)(+10)\,0$ *Ans.* 0 **(Rule 6)**

6.5 Using Signed Numbers to Solve Problems

Complete each statement, using signed numbers to obtain the answer:

a) If George deposits $5 each week, then after 3 weeks his bank balance will be (   ).

   Let $+5 = 5 weekly deposit   Then, $(+5)(+3) = +15$

   and $+3 = 3$ weeks later   *Ans.* $15 more

b) If Henry has been spending $5 a day, then 4 days ago he had (   ).

   Let $-5 = 5 daily spending   Then, $(-5)(-4) = +20$

   and $-4 = 4$ days earlier   *Ans.* $20 more

c) If the temperature falls 6° each day, then after 3 days it will be (   ).

   Let $-6 = 6°$ daily fall   Then, $(-6)(+3) = -18$

   and $+3 = 3$ days later   *Ans.* 18° lower

d) If a team has been gaining 10 yd. on each play, then 3 plays ago it was (   ).

   Let $+10 = 10$ yd. gain per play   Then, $(+10)(-3) = -30$

   and $-3 = 3$ plays earlier   *Ans.* 30 yd. farther back

e) If a car has been traveling west at 30 mph, then 3 hr. ago it was (   ).

   Let $-30 = 30$ mph rate westward   Then, $(-30)(-3) = +90$

   and $-3 = 3$ hr. earlier   *Ans.* 90 mi. farther east

7. FINDING POWERS OF SIGNED NUMBERS

The following rules apply to powers whose exponent is a positive integer:

Rules for Powers of Signed Numbers

Rule 1. For positive base, power is always positive.

Thus, $(+2)^3$ or $2^3 = +8$ since $(+2)^3 = (+2)(+2)(+2)$.

Rule 2. For negative base having even exponent, power is positive.

Thus, $(-2)^4 = +16$ since $(-2)^4 = (-2)(-2)(-2)(-2)$.

Note. -2^4 means "the negative of 2^4". Hence, $-2^4 = -16$.

Rule 3. For negative base having odd exponent, power is negative.

Thus, $(-2)^5 = -32$ since $(-2)^5 = (-2)(-2)(-2)(-2)(-2)$.

THINK!

| FOR NEGATIVE BASE: |
| Power is Positive when Exponent is Even, Negative when Odd. |

7.1 Rule 1. Finding Powers When Base Is Positive

Find each power:

a) 3^2 *Ans.* 9

b) 2^4 *Ans.* 16

c) 10^3 *Ans.* 1000

d) $(+5)^3$ *Ans.* 125

e) $(+7)^2$ *Ans.* 49

f) $(+1)^{10}$ *Ans.* 1

g) $(\frac{2}{3})^2$ *Ans.* $\frac{4}{9}$

h) $(\frac{1}{2})^3$ *Ans.* $\frac{1}{8}$

i) $(\frac{1}{10})^4$ *Ans.* $\frac{1}{10,000}$

7.2 Rules 2 and 3. Finding Powers When Base is Negative

Find each power:

a) $(-3)^2$ *Ans.* 9

b) $(-3)^3$ *Ans.* -27

c) $(-1)^{100}$ *Ans.* 1

d) $(-1)^{105}$ *Ans.* -1

e) $(-.5)^2$ *Ans.* .25

f) $(-.2)^3$ *Ans.* $-.008$

g) $(-\frac{1}{2})^2$ *Ans.* $\frac{1}{4}$

h) $(-\frac{1}{3})^3$ *Ans.* $-\frac{1}{27}$

i) $(-\frac{2}{5})^3$ *Ans.* $-\frac{8}{125}$

7.3 Rules 1 to 3. Finding Powers of Signed Numbers

Find each power:

a) 3^2 *Ans.* 9

b) -3^2 *Ans.* -9

c) $(-3)^2$ *Ans.* 9

d) $(\frac{1}{2})^3$ *Ans.* $\frac{1}{8}$

e) $(-\frac{1}{2})^3$ *Ans.* $-\frac{1}{8}$

f) $-(\frac{1}{2})^3$ *Ans.* $-\frac{1}{8}$

g) $(-1)^{100}$ *Ans.* 1

h) -1^{100} *Ans.* -1

i) $(-1)^{111}$ *Ans.* -1

7.4 Finding Bases, Exponents or Powers

Complete each:

a) $(-3)^? = 81$ *Ans.* 4

b) $2^? = 128$ *Ans.* 7

c) $(?)^5 = -32$ *Ans.* -2

d) $(?)^{121} = -1$ *Ans.* -1

e) $(-\frac{3}{4})^3 = ?$ *Ans.* $-\frac{27}{64}$

f) $-.2^4 = ?$ *Ans.* $-.0016$

8. DIVIDING SIGNED NUMBERS

Rules for Dividing Signed Numbers

Rule 1. To divide two signed numbers with like signs, divide the absolute value of the first by that of the second. The required quotient is positive.

Thus, $\dfrac{+8}{+2} = +4$ and $\dfrac{-8}{-2} = +4$.

Rule 2. To divide two signed numbers with unlike signs, divide the absolute value of the first by that of the second. The required quotient is negative.

Thus, $\dfrac{+12}{-4} = -3$ and $\dfrac{-12}{+4} = -3$.

THINK!

> IN DIVIDING SIGNED NUMBERS:
> **Like Signs Result in Positive Quotient, Unlike Signs in Negative.**

Rule 3. Zero divided by any signed number is zero.

Thus, $\dfrac{0}{+17} = 0$ and $\dfrac{0}{-17} = 0$.

Rule 4. Dividing a signed number by zero is an impossible operation.

Thus, $(+18) \div 0$ or $(-18) \div 0$ are impossible.

$\dfrac{18}{0}$, $\dfrac{+18}{0}$ or $\dfrac{-18}{0}$ are meaningless.

Combining Multiplying and Dividing of Signed Numbers

To multiply and divide signed numbers at the same time:

(1) Isolate their absolute values to obtain the absolute value of the answer.
(2) Find the sign of the answer, as follows:

Rule 5. The quotient is positive if all the numbers are positive or if there is an even number of negatives.

Thus, $\dfrac{(+12)(+5)}{(+3)(+2)}$, $\dfrac{(+12)(+5)}{(-3)(-2)}$, and $\dfrac{(-12)(-5)}{(-3)(-2)}$ equal $+10$.

Rule 6. The quotient is negative if there is an odd number of negatives.

Thus, $\dfrac{(+12)(+5)}{(+3)(-2)}$, $\dfrac{(+12)(-5)}{(-3)(-2)}$, and $\dfrac{(-12)(-5)}{(+3)(-2)}$ equal -10.

Rule 7. The quotient is zero if one of the numbers in the dividend is 0.

Thus, $\dfrac{(+53)(0)}{(-17)(-84)} = 0$.

Rule 8. A zero divisor makes the operation impossible.

Thus, $\dfrac{(+53)(-17)}{(+84)0}$ is meaningless.

8.1 Rule 1. Dividing Signed Numbers with Like Signs

Divide: $a)$ (+12) by (+6) $b)$ (−12) by (−4) $c)$ (−24.6) by (−3)

Procedure: Solutions:

$a)$ $\dfrac{+12}{+6}$ $b)$ $\dfrac{-12}{-4}$ $c)$ $\dfrac{-24.6}{-3}$

1. Divide absolute values: $\dfrac{12}{6} = 2$ $\dfrac{12}{4} = 3$ $\dfrac{24.6}{3} = 8.2$

2. Make quotient positive: **Ans.** $+2$ **Ans.** $+3$ **Ans.** $+8.2$

8.2 Rule 2. Dividing Signed Numbers with Unlike Signs

Divide: *a*) (+20) by (−5)   *b*) −24 by +8   *c*) +8 by −16

Procedure: Solutions:

a) $\dfrac{+20}{-5}$ *b*) $\dfrac{-24}{+8}$ *c*) $\dfrac{+8}{-16}$

1. Divide absolute values: $\dfrac{20}{5} = 4$ $\dfrac{24}{8} = 3$ $\dfrac{8}{16} = \dfrac{1}{2}$

2. Make quotient negative: **Ans. −4**   **Ans. −3**   **Ans. −$\dfrac{1}{2}$**

8.3 Rules 1 to 4. Dividing Signed Numbers

Divide +9 by *a*) +3, *b*) 0, *c*) −10   Divide each by −12: *d*) +36, *e*) 0, *f*) −3

Ans. a) $\dfrac{+9}{+3} = +3$ **(Rule 1)**   *d*) $\dfrac{+36}{-12} = -3$ **(Rule 2)**

b) $\dfrac{+9}{0}$ is meaningless   **(Rule 4)**   *e*) $\dfrac{0}{-12} = 0$ **(Rule 3)**

c) $\dfrac{+9}{-10} = -\dfrac{9}{10}$ **(Rule 2)**   *f*) $\dfrac{-3}{-12} = +\dfrac{1}{4}$ **(Rule 1)**

8.4 Rules 5 and 6: Combining Multiplying and Dividing Signed Numbers

Solve: *a*) $\dfrac{(+12)(+8)}{(-3)(-4)}$ *b*) $\dfrac{(-4)(-2)(-3)}{(-5)(-10)}$

Procedure:

1. Isolate absolute values: $\dfrac{(12)(8)}{(3)(4)} = 8$ $\dfrac{(4)(2)(3)}{(5)(10)} = \dfrac{12}{25}$

2. Find the sign of the answer: $\dfrac{(+)(+)}{(-)(-)} = +$ $\dfrac{(-)(-)(-)}{(-)(-)} = -$

Ans. +8   **Ans. −$\dfrac{12}{25}$**

8.5 Rules 7 and 8. Zero in Dividend or Divisor

Solve: *a*) $\dfrac{(+27)0}{(-3)(+15)}$ *Ans.* 0 **(Rule 7)**   *b*) $\dfrac{(+27)(-3)}{(+15)0}$ *Ans.* meaningless **(Rule 8)**

9. EVALUATING EXPRESSIONS HAVING SIGNED NUMBERS

To evaluate an expression having signed numbers:

1) Substitute the values given for the variables, enclosing them in parentheses.
2) Perform the operations in the correct order, doing the power operations first.

9.1 Evaluating Expressions Having One Variable

Evaluate if $y = -2$:

a) $2y + 5$ *b*) $20 - 3y$ *c*) $4y^2$ *d*) $2y^3$ *e*) $20 - y^5$

$2(-2) + 5$ $20 - 3(-2)$ $4(-2)^2$ $2(-2)^3$ $20 - (-2)^5$

$-4 + 5$ $20 + 6$ $4(4)$ $2(-8)$ $20 - (-32)$

Ans. 1   *Ans.* 26   *Ans.* 16   *Ans.* −16   *Ans.* 52

9.2 Evaluating Expressions Having Two Variables

Evaluate if $x = -3$ and $y = +2$:

a) $\quad 2x - 5y$
$\quad 2(-3) - 5(+2)$
$\quad\quad -6 - 10$
Ans. -16

b) $\quad 20 - 2xy$
$\quad 20 - 2(-3)(+2)$
$\quad\quad 20 + 12$
Ans. 32

c) $\quad 3xy^2$
$\quad 3(-3)(+2)^2$
$\quad 3(-3)(4)$
Ans. -36

d) $\quad 2x^2 - y^2$
$\quad 2(-3)^2 - (+2)^2$
$\quad 2(+9) - (+4)$
Ans. 14

9.3 Evaluating Expressions Having Three Variables

Evaluate if $x = +1$, $y = -2$, $z = -3$:

a) $\quad 4xy^2 + z$
$\quad 4(+1)(-2)^2 + (-3)$
$\quad\quad 4(1)(4) - 3$
Ans. 13

b) $\quad x^2 + y^2 - z^2$
$\quad (+1)^2 + (-2)^2 - (-3)^2$
$\quad\quad 1 + 4 - 9$
Ans. -4

c) $\dfrac{3x - 5y}{2z}$
$\dfrac{3(+1) - 5(-2)}{2(-3)}$
$\dfrac{3 + 10}{-6}$
Ans. $-2\frac{1}{6}$

d) $\dfrac{2y^2}{x - z}$
$\dfrac{2(-2)^2}{+1 - (-3)}$
$\dfrac{2 \cdot 4}{1 + 3}$
Ans. 2

SUPPLEMENTARY PROBLEMS

1. State the words that are opposite in meaning to the following: **(1.1)**

a) farther   *d)* longer   *g)* wider   *j)* stronger
b) slower   *e)* cheaper   *h)* credit
c) hotter   *f)* younger   *i)* heavier

Ans. a) nearer   *d)* shorter   *g)* narrower   *j)* weaker
b) faster   *e)* dearer   *h)* debit
c) colder   *f)* older   *i)* lighter

2. State the quantity represented by each signed number: **(1.2)**

a) By $+12$, if -12 means 12 yd. lost.
b) By -7, if $+7$ means 7 flights up.
c) By $+25$, if -25 means 25 mi. westward.
d) By -32, if $+32$ means \$32 earned.
e) By $+15$, if -15 means \$15 withdrawn.
f) By -13, if $+13$ means 13 steps forward.

Ans. a) 12 yd. gained   *c)* 25 mi. eastward   *e)* \$15 deposited
b) 7 flights down   *d)* \$32 spent   *f)* 13 steps backward

3. Evaluate: **(1.3)**

a) $\left|3\frac{1}{2}\right| + \left|-3\frac{1}{2}\right|$ *Ans.* $3\frac{1}{2} + 3\frac{1}{2} = 7$

b) $|97| - |-97|$ *Ans.* $97 - 97 = 0$

c) $-5|-3|\,|-2|\,|+4|$ *Ans.* $-5(3)(2)(4) = -120$

d) $\dfrac{18(|+9|)}{6(|-9|)}$ *Ans.* $\dfrac{18(9)}{6(9)} = 3$

e) $|-5|^2$ *Ans.* $5^2 = 25$

f) $\dfrac{2|+2| + 3|-3|}{4|-4| - 5|+3|}$ *Ans.* $\dfrac{2(2) + 3(3)}{4(4) - 5(3)} = \dfrac{13}{1} = 13$

4. Using the number line with reference to the graphs and coordinates shown, name **(1.4)**

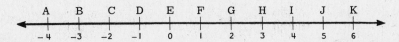

a) the graphs of the whole numbers,   *b*) the coordinates of points midway between (1) B and D, (2) E and K, (3) D and E, (4) G and J,   *c*) the graphs of coordinates that are at least −1 and no more than 3,   *d*) the graphs of coordinates whose absolute value is equal to or less than 2,   *e*) the graphs of the coordinates that differ from −1 by 3.

Ans. a) E, F, G, H, I, J, K,   *b*) (1) −2, (2) 3, (3) −$\frac{1}{2}$, (4) 3$\frac{1}{2}$,   *c*) D, E, F, G, H,   *d*) C, D, E, F, G.
   e) A, G

5. On a temperature scale, state the meanings of *a*) −17, *b*) +15 . **(2.1)**

Ans. a) −17 means (*1*) 17° below zero or (*2*) a drop of 17° from any temperature.
   b) +15 means (*1*) 15° above zero or (*2*) a rise of 15° from any temperature.

6. With reference to a temperature scale, what real number indicates **(2.2)**

a) 24° above zero,   *b*) a rise of 24°,   *c*) no change in temperature and also zero degrees,   *d*) the equivalent of a drop of 10° followed by a drop of 10° more,   *e*) the new temperature reached when after starting from 5° below zero, the temperature rose 25°.

Ans. a) 24,   *b*) 24,   *c*) 0,   *d*) (−10) + (−10) = −20, meaning a combined effect equivalent to a 20° drop,   *e*) (−5) + (+25) = (+20) indicating the new temperature of 20° above zero.

7. Which is greater? *a*) − $\frac{1}{2}$ or 0,   *b*) − $\frac{1}{2}$ or − 30,   *c*) + $\frac{1}{2}$ or − 2$\frac{1}{2}$,   *d*) −110 or −120 . **(2.3)**

   Ans.   *a*) 0   *b*) − $\frac{1}{2}$ *c*) + $\frac{1}{2}$ *d*) −110

8. In each, obtain a true statement by replacing the question mark with either =, <, or > : **(2.4)**

a) −2 ? −1   *Ans.* <   *e*) 50 + 0 ? 50 × 1   *Ans.* =   *h*) |−7| ? |−8| *Ans.* <
b) −100 ? 0   *Ans.* <   *f*) $\frac{1}{2}$? $\frac{1}{4}$ × $\frac{1}{4}$ *Ans.* >   *i*) 2(−7) ? 0   *Ans.* <
c) 0 ? − $\frac{1}{4}$ *Ans.* >   *g*) −7 ? −8   *Ans.* >   *j*) 2|−7| ? 0   *Ans.* >
d) 50 × 0 ? 0   *Ans.* =

9. Express each symbol, verbally and state whether each statement is true or false: **(2.5)**

a) − $\frac{1}{2}$ < − $\frac{1}{4}$ *Ans.* − $\frac{1}{2}$ is less than − $\frac{1}{4}$. True

b) −3 < 0 < 3   *Ans.* −3 is less than 0, which is less than 3. True

c) −3 < −4 < −5   *Ans.* −3 is less than −4, which is less than −5. False

d) −100 > −1000 > 1,000,000   *Ans.* −100 is less than −1000, which is less than 1,000,000
               False

e) 2 × 1 ≠ 2 + $\frac{1}{2}$ *Ans.* 2 × 1 does not equal 2 + $\frac{1}{2}$. True since 2 ≠ 2$\frac{1}{2}$.

f) |−3| ≠ |+3| *Ans.* Absolute value of −3 does not equal the absolute value
   since 3 = 3   of +3. False since 3 = 3.

10. Beginning with the main floor, an elevator went up 5 floors, then up 10 more, then down 6, and then down 12. Find its location after making these changes. **(2.6)**

Ans. 3 floors below the main floor.

11. Beginning with 5° above zero, the temperature rose 2°, then dropped 8° and finally rose 4°. Find the change in temperature and the final temperature after the changes. **(2.7)**

Ans. Change in temperature was a drop of 2° from the initial temperature of +5°. Final temperature after the changes was 3° above zero.

12. A plane starting from a point 200 mi. east of its base flew directly west to a point 300 mi. west of the base. How far did it travel? **(2.8)**

Ans. 500 mi. westward.

13. List the numbers described in each set and graph the set: **(2.9)**

    a) the set of natural odd numbers less than 10

    b) the set of whole numbers greater than 6 and less than or equal to 9

    c) the set of negative even integers less than −1 and greater than −10

    d) the set of powers of 2

    e) the set of integers whose absolute values are between 2 and 6

    f) the set of positive integers whose final digit is 5

    g) the set of negative integers whose final digit is 0

    h) the set of natural numbers represented by $3n$ if n represents the set $\{1, 2, 3, 4\}$

    i) the set of whole numbers represented by $2n - 3$ if n represents the set $\{0, 1, 2, 3, 4\}$

Ans.   (The graph of each set is left to the student. Refer for help to Set 2.10.)

    a) $\{1, 3, 5, 7, 9\}$ **d) $\{2, 4, 8, 16, 32, \dots ,\}$ *g*) $\{\dots, -50, -40, -30, -20, -10\}$

    b) $\{7, 8, 9\}$ *e*) $\{-5, -4, -3, 3, 4, 5\}$ *h*) $\{3, 6, 9, 12\}$

    c) $\{-8, -6, -4, -2\}$ *f*) $\{5, 15, 25, 35, \dots\}$ *i*) $\{1, 3, 5\}$

**The unit length on a number line may have a value that is suitable to the problem. Thus, in (*d*) use a value of 4 for each unit length:

14. Graph each set and write the set, using set-builder notation: **(2.10)**

    a) the set of real numbers less than or equal to 3

    b) the set of real numbers whose absolute value is greater than or equal to 4

    c) the set of real numbers whose absolute value is less than 4

    d) the set of real numbers between −2 and 7

Ans.

    a)

               $\{x : x \leq 3,\ x$ is a real number $\}$

    b)

               $\{x : |x| \geq 4,\ x$ is a real number $\}$

    c)

               $\{x : |x| < 4,\ x$ is a real number $\}$ or $\{x : -4 < x < 4,\ x$ is a real number $\}$

    d)

               $\{x : -2 < x < 7,\ x$ is a real number $\}$

15. Using signed numbers, find each sum: **(3.1)**

    a) 20 lb. gained plus 7 lb. lost.   *d*) \$5 gained plus \$15 spent.

    b) 17 lb. lost plus 3 lb. gained.   *e*) 8° rise plus 20° rise.

    c) \$5 spent plus \$15 spent.   *f*) 8° drop plus 8° rise.

Ans. *a*) $(+20) + (-7) = +13$ or 13 lb. gained   *d*) $(+5) + (-15) = -10$ or \$10 spent

       b) $(-17) + (+3) = -14$ or 14 lb. lost   *e*) $(+8) + (+20) = +28$ or 28° rise

       c) $(-5) + (-15) = -20$ or \$20 spent   *f*) $(-8) + (+8) = 0$ or no change

16. Add: *a*) $(+10\frac{1}{2}), (+7\frac{1}{2})$ *b*) $(-1.4), (-2.5)$ *c*) $(+5), (+3), (+12)$ *d*) $(-1), (-2), (-3)$ **(3.2)**

Ans. *a*) $+18$ *b*) -3.9 *c*) $+20$ *d*) -6

17. Add: *a*) $(+6\frac{1}{4}), (-3\frac{1}{2})$ *b*) $(-.23), (+.18)$ *c*) $(+23), (-13), (+12)$ *d*) $(+5), (-8), (+17)$ **(3.3)**

Ans. *a*) $+2\frac{3}{4}$ *b*) $-.05$ *c*) $+22$ *d*) $+14$

18. Add: a) $(+25.7),(-25.7)$ b) $(+120),(-120),(+19)$ c) $(+28),(-16),(-28),(+16)$ **(3.4)**

Ans. a) 0 b) $+19$ c) 0

19. Add -32 to   To $+11$, add   **(3.5)**

a) -25 *Ans.* -57 c) $+32$ *Ans.* 0 e) -29 *Ans.* -18 g) $+117$ *Ans.* $+128$
b) $+25$ *Ans.* -7 d) $+100$ *Ans.* $+68$ f) -11 *Ans.* 0 h) -108 *Ans.* -97

20. Express in simplified vertical form and add: **(4.1)**

a) $(+11)+(+3)+(-9)+(-8)$ b) $(-42)+(+42)+(-85)$ c) $(+13.7)+(+2.4)-(8.9)$

Ans. a)

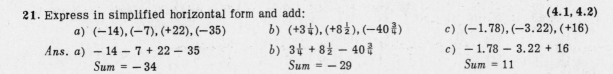

a)
$$\begin{array}{r} 11 \\ 3 \\ -9 \\ -8 \\ \hline \end{array}$$
$Sum = -3$

b)
$$\begin{array}{r} -42 \\ +42 \\ -85 \\ \hline \end{array}$$
$Sum = -85$

c)
$$\begin{array}{r} 13.7 \\ 2.4 \\ -8.9 \\ \hline \end{array}$$
$Sum = 7.2$

21. Express in simplified horizontal form and add: **(4.1, 4.2)**

a) $(-14),(-7),(+22),(-35)$ b) $(+3\frac{1}{4}),(+8\frac{1}{2}),(-40\frac{3}{4})$ c) $(-1.78),(-3.22),(+16)$

Ans. a) $-14-7+22-35$ b) $3\frac{1}{4}+8\frac{1}{2}-40\frac{3}{4}$ c) $-1.78-3.22+16$
$Sum=-34$ $Sum=-29$ $Sum=11$

22. In a football game, a team gained 8 yd. on the first play, gained 1 yd. on the second play, lost 12 yd. on the third play and lost 6 yd. on the fourth play. Find the change in position due to these changes, using a) signed numbers and b) a number scale: **(4.3)**

a) $(+8)+(+1)+(-12)+(-6)$
$\quad\; 8\; +\; 1\; -\; 12\; -\; 6$
$\qquad\qquad -9$

b)
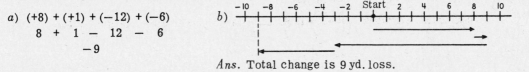

Ans. Total change is 9 yd. loss.

23. Subtract: **(5.1)**

a) $(+11)$ from $(+16)$ c) $(+3.5)$ from $(+7.2)$ e) $(+3\frac{1}{3})$ from $(+11\frac{2}{3})$
b) $(+47)$ from (-47) d) $(+7.2)$ from (-3.5) f) $(+17\frac{2}{3})$ from (-8)

Ans. a) $+5$ b) -94 c) $+3.7$ d) -10.7 e) $+8\frac{1}{3}$ f) $-25\frac{2}{3}$

24. Subtract: **(5.2)**

a) (-11) from $(+16)$ c) $(-.81)$ from $(+.92)$ e) $(-7\frac{1}{5})$ from $(+2\frac{4}{5})$
b) (-47) from $(+47)$ d) $(-.23)$ from $(-.27)$ f) $(-3\frac{5}{6})$ from (-4)

Ans. a) $+27$ b) $+94$ c) $+1.73$ d) $-.04$ e) $+10$ f) $-\frac{1}{6}$

25. Subtract the lower number from the upper: **(5.3)**

a) $+22$ b) $+17$ c) -30.7 d) $-.123$ e) $-13\frac{2}{3}$ f) $-27\frac{1}{2}$
$\quad\;\underline{+17}$ $\underline{+22}$ $\underline{+30.7}$ $\underline{+.265}$ $\underline{-10\frac{1}{3}}$ $\underline{+\;3\frac{3}{4}}$

Ans. a) $+5$ b) -5 c) -61.4 d) $-.388$ e) $-3\frac{1}{3}$ f) $-31\frac{1}{4}$

26. Subtract $+4$ from a) $+8\frac{1}{2}$, b) $+4$, c) $+2.3$, and d) -25.   **(5.4)**
From -10 subtract e) -23, f) -8, g) -3.9, and h) $+20\frac{1}{4}$.

Ans. a) $+4\frac{1}{2}$, b) 0, c) -1.7, d) -29, e) $+13$, f) -2, g) -6.1, h) $-30\frac{1}{4}$

27. Combine: a) $(+11)+(+7)-(+24)$ d) $(+25)-(-6)-(-22)+(+40)$ **(5.5)**
b) $(-11)-(-5)-(-14)$ e) $(-3.7)+(-2.4)-(+7.8)+(-11.4)$
c) $(+.13)-(+.07)-(+.32)$ f) $(+2\frac{1}{2})-(-1\frac{1}{4})-(+5\frac{3}{4})-(-7)$

Ans. a) -6, b) $+8$, c) $-.26$ d) $+93$, e) -25.3, f) $+5$

28. Find the change from: **(5.6)**

    a) +10 to −20   *Ans.* −30, a decrease of 30

    b) −10 to +20   *Ans.* +30, an increase of 30   *g)* $-\frac{1}{2}$ to $+5\frac{1}{2}$ *Ans.* +6, an increase of 6

    c) +45 to 0   *Ans.* −45, a decrease of 45   *h)* $+5\frac{1}{2}$ to $+4\frac{1}{2}$ *Ans.* −1, a decrease of 1

    d) −45 to 0   *Ans.* +45, an increase of 45

    e) −45 to +45   *Ans.* +90, an increase of 90   *i)* $+62\frac{1}{4}$ to $+112\frac{1}{2}$ *Ans.* $+50\frac{1}{4}$, an increase of

    f) +45 to −45   *Ans.* −90, a decrease of 90 $50\frac{1}{4}$

29. Find the distance from 500 ft. above sea level to *a)* 1200 ft. above sea level, *b)* sea level, **(5.7)**
    c) 2000 ft. below sea level.   *Ans. a)* 700 ft. up, *b)* 500 ft. down, *c)* 2500 ft. down

30. On a Monday, the hourly temperatures from 1 P.M. to 6 P.M. were   **(5.8)**

1 P.M.	2 P.M.	3 P.M.	4 P.M.	5 P.M.	6 P.M.
−8°	−5°	0°	4°	−4°	−20°

Find each hourly temperature change.

  Ans. a) 3° rise from 1 to 2 P.M., *b)* 5° rise from 2 to 3 P.M., *c)* 4° rise from 3 to 4 P.M.,
    d) 8° drop from 4 to 5 P.M., *e)* 16° drop from 5 to 6 P.M.

31. Multiply: *a)* (+3)(+22)   *c)* (−5)(−4)   *e)* $(+8)(+2\frac{1}{2})$ *g)* $(-2\frac{1}{2})(-1\frac{1}{2})$ **(6.1)**

           b) (+.3)(+2.2)   *d)* (−.05)(−.04)   *f)* $(-35)(-2\frac{1}{5})$ *h)* $(+\frac{5}{4})(+\frac{15}{2})$

  Ans. a) +66, *b)* +.66,   *c)* +20, *d)* +.002,   *e)* +20, *f)* +77,   *g)* $+3\frac{3}{4}$, *h)* $+9\frac{3}{8}$

32. Multiply: *a)* (−20)(+6)   *c)* (−.8)(+.11)   *e)* $(+6)(-7\frac{2}{3})$ *g)* $(-\frac{7}{2})(+\frac{11}{4})$ **(6.2)**

           b) (+13)(−8)   *d)* (+3.4)(−21)   *f)* $(-2\frac{1}{7})(+21)$ *h)* $(+2\frac{1}{5})(-3\frac{2}{5})$

  Ans. a) −120, *b)* −104, *c)* −.088, *d)* −71.4, *e)* −46, *f)* −45,   *g)* $-\frac{77}{8}$, *h)* $-7\frac{12}{25}$

33. Multiply +8 by *a)* +7, *b)* 0, *c)* −4.   Multiply −12 by *d)* +.9,   *e)* $-1\frac{1}{2}$, *f)* −8.21   **(6.3)**

      Ans. a) +56, *b)* 0, *c)* −32   *Ans.*   *d)* −10.8, *e)* +18, *f)* +98.52

34. Multiply: *a)* (+3)(+4)(+12)   *d)* (−1)(−1)(+1)(−1)   *g)* $(+\frac{1}{2})(+\frac{1}{2})(+\frac{1}{2})(-\frac{1}{2})$ **(6.4)**

           b) (+.3)(+.4)(+1.2)   *e)* (−2)(−2)(−2)(−2)   *h)* $(-\frac{1}{2})(+8)(-\frac{1}{4})(+16)$

           c) (+.3)(−4)(−.12)   *f)* (−2)(+5)(−5)(+4)   *i)* $(-1\frac{1}{2})(+2\frac{1}{2})(+3\frac{1}{2})$

  Ans. a) +144, *b)* +.144, *c)* +.144, *d)* −1, *e)* +16, *f)* +200, *g)* $-\frac{1}{16}$, *h)* +16, *i)* $-13\frac{1}{8}$

35. Complete each statement. In each case, indicate how signed numbers may be used to obtain the answer.   **(6.5)**

    a) If George withdraws $10 each week, then after 5 weeks, his bank balance will be ( ).

    b) If Tom has been earning $15 a day, then in 3 days, he will have ( ).

    c) If the temperature has risen 8° each day, then five days ago, it was ( ).

    d) If a car has been traveling east at 40 m.p.h., then 3 hours ago, it was ( ).

    e) If a school decreases in register 20 pupils per day, then 12 days ago, the register was ( ).

  Ans. a) $50 less   *b)* $45 more   *c)* 40° less   *d)* 120 mi. farther west *e)* 240 pupils more

        (−10)(+5) = −50   (+15)(+3) = +45   (+8)(−5) = −40   (+40)(−3) = −120   (−20)(−12) = +240

36. Find each power: *a)* 2^3, *b)* $(+4)^2$, *c)* 10^4, *d)* $.3^2$, *e)* $(+.2)^3$, *f)* $(\frac{1}{4})^2$, *g)* $(\frac{1}{10})^3$, *h)* $(\frac{2}{5})^2$ **(7.1)**

  Ans. a) 8, *b)* 16, *c)* 10,000, *d)* .09, *e)* .008, *f)* $\frac{1}{16}$, *g)* $\frac{1}{1000}$, *h)* $\frac{4}{25}$

37. Find each power: *a)* $(-1)^5$, *b)* $(-1)^{82}$, *c)* $(-.3)^3$, *d)* $(-.1)^4$, *e)* $(-.12)^2$, *f)* $(-\frac{2}{5})^3$, *g)* $(-\frac{1}{3})^4$ **(7.2)**

  Ans. a) −1, *b)* +1, *c)* −.027, *d)* +.0001, *e)* +.0144, *f)* $-\frac{8}{125}$, *g)* $+\frac{1}{81}$

(7.3)

38. Find each power:

a) 5^2 *Ans.* 25   f) $(-1)^{100}$ *Ans.* 1   k) $-(-1)^{103}$ *Ans.* 1

b) $(-5)^2$ *Ans.* 25   g) -1^{100} *Ans.* -1 l) $-(\frac{2}{3})^3$ *Ans.* $-\frac{8}{27}$

c) -5^2 *Ans.* -25 h) -1^{101} *Ans.* -1 m) $-(-\frac{2}{3})^2$ *Ans.* $-\frac{4}{9}$

d) $(\frac{1}{3})^2$ *Ans.* $\frac{1}{9}$ i) $(-1)^{101}$ *Ans.* -1

e) $(-\frac{1}{3})^2$ *Ans.* $\frac{1}{9}$ j) $-(-1)^{102}$ *Ans.* -1

(7.4)

39. Complete each:

a) $(-5)^? = -125$ c) $(-?)^4 = +.0001$ e) $(+\frac{2}{3})^4 = ?$ g) $(?)^{171} = -1$

b) $(+10)^? = 10,000$ d) $(-?)^3 = -.343$ f) $(-\frac{1}{2})^5 = ?$ h) $(?)^{242} = +1$

Ans. a) 3, b) 4,   c) $-.1$, d) $-.7$,   e) $\frac{16}{81}$, f) $-\frac{1}{32}$, g) -1, h) $+1$ or -1

(8.1)

40. Divide: a) $(+24)$ by $(+3)$ c) (-49) by (-7) e) $(+4.8)$ by $(+.2)$ g) (-18) by (-4)

b) $(+88)$ by $(+8)$ d) (-78) by (-6) f) (-95) by $(-.5)$ h) $(+8)$ by $(+12)$

Ans. a) $+8$, b) $+11$,   c) $+7$, d) $+13$,   e) $+24$, f) $+190$,   g) $+4\frac{1}{2}$, h) $+\frac{2}{3}$

(8.2)

41. Divide: a) $(+30)$ by (-5) c) $(+13)$ by (-2) e) $(+.2)$ by $(-.04)$ g) (-100) by $(+500)$

b) (-30) by $(+5)$ d) (-36) by $(+8)$ f) (-30) by $(+.1)$ h) $(+100)$ by (-3)

Ans. a) -6, b) -6,   c) $-6\frac{1}{2}$, d) $-4\frac{1}{2}$, e) -5, f) -300,   g) $-\frac{1}{5}$, h) $-33\frac{1}{3}$

(8.3)

42. Divide $+12$ by   a) $+24$,   b) $+12$,   c) $+4$,   d) -1,   e) -3,   f) -48

Divide each by -20 g) $+60$,   h) $+20$,   i) $+5$,   j) -225,   k) -10,   l) -100

Ans. a) $+\frac{1}{2}$, b) $+1$, c) $+3$, d) -12, e) -4, f) $-\frac{1}{4}$, g) -3, h) -1, i) $-\frac{1}{4}$, j) $+11\frac{1}{4}$, k) $+\frac{1}{2}$, l) $+5$

(8.3)

43. Divide: a) $\frac{+25}{+5}$ b) $\frac{-25}{+5}$ c) $\frac{-2.5}{-.5}$ d) $\frac{-.25}{+.5}$ e) $\frac{-25}{-.5}$ f) $\frac{-.025}{+.5}$

Ans. a) $+5$ b) -5 c) $+5$ d) $-\frac{1}{2}$ e) $+50$ f) $-.05$

(8.4, 8.5)

44. Multiply and divide as indicated:

a) $\dfrac{(+20)(+12)}{(+3)(+5)}$ c) $\dfrac{(+3)(+6)(+10)}{(+12)(-3)}$ e) $\dfrac{0}{(-17)(-24)}$ g) $\dfrac{(+1)(+2)(+3)}{(-4)(-6)}$

b) $\dfrac{(+20)(-12)}{(-3)(-5)}$ d) $\dfrac{(-3)(-6)(+18)}{(+12)(+3)}$ f) $\dfrac{(-120)(+31)\,0}{(-5)(-8)(-9)}$ h) $\dfrac{(+.1)(+.2)(-30)}{(-.4)(-.1)}$

Ans. a) $+16$, b) -16,   c) -5, d) $+9$,   e) 0, f) 0,   g) $+\frac{1}{4}$, h) -15

(9.1)

45. Evaluate if $y = -3$:

a) $3y + 1$ c) $2y^2$ e) $(-y)^2$ g) $\dfrac{7y}{3}$ i) $\dfrac{3y + 15}{y}$

b) $20 - 4y$ d) $3y^3$ f) $2 - y^3$ h) $y(y^2 - 2)$ j) $2y^2 - 5y + 27$

Ans. a) -8, b) 32,   c) 18, d) -81, e) 9, f) 29,   g) -7, h) -21,   i) -2, j) 60

(9.2)

46. Evaluate if $x = -1$ and $y = +3$:

a) $x + y$ c) $x^2 + y^2$ e) $4xy - x^2$ g) $3xy^2$ i) $\dfrac{y^2}{6x}$

b) $y - 2x$ d) $3xy$ f) $x^2y + 10$ h) $x^3 + 10y$ j) $\dfrac{y + x}{y - x}$

Ans. a) 2, b) 5,   c) 10, d) -9,   e) -13, f) 13,   g) -27, h) 29,   i) $-\frac{3}{2}$, j) $\frac{1}{2}$

(9.3)

47. Evaluate if $x = -2$, $y = -1$, and $z = +3$:

a) $x + y + z$ c) $x^2 + y^2 + z^2$ e) $2xyz$ g) $xy + z^2$ i) $\dfrac{2x - 3y}{4z}$

b) $2x + 2y - 2z$ d) $x^3 - y^2 + z$ f) $xy + yz$ h) $y^2 - 5xz$ j) $\dfrac{x^2 - y^2}{z^2}$

Ans. a) 0, b) -12,   c) 14, d) -6,   e) 12, f) -1,   g) 11, h) 31,   i) $-\frac{1}{12}$, j) $\frac{1}{3}$

Chapter 4

Monomials and Polynomials

1. UNDERSTANDING MONOMIALS AND POLYNOMIALS

A sentence in English may be a word or a combination of words. In mathematics, an expression may be a term or a combination of terms. In English, *run* is a word of three letters. In mathematics, *run* is a term which is the product of three variables, r, u, and n.

A **term** is a number, a variable, or the product or quotient of variables.

Thus, 5, y, $5y$, $\frac{y}{5}$, $\frac{5}{y}$, $5xy$, $\frac{5x}{y}$, and $5x^3y^2$ are terms.

Terms such as 7, $.07$, or $\frac{1}{7}$ are constants.

A **factor of a term** is each of the numbers or variables multiplied to form the term.

Thus, the factors of $5xy$ are 5, x, and y.

Any factor of a term is the **coefficient** of the product of the remaining factors.

Thus, in $5xy$, 5 is the **numerical coefficient** of xy; and xy is the **literal coefficient** of 5.

An **expression** may be a term or a combination of terms.

Thus, $\frac{10}{x} + 3y + 4$ is an expression of three terms, $3y + 4$ is an expression of two terms, and $\frac{10}{x}$ is an expression of one term. Since the variable, x, appears in the denominator, the expression $\frac{10}{x} + 3y + 4$ is not a polynomial according to the following definition:

A **polynomial** is an expression formed from numbers and variables in which

1. no operations are indicated other than addition, subtraction, and multiplication,
2. the exponents of variables are positive integers, and
3. no variable appears in the denominator, or in the radicand of a root expression.

Thus, $5x^2 + 4x - 2$ is a polynomial in x, and $5x + 2y$ is a polynomial in x and y. The expression $4\sqrt{x} + 3$ is not a polynomial since the variable x is the radicand of a root expression; however, $4x + \sqrt{3}$ is a polynomial.

A **monomial** is any one of the terms of a polynomial.

Thus, $5x$, $5x^2y$, and $\frac{x}{5}$ are monomials. However, $\frac{5}{x}$ is not a monomial since division by a variable is involved.

A **binomial** is a polynomial of two terms. A **trinomial** is a polynomial of three terms.

Thus, $3x^2 + 5x$ is a binomial and $3x^2 + 5x + 7$ is a trinomial. Although "poly" is a prefix meaning many, it is sometimes convenient to consider a monomial as a polynomial of one term.

In general, a **monomial in x** is an expression of the form ax^n where a is a nonzero real number and n is a positive integer. The number denoted by a is the numerical coefficient and is referred to as the **coefficient of the monomial** while the number denoted by n is the **degree of the monomial**.

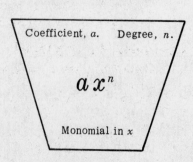

Coefficient, a.   Degree, n.

$$a\,x^n$$

Monomial in x

Thus, $\frac{1}{2}x^2$ is a monomial in x of degree 2 and coefficient $\frac{1}{2}$. A number such as 5 is a monomial of degree 0. However, 0 has no degree.

A **monomial in** x **and** y is of the form ax^ny^q where a is a nonzero real number and both n and q are positive integers. The degree of a monomial in more than one variable is the sum of the exponents of each of the variables. Note that the degree of ax^ny^q is $n + q$.

Thus, $9x^2y^3$ is a monomial in x and y of degree 5.

The **degree of a polynomial** is the degree of the monomial of greatest degree. Thus, the degree of the polynomial $7x^3 + 3x^2 + 5x - 1$ is 3 since the monomial of greatest degree is $7x^3$.

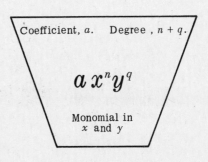

Coefficient, a.   Degree , $n + q$.

$$a\,x^n y^q$$

Monomial in x and y

Like monomials are monomials having a common literal coefficient. Like monomials may differ only in their numerical coefficients.

Like Monomials	Unlike Monomials
$7x$ and $5x$	$7x$ and $5y$
$8a^2$ and a^2	$8a^2$ and a^3
$5rs^2$ and $2rs^2$	$5rs^2$ and $2r^2s$

A polynomial is **in simple form** when no two of its terms are like monomials. **To simplify a polynomial,** change the polynomial into an equivalent polynomial in simple form.

Thus, $x^2 + 5x + 3x + 7$, by combining like monomials, can be simplified by changing it into the equivalent polynomial $x^2 + 8x + 7$.

1.1 Properties of Monomials

State the coefficient and degree of each expression if it is a monomial:

a) 25   *Ans.* a constant monomial of degree 0

b) $5x$ *Ans.* a monomial of degree 1 and a coefficient 5

c) $\frac{1}{2}xy$ *Ans.* a monomial of degree 2 and coefficient $\frac{1}{2}$

d) $-2x^2y$ *Ans.* a monomial of degree 3 and a coefficient of -2

e) $\frac{3x^2}{y}$ *Ans.* not a monomial because of division by a variable

f) $\sqrt{5}\,x^5$ *Ans.* a monomial of degree 5 and a coefficient $\sqrt{5}$

g) $\frac{6}{x^2}$ *Ans.* not a monomial because of division by a variable

h) $x^2 + 6$ *Ans.* a binomial

1.2 Selecting Like Monomials in a Polynomial

Select like monomials in each polynomial, if any:

a) $10 - 5x + 2$ *Ans. a*) 10 and $+2$

b) $x + 3y - z + y$ *Ans. b*) $3y$ and $+y$

c) $2ab - 3ac + 4bc - bc$ *Ans. c*) $+4bc$ and $-bc$

d) $2abc + 3acd + 5bcd + 7acd$ *Ans. d*) $3acd$ and $7acd$

e) $y^2 - 2x^2 + 4z^2 - 5y^2$ *Ans. e*) y^2 and $-5y^2$

f) $xy^2 + x^2y^2 - 3x^2y + 7x^2y$ *Ans. f*) $-3x^2y$ and $7x^2y$

g) $2ab^2c^2 - 5a^2b^2c + 8a^2bc^2$ *Ans. g*) no like terms

h) $3(x+y) - 5(x+y) + 2(x-y)$ *Ans. h*) $3(x+y)$ and $-5(x+y)$

1.3 Degree of a Polynomial

State the degree of each polynomial:

a) $y^2 + y^3 - 7$ *Ans.* degree 3 since monomial of greatest degree is y^3

b) $6 + 3x + x^2$ *Ans.* degree 2 since monomial of greatest degree is x^2

c) $5x^2 + 7y^3$ *Ans.* degree 3 since monomial of greatest degree is y^3

d) $5x^3y^2 + x^4$ *Ans.* degree 5 since the degree of $5x^3y^2$ is $3 + 2$ or 5

e) $2x^5 + x - 2x^5 + 8$ *Ans.* degree 1 since the polynomial in simple form is $x + 8$.

2. DISTRIBUTIVE LAW

On one job, George found that he had earned 3 $10 bills. On a second job, he earned 2 $10 bills. To compute his total earnings, he added the separate earnings, as follows: $3 \cdot \$10 + 2 \cdot \$10 = \$30 + \$20 = \$50$. However, he discovered a simpler method which involved adding the bills first, then multiplying by $10, as follows:

$$(3 + 2) \cdot \$10 = 5 \cdot \$10 = \$50$$

Since the results are equal, then we can conclude by using the commutative law that

$$10(3 + 2) = 10 \cdot 3 + 10 \cdot 2$$

The final result is an illustration of the **distributive law of multiplication over addition**. Since any real numbers could have been used, we generalize the distributive law as follows:

Distributive Law
If a, b, and c are real numbers, then $a(b + c) = ab + ac$

By applying the Commutative Law, we obtain $(b + c)a = ba + ca$. According to the symmetric property of equality, the sides of an equation can be interchanged. Hence, since $a(b + c) = ab + ac$, then $ab + ac = a(b + c)$.

The distributive law is useful in understanding numerical products and in supplying shortcuts:

$$20 \cdot 8\tfrac{1}{2} = 20(8 + \tfrac{1}{2})$$
$$= 20 \cdot 8 + 20 \cdot \tfrac{1}{2}$$
$$= 160 + 10 = 170$$

The distributive law, which is one of the most important of the fundamental principles of mathematics may be stated verbally in the following way when it is applied to the multiplying of a monomial by a polynomial:

To multiply a monomial by a polynomial, multiply the monomial by each term of the polynomial; the result being the sum of the products thus obtained.

Thus, $5(x + 2y) = 5x + 10y$, $x(5x - 4) = 5x^2 - 4x$, and $20y(\tfrac{1}{2}x + \tfrac{1}{4}y) = 10xy + 5y^2$.

By repeated application of the distributive law, it may be extended to cover the product of a monomial and a polynomial of more than 2 terms.

Extended Distributive Law
If a, b, and c are real numbers.
$a(b + c + d + \cdots) = ab + ac + ad + \cdots$
and $ab + ac + ad + \cdots = a(b + c + d + \cdots)$

Thus, $5(2x + 3y + 4z + 5) = 10x + 15y + 20z + 25$, and $10x + 15y + 20z + 25 = 5(2x + 3y + 4z + 5)$

The distributive law may be used **to combine like terms** in the expression $7x + 4x - x$ into $10x$, as follows:

$$7x + 4x - x$$

Make the common literal coefficient, x, a factor of an equivalent expression.

$$(7 + 4 - 1)x$$

Using the substitution principle, substitute 10 for $(7 + 4 - 1)$

$$10x$$

To Combine Monomials Being Added or Subtracted

Combine: a) $7x + 5x - 3x$ b) $8a^2 - a^2$

Procedure:

1) **Add or subtract numerical coefficients :**

2) **Keep common literal coefficient:**

Solutions:

1) $7 + 5 - 3 = 9$ 1) $8 - 1 = 7$

2) $9x$ *Ans.*   2) $7a^2$ *Ans.*

2.1 Combining Like Terms with Integral Coefficients

Combine:
a) $8+5-3$ *Ans.* 10   e) $7x-4x-x$ *Ans.* $2x$ i) $12c^2+c^2-7c^2$ *Ans.* $6c^2$

b) $7-4-1$ *Ans.* 2   f) $20r+30r-40r$ *Ans.* $10r$ j) $8ab+7ab$ *Ans.* $15ab$

c) $20+30-45$ *Ans.* 5   g) $2a^2+a^2$ *Ans.* $3a^2$ k) $6r^2s-2r^2s$ *Ans.* $4r^2s$

d) $8b+5b-3b$ *Ans.* $10b$ h) $13y^2-2y^2$ *Ans.* $11y^2$ l) $30x^3y^2-25x^3y^2$ *Ans.* $5x^3y^2$

2.2 Simplifying Expressions by Combining Like Terms

Simplify each expression by combining like terms:

a) $18a+12a-10$ *Ans.* $30a-10$ d) $2x^2+3x^2-y^2$ *Ans.* $5x^2-y^2$ g) $6b+20b+2c-c$ *Ans.* $26b+c$

b) $18a+12-10$ *Ans.* $18a+2$ e) $2x^2+3y^2-x^2$ *Ans.* x^2+3y^2 h) $6b+20c+2b-c$ *Ans.* $8b+19c$

c) $18a+12-10a$ *Ans.* $8a+12$ f) $2x^2+3y^2-y^2$ *Ans.* $2x^2+2y^2$ i) $6c+20b+2b-c$ *Ans.* $22b+5c$

2.3 Combining Like Terms with Fractional and Decimal Coefficients

Combine like terms:

a) $8x + 3\frac{1}{4}x$ e) $\frac{2}{3}b^2 + \frac{1}{2}b^2$ i) $4.8w + 6.5w - 6.3w$

b) $7x - 2\frac{1}{3}x$ f) $1\frac{2}{3}c^2 - 1\frac{1}{3}c^2$ j) $1\frac{1}{2}y^2 + 3\frac{3}{4}y^2 - 2\frac{3}{4}y^2$

c) $\frac{5}{3}b - b$ g) $2.3ab + 11.6ab$ k) $3xy + 1.2xy - .6xy$

d) $3c - \frac{2}{3}c$ h) $.58cd^2 - .39cd^2$ l) $1.7x^2y + .9x^2y - 2.05x^2y$

Ans. a) $11\frac{1}{4}x$ e) $1\frac{1}{6}b^2$ i) $5w$

b) $4\frac{2}{3}x$ f) $\frac{1}{3}c^2$ j) $2\frac{1}{2}y^2$

c) $\frac{2}{3}b$ g) $13.9ab$ k) $3.6xy$

d) $2\frac{1}{3}c$ h) $.19cd^2$ l) $.55x^2y$

2.4 Combining Like Terms Representing the Lengths of Line Segments

Represent the length of each entire line:

a) $\underset{a \quad\quad a}{\rule{3cm}{0.4pt}}$ d) $\underset{x \quad 1.5x \quad 2x}{\rule{3cm}{0.4pt}}$ g) $\underset{a\ a\ a\ a\ a\quad b\quad b\quad c}{\rule{4cm}{0.4pt}}$

b) $\underset{a \quad b \quad a}{\rule{3cm}{0.4pt}}$ e) $\underset{y \quad y \quad .7y \quad 1.3y}{\rule{3cm}{0.4pt}}$ h) $\underset{a\ a\ b\ b\quad 2b\quad\quad 4a}{\rule{4cm}{0.4pt}}$

c) $\underset{a \quad a \quad a\ b\ b}{\rule{3cm}{0.4pt}}$ f) $\underset{1\frac{1}{2}c \quad \frac{3}{4}c \quad c}{\rule{3cm}{0.4pt}}$ i) $\underset{b\quad a\quad b\quad 3c\quad\quad 8c\quad\quad c}{\rule{4cm}{0.4pt}}$

Ans. a) $2a$ d) $4.5x$ g) $5a + 2b + c$

b) $2a + b$ e) $4y$ h) $6a + 4b$

c) $3a + 2b$ f) $3\frac{1}{4}c$ i) $a + 2b + 12c$

2.5 Applying the Distributive Law to Numerical Problems

Use the distributive law to find each product:

a) $10(3\frac{1}{2})$,   b) $25(44)$,   c) $20(99\frac{1}{2})$,   d) $12(98\frac{1}{4})$,   e) $\frac{1}{4}(84\frac{1}{2})$,   f) $50(101)$

Solutions:

a) $10(3 + \frac{1}{2}) = 30 + 5 = 35$

b) $25(40 + 4) = 1000 + 100 = 1100$

c) $20(100 - \frac{1}{2}) = 2000 - 10 = 1990$

d) $12(100 + \frac{1}{4} - 2) = 1200 + 3 - 24 = 1179$

e) $\frac{1}{4}(80 + 4 + \frac{1}{2}) = 20 + 1 + \frac{1}{8} = 21\frac{1}{8}$

f) $50(100 + 1) = 5000 + 50 = 5050$

3. ADDING MONOMIALS

To add like terms:
1. Add their numerical coefficients.
2. Keep the common literal coefficient.

Thus, $3a^2 - 5a^2 + 4a^2 = (3 - 5 + 4)a^2$ or $2a^2$.

To simplify monomials being added:
(1) Parentheses may be omitted.
(2) "+" meaning "add" may be omitted.
(3) If the first monomial is positive, its + sign may be omitted.

Thus, to simplify $(+8x) + (+9x) + (-10x)$ write $8x + 9x - 10x$.

3.1 Adding Like Terms

Add: a) $5a^2$ and $3a^2$ b) $13(x+y)$ and $-7(x+y)$

Procedure:
1. Add the numerical coefficients: 1. $5 + 3 = 8$ 1. $13 - 7 = 6$
2. Keep common literal coefficient.   **Ans.** $8a^2$ **Ans.** $6(x+y)$

3.2 Adding Like Terms Horizontally

Simplify and add:

a) $(+5a) + (+2a) + (-4a)$ b) $(-8x^2) + (-12x^2)$ c) $(-3wy) + (+11wy)$ d) $(+16r^2s) + (-13r^2s)$

Solutions: (*First, simplify.*)

a) $(+5a) + (+2a) + (-4a)$	b) $(-8x^2) + (-12x^2)$	c) $(-3wy) + (+11wy)$	d) $(+16r^2s) + (-13r^2s)$
$5a + 2a - 4a$	$-8x^2 - 12x^2$	$-3wy + 11wy$	$16r^2s - 13r^2s$
Ans. $3a$	**Ans.** $-20x^2$	**Ans.** $8wy$	**Ans.** $3r^2s$

3.3 Adding Like Terms Vertically

Add:

a) $8xy$	b) $-2abc$	c) $12c^3d^2$	d) $15(x-y)$	e) $-3(a^2+b^2)$
$-3xy$	$5abc$	$-10c^3d^2$	$-18(x-y)$	$-(a^2+b^2)$
$12xy$	$-8abc$	$-c^3d^2$	$14(x-y)$	$-8(a^2+b^2)$
Ans. $17xy$	$-5abc$	c^3d^2	$11(x-y)$	$-12(a^2+b^2)$

3.4 Adding Like and Unlike Terms

Simplify and add: (*Combine only like terms.*)

a) $(+10x) + (+5x) + (-7)$	b) $(+3a^2) + (-4a^2) + (-3b^2)$	c) $(-8a^2c) + (-6ac^2) + (-3ac^2)$
$10x + 5x - 7$	$3a^2 - 4a^2 - 3b^2$	$-8a^2c - 6ac^2 - 3ac^2$
Ans. $15x - 7$	*Ans.* $-a^2 - 3b^2$	*Ans.* $-8a^2c - 9ac^2$

4. ARRANGING AND ADDING POLYNOMIALS

Arranging the Terms of a Polynomial in Descending or Ascending Order

A polynomial may be arranged as follows:
1. In **descending order**, by having the exponents of the same variable decrease in successive terms.
2. In **ascending order**, by having the exponents of the same variable increase in successive terms.

Thus, $2x^2 + 3x^3 - 5x + 8$ becomes

$3x^3 + 2x^2 - 5x + 8$ in descending order

or $8 - 5x + 2x^2 + 3x^3$ in ascending order.

To Add Polynomials

Add: $5x - 2y$ and $y + 3x$

Procedure:

Solution:

1. Arrange polynomials in order, placing like terms in same column:

1. $5x - 2y$
$\underline{3x + y}$

2. Add like terms:

2. $8x - y$ **Ans.**

To check addition of polynomials, substitute any convenient value, except 1 or 0, for each of the variables.

Note. If 1 is substituted for a variable, an incorrect exponent will not be detected.

If $x = 1$, then $x^2 = 1$, $x^3 = 1$, $x^4 = 1$, etc.

In Sets 4.4 and 4.5, checking is shown.

4.1 Arranging Polynomials and Combining Like Terms

Rearrange in descending order and combine:

a) $3a^2 + 2a^2 - 10a - 5a$

b) $5x + 8 - 6x + 10x^2$

c) $-5y^2 + 8x^2 + 5y^2 + x$

a) No rearrangement needed.
Ans. $5a^2 - 15a$

b) $10x^2 + 5x - 6x + 8$
Ans. $10x^2 - x + 8$

c) $8x^2 + x - 5y^2 + 5y^2$
Ans. $8x^2 + x$

4.2 Adding Arranged Polynomials

Add:

a) $3x - 10$
$\underline{2x + 4}$
Ans. a) $5x - 6$

b) $5x^2 + 5x$
$\underline{-x^2 - x}$
Ans. b) $4x^2 + 4x$

c) $5x^3 + 7x^2 - 4$
$\underline{-6x^3 \qquad - 10}$
Ans. c) $-x^3 + 7x^2 - 14$

d) $10x + 3y$
$\underline{7x - 6y + 1}$
Ans. d) $17x - 3y + 1$

4.3 Adding Polynomials

Add: a) $3a + 5b$, $6b - 2a$ and $10b - 25$ b) $x^2 + x^3 - 3x$, $4 - 5x^2 + 3x^3$ and $10 - 8x^2 - 5x$

Procedure:

Solutions:

1. Rearrange polynomials with like terms in the same column:

a) $\quad 3a + 5b$
$\quad -2a + 6b$
$\underline{\qquad 10b - 25}$

b) $x^3 + x^2 - 3x$
$3x^3 - 5x^2 \qquad + 4$
$\underline{\qquad -8x^2 - 5x + 10}$

2. Add like terms:

Ans. a) $\quad a + 21b - 25$

Ans. b) $4x^3 - 12x^2 - 8x + 14$

4.4 Checking the Addition of Polynomials

3.4. Check by letting $x = 2$ and $y = 3$: $(25x - 10y) + (5x - 2y) = 30x - 12y$

Check: Let $x = 2$ and $y = 3$.
$25x - 10y \longrightarrow 50 - 30 = 20$
$\underline{5x - 2y \longrightarrow 10 - 6 = 4}$
$30x - 12y \longrightarrow 60 - 36 = \boxed{24}$

By adding vertically and horizontally, the sum is 24.

3.5. Check by letting $a = 2$, $b = 4$ and $c = 3$: $(a^2 + b^2 - c^2) + (3a^2 - b^2 + 4c^2) = 4a^2 + 3c^2$

Check: Let $a = 2$, $b = 4$ and $c = 3$.
$a^2 + b^2 - c^2 \longrightarrow 4 + 16 - 9 = 11$
$\underline{3a^2 - b^2 + 4c^2 \longrightarrow 12 - 16 + 36 = 32}$
$4a^2 \qquad + 3c^2 \longrightarrow 16 \qquad + 27 \quad \boxed{43}$

By adding vertically and horizontally, the sum is 43.

5. SUBTRACTING MONOMIALS

Monomials are **opposites** if they differ only in sign.

Thus, $(-3x)$ and $(+3x)$ are opposites.

Rule. The sum of monomials that are opposites is zero.

Thus, $(+3x) + (-3x) = 3x - 3x$ Simplifying the writing of the expression

$$= (3 - 3)x \quad \text{Distributive Law}$$
$$= 0x \qquad\quad \text{Substitution Principle}$$
$$= 0 \qquad\quad\ \text{Multiplicative Property of 0.}$$

Hence, monomials that are opposites are also additive inverses.

Subtraction Rule

To subtract a term, add its opposite or additive inverse.

Thus, to subtract $(-3x)$, add $(+3x)$; or, to subtract $(+5x^2)$, add $(-5x^2)$.

5.1 Subtracting Like Terms

Subtract: $a)\ (+2a)-(-5a)$ $b)\ (-3x^2)-(+5x^2)$ $c)\ (-15cd)-(-10cd)$ $d)\ (+3a^2b)-(+8a^2b)$

$a)\ (+2a)-(-5a)$	$b)\ (-3x^2)-(+5x^2)$	$c)\ (-15cd)-(-10cd)$	$d)\ (+3a^2b)-(+8a^2b)$
$(+2a) + (+5a)$	$(-3x^2) + (-5x^2)$	$(-15cd) + (+10cd)$	$(+3a^2b) + (-8a^2b)$
$2a + 5a$	$-3x^2 - 5x^2$	$-15cd + 10cd$	$3a^2b - 8a^2b$
Ans. $7a$	*Ans.* $-8x^2$	*Ans.* $-5cd$	*Ans.* $-5a^2b$

5.2 Different Subtraction Forms

$a)$ Subtract $(-5a)$ from $(+2a)$

$b)$ From $(-3x^2)$ take $(+5x^2)$

$c)$ Reduce $(+7mn)$ by $(-2mn)$

$d)$ How much does $(-8cd)$ exceed $(+3cd)$?

Solutions:

$a)\ (+2a) - (-5a)$	$b)\ (-3x^2) - (+5x^2)$	$c)\ (+7mn) - (-2mn)$	$d)\ (-8cd) - (+3cd)$
$(+2a) + (+5a)$	$(-3x^2) + (-5x^2)$	$(+7mn) + (+2mn)$	$(-8cd) + (-3cd)$
$2a + 5a$	$-3x^2 - 5x^2$	$7mn + 2mn$	$-8cd - 3cd$
Ans. $7a$	**Ans.** $-8x^2$	**Ans.** $9mn$	**Ans.** $-11cd$

5.3 Combining Adding and Subtracting of Like Terms

Combine:

$a)\ (+6x)+(+8x)-(-3x)$ $b)\ (-3a^2)-(-a^2)-(+10a^2)$ $c)\ (+13ab)-(-ab)-(-2ab)+(-3ab)$

Solutions:

$a)\ (+6x)+(+8x)-(-3x)$	$b)\ (-3a^2)-(-a^2)-(+10a^2)$	$c)\ (+13ab)-(-ab)-(-2ab)+(-3ab)$
$(+6x) + (+8x) + (+3x)$	$(-3a^2) + (+a^2) + (-10a^2)$	$(+13ab) + (+ab) + (+2ab) + (-3ab)$
$6x + 8x + 3x$	$-3a^2 + a^2 - 10a^2$	$13ab + ab + 2ab - 3ab$
Ans. $17x$	**Ans.** $-12a^2$	**Ans.** $13ab$

6. SUBTRACTING POLYNOMIALS

To Subtract Polynomials

Procedure:

1. Arrange polynomials in order, placing like terms in same column:

2. Subtract like terms:

Subtract $5x - 2y$ from $8x - 4y$

Solution:

$$(8x - 4y) - (5x - 2y)$$

1. $8x - 4y$ **Minuend**

(S) $\underline{5x - 2y}$ **Subtrahend**

2. $3x - 2y$ **Difference (Ans.)**

Notes. *1)* Use **(S)** to indicate subtraction.

2) To subtract a polynomial, change each of its signs **mentally**, then add.

To check subtraction, add the difference obtained to the subtrahend.

Their sum should be the minuend.

6.1 Subtracting Arranged Polynomials

Subtract:

a)	$5b + 7$	b)	$y^2 - 3y$	c)	$8x^3 - 2x^2 + 5x$	d)	$3x^2y + 4xy^2$
(S)	$3b - 2$	(S)	$-2y^2 - 4y$	(S)	$6x^3 \qquad + 9x$	(S)	$x^2y + xy^2 + y^3$
Ans.	$2b + 9$	Ans.	$3y^2 + y$	Ans.	$2x^3 - 2x^2 - 4x$	Ans.	$2x^2y + 3xy^2 - y^3$

6.2 Arranging Polynomials and Subtracting

Arrange and subtract:

a) $2x - y + 8$ from $13x + 4y + 9$

b) $10 + 3a - 5b$ from $7b + 2a - 8$

c) $x^3 - 10$ from $25x^2 + 3x^3$

d) $m^2 - 18m$ from $12 + 3m^2$

Solutions:

a)	$13x + 4y + 9$	b)	$2a + 7b - 8$	c)	$3x^3 + 25x^2$	d)	$3m^2 \qquad + 12$
(S)	$2x - y + 8$	(S)	$3a - 5b + 10$	(S)	$x^3 \qquad - 10$	(S)	$m^2 - 18m$
Ans.	$11x + 5y + 1$	Ans.	$-a +12b - 18$	Ans.	$2x^3 + 25x^2 + 10$	Ans.	$2m^2 + 18m + 12$

6.3 Different Subtraction Forms

a) From $9 + x^2$ take $-3x^2 - 5x + 12$

b) Reduce $17ab$ by $-8ab + 15$

c) Find $8x^2 - 15x$ less $20x - 7$

d) Subtract $10 - 4x + x^2$ from 0.

Solutions:

a)	$x^2 \qquad + 9$	b)	$17ab$	c)	$8x^2 - 15x$	d)	0
(S)	$-3x^2 - 5x + 12$	(S)	$-8ab + 15$	(S)	$20x - 7$	(S)	$10 - 4x + x^2$
Ans.	$4x^2 + 5x - 3$	Ans.	$25ab - 15$	Ans.	$8x^2 - 35x + 7$	Ans.	$-10 + 4x - x^2$

6.4 Checking the Subtraction of Polynomials

Check each subtraction, using addition:

a)	$8c - 3$	b)	$5x^2 + 20$	c)	$3y^2 + 5y$
(S)	$5c - 8$	(S)	$x^2 + 15$	(S)	$y^2 - 8y + 5$
	$3c + 5$ (?)		$4x^2 + 5$ (?)		$2y^2 +13y + 5$ (?)

Checking: (Difference + Subtrahend = Minuend)

a)	$3c + 5$	b)	$4x^2 + 5$	c)	$2y^2 + 13y + 5$
(A)	$5c - 8$	(A)	$x^2 + 15$	(A)	$y^2 - 8y + 5$
	$8c - 3$		$5x^2 + 20$		$3y^2 + 5y + 10$
	(Correct)		*(Correct)*		*(Incorrect)*

Correct difference = $2y^2 + 13y - 5$

7.   USING PARENTHESES AND OTHER GROUPING SYMBOLS
TO ADD OR SUBTRACT POLYNOMIALS

Symbols of grouping include:

1. **Parentheses,** ( ), as in $\frac{1}{2}(8 - 4x)$ or $5 - (10x - 4)$.

2. **Brackets,** [ ], to include parentheses as in $8 - [5 + (x - 2)]$.

3. **Braces,** { }, to include brackets as in $x - \{3 + [x - (y + 4)]\}$.

4. **Bar,** ———, as in the fraction $\frac{8 - 4x}{2}$ or $5 - \overline{10x - 4}$.

Symbols of grouping may be used to show the addition or subtraction of polynomials. Thus:

1. To add $3a + 4b$ and $5a - b$, write $(3a + 4b) + (5a - b)$.

2. To subtract $2x - 5$ from $x^2 + 10x$, write $(x^2 + 10x) - (2x - 5)$.

3. To subtract the sum of $8x^2 + 9$ and $6 - x^2$ from $3x^2 - 12$,

write $(3x^2 - 12) - [(8x^2 + 9) + (6 - x^2)]$.

Rules for Removing Parentheses and Grouping Symbols

Rule 1. When removing parentheses preceded by a plus sign, **do not change** the signs of the enclosed terms.

Thus, $3a + (+5a - 10)$ $3x^2 + (-x^2 - 5x + 8)$
         $3a + 5a - 10$ $3x^2 - x^2 - 5x + 8$
         $8a - 10$ **Ans.** $2x^2 - 5x + 8$ **Ans.**

Rule 2. When removing parentheses preceded by a minus sign, **change** the sign of each enclosed term.

Thus, $3a - (+5a - 10)$ $3x^2 - (-x^2 - 5x + 8)$
         $3a - 5a + 10$ $3x^2 + x^2 + 5x - 8$
         $-2a + 10$ **Ans.** $4x^2 + 5x - 8$ **Ans.**

Rule 3. When more than one set of grouping symbols is used, remove one set at a time beginning with the innermost one.

Thus, $2 + [r - (3 - r)]$ $6s - \{5 - [3 + (7s - 8)]\}$
         $2 + [r - 3 + r]$ $6s - \{5 - [3 + 7s - 8]\}$
         $2 + r - 3 + r$ $6s - \{5 - 3 - 7s + 8\}$
         $2r - 1$ **Ans.** $6s - 5 + 3 + 7s - 8$
                                     $13s - 10$ **Ans.**

7.1 Rule 1. Removing Parentheses Preceded by a Plus Sign

Simplify: (*Do not change the sign of the enclosed terms.*)

a) $13x + (5x - 2)$ b) $(15a^2 - 3a) + (-7 - 2a)$ c) $3 + (6 - 5x) - 2x^2$
   $13x + 5x - 2$ $15a^2 - 3a - 7 - 2a$ $3 + 6 - 5x - 2x^2$

Ans. a) $18x - 2$ **Ans.** b) $15a^2 - 5a - 7$ **Ans.** c) $9 - 5x - 2x^2$

7.2 Rule 2. Removing Parentheses Preceded by a Minus Sign

Simplify: (*Change the sign of each enclosed term.*)

a) $13x - (5x - 2)$ b) $-(15a^2 - 3a) - (-7 - 2a)$ c) $3 - (5 - 5x) - 2x^2$
   $13x - 5x + 2$ $-15a^2 + 3a + 7 + 2a$ $3 - 5 + 5x - 2x^2$

Ans. a) $8x + 2$ **Ans.** b) $-15a^2 + 5a + 7$ **Ans.** c) $-2 + 5x - 2x^2$

7.3 Rule 3. Brackets Containing Parentheses

Simplify:

Procedure: a) $2 - [r - (3 - r)]$ b) $5 - [(8 + 4x) - (3x - 2)]$
1. Remove ( ): $2 - [r - 3 + r]$ $5 - [8 + 4x - 3x + 2]$
2. Remove [ ] : $2 - r + 3 - r$ $5 - 8 - 4x + 3x - 2$
3. Combine: **Ans.** a) $-2r + 5$ **Ans.** b) $-x - 5$

7.4 Using Grouping Symbols to Add or Subtract Polynomials

a) Subtract $2x - 5$ from the sum of $15x + 10$ and $3x - 5$.

Solution Using Parentheses

$[(15x + 10) + (3x - 5)] - (2x - 5)$
$15x + 10 + 3x - 5 - 2x + 5$

Ans. $16x + 10$

Solution Without Parentheses

	$15x + 10$			$18x + 5$
(A)	$3x - 5$		**(S)**	$2x - 5$
	$18x + 5$		**Ans.**	$16x + 10$

b) From the sum of $3a - 5b$ and $8a + 10$ subtract the sum of $2b - 8$ and $7a + 9$.

Solution Using ( ) and [ ]

$$[(3a - 5b) + (8a + 10)] - [(2b - 8) + (7a + 9)]$$
$$[3a - 5b + 8a + 10] - [2b - 8 + 7a + 9]$$
$$[11a - 5b + 10] - [7a + 2b + 1]$$
$$11a - 5b + 10 - 7a - 2b - 1$$

Ans. $4a - 7b + 9$

Solution Without ( ) and [ ]

$$\begin{array}{ll} & 3a - 5b \qquad\qquad 2b - 8 \\ \text{(A)} & 8a \quad\;\; + 10 \quad \text{(A)} \;\; 7a \qquad + 9 \\ \hline & 11a - 5b + 10 \qquad 7a + 2b + 1 \end{array}$$

$$\begin{array}{ll} & 11a - 5b + 10 \\ \text{(S)} & \;\;7a + 2b + \;1 \\ \hline \end{array}$$

Ans. $4a - 7b + 9$

7.5 Removing Symbols of Grouping

Simplify: (*Remove innermost symbols first.*)

Procedure:

1. Remove ⎯ :
2. Remove ( ):
3. Remove [ ] :
4. Remove { } :
5. Combine:

$$5x - \{8x - [7 - (4x - \overline{8 - 2x})]\} - 5$$
$$5x - \{8x - [7 - (4x - 8 + 2x)]\} - 5$$
$$5x - \{8x - [7 - 4x + 8 - 2x]\} - 5$$
$$5x - \{8x - 7 + 4x - 8 + 2x\} - 5$$
$$5x - 8x + 7 - 4x + 8 - 2x - 5$$

Ans. $-9x + 10$

8. MULTIPLYING MONOMIALS AND POWERS OF THE SAME BASE

Rule 1. **To multiply the powers of the same base,** keep the base and add the exponents.

Thus, $x^4 \cdot x^3 = x^7$ $\qquad a^5 \cdot a \cdot b^2 \cdot b^3 = a^6 b^5$
$3^{10} \cdot 3^2 = 3^{12}$ $\qquad 2^4 \cdot 2^5 \cdot 10^2 \cdot 10^4 = 2^9 \cdot 10^6$

$$\boxed{x^a x^b = x^{a+b}}$$

Rule 2. **To find the power of a power of a base,** keep the base and multiply the exponents.

Thus, $(x^4)^3 = x^{12}$ since $(x^4)^3 = (x^4)(x^4)(x^4)$
$(5^2)^4 = 5^8$ since $(5^2)^4 = (5^2)(5^2)(5^2)(5^2)$

$$\boxed{(x^a)^b = x^{ab}}$$

Rule 3. Changing the order of factors does not change their product.

Rule 3 is based on the associative and commutative laws of multiplication.

Thus, the product $x(5x)$ can be reordered into $5x^2$, as follows:

$$\begin{aligned} x(5x) &= (x \cdot 5)x \quad \text{Associative Law of Multiplication} \\ &= (5x)x \quad \text{Commutative Law of Multiplication} \\ &= 5(xx) \quad \text{Associative Law of Multiplication} \\ &= 5x^{1+1} = 5x^2 \text{ Rule 1.} \end{aligned}$$

Rule 3 applies to products having powers that are factors.

Thus, $x^3 y\; x^2 y^2 = x^3 x^2 y\; y^2$ $\qquad$ Rule 3
$$= x^{3+2} y^{1+2} = x^5 y^3 \qquad \text{Rule 1}$$

To Multiply Monomials

Multiply $2x$ by $-3x^2$.

Procedure:

1. Multiply numerical coefficients:
2. Multiply literal coefficients:
3. Multiply results:

Solution:

$$\begin{aligned} & (2x)(-3x^2) \\ 1. \quad & (2)(-3) = -6 \\ 2. \quad & (x)(x^2) = x^3 \\ 3. \quad & -6x^3 \;\text{ Ans.} \end{aligned}$$

8.1 Rule 1. Multiplying Powers of the Same Base

Multiply: (*Keep base and add exponents.*)

a) $b \cdot b^2$ *Ans.* b^3
b) $x^2 \cdot x^3 \cdot x$ *Ans.* x^6
c) $x^b x^c$ *Ans.* x^{b+c}

d) $x^2 \cdot x^3 \cdot y$ *Ans.* $x^5 y$
e) $c^4 \cdot c \cdot d^5 \cdot d$ *Ans.* $c^5 d^6$
f) $x^3 x^2 x^4 y$ *Ans.* $x^9 y$

g) $4^5 \cdot 4^2$ *Ans.* 4^7
h) $2^3 \cdot 2 \cdot 5$ *Ans.* $2^4 \cdot 5$
i) $3^2 3^3 y^4 y^5$ *Ans.* $3^5 y^9$

8.2 Rule 2. Finding the Power of a Power of a Base

Raise to a power: (*Keep base and multiply exponents.*)

a) $(a^4)^2$ *Ans.* a^8
b) $(b^3)^5$ *Ans.* b^{15}
c) $(x^d)^e$ *Ans.* x^{de}

d) $(3^5)^4$ *Ans.* 3^{20}
e) $(10^4)^{10}$ *Ans.* 10^{40}
f) $(5^m)^n$ *Ans.* 5^{mn}

g) $(x^2)^3 (y^3)^2$ *Ans.* $x^6 y^6$
h) $(4^2)^3 (x^3)^4$ *Ans.* $4^6 x^{12}$
i) $(y^3)^4 y^3 y^4$ *Ans.* y^{19}

8.3 Rule 3. Reordering Factors When Multiplying Monomials Containing Powers

Multiply:

a) $2(-3b)$ *Ans.* $-6b$
b) $(-2b)(5b)$ *Ans.* $-10b^2$
c) $(4x)(-7y)$ *Ans.* $-28xy$

d) $(4x^2)(5x^3)$ *Ans.* $20x^5$
e) $(-\frac{1}{2}y^3)(-10y^5)$ *Ans.* $5y^8$
f) $(10r^4)(-\frac{2}{5}rs)$ *Ans.* $-4r^5 s$

g) $(3a)(2b)(-10c)$ *Ans.* $-60abc$
h) $(2x^2)(3x^3)(4x^4)$ *Ans.* $24x^9$
i) $(-3)(-r^4)(-s^5)$ *Ans.* $-3r^4 s^5$

9. MULTIPLYING A MONOMIAL BY A POLYNOMIAL

Extended Distributive Law: $a(b + c + d + \cdots) = ab + ac + ad + \cdots$

Rule: To multiply a monomial by a polynomial, multiply the monomial by each term of the polynomial; the result being the sum of the products thus obtained.

Using the extended distributive law, a monomial may be multiplied by a polynomial having any number of terms.

Thus, $5(x^3 + 2x^2 + 3x - 4) = 5x^3 + 10x^2 + 15x - 20$.

The extended distributive law is used in the multiplication of two numbers such as the multiplying of 1234 by 5: $5(1234) = 5(1000 + 200 + 30 + 4)$
$$= 5000 + 1000 + 150 + 20 = 6{,}170.$$

9.1 Multiplying a Polynomial by a Monomial Horizontally

Multiply:

a) $10(a+b)$ *Ans.* $10a+10b$
b) $x(y-7)$ *Ans.* $xy-7x$
c) $-c(d-5e)$ *Ans.* $-cd+5ce$

d) $\pi r(r+h)$ *Ans.* $\pi r^2+\pi rh$
e) $-ab(a+b)$ *Ans.* $-a^2 b-ab^2$
f) $\frac{2}{3}(9k-30m)$ *Ans.* $6k-20m$

g) $3(x^2-2x+8)$ *Ans.* $3x^2-6x+24$
h) $a(a^2+a+5)$ *Ans.* a^3+a^2+5a
i) $-x^2(3-2x+x^2)$ *Ans.* $-3x^2+2x^3-x^4$

9.2 Multiplying a Polynomial by a Monomial Vertically

Multiply: a) $y^2 + 8y - 7$
               $\underline{ 3y}$
Ans. $3y^3 + 24y^2 - 21y$

b) $d^3 - 2d^2 - 20$
        $\underline{ -d^2}$
Ans. $-d^5 + 2d^4 + 20d^2$

c) $5a + 2b - 3c + 8$
             $\underline{ -2abc}$
Ans. $-10a^2 bc - 4ab^2 c + 6abc^2 - 16abc$

9.3 Removing Parentheses

Simplify: a) $3x + 2(x-3)$
              $3x + 2x - 6$
Ans. $5x - 6$

b) $3x^2 - x(5-x)$
   $3x^2 - 5x + x^2$
Ans. $4x^2 - 5x$

c) $a(4a-5) - 8(a^2-10)$
   $4a^2 - 5a - 8a^2 + 80$
Ans. $-4a^2 - 5a + 80$

MONOMIALS AND POLYNOMIALS

9.4 Removing Brackets Containing Parentheses

Simplify: (*Remove parentheses first.*)

a) $3[5x - 2(x-4)]$
$3[5x - 2x + 8]$
$3[3x + 8]$
Ans. $9x + 24$

b) $3 + 5[2 - 4(a-6)]$
$3 + 5[2 - 4a + 24]$
$3 + 5[26 - 4a]$
Ans. $133 - 20a$

c) $a[ab - a(b-c)]$
$a[ab - ab + ac]$
$a[ac]$
Ans. a^2c

9.5 Removing Symbols of Grouping

Simplify: (*Remove innermost symbols first.*)

$$120y - 2\{y + 8[-7y - 5(y - \overline{3y + 4})]\} + 320$$

1. Remove $\overline{}$: $120y - 2\{y + 8[-7y - 5(y - 3y - 4)]\} + 320$
2. Remove ( ) : $120y - 2\{y + 8[-7y - 5y + 15y + 20]\} + 320$
3. Combine : $120y - 2\{y + 8[3y + 20]\} + 320$
4. Remove [ ] : $120y - 2\{y + 24y + 160\} + 320$
5. Remove { } : $120y - 2y - 48y - 320 + 320$
6. Combine : $70y$ *Ans.*

10. MULTIPLYING POLYNOMIALS

To Multiply Polynomials

Multiply $3x + 4$ by $1 + 2x$

Procedure:

Solution:

1. Arrange each polynomial in order:

2. Multiply each term of one polynomial by each term of the other:

3. Add like terms:

$$3x + 4$$
$$2x + 1$$
$$\overline{6x^2 + 8x}$$
$$\underline{ + 3x + 4}$$

Ans. $6x^2 + 11x + 4$

To check multiplication of polynomials, interchange the polynomials and multiply again, or substitute any convenient value for the variable, except 1 or 0.

The multiplication of two polynomials such as the previous multiplication of $(3x + 4)$ by $(2x + 1)$ is based on the repeated application of the distributive law, as follows:

Multiply $(3x + 4)$ by $(2x + 1)$ by treating $(3x + 4)$ as a monomial, when applying the distributive law, thus: $(3x + 4)(2x + 1) = (3x + 4)2x + (3x + 4)1$

Apply the distributive law a second time, and then combine:

$(3x + 4)(2x + 1) = 6x^2 + 8x + 3x + 4 = 6x^2 + 11x + 4$ *Ans.*

An understanding of the process of multiplying two polynomials is an aid to an understanding of the process of multiplying two numbers, such as 34 and 21. Note in the multiplication shown

$$
\begin{array}{ll}
34 & 30 + 4 \\
\times\,21 & \times\;20 + 1 \\
\hline
34 & 30 + 4 \\
68(0) & 600 + 80 \\
\hline
714 = & 600 + 110 + 4
\end{array}
$$

how each term of the polynomial $(30 + 4)$ is multiplied by each term of the polynomial $(20 + 1)$. Hence, the multiplying of two numbers is a special application of the general process of multiplying two polynomials.

10.1 Multiplying Polynomials

Multiply:

a) $3x + 4$
$\underline{2x - 1}$
$6x^2 + 8x$
$-3x - 4$
$\overline{}$
Ans. $6x^2 + 5x - 4$

b) $8 + c$
$\underline{3 - 2c}$
$24 + 3c$
$- 16c - 2c^2$
$\overline{}$
Ans. $24 - 13c - 2c^2$

c) $4r + 7s$
$\underline{4r - 7s}$
$16r^2 + 28rs$
$- 28rs - 49s^2$
$\overline{}$
Ans. $16r^2 - 49s^2$

d) $a^2 - 3a + 5$
$\underline{5a - 2}$
$5a^3 - 15a^2 + 25a$
$- 2a^2 + 6a - 10$
$\overline{}$
Ans. $5a^3 - 17a^2 + 31a - 10$

10.2 Checking Multiplication

Multiply and check: $(5r - 8)(3r - 2)$

Solution:

$5r - 8$
$\underline{3r - 2}$
$15r^2 - 24r$
$- 10r + 16$
$\overline{}$
Ans. $15r^2 - 34r + 16$

Check by multiplication:

$3r - 2$
$\underline{5r - 8}$
$15r^2 - 10r$
$- 24r + 16$
$\overline{}$
$15r^2 - 34r + 16$

Check by substitution:

Let $r = 10$.

$5r - 8 \rightarrow 42$
$3r - 2 \rightarrow 28$
$15r^2 - 34r + 16 \rightarrow 1500 - 340 + 16 = 1176$
Correct since $1176 = (42 \times 28)$

10.3 Extended Multiplication

Multiply $5p + 2$, $2p - 1$ and $p + 1$ and check.

Solution:

$5p + 2$
$\underline{2p - 1}$
$10p^2 + 4p$
$- 5p - 2$
$\overline{}$
$10p^2 - p - 2$

$10p^2 - p - 2$
$\underline{p + 1}$
$10p^3 - p^2 - 2p$
$+ 10p^2 - p - 2$
$\overline{}$
$10p^3 + 9p^2 - 3p - 2$
Ans.

Check by substitution:

Let $p = 10$.

$5p + 2 \rightarrow 50 + 2 = 52$
$2p - 1 \rightarrow 20 - 1 = 19$
$p + 1 \rightarrow 10 + 1 = 11$

$10p^3 + 9p^2 - 3p - 2 \rightarrow 10{,}000 + 900 - 30 - 2 = 10{,}868$
The check is correct since $52(19)(11) = 10{,}868$.

11. DIVIDING POWERS AND MONOMIALS

The following rules apply to powers whose exponent is a positive integer. Hence, the set of positive integers is the replacement set of variables used as exponents. Thus, in $\dfrac{x^a}{x^b}$, a and b are positive integers.

When dividing powers having the same base, arrange them into a fraction and apply the following rules:

Rule 1. If the exponent of the numerator is **larger than** the exponent of the denominator, keep the base and subtract the smaller exponent from the larger.

Thus, $\dfrac{x^7}{x^4} = x^3$

If a is larger than b,
$$\frac{x^a}{x^b} = x^{a-b}$$

Rule 2. If the exponents **are equal**, then we have a number divided by itself; the quotient is 1.

Thus, $\dfrac{x^4}{x^4} = 1$

$$\frac{x^a}{x^a} = 1$$

Rule 3. If the exponent of the denominator is larger, make the numerator of the quotient 1, and to obtain its denominator, keep the base and subtract the smaller exponent from the larger.

Thus, $\dfrac{x^4}{x^7} = \dfrac{1}{x^3}$

If a is smaller than b,
$$\frac{x^a}{x^b} = \frac{1}{x^{b-a}}$$

To Divide Monomials

Divide $21ab^2$ by $-7a^2b$.

Procedure:

1. Arrange in fractional form:

2. Divide numerical coefficients:

3. Divide literal coefficients:

4. Multiply the results:

Solution:

1. $\dfrac{21ab^2}{-7a^2b}$ **Dividend**
$\overline{\phantom{\dfrac{21ab^2}{-7a^2b}}}$ **Divisor**

2. $\dfrac{21}{-7} = -3$

3. $\dfrac{ab^2}{a^2b} = \dfrac{b}{a}$

Ans. 4. $-\dfrac{3b}{a}$ **Quotient**

To Check Division of Monomials

Multiply the quotient by the divisor. The result should be the dividend.

Thus, to check $\dfrac{15ab}{3a} = 5b$, multiply $3a$ by $5b$ to obtain $15ab$.

11.1 Rules 1 to 3. Dividing Powers of the Same Base

Divide:

(Rule 1)

a) $\dfrac{x^8}{x^2}$ $Ans.$ x^6

b) $\dfrac{8^7}{8^3}$ $Ans.$ 8^4

c) $\dfrac{a^3b^4}{a^2b^2}$ $Ans.$ ab^2

d) $\dfrac{x^{2a}}{x^a}$ $Ans.$ x^a

(Rule 2)

e) $\dfrac{x^2}{x^2}$ $Ans.$ 1

f) $\dfrac{-8^3}{8^3}$ $Ans.$ -1

g) $\dfrac{a^2b^2}{-a^2b^2}$ $Ans.$ -1

h) $\dfrac{-x^a}{-x^a}$ $Ans.$ 1

(Rule 3)

i) $\dfrac{x^2}{x^8}$ $Ans.$ $\dfrac{1}{x^6}$

j) $\dfrac{8^3}{8^7}$ $Ans.$ $\dfrac{1}{8^4}$

k) $\dfrac{a^2b^2}{a^3b^4}$ $Ans.$ $\dfrac{1}{ab^2}$

l) $\dfrac{x^a}{x^{2a}}$ $Ans.$ $\dfrac{1}{x^a}$

11.2 Dividing Monomials

Divide:

a) $\dfrac{24b^2}{3b}$ $Ans.$ $8b$

b) $\dfrac{24b}{8b^2}$ $Ans.$ $\dfrac{3}{b}$

c) $\dfrac{-24b^2}{-24b^2}$ $Ans.$ 1

d) $\dfrac{28x^2y^4}{28x^2y^2}$ $Ans.$ y^2

e) $\dfrac{28x^2y^2}{-28x^2y^2}$ $Ans.$ -1

f) $\dfrac{-25u^5w}{-25uw^5}$ $Ans.$ $\dfrac{u^4}{w^4}$

g) $\dfrac{-14abc}{7abcd}$ $Ans.$ $-\dfrac{2}{d}$

h) $\dfrac{-7a^2bc}{14ab^2c^2}$ $Ans.$ $-\dfrac{a}{2bc}$

i) $\dfrac{a^3b^4c^5}{a^3b^7c^2}$ $Ans.$ $\dfrac{c^3}{b^3}$

11.3 Checking Division Using Multiplication

Check each division, using multiplication:

a) Does $\dfrac{24b^2}{3b} = 8b$?   b) Does $\dfrac{28x^2y^4}{28x^2y^2} = y^2$?   c) Does $\dfrac{a^3b^4c^6}{-ab^2c^2} = -a^2b^2c^3$?

Check: (Quotient × Divisor = Dividend)

a) Multiply:
$(8b)(3b) = 24b^2$
Correct.

b) Multiply:
$y^2(28x^2y^2) = 28x^2y^4$
Correct.

c) Multiply:
$(-a^2b^2c^3)(-ab^2c^2) = a^3b^4c^5$
Incorrect. The quotient should be $-a^2b^2c^4$.

12. DIVIDING A POLYNOMIAL BY A MONOMIAL

The following rule used to divide a polynomial by a monomial is a further application of the distributive law.

To divide a polynomial by a monomial, divide each term of polynomial by the monomial; the result being the sum of the quotients thus obtained.

Thus, $\dfrac{10x + 15}{5} = \dfrac{1}{5}(10x + 15) = \dfrac{1}{5}(10x) + \dfrac{1}{5}(15)$ (Apply the distributive law.)

$$= \dfrac{10x}{5} + \dfrac{15}{5} = 2x + 3$$

Note. Dividing by 5 is equivalent to multiplying by $\dfrac{1}{5}$, the reciprocal of 5.

In actual practice, only the following steps need be taken:

$$\dfrac{10x + 15}{5} = \dfrac{10x}{5} + \dfrac{15}{5} = 2x + 3.$$

Also,
$$\dfrac{ax + bx}{x} = \dfrac{ax}{x} + \dfrac{bx}{x} = a + b.$$

To check the division, multiply the quotient by the divisor. The result should be the dividend.

Thus, to check $\dfrac{10x + 15}{5} = 2x + 3$, multiply $2x + 3$ by 5 to obtain $10x + 15$.

12.1 Dividing a Polynomial by a Monomial

Divide:

a) $\dfrac{3a + 6b}{3}$ *Ans.* $a + 2b$

b) $\dfrac{r - rt}{r}$ *Ans.* $1 - t$

c) $\dfrac{pq + pr}{-p}$ *Ans.* $-q - r$

d) $\dfrac{2\pi r + 2\pi R}{2\pi}$ *Ans.* $r + R$

e) $\dfrac{ab - abc}{ab}$ *Ans.* $1 - c$

f) $\dfrac{9x^2y - 36xy^2}{9xy}$ *Ans.* $x - 4y$

g) $\dfrac{7x - 14y + 56}{7}$ *Ans.* $x - 2y + 8$

h) $\dfrac{x^3 + 2x^2 + 5x}{x}$ *Ans.* $x^2 + 2x + 5$

i) $\dfrac{3x^5 - x^3 + 5x^2}{-x^2}$ *Ans.* $-3x^3 + x - 5$

12.2 Checking Division

Check each, using multiplication:

a) Does $\dfrac{r - rt}{r} = 1 - t$?   b) Does $\dfrac{x^2y - 2xy^2}{xy} = x - y$?   c) Does $\dfrac{2x - 4y + 10}{-2} = -x + 2y - 5$?

Check: (Quotient × Divisor = Dividend)

a) Multiply:
$r(1 - t) = r - rt$
Correct.

b) Multiply:
$xy(x - y) = x^2y - xy^2$
Incorrect. The quotient should be $x - 2y$.

c) Multiply:
$-2(-x + 2y - 5) = 2x - 4y + 10$
Correct.

12.3 Multiplying and Dividing Polynomials by a Monomial

Simplify: a) $5(x - 2) + \dfrac{3x - 12}{3}$

$5x - 10 + x - 4$
Ans. $6x - 14$

b) $\dfrac{x^2 - 5x}{x} - x(3 - x)$

$x - 5 - 3x + x^2$
Ans. $x^2 - 2x - 5$

c) $\dfrac{a^3 - a^2bc}{a} - b(b - ac)$

$a^2 - abc - b^2 + abc$
Ans. $a^2 - b^2$

13. DIVIDING A POLYNOMIAL BY A POLYNOMIAL

To Divide Polynomials

Divide $x^2 - 5x + 6$ by $x - 2$.

Procedure:

Solution: (*By Steps*)

Full Solution:

1. Set up as a form of long division in which the polynomials are arranged in descending order, leaving space for missing terms:

1. $x - 2 \overline{)\, x^2 - 5x + 6}$

$$\begin{array}{r} x - 3 \\ x-2 \overline{)\, x^2 - 5x + 6} \\ x^2 - 2x \\ \hline -3x + 6 \\ -3x + 6 \end{array}$$

2. Divide the first term of the divisor into the first term of the dividend to obtain the first term of the quotient:

2. $\begin{array}{r} x \\ x-2 \overline{)\, x^2 - 5x + 6} \end{array}$

3. Multiply the first term of the quotient by each term of the divisor:

3. $\begin{array}{r} x \\ x-2 \overline{)\, x^2 - 5x + 6} \\ x^2 - 2x \end{array}$

Ans. $x - 3$

4. Subtract like terms and bring down one or more terms as needed:

4. $\qquad -3x + 6$

5. Repeat steps **2** to **4**, using the remainder as the new dividend: that is, divide, multiply, subtract and bring down:

5. $\begin{array}{r} -3 \\ x-2 \overline{)\,} \end{array}$

$\qquad -3x + 6$
$\qquad -3x + 6$

6. Continue repeating steps **2** to **4** as long as it is possible.

6. No further steps needed.

To Check the Division

1) If no final remainder exists, then multiply the quotient by the divisor. The result should equal the dividend.

Thus, to check $\dfrac{18}{3} = 6$, multiply 3 by 6 to obtain 18.

2) If there is a final remainder, add this to the product of the quotient and divisor. The result should equal the dividend.

Thus, to check $\dfrac{19}{3} = 6\frac{1}{3}$, multiply 3 by 6 and then add 1 to obtain 19.

The process of dividing a polynomial by another polynomial is a further application of the distributive law. Note the use of the distributive law in the previous division of $x^2 - 5x + 6$ by $x - 2$, as follows:

$$\frac{x^2 - 5x + 6}{x - 2} = \frac{(x^2 - 2x) + (-3x + 6)}{x - 2}$$

Apply the rule for the division of a polynomial by a monomial.

(See Section 12)

$$= \frac{x^2 - 2x}{x - 2} + \frac{-3x + 6}{x - 2}$$

$$= x + (-3) = x - 3$$

An understanding of the process of dividing two polynomials is an aid to an understanding of the process of dividing one number by another number. Note how steps used in the procedure of the previous example parallel the steps taken in the customary long division process.

13.1 Dividing a Polynomial by a Polynomial (No Remainder)

Divide: *a)* $x^2 - 9x + 14$ by $x - 7$ *b)* $x^3 - 6x^2 + 11x - 6$ by $x - 3$ and check.

Solutions: *a)*

$$
\begin{array}{r}
x - 2 \\
x-7 \overline{\smash{)}\ x^2 - 9x + 14} \\
\underline{x^2 - 7x} \\
-2x + 14 \\
\underline{-2x + 14}
\end{array}
$$

Ans. $x - 2$

Check:

$$
\begin{array}{r}
x - 2 \\
\underline{x - 7} \\
x^2 - 2x \\
\underline{-7x + 14} \\
x^2 - 9x + 14
\end{array}
$$

(Dividend)

b)

$$
\begin{array}{r}
x^2 - 3x + 2 \\
x-3 \overline{\smash{)}\ x^3 - 6x^2 + 11x - 6} \\
\underline{x^3 - 3x^2} \\
-3x^2 + 11x \\
\underline{-3x^2 + 9x} \\
2x - 6 \\
\underline{2x - 6}
\end{array}
$$

Ans. $x^2 - 3x + 2$

Check:

$$
\begin{array}{r}
x^2 - 3x + 2 \\
\underline{x - 3} \\
x^3 - 3x^2 + 2x \\
\underline{-3x^2 + 9x - 6} \\
x^3 - 6x^2 + 11x - 6
\end{array}
$$

(Dividend)

13.2 Arranging Polynomials and Dividing

Divide: $20a^2 - 3b^2 + 7ab$ by $-b + 4a$ and check:

Solution: Arrange both dividend and divisor in descending powers of *a*:

$$
\begin{array}{r}
5a + 3b \\
4a-b \overline{\smash{)}\ 20a^2 + 7ab - 3b^2} \\
\underline{20a^2 - 5ab} \\
12ab - 3b^2 \\
\underline{12ab - 3b^2}
\end{array}
$$

Ans. $5a + 3b$

Check:

$$
\begin{array}{r}
5a + 3b \\
\underline{4a - b} \\
20a^2 + 12ab \\
\underline{-5ab - 3b^2} \\
20a^2 + 7ab - 3b^2
\end{array}
$$

(Dividend)

13.3 Terms Missing in Dividend

Divide $x^3 - 64$ by $x - 4$ and check:

Solution: Leave spaces for missing x^2 and x terms:

$$
\begin{array}{r}
x^2 + 4x + 16 \\
x-4 \overline{\smash{)}\ x^3 \qquad\quad - 64} \\
\underline{x^3 - 4x^2} \\
4x^2 \\
\underline{4x^2 - 16x} \\
16x - 64 \\
\underline{16x - 64}
\end{array}
$$

Ans. $x^2 + 4x + 16$

Check:

$$
\begin{array}{r}
x^2 + 4x + 16 \\
\underline{x - 4} \\
x^3 + 4x^2 + 16x \\
\underline{-4x^2 - 16x - 64} \\
x^3 \qquad\quad - 64
\end{array}
$$

(Dividend)

13.4 Dividing Polynomials (With Remainder)

Divide $8x^2 - 10x + 8$ by $2x - 4$ and check:

Solution:

$$
\begin{array}{r}
4x + 3 + \frac{20}{2x-4} \\
2x-4 \overline{\smash{)}\ 8x^2 - 10x + 8} \\
\underline{8x^2 - 16x} \\
+6x + 8 \\
\underline{+6x - 12}
\end{array}
$$

Remainder: 20

Complete quotient by adding $\frac{20}{2x-4}$

Ans. $4x + 3 + \frac{20}{2x-4}$

Check:

$$
\begin{array}{r}
4x + 3 \\
\underline{2x - 4} \\
8x^2 + 6x \\
\underline{-16x - 12} \\
8x^2 - 10x - 12
\end{array}
$$

Add Remainder: + 20

$8x^2 - 10x + 8$ (Dividend)

SUPPLEMENTARY PROBLEMS

1. State the coefficient and degree of each expression, if it is a monomial: (1.1)

a) 5 — *Ans.* a constant monomial of degree 0

b) $\frac{y}{5}$ — *Ans.* a monomial of degree 1 and coefficient $\frac{1}{5}$

c) $\frac{1}{5}xy$ — *Ans.* a monomial of degree 2 and coefficient $\frac{1}{5}$

d) $.5\frac{x}{y}$ — *Ans.* not a monomial because of division by a variable

e) $.5\,x\sqrt{y}$ — *Ans.* not a monomial since variable is in the radicand

f) $.5x^3$ — *Ans.* monomial of degree 3 and coefficient $.5$

g) $\sqrt{5}\,x^3y^2$ — *Ans.* monomial of degree 5 and coeficient $\sqrt{5}$

h) $5x^3 + y^2$ — *Ans.* a binomial having two monomials, $5x^3$ and y^2.

2. Select like monomials in each polynomial, if any: (1.2)

a) $16 - 4y + 3y - y^2$

b) $16y^2 - 4y + 20y^2 + 8$

c) $5x^2 - 8xy + 7y^2 - 2$

d) $7a - 3b + 12ab + 10$

e) $a^2b + ab^2 - 2ab + 3ab^2$

f) $4(x+y) - 5(x+y) + 2(x^2+y^2)$

g) $3xy + xz - 3x - 5z$

h) $3x^2y^2 + 2(x^2+y^2) - 4(x^2+y^2)$

Ans. a) $-4y$ and $+3y$

b) $16y^2$ and $20y^2$

c) no like terms

d) no like terms

e) $+ab^2$ and $+3ab^2$

f) $4(x+y)$ and $-5(x+y)$

g) no like terms

h) $2(x^2+y^2)$ and $-4(x^2+y^2)$

3. State the degree of each polynomial: (1.3)

a) $2x^3 + 4$, b) $4 + 3x + 2x^2$, c) $3x^2 + 4y^3$, d) $3x^2y^3 + 4$, e) $x^8 + y^5 - x^8 + 20$

Ans. a) degree 3, b) degree 2, c) degree 3 since term of greatest degree is $4y^3$

d) degree 5, e) degree 5 (Simplify into $y^5 + 20$.)

4. Combine: (2.1)

a) $20 + 10 - 18$

b) $10 - 6 - 1$

c) $6x + 5x + x$

d) $6x^2 + 5x^2 + x^2$

e) $13y^2 - y^2 + 10y^2$

f) $27w^5 - 22w^5$

g) $3pq + 11pq - pq$

h) $2abc + abc - 3abc$

i) $36a^2b^2c - 23a^2b^2c$

j) $8(a+b) - 2(a+b)$

k) $11(x^2+y^2) + 4(x^2+y^2)$

l) $5(x+y)^2 - (x+y)^2$

Ans. a) 12 b) 3 c) $12x$ d) $12x^2$ e) $22y^2$ f) $5w^5$ g) $13pq$ h) 0 i) $13a^2b^2c$ j) $6(a+b)$ k) $15(x^2+y^2)$ l) $4(x+y)^2$

5. Simplify each expression by combining like terms: (2.2)

a) $13b + 7b - 6$ *Ans.* $20b - 6$

b) $13b + 7 - 6$ *Ans.* $13b + 1$

c) $13b + 7b - 6b$ *Ans.* $14b$

d) $13b^2 + 7b^2 - 6b$ *Ans.* $20b^2 - 6b$

e) $13b^2 + 7b - 6b^2$ *Ans.* $7b^2 + 7b$

f) $5y^2 + 3y^2 + 10y - 2$ *Ans.* $8y^2 + 10y - 2$

g) $5y^2 + 3y + 10y - 2y$ *Ans.* $5y^2 + 11y$

h) $5y^2 + 3y + 10y^2 - 2y$ *Ans.* $15y^2 + y$

i) $5y + 3y^2 + 10y^2 - 2y^2$ *Ans.* $11y^2 + 5y$

j) $5 + 3y + 10y^2 - 2$ *Ans.* $10y^2 + 3y + 3$

6. Combine like terms: (2.3)

a) $3y + 7\frac{2}{3}y$

b) $20\frac{1}{2}a - 11a$

c) $\frac{7}{3}c - \frac{1}{3}c$

d) $5d - \frac{d}{5}$

e) $\frac{x^2}{2} - \frac{x^2}{3}$

f) $\frac{y^2}{2} + \frac{y^2}{6}$

g) $7.1ab + 3.9ab - 2.7ab$

h) $2.12c^2 - 1.09c^2 - .55c^2$

i) $3\frac{5}{12}xy^2 + 4\frac{1}{6}xy^2 - 2xy^2$

Ans. a) $10\frac{2}{3}y$ b) $9\frac{1}{2}a$ c) $2c$ d) $4\frac{4}{5}d$ e) $\frac{x^2}{6}$ f) $\frac{2}{3}y^2$ g) $8.3\,ab$ h) $.48c^2$ i) $5\frac{7}{12}xy^2$

7. Represent the length of each entire line: **(2.4)**

a) $\overline{ d | d | d }$ d) $\overline{ u | \frac{3}{4}u }$ g) $\overline{ 2a | 6a | 4a | 3b }$

b) $\overline{ p | q | q | q }$ e) $\overline{ x | .5x | 1.5x }$ h) $\overline{ 3b | 5b | 7c | 4b }$

c) $\overline{ r | t | r | t }$ f) $\overline{ y | 2y | 3y }$ i) $\overline{ a+b | a+c | b+c }$

Ans. a) $3d$ d) $1\frac{3}{4}u$ g) $12a + 3b$

      b) $p + 3q$ e) $3x$ h) $12b + 7c$

      c) $2r + 2t$ f) $6y$ i) $2a + 2b + 2c$

8. Use the distributive law to find each product: **(2.5)**

     a) $20\left(4\frac{1}{4}\right)$ *Ans.* $20\left(4 + \frac{1}{4}\right) = 80 + 5 = 85$

     b) $25(1002)$ *Ans.* $25(1000 + 2) = 25,000 + 50 = 25,050$

     c) $40\left(99\frac{1}{4}\right)$ *Ans.* $40\left(100 - \frac{3}{4}\right) = 4000 - 30 = 3970$

     d) $\frac{1}{2}(864.5)$ *Ans.* $\frac{1}{2}\left(800 + 60 + 4 + \frac{1}{2}\right) = 400 + 30 + 2 + \frac{1}{4} = 432.25$

     e) $240(9.95)$ *Ans.* $240\left(10 - \frac{1}{20}\right) = 2400 - 12 = 2388$

9. Add: a) $(+5b) + (+16b)$ e) $+ 8x^2y^2$ f) $+3.2h$ g) $-3(a+b)$ **(3.1 to 3.3)**

         b) $(-10y^3) + (-7y^3)$ $+11x^2y^2$ $-2.2h$ $+5(a+b)$

         c) $(+7rs) + (-10rs)$ $\underline{+30x^2y^2}$ $\underline{+7.5h}$ $\underline{+2(a+b)}$

         d) $(-20abc) + (-abc)$

Ans. a) $21b$,   b) $-17y^3$,   c) $-3rs$,   d) $-21abc$,   e) $49x^2y^2$,   f) $8.5h$,   g) $4(a+b)$

10. Simplify and add: **(3.2)**

     a) $(+13a) + (-2a) + (-a)$ d) $(+xy^2) + (+xy^2) + (-xy^2)$

     b) $(-2x^2) + (-8x^2) + (-15x^2)$ e) $(+2.3ab) + (+7.1ab) + (-3.7ab)$

     c) $(+a^3) + (+3a^3) + (-7a^3)$ f) $\left(+\frac{3}{4}r^2s\right) + \left(-\frac{1}{2}r^2s\right) + \left(1\frac{1}{8}r^2s\right)$

Ans. a) $13a - 2a - a = 10a$ d) $xy^2 + xy^2 - xy^2 = xy^2$

       b) $-2x^2 - 8x^2 - 15x^2 = -25x^2$ e) $2.3ab + 7.1ab - 3.7ab = 5.7ab$

       c) $a^3 + 3a^3 - 7a^3 = -3a^3$ f) $\frac{3}{4}r^2s - \frac{1}{2}r^2s + 1\frac{1}{8}r^2s = +1\frac{3}{8}r^2s$

11. Simplify and add: **(3.4)**

     a) $(+12a) + (-3a) + (+10)$ e) $(-10x^2) + (-3x) + (-5x^2)$

     b) $(+12) + (-3a) + (+10a)$ f) $(+5r^2s) + (-2r^2s) + (+rs^2)$

     c) $(+12b) + (-3) + (+10b)$ g) $(+5rs^2) + (-2r^2s) + (+rs^2)$

     d) $(-10x^2) + (-3x^2) + (-5x)$ h) $(+5rs^2) + (-2rs^2) + (+rs^2)$

Ans. a) $12a - 3a + 10 = 9a + 10$ e) $-10x^2 - 3x - 5x^2 = -15x^2 - 3x$

       b) $12 - 3a + 10a = 12 + 7a$ f) $5r^2s - 2r^2s + rs^2 = 3r^2s + rs^2$

       c) $12b - 3 + 10b = 22b - 3$ g) $5rs^2 - 2r^2s + rs^2 = 6rs^2 - 2r^2s$

       d) $-10x^2 - 3x^2 - 5x = -13x^2 - 5x$ h) $5rs^2 - 2rs^2 + rs^2 = 4rs^2$

12. Rearrange in descending order and combine: **(4.1)**

     a) $-6y + 2y^2 + y^3 + 3y^2$ b) $2x^3 + 3x^4 - x^3 - 10 + 5x^2$ c) $6y^2 - x^2 + 10xy + 8x^2$

                                                                               (order in terms of x)

     a) $y^3 + 2y^2 + 3y^2 - 6y$ b) $3x^4 + 2x^3 - x^3 + 5x^2 - 10$ c) $8x^2 - x^2 + 10xy + 6y^2$

Ans. $y^3 + 5y^2 - 6y$ *Ans.* $3x^4 + x^3 + 5x^2 - 10$ *Ans.* $7x^2 + 10xy + 6y^2$

13. Add: a) $\begin{array}{r} 5y + 12 \\ \underline{-3y - 10} \end{array}$ b) $\begin{array}{r} 6x - 2y \\ \underline{3x + 10y} \end{array}$ c) $\begin{array}{r} 8x^3 + 5x^2 - 10x \\ \underline{x^3 - 6x^2 + 11x} \end{array}$ d) $\begin{array}{r} x^2 - 3x + 25 \\ \underline{-3x^2 - 10x - 30} \end{array}$ **(4.2)**

Ans. a) $2y + 2$ b) $9x + 8y$ c) $9x^3 - x^2 + x$ d) $-2x^2 - 13x - 5$

14. Add: *a*) $6x^2 - 7x$ and $-2x^2 - x$ *c*) $x^2 - x + 1$ and $7x - 4x^2 + 9$ **(4.3)**

   b) $5a + 2$, $3a - 7$ and $-6a + 4$ *d*) $5y - 3x + 6$ and $-8 - 4x + y$

Ans. a) $6x^2 - 7x$ *b*) $5a + 2$ *c*) $x^2 - x + 1$ *d*) $-3x + 5y + 6$

$\underline{-\ 2x^2 -\ x}$ $3a - 7$ $\underline{-4x^2 + 7x +\ 9}$ $\underline{-4x +\ y - 8}$

$4x^2 - 8x$ $\underline{-6a + 4}$ $-3x^2 + 6x + 10$ $-7x + 6y - 2$

$2a - 1$

15. *a*) Check, letting $x = 2$, $y = 3$ and $z = 4$:   **(4.4)**

   a) $5x - 3y + \ \ z$ *b*) $x^2 + 2y^2 - \ \ z^2$

$\underline{2x - 2y - 10z}$ $x^2 - \ \ y^2 + 2z^2$

$7x - 5y - \ \ 9z$ $\underline{2x^2 + \ \ y^2 + \ \ z^2}$

b) *Check*: *a*) $5x - 3y + \ \ z \rightarrow 10 - 9 + \ 4 \ = \quad \ \ 5$ *b*) $x^2 + 2y^2 - \ z^2 \rightarrow 4 + 18 - 16 = \quad \ 6$

$2x - 2y - 10z \rightarrow \ 4 - 6 - 40 \ = -42$ $x^2 - \ \ y^2 + 2z^2 \rightarrow \ 4 - \ 9 + 32 = \ 27$

$\underline{7x - 5y - \ \ 9z \rightarrow 14 - 15 - 36} = \boxed{-37}$ $\underline{2x^2 + \ \ y^2 + \ \ z^2 \rightarrow \ 8 + \ 9 + 16} = \boxed{33}$

By adding vertically and horizontally,   By adding vertically and horizontally,

the sum is -37.   the sum is 33.

16. Subtract: *a*) $(+5c) - (-3c)$ *c*) $(-3rs) - (+2rs)$ *e*) $(+2x^2y) - (+12x^2y)$ **(5.1)**

   b) $(-x^2) - (-4x^2)$ *d*) $(+cd^2) - (+7cd^2)$ *f*) $(+5abc) - (-7abc)$

   Ans. a) $8c$, *b*) $3x^2$,   *c*) $-5rs$, *d*) $-6cd^2$,   *e*) $-10x^2y$, *f*) $12abc$

17. Subtract: *a*) $+3cd$ *b*) $+5x^2$ *c*) $-\ xy^2$ *d*) $-2pqr$ *e*) $-\ 4(m-n)$ **(5.1)**

   (S) $\underline{+\ cd}$ **(S)** $\underline{-7x^2}$ **(S)** $\underline{-4xy^2}$ **(S)** $\underline{+7pqr}$ **(S)** $\underline{-14(m-n)}$

   Ans. a) $2cd$ *b*) $12x^2$ *c*) $3xy^2$ *d*) $-9pqr$ *e*) $10(m-n)$

18. *a*) From $(5y^2)$ take $(-2y^2)$ *Ans.* $5y^2 - (-2y^2) = 7y^2$ **(5.2)**

   b) Reduce $(-2ab)$ by $(-5ab)$ *Ans.* $-2ab - (-5ab) = \ 3ab$

   c) How much less than $+x^2$ is $+3x^2$?   *Ans.* $x^2 - (+3x^2) = \ -2x^2$

   d) How much does $-17y$ exceed $-30y$?   *Ans.* $-17y - (-30y) = 13y$

19. Combine: *a*) $(+4b) + (-2b) - (-3b)$ *c*) $(+2cd) - (-3cd) + (-10cd) - (+5cd)$ **(5.3)**

   b) $(-5x^2) - (-x^2) - (+3x^2)$ *d*) $(-4abc^2) - (-abc^2) - (+3abc^2) - (-12abc^2)$

   Ans. a) $4b - 2b + 3b = \ 5b$ *c*) $2cd + 3cd - 10cd - 5cd = \ -10cd$

   b) $-5x^2 + x^2 - 3x^2 = -7x^2$ *d*) $-4abc^2 + abc^2 - 3abc^2 + 12abc^2 = \ 6abc^2$

20. Subtract: *a*) $3k - 5$ *b*) $k^2 - 2k$ *c*) $-2a^2 - 5a + 12$ *d*) $3r^2 - 5rt$ **(6.1)**

   (S) $\underline{k - 8}$ **(S)** $\underline{-k^2 - 8k}$ **(S)** $\underline{-\ a^2 \qquad \ -\ 7}$ **(S)** $\underline{-10r^2 - \ rt + 7t^2}$

   Ans. a) $2k + 3$ *b*) $2k^2 + 6k$ *c*) $-\ a^2 - 5a + 19$ *d*) $13r^2 - 4rt - 7t^2$

21. Arrange and subtract: **(6.2)**

   a) $5k - 3l - 2$ from $4l - 7 - k$ *c*) $3x + 5$ from $x^2 - 4x$

   b) $3x + 4y - 5$ from $16 - 2x - y$ *d*) $m^3 - 18m$ from $8m^2 + 10m$

Ans. a) $-\ k + 4l - 7$ *b*) $-2x - \ y + 16$ *c*) $x^2 - 4x$ *d*) $8m^2 + 10m$

   (S) $\underline{5k - 3l - 2}$ **(S)** $\underline{3x + 4y - \ 5}$ **(S)** $\underline{\qquad 3x + 5}$ **(S)** $\underline{m^3 \qquad \ \ -\ 18m}$

$-6k + 7l - 5$ $-5x - 5y + 21$ $x^2 - 7x - 5$ $-m^3 + 8m^2 + 28m$

22. *a*) Reduce $8x^2$ by $3x^2 + 5$. *Ans.* $5x^2 - 5$ *c*) Subtract $a^3 - 2a^2 + 5$ from 0. *Ans.* $-a^3 + 2a^2 - 5$ **(6.3)**

   b) From $2x - 3y$ take $4y - 7x$. *Ans.* $9x - 7y$ *d*) What is $5h^3 - 12h$ less $h^2 + 5h$? *Ans.* $5h^3 - h^2 - 17h$

23. Check each subtraction, using addition: **(6.4)**

$$a)\ 3x - 2 \qquad b)\ 8a^2 - 1 \qquad c)\ 5y^2 - 3y \qquad d)\ 2h^2 \quad + 5$$

$$(S)\ \underline{x - 5} \qquad (S)\ \underline{-a^2 + 7} \qquad (S)\ \underline{8y^2 \quad + 15} \qquad (S)\ \underline{-3h^2 - h}$$

$$2x + 3\ (?) \qquad 9a^2 - 8\ (?) \qquad -3y^2 + 3y - 15\ (?) \qquad 5h^2 - h + 5\ (?)$$

Check by addition:

$$a)\ 2x + 3 \qquad b)\ 9a^2 - 8 \qquad c)\ -3y^2 + 3y - 15 \qquad d)\ 5h^2 - h + 5$$

$$(A)\ \underline{x - 5} \qquad (A)\ \underline{-a^2 + 7} \qquad (A)\ \underline{8y^2 \quad + 15} \qquad (A)\ \underline{-3h^2 - h}$$

$$3x - 2 \qquad 8a^2 - 1 \qquad 5y^2 + 3y \qquad 2h^2 - 2h + 5$$

$$\textit{(Correct)} \qquad \textit{(Correct)} \qquad \textit{(Incorrect)} \qquad \textit{(Incorrect)}$$

$$\qquad\qquad\qquad\qquad\qquad \text{Difference should be} \qquad \text{Difference should be}$$

$$\qquad\qquad\qquad\qquad\qquad -3y^2 - 3y - 15 \qquad\qquad 5h^2 + h + 5$$

24. Simplify: $a)\ 2r + (3 - 7r) \qquad b)\ (7x^2 + 4) + (10 - 2x^2) \qquad c)\ 8y + (7y - 20) + (40 - 3y)$ **(7.1)**

$Ans.\ a)\ -5r + 3 \qquad b)\ 5x^2 + 14 \qquad c)\ 12y + 20$

25. Simplify: $a)\ 17 - (3a + 4) \qquad c)\ (5x^2 - 2) - (3 - 4x^2) \qquad e)\ 24h - (3h - 2) - 6(h - 1)$ **(7.2)**

$\qquad\qquad b)\ 17a - (6 - 2a) \qquad d)\ 3 - (7y + 10) - (18 - y) \qquad f)\ 80 - (30 - 5y) - (3y - y^2)$

$Ans.\ a)\ 13 - 3a \qquad c)\ 9x^2 - 5 \qquad e)\ 15h + 8$

$\qquad\quad b)\ 19a - 6 \qquad d)\ -6y - 25 \qquad f)\ y^2 + 2y + 50$

26. Simplify: **(7.3, 7.5)**

$\qquad a)\ 5a - [2a - (3a + 4)] \qquad b)\ 12x + 4 - [(3 - x) - (5x + 7)] \qquad c)\ 20 - \{[-(d-1) + 3d] - 5d\}$

$Ans.\ a)\ 6a + 4 \qquad\qquad b)\ 18x + 8 \qquad\qquad c)\ 3d + 19$

27. $a)$ Subtract $3b - 8$ from the sum of $5b - 2$ and $-6b + 5$.   **(7.4)**

$\qquad b)$ From the sum of $8x^2 + 5$ and $7x^2 - 2$, subtract the sum of $20x - 8$ and $-x^2 + 5x$.

$Ans.\ a)\ [(5b - 2) + (-6b + 5)] - (3b - 8) = -4b + 11$

$\qquad\quad b)\ [(8x^2 + 5) + (7x^2 - 2)] - [(20x - 8) + (-x^2 + 5x)] = 16x^2 - 25x + 11$

28. Multiply: $a)\ c^2 \cdot c \cdot c \qquad\qquad d)\ x^2 \cdot y^3 \cdot x^5 \qquad\qquad g)\ 7^2\, 7$ **(8.1)**

$\qquad\qquad\quad b)\ y^3 \cdot y^4 \cdot y \qquad\qquad e)\ m^2\, p m^8\, p \qquad\qquad h)\ 8^3 \cdot 8 \cdot 10^2$

$\qquad\qquad\quad c)\ a^x a^y \qquad\qquad\quad f)\ a^3 b a b^4 \qquad\qquad i)\ 3^5\, 3^4 x^2 x^9$

$Ans.\ a)\ c^4, \quad b)\ y^8, \quad c)\ a^{x+y}, \quad d)\ x^7 y^3, \quad e)\ m^{10} p^2, \quad f)\ a^4 b^5, \quad g)\ 7^3, \quad h)\ 8^4 10^2, \quad i)\ 3^9 x^{11}$

29. Raise to a power: $a)\ (x^2)^3 \qquad c)\ (b^2)^6 \qquad e)\ (3^3)^3 \qquad g)\ (r^3)^6 (t^2)^2$ **(8.2)**

$\qquad\qquad\qquad\qquad\quad b)\ (x^3)^2 \qquad d)\ (a^x)^y \qquad f)\ (5^2)^5 \qquad h)\ (4^7)^2 (10^2)^4$

$Ans.\ a)\ x^6, \quad b)\ x^6, \quad c)\ b^{12}, \quad d)\ a^{xy}, \quad e)\ 3^9, \quad f)\ 5^{10}, \quad g)\ r^{18} t^4, \quad h)\ 4^{14} 10^8$

30. Multiply: $a)\ 3(-5a) \qquad\qquad d)\ 5y(-y)(-y) \qquad\qquad g)\ (-7ab)(-3a)(-b)$ **(8.3)**

$\qquad\qquad\quad b)\ (-6x)(-x) \qquad\quad e)\ (.2x^2)(.3x^3) \qquad\quad h)\ (3r^3)(5s^5)$

$\qquad\qquad\quad c)\ (-4y)(+3y^2) \qquad f)\ (\tfrac{2}{3}x)(3x)(-5y) \qquad i)\ (-5xy^2)^2$

$Ans.\ a)\ -15a \qquad\qquad d)\ 5y^3 \qquad\qquad g)\ -21a^2 b^2$

$\qquad\quad b)\ 6x^2 \qquad\qquad e)\ .06x^5 \qquad\qquad h)\ 15r^3 s^5$

$\qquad\quad c)\ -12y^3 \qquad\qquad f)\ -10x^2 y \qquad\qquad i)\ 25x^2 y^4$

31. Multiply: $a)\ 2(a - b) \qquad d)\ 3a(b - 2c) \qquad g)\ \tfrac{1}{2}(a^2 + 6b^2) \qquad j)\ -5(x^2 + y^2 - z^2)$ **(9.1)**

$\qquad\qquad\quad b)\ -3(x - 5) \qquad e)\ -5x(x - 4) \qquad h)\ ab(a - 2b) \qquad k)\ -a(a^3 + a^2 - 5a)$

$\qquad\qquad\quad c)\ a(c - 3d) \qquad f)\ \tfrac{1}{2}(6y - 8z) \qquad i)\ -4r^2(r^3 + 2r^2) \qquad l)\ 4x(5 - x - 10x^2)$

$Ans.\ a)\ 2a - 2b \qquad d)\ 3ab - 6ac \qquad g)\ \tfrac{a^2}{2} + 3b^2 \qquad j)\ -5x^2 - 5y^2 + 5z^2$

$\qquad\quad b)\ -3x + 15 \qquad e)\ -5x^2 + 20x \qquad h)\ a^2 b - 2ab^2 \qquad k)\ -a^4 - a^3 + 5a^2$

$\qquad\quad c)\ ac - 3ad \qquad f)\ 3y - 4z \qquad i)\ -4r^5 - 8r^4 \qquad l)\ 20x - 4x^2 - 40x^3$

32. Multiply: *a)* $s^2 - s - 1$ *b)* $x^3 - 3x^2 + 11$ *c)* $7h + 5k - 3m + 5$ **(9.2)**

$\underline{\hspace{2em} -3s}$ $\underline{\hspace{3em} 7x^2}$ $\underline{\hspace{4em} 2hkm}$

Ans. *a)* $-3s^3 + 3s^2 + 3s$ *b)* $7x^5 - 21x^4 + 77x^2$ *c)* $14h^2km + 10hk^2m - 6hkm^2 + 10hkm$

33. Simplify: *a)* $5 + 3(y - 2)$ *c)* $3x + 10(2x - 1)$ *e)* $-a(a - 2) + 6(a^2 - 5)$ **(9.3)**

b) $x + 2(3 - 4x)$ *d)* $-4(a - 3) - 2(5 - a)$ *f)* $\frac{1}{2}(6c - 10d) - \frac{2}{3}(9d - 30c)$

Ans. *a)* $3y - 1$ *c)* $23x - 10$ *e)* $5a^2 + 2a - 30$

b) $-7x + 6$ *d)* $-2a + 2$ *f)* $23c - 11d$

34. Simplify: *a)* $2[3b + 5(b - 2)]$ *c)* $4(5 - c) - 3[8 - 7(c - 2)]$ **(9.4, 9.5)**

b) $-a[2(a - 3) + 6a]$ *d)* $10\{25 - [5(y + 4) - 3(y - 1)]\}$

Ans. *a)* $16b - 20$,   *b)* $-8a^2 + 6a$,   *c)* $17c - 46$,   *d)* $-20y + 20$

35. Multiply: *a)* $(5y + 2)(3y + 1)$ *d)* $(a + 2b)(a - b)$ *g)* $(x^2 + x + 1)(x + 2)$ **(10.1)**

b) $(x + 7)(x - 4)$ *e)* $(x - 4y)(x - y)$ *h)* $(r^2 - 2r + 3)(r - 1)$

c) $(1 + y)(2 - y)$ *f)* $(ab - 5)(ab + 2)$ *i)* $(t^2 + 5t - 6)(2t + 1)$

Ans. *a)* $15y^2 + 11y + 2$ *d)* $a^2 + ab - 2b^2$ *g)* $x^3 + 3x^2 + 3x + 2$

b) $x^2 + 3x - 28$ *e)* $x^2 - 5xy + 4y^2$ *h)* $r^3 - 3r^2 + 5r - 3$

c) $2 + y - y^2$ *f)* $a^2b^2 - 3ab - 10$ *i)* $2t^3 + 11t^2 - 7t - 6$

36. Check each multiplication, letting $x = 10$.   **(10.2)**

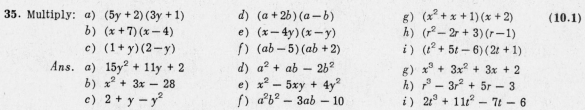

a) $3x + 1$ *b)* $x^2 + x - 1$

(M) $\underline{2x + 2}$ **(M)** $\underline{3x - 2}$

$6x^2 + 8x + 2$ $3x^3 + x^2 - 5x + 2$

Check: *a)* $3x + 1 \rightarrow 30 + 1 = 31$ *b)* $x^2 + x - 1 \rightarrow 100 + 10 - 1 = 109$

$\underline{2x + 2 \rightarrow 20 + 2 = 22}$ $\underline{3x - 2 \rightarrow \quad 30 - 2 \quad = \quad 28}$

$6x^2 + 8x + 2 \rightarrow 600 + 80 + 2 = 682$ $3x^3 + x^2 - 5x + 2 \rightarrow 3000 + 100 - 50 + 2 = 3052$

Correct since $682 = (31 \times 22)$ Correct since $3052 = (109 \times 28)$

37. Multiply: *a)* $(x + 2)(x + 3)(x + 4)$ *b)* $(y - 1)(y - 2)(y + 5)$ *c)* $(2a + 3)(3a - 4)(a - 5)$ **(10.3)**

Ans. *a)* $(x^2 + 5x + 6)(x + 4)$ *b)* $(y^2 - 3y + 2)(y + 5)$ *c)* $(6a^2 + a - 12)(a - 5)$

$x^3 + 9x^2 + 26x + 24$ $y^3 + 2y^2 - 13y + 10$ $6a^3 - 29a^2 - 17a + 60$

38. Divide: *a)* $\frac{x^5}{x^3}$ *b)* $\frac{x^3}{x^3}$ *c)* $\frac{x^3}{x^5}$ *d)* $\frac{a^4b^5}{ab^2}$ *e)* $\frac{ab^2}{a^4b^5}$ *f)* $\frac{10^5}{10^9}$ *g)* $\frac{10^9}{10^5}$ *h)* $\frac{10^5}{10^5}$ **(11.1)**

Ans. *a)* x^2 *b)* 1 *c)* $\frac{1}{x^2}$ *d)* a^3b^3 *e)* $\frac{1}{a^3b^3}$ *f)* $\frac{1}{10^4}$ *g)* 10^4 *h)* 1

39. Divide: *a)* $\frac{32a}{4a}$ *b)* $\frac{4a}{32a}$ *c)* $\frac{32a^4}{-8a^3}$ *d)* $\frac{-a^2b^2c^2}{-ab^3}$ *e)* $\frac{7xy}{-7xy}$ *f)* $\frac{-56c^4d}{7cd^4}$ **(11.2)**

Ans. *a)* 8 *b)* $\frac{1}{8}$ *c)* $-4a$ *d)* $\frac{ac^2}{b}$ *e)* -1 *f)* $-\frac{8c^3}{d^3}$

40. Divide: *a)* r^{10} by r^3 *d)* u^2 by u^8 *g)* $(-8x^2y^2) \div (-2xy)$ *j)* $a^5 \div a^b$ **(11.1, 11.2)**

b) s^5 by s *e)* $2ab \div ab^2$ *h)* $10r^4s^4 \div 4r^4s^4$ *k)* $3^a \div 3^5$

c) $-t^2$ by t^2 *f)* $-a^2b \div ab^2$ *i)* $x^a \div x^2$ *l)* $x^a \div x^b$

Ans. a) r^7,   *b)* s^4,   *c)* -1,   *d)* $\frac{1}{u^4}$,   *e)* $\frac{2}{b}$,   *f)* $-\frac{a}{b}$,   *g)* $4xy$,   *h)* $2\frac{1}{2}$,   *i)* x^{a-2},   *j)* a^{5-b},   *k)* 3^{a-5},   *l)* x^{a-b}

41. Check each division, using multiplication: **(11.3)**

a) Does $\frac{18x^3}{3x} = 6x^2$ (?)   *b)* Does $\frac{6a^2b^2}{-2ab} = -3ab$ (?)   *c)* Does $\frac{-27a^2}{-9a^6} = \frac{3}{a^3}$ (?)

Check, using multiplication:

a) $(3x)(6x^2) = 18x^3$ *b)* $(-2ab)(-3ab) = 6a^2b^2$ *c)* $(-9a^6)\left(\frac{3}{a^3}\right) = -27a^3$

(Correct)   *(Correct)*   *(Incorrect)*. Quotient should be $\frac{3}{a^4}$.

42. Divide: *a)* $\dfrac{5a + 15c}{5}$ *c)* $\dfrac{xy^2 + x^2y}{xy}$ *e)* $\dfrac{P + Prt}{P}$ *g)* $\dfrac{20r + 30s - 40}{-10}$ **(12.1)**

b) $\dfrac{xy + x}{x}$ *d)* $\dfrac{\pi R^2 - \pi r^2}{\pi}$ *f)* $\dfrac{5x^3 - 5x}{5x}$ *h)* $\dfrac{y^5 + 2y^4 - y^3}{y^3}$

Ans. *a)* $a + 3c$, *b)* $y + 1$, *c)* $y + x$, *d)* $R^2 - r^2$, *e)* $1 + rt$, *f)* $x^2 - 1$, *g)* $-2r - 3s + 4$, *h)* $y^2 + 2y - 1$

43. Divide: *a)* $2x - 4$ by 2   *d)* $(45x^2 - 15) \div 15$ *g)* $4\,)\,\overline{8a^2 - 4a + 12}$ **(12.2)**

b) $3a - 6$ by -3 *e)* $(15x^2 - 45x) \div 15x$ *h)* $-x\,)\,\overline{x^3 - 7x^2 + 10x}$

c) $-7x^3 + 7x^2$ by $-7x$ *f)* $(27xy - 18y^2) \div 9y$ *i)* $3a^2\,)\,\overline{30a^4 - 33a^3 + 3a^2}$

Ans. *a)* $x - 2$, *b)* $-a + 2$, *c)* $x^2 - x$, *d)* $3x^2 - 1$, *e)* $x - 3$, *f)* $3x - 2y$,

g) $2a^2 - a + 3$, *h)* $-x^2 + 7x - 10$, *i)* $10a^2 - 11a + 1$

44. Simplify: *a)* $2(x + 4) + \dfrac{6x - 8}{2}$ *b)* $\dfrac{r^2 - 10r}{r} + r(3 + r)$ *c)* $\dfrac{a^4 - a^3 + a^2}{a} - 2a(a^2 - 1)$ **(12.3)**

a) $2x + 8 + 3x - 4$ *b)* $r - 10 + 3r + r^2$ *c)* $a^3 - a^2 + a - 2a^3 + 2a$

Ans. $5x + 4$ Ans. $r^2 + 4r - 10$ Ans. $-a^3 - a^2 + 3a$

45. Divide: **(13.1a, 13.2)**

a) $d^2 + 9d + 14$ by $d + 7$ *e)* $2r^2 + 7r + 6$ by $r + 2$ *i)* $15a^2b^2 - 8ab + 1$ by $3ab - 1$

b) $d^2 - 8d + 7$ by $d - 7$ *f)* $6y^2 - 29y + 28$ by $2y - 7$ *j)* $3x^2 - 40 - 2x$ by $3x + 10$

c) $r^2 - 13r + 30$ by $r - 10$ *g)* $x^2 + xy - 20y^2$ by $x - 4y$ *k)* $3 + 7y^2 - 22y$ by $3 - y$

d) $x^2 - 3x - 10$ by $x - 5$ *h)* $45 - 14b + b^2$ by $9 - b$ *l)* $x^4 + 4x^2 - 45$ by $x^2 + 9$

Ans. *a)* $d + 2$ *c)* $r - 3$ *e)* $2r + 3$ *g)* $x + 5y$ *i)* $5ab - 1$ *k)* $1 - 7y$

b) $d - 1$ *d)* $x + 2$ *f)* $3y - 4$ *h)* $5 - b$ *j)* $x - 4$ *l)* $x^2 - 5$

46. Divide: *a)* $x^3 + 5x^2 + 7x + 2$ by $x + 2$ *d)* $6a^3 + 7a^2 + 12a - 5$ by $3a - 1$ **(13.1b)**

b) $x^3 - 2x^2 - 5x + 6$ by $x - 1$ *e)* $6a^3 + 17a^2 + 27a + 20$ by $3a + 4$

c) $x^3 - 2x^2 - 5x + 6$ by $x - 3$ *f)* $21y^3 - 38y^2 + 29y - 40$ by $3y - 5$

Ans. *a)* $x^2 + 3x + 1$ *d)* $2a^2 + 3a + 5$

b) $x^2 - x - 6$ *e)* $2a^2 + 3a + 5$

c) $x^2 + x - 2$ *f)* $7y^2 - y + 8$

47. Divide: *a)* $x^2 - 9$ by $x - 3$ *d)* $x^3 - 8$ by $x - 2$ **(13.3)**

b) $x^3 - 4x$ by $x + 2$ *e)* $x^4 - 1$ by $x + 1$

c) $7x^2 - 63$ by $x + 3$ *f)* $2x^3 - 30x - 8$ by $x - 4$

Ans. *a)* $x + 3$ *b)* $x^2 - 2x$ *c)* $7x - 21$ *d)* $x^2 + 2x + 4$ *e)* $x^3 - x^2 + x - 1$ *f)* $2x^2 + 8x + 2$

48. Divide: **(13.4)**

a) $x^2 - 5x + 2$ by $x - 3$ *c)* $x^2 + 1$ by $x + 1$ *e)* $x^3 - 5x^2 + 6x + 5$ by $x - 3$

b) $2x^2 + 5x - 15$ by $x - 2$ *d)* $x^2 + 9$ by $x + 3$ *f)* $2x^3 + 3x^2 - x - 2$ by $2x - 3$

Ans. *a)* $x - 2 + \dfrac{-4}{x - 3}$ *c)* $x - 1 + \dfrac{2}{x + 1}$ *e)* $x^2 - 2x + \dfrac{5}{x - 3}$

b) $2x + 9 + \dfrac{3}{x - 2}$ *d)* $x - 3 + \dfrac{18}{x + 3}$ *f)* $x^2 + 3x + 4 + \dfrac{10}{2x - 3}$

49. Check each division, using multiplication: **(13.2, 13.4)**

a) Does $\dfrac{21x^2 + 11xy - 2y^2}{3x + 2y} = 7x - y$?   *b)* Does $\dfrac{x^3 - 6}{x - 2} = x^2 + 2x + 4 + \dfrac{2}{x - 2}$?

Check, using multiplication:

a) $3x + 2y$

$\underline{7x - y}$

(Correct) $21x^2 + 11xy - 2y^2$

b) $\quad x^2 + 2x + 4$

$\underline{\qquad\qquad x - 2}$

$\qquad x^3 \qquad\qquad - 8$

Add remainder: $+ 2$

(Correct) $x^3 \qquad\qquad - 6$

Chapter 5

Equations and Inequalities of the First Degree In One Variable

1. ### REVIEWING THE SOLUTION OF FIRST DEGREE EQUATIONS HAVING POSITIVE ROOTS

A first degree equation in one variable is one which can be transformed into an equivalent equation of the form $ax = b$ where a and b are real numbers, and $a \neq 0$.

Thus, $-\frac{1}{2}x = 8$ is an equation of the first degree in one variable of the form $ax = b$, where $a = -\frac{1}{2}$ and $b = 8$. However, the equation $2x^2 = 8$ is an equation of the second degree. The equation $2x = \frac{8}{x}$ is not a first degree equation because it is transformable into $2x^2 = 8$.

In Chapter 2, simple equations were solved using the equality rules and inverse operations. In this chapter, these methods of solution will be extended to equations having signed numbers and to more difficult equations.

Inverse Operations

Since addition and subtraction are inverse operations:
1. Use subtraction (S) to undo addition (A).
2. Use addition (A) to undo subtraction (S).

Since multiplication and division are inverse operations:
3. Use division (D) to undo multiplication (M).
4. Use multiplication (M) to undo division (D).

Order of Inverse Operations

Generally, undo addition and subtraction before undoing multiplication and division.

1.1 Using Subtraction (S) to Undo Addition (A)

Solve:

	$a)$		$b)$		$c)$		$d)$	
	$n + 2 = 8$		$n + 5 = 2n$		$2n + 6 = n + 10$		$n^2 + 8 = n^2 + n$	
S_2	$\underline{\quad 2 = 2}$	S_n	$\underline{n \quad = \quad n}$	S_{n+6}	$\underline{n + 6 = n + 6}$	S_{n^2}	$\underline{n^2 \quad = n^2}$	
Ans. n	$= 6$	*Ans.*	$5 = n$	*Ans.* n	$= 4$	*Ans.*	$8 = n$	

1.2 Using Addition (A) to Undo Subtraction (S)

Solve:

	$a)$		$b)$		$c)$		$d)$	
	$x - 2 = 8$		$5 - x = 0$		$5 - n = -7$		$8 - n^2 = n - n^2$	
A_2	$\underline{\quad 2 = 2}$	A_x	$\underline{\quad x = x}$	A_{7+n}	$\underline{7 + n = \quad 7 + n}$	A_{n^2}	$\underline{n^2 = \quad n^2}$	
Ans. x	$= 10$	*Ans.* 5	$= x$	*Ans.* 12	$= n$	*Ans.* 8	$= n$	

1.3 Using Division (D) to Undo Multiplication (M)

Solve:

	$a)$		$b)$		$c)$		$d)$	
	$2y = 10$		$10w = 5$		$.7a = 77$		$3\frac{1}{4}b = 32\frac{1}{2}$	
D_2	$\dfrac{2y}{2} = \dfrac{10}{2}$	D_{10}	$\dfrac{10w}{10} = \dfrac{5}{10}$	$D_{.7}$	$\dfrac{.7a}{.7} = \dfrac{77}{.7}$	$D_{3.25}$	$\dfrac{3.25b}{3.25} = \dfrac{32.5}{3.25}$	
Ans.	$y = 5$	*Ans.*	$w = \frac{1}{2}$	*Ans.*	$a = 110$	*Ans.*	$b = 10$	

1.4 Using Multiplication (M) to Undo Division (D)

Solve: a) $\dfrac{n}{3} = 6$ | b) $\dfrac{6}{n} = 1$ | c) $7 = \dfrac{1}{8}z$ | d) $\dfrac{b}{.5} = 100$

M_3 $3\left(\dfrac{n}{3}\right) = 6\cdot 3$ | M_n $n\left(\dfrac{6}{n}\right) = 1\cdot n$ | M_8 $8\cdot 7 = 8\left(\dfrac{1}{8}z\right)$ | $M_{.5}$ $.5\left(\dfrac{b}{.5}\right) = 100(.5)$

Ans. $n = 18$ | *Ans.* $6 = n$ | *Ans.* $56 = z$ | *Ans.* $b = 50$

1.5 Using Two Operations to Solve Equations

Solve: a) $5x + 2 = 17$ | b) $\dfrac{x}{6} - 2 = 8$ | c) $12 - x = 8$ | d) $\dfrac{12}{x} = 8$

S_2 $\underline{\quad 2 = 2\quad}$ | A_2 $\underline{\quad 2 = 2\quad}$ | A_x $\underline{\quad x = +x\quad}$ | M_x $x\left(\dfrac{12}{x}\right) = 8x$

   $5x = 15$ | $\dfrac{x}{6} = 10$ | $12 = 8 + x$ | $12 = 8x$

D_5 $\dfrac{5x}{5} = \dfrac{15}{5}$ | M_6 $6\left(\dfrac{x}{6}\right) = 10(6)$ | S_8 $\underline{\quad 8 = 8\quad}$ | D_8 $\dfrac{12}{8} = \dfrac{8x}{8}$

Ans. $x = 3$ | *Ans.* $x = 60$ | *Ans.* $4 = x$ | *Ans.* $1\frac{1}{2} = x$

1.6 Equations Containing More Than One Term in the Variable

Solve: a) $8y = 3y + 35$ | b) $3y + y + 70 = 11y$ | c) $5y - 2 = 2y + 22$

S_{3y} $\underline{3y = 3y\quad}$ | *Combine:* $4y + 70 = 11y$ | S_{2y} $\underline{2y \quad\quad = 2y\quad}$

   $5y = \quad 35$ | S_{4y} $\underline{\quad 4y \quad = 4y\quad}$ | $3y - 2 = \quad 22$

D_5 $\dfrac{5y}{5} = \dfrac{35}{5}$ | $70 = 7y$ | A_2 $\underline{\quad\quad 2 = \quad 2\quad}$

Ans. $y = 7$ | D_7 $\dfrac{70}{7} = \dfrac{7y}{7}$ | $3y = \quad 24$

   | *Ans.* $10 = y$ | D_3 $\dfrac{3y}{3} = \dfrac{24}{3}$

   | | *Ans.* $y = 8$

1.7 Equations Having Fractional Coefficients

Find each solution set:

a) $\dfrac{1}{8}a = 3$ | b) $\dfrac{3}{8}b = 12$ | c) $\dfrac{2}{3}c - 3 = 7$ | d) $\dfrac{8}{5}d + 12 = 36$

M_8 $8\left(\dfrac{1}{8}a\right) = 3(8)$ | $M_{8/3}$ $\dfrac{8}{3}\left(\dfrac{3}{8}b\right) = 12\left(\dfrac{8}{3}\right)$ | A_3 $\underline{\quad\quad 3 = 3\quad}$ | S_{12} $\underline{\quad\quad 12 = 12\quad}$

   $a = 24$ | $b = 32$ | $\dfrac{2}{3}c = 10$ | $\dfrac{8}{5}d = 24$

Ans. $\{24\}$ | *Ans.* $\{32\}$ | $M_{3/2}$ $\dfrac{3}{2}\left(\dfrac{2}{3}c\right) = \dfrac{3}{2}\cdot 10$ | $M_{5/8}$ $\dfrac{5}{8}\left(\dfrac{8}{5}d\right) = 24\left(\dfrac{5}{8}\right)$

   | | $c = 15$ | $d = 15$

   | | *Ans.* $\{15\}$ | *Ans.* $\{15\}$

1.8 Number Problems Leading to First Degree Equations

a)   Twice a number is equal to 81 less than five times the same number. Find the number.

Solutions:

a)   Let $n =$ the number.

A_{81} $2n = 5n - 81$
S_{2n} $2n + 81 = 5n$
D_3 $81 = 3n$
           $27 = n$

Ans. The number is 27.

b)   Three times a number decreased by 8 equals the number increased by 12. Find the number.

b)   Let $n =$ the number.

A_8 $3n - 8 = n + 12$
S_n $3n = n + 20$
D_2 $2n = 20$
         $n = 10$

Ans. The number is 10.

2. SOLVING FIRST DEGREE EQUATIONS HAVING NEGATIVE ROOTS

Rule. When a and b are real numbers and $a \neq 0$, an equation of the form $ax = b$ can be transformed into $x = \frac{b}{a}$ by dividing both sides by a, the coefficient of the variable x.

Thus, to solve $-3x = 15$, divide both sides by -3, the coefficient of x, as follows:

$$\mathbf{D}_{-3} \qquad \frac{-3x}{-3} = \frac{15}{-3}$$

$$x = -5$$

2.1 Using Addition or Subtraction to Solve Equations

Solve:

a)	b)	c)	d)
$n + 8 = 2$	$n - 8 = -13$	$n - 15 = 2n - 9$	$14 = -n + 10$
$\mathbf{S}_8 \quad \underline{8 = 8}$	$\mathbf{A}_8 \quad \underline{8 = 8}$	$\mathbf{S}_{n-9} \quad n - 9 = n - 9$	$\mathbf{A}_{n-14} \quad n - 14 = n - 14$
$Ans.\ n = -6$	$Ans.\ n = -5$	$Ans.\ -6 = n$	$Ans.\ n = -4$

2.2 Using Multiplication or Division to Solve Equations

Solve:

a)	b)	c)	d)
$2x = -8$	$\frac{x}{2} = -8$	$-12x = 3$	$-81 = 2.7x$
$\mathbf{D}_2 \quad \frac{2x}{2} = \frac{-8}{2}$	$\mathbf{M}_2 \quad 2(\frac{x}{2}) = (-8)2$	$\mathbf{D}_{-12} \quad \frac{-12x}{-12} = \frac{3}{-12}$	$\mathbf{D}_{2.7} \quad \frac{-81}{2.7} = \frac{2.7x}{2.7}$
$Ans.\ x = -4$	$Ans.\ x = -16$	$Ans.\ x = -\frac{1}{4}$	$Ans.\ -30 = x$

2.3 Using Two Operations to Solve Equations

Find each solution set:

a)	b)	c)	d)
$3y + 20 = 11$	$8 - 3y = 29$	$\frac{18}{y} = -6$	$20 + 5y = 2y$
$\mathbf{S}_{20} \quad \underline{20 = 20}$	$\mathbf{S}_8 \quad \underline{8 = 8}$	$\mathbf{M}_y \quad \frac{18}{y} \cdot y = -6y$	$\mathbf{S}_{5y} \quad \underline{5y = 5y}$
$3y = -9$	$-3y = 21$	$18 = -6y$	$20 = -3y$
$\mathbf{D}_3 \quad \frac{3y}{3} = \frac{-9}{3}$	$\mathbf{D}_{-3} \quad \frac{-3y}{-3} = \frac{21}{-3}$	$\mathbf{D}_{-6} \quad \frac{18}{-6} = \frac{-6y}{-6}$	$\mathbf{D}_{-3} \quad \frac{20}{-3} = \frac{-3y}{-3}$
$y = -3$	$y = -7$	$-3 = y$	$-6\frac{2}{3} = y$
$Ans.\ \{-3\}$	$Ans.\ \{-7\}$	$Ans.\ \{-3\}$	$Ans.\ \{-6\frac{2}{3}\}$

2.4 Equations Having Fractional Coefficients

Solve:

a)	b)	c)
$5 + \frac{y}{3} = 3$	$\frac{3y}{4} - 14 = -23$	$5\frac{3}{4}y = -10 + 5\frac{1}{2}y$
$\mathbf{S}_5 \quad \underline{5 = 5}$	$\mathbf{A}_{14} \quad \underline{14 = 14}$	$\mathbf{S}_{5\frac{1}{2}y} \quad 5\frac{1}{2}y = \underline{5\frac{1}{2}y}$
$\frac{y}{3} = -2$	$\frac{3y}{4} = -9$	$\frac{1}{4}y = -10$
$\mathbf{M}_3 \quad 3(\frac{y}{3}) = (-2)3$	$\mathbf{M}_{4/3} \quad \frac{4}{3}(\frac{3y}{4}) = (-9)\frac{4}{3}$	$\mathbf{M}_4 \quad 4(\frac{1}{4}y) = (-10)4$
$Ans.\ y = -6$	$Ans.\ y = -12$	$Ans.\ y = -40$

2.5 More Difficult Equations

Solve:

a)
$$5y - 2y + 11 = 8y + 26$$
$Combine:\quad 3y + 11 = 8y + 26$
$$\mathbf{S}_{3y+26} \quad \frac{3y + 26 = 3y + 26}{-15 = 5y}$$
$$\mathbf{D}_5 \quad \frac{-15}{5} = \frac{5y}{5}$$
$$Ans. \qquad -3 = y$$

b)
$$4\frac{3}{4}a + 11 = 3a - 24$$
$$\mathbf{S}_{3a+11} \quad \frac{3a + 11 = 3a + 11}{1\frac{3}{4}a = -35}$$
$$\mathbf{M}_{4/7} \quad \frac{4}{7}(\frac{7}{4}a) = (-35)\frac{4}{7}$$
$$Ans. \qquad a = -20$$

2.6 Problems Having Negative Roots

a) The sum of three numbers, represented by n, $n-4$ and $3n+7$, is -2. Find the numbers.

b) A merchant's profits in dollars on three articles are represented by p, $p-3$ and $2p-4$. If the total profit is \$1, find the profit on each.

Solutions:

a) $n + (n-4) + (3n+7) = -2$

$\qquad n + n - 4 + 3n + 7 = -2$

$S_3 \qquad\qquad\quad 5n + 3 = -2$

$D_5 \qquad\qquad\quad\; 5n = -5$

$\qquad\qquad\qquad n = -1 \begin{cases} n-4 = -5 \\ 3n+7 = 4 \end{cases}$

Ans. Numbers are, $-1, -5$ and 4.

b) $p + (p-3) + (2p-4) = 1$

$\qquad p + p - 3 + 2p - 4 = 1$

$A_7 \qquad\qquad\quad 4p - 7 = 1$

$D_4 \qquad\qquad\quad\; 4p = 8$

$\qquad\qquad\qquad p = 2 \begin{cases} p-3 = -1 \\ 2p-4 = 0 \end{cases}$

Ans. The merchant made \$2 on the first article, lost \$1 on the second and made no profit on the third.

3. SOLVING EQUATIONS BY USING THE RULE OF TRANSPOSITION

> **Rule of Transposition**
>
> To eliminate a term from one side of an equation, add its opposite to the other.

Thus, by transposing, $13x = 24 + 5x$ is transformed into $13x - 5x = 24$. In this way, like terms can be collected on one side of an equation and combined. Also, by transposing, the equation $13x = 24 - 5x$ becomes $13x + 5x = 24$.

The rule of transposing is useful because it makes the second step of each of the following transformations unnecessary:

$$\begin{array}{llll} & 13x = 24 + 5x & & 13x = 24 - 5x \\ A_{-5x} & \underline{-5x = \quad -5x} & A_{5x} & \underline{+5x = \quad + 5x} \\ & 13x - 5x = 24 & & 13x + 5x = 24 \end{array}$$

Note in the first transformation that $5x$ is eliminated from the right side and its opposite, $-5x$, is included in the left side; while in the second transformation, $-5x$ is eliminated from the right side and its opposite, $5x$, is included in the left side.

The symbol $"\mathbf{Tr}"$ indicates the use of the rule of transposition.

Note. The student should understand that "transposing a term" does **not** indicate that a term somehow has been "carried across" from one side of the equation to the other, and at the same time a change of sign occurs in the transposed term. Rather should he understand that the rule of transposition is based on the addition rule of equality, and that, in "transposing a term", he is eliminating it from one side and adding its opposite or additive inverse to the other.

To Solve Equations by Transposing Terms

Procedure:

1. Transpose (**Tr**) so that like terms will be on the same side of equation: (*Change signs of transposed terms.*)

2. Combine like terms:

3. Divide by the coefficient of the variable:

Solve: $8a - 55 = 3a - 40$

Solution:

1. $\qquad\qquad 8a - 55 = 3a - 40$

$\; \mathbf{Tr} \qquad\quad 8a - 3a = 55 - 40$

2. **Combine:** $\qquad\quad 5a = 15$

3. $\mathbf{D_5} \qquad\qquad\quad \dfrac{5a}{5} = \dfrac{15}{5}$

Ans. $\qquad\qquad\qquad\; a = 3$

3.1 Transposing Terms in an Equation

Solve, using transposition:

a) $31 - 6x = 25$
Tr $31 - 25 = 6x$
$\mathbf{D_6} \quad\quad 6 = 6x$
Ans. $\quad 1 = x$

b) $2y - 28 = 42 - 5y$
Tr $2y + 5y = 42 + 28$
$\mathbf{D_7} \quad\quad 7y = 70$
Ans. $\quad y = 10$

c) $11z + 3 - 4z = 5z$
Tr $11z - 4z - 5z = -3$
$\mathbf{D_2} \quad\quad 2z = -3$
Ans. $\quad z = -1\frac{1}{2}$

3.2 More Difficult Equations

Find each solution set and check:

a) $\quad\quad 5a - 7 + 4a = 2a - 28 + 4a$
Tr $5a + 4a - 4a - 2a = 7 - 28$
$\mathbf{D_3} \quad\quad\quad 3a = -21$
$\quad\quad\quad\quad a = -7$

Check:
$$5a - 7 + 4a = 2a - 28 + 4a$$
$$5(-7) - 7 + 4(-7) \overset{?}{=} 2(-7) - 28 + 4(-7)$$
$$-35 - 7 - 28 \overset{?}{=} -14 - 28 - 28$$
$$-70 = -70$$

Ans. $\{-7\}$

b) $\quad\quad n^2 + 3n - 8 = n^2 - 5n - 32$
Tr $n^2 - n^2 + 3n + 5n = -32 + 8$
$\mathbf{D_8} \quad\quad\quad 8n = -24$
$\quad\quad\quad\quad n = -3$

Check:
$$n^2 + 3n - 8 = n^2 - 5n - 32$$
$$(-3)^2 + 3(-3) - 8 \overset{?}{=} (-3)^2 - 5(-3) - 32$$
$$9 - 9 - 8 \overset{?}{=} 9 + 15 - 32$$
$$-8 = -8$$

Ans. $\{-3\}$

4. SOLVING EQUATIONS CONTAINING PARENTHESES

To Solve Equations by Removing Parentheses

Procedure:

1. Remove parentheses:

2. Solve the resulting equation:

Solve: $\quad 8 + 2(x-5) = 14$

Solution:

1. $\quad\quad 8 + 2(x-5) = 14$
Remove ( ): $\quad 8 + 2x - 10 = 14$
2. $\quad\quad\quad\quad 2x - 2 = 14$
Ans. $\quad\quad\quad\quad x = 8$

Note the use of the distributive law in the removal of parentheses.

4.1 Removing Parentheses to Solve Equations

Remove parentheses, then solve:

a) **Remove ( ):** $3(n+2) = 30 + n$
Tr
$\quad\quad 3n + 6 = 30 + n$
$\quad\quad 3n - n = 30 - 6$
$\quad\quad\quad 2n = 24$
Ans. $\quad\quad n = 12$

b) **Remove ( ):** $-18 = 10 - 2(3-x)$
$\quad\quad -18 = 10 - 6 + 2x$
$\quad\quad -18 = 4 + 2x$
$\quad\quad -22 = 2x$
Ans. $\quad -11 = x$

4.2 More Difficult Equations with Parentheses

Find each solution set and check:

a) **Remove ( ):** $\quad 6y(y-2) = 3y(2y-1) + 27$
Tr $\quad\quad 6y^2 - 12y = 6y^2 - 3y + 27$
Combine: $6y^2 - 6y^2 - 12y + 3y = 27$
$\quad\quad\quad\quad -9y = 27$
$\quad\quad\quad\quad\quad y = -3$

Check:
$$6y(y-2) = 3y(2y-1) + 27$$
$$6(-3)(-5) \overset{?}{=} 3(-3)(-7) + 27$$
$$90 \overset{?}{=} 63 + 27$$
$$90 = 90$$

Ans. $\{-3\}$

b) **Remove ( ):** $(a+1)(a-5) + 7 = 44 - a(7-a)$
Tr $\quad\quad a^2 - 4a - 5 + 7 = 44 - 7a + a^2$
Combine: $\quad a^2 - a^2 - 4a + 7a = 44 + 5 - 7$
$\quad\quad\quad\quad 3a = 42$
$\quad\quad\quad\quad a = 14$

Check:
$$(a+1)(a-5) + 7 = 44 - a(7-a)$$
$$(15)(9) + 7 \overset{?}{=} 44 - 14(-7)$$
$$135 + 7 \overset{?}{=} 44 + 98$$
$$142 = 142$$

Ans. $\{14\}$

4.3 and 4.4 Problems Leading to Equations with Parentheses

4.3. *a*) Find a number if twice the sum of the number and 7 equals three times the difference of the number and 10.

b) Find a number if 20 minus twice the number equals three times the sum of twice the number and 20.

Solutions:

a)   Let n = the number

Remove ( ): $2(n+7) = 3(n-10)$

Tr $2n + 14 = 3n - 30$

           $14 + 30 = 3n - 2n$

              $44 = n$

Ans. Number is 44.

b)   Let n = the number

Remove ( ): $20 - 2n = 3(2n+20)$

Tr $20 - 2n = 6n + 60$

           $20 - 60 = 6n + 2n$

             $-40 = 8n$ or $n = -5$

Ans. Number is -5.

4.4. John, George and Tom earned \$120 together. George earned \$20 less than John and Tom earned twice as much as George. Find the earnings of each.

Solution: Let n = John's earnings in \$

           $n - 20$ = George's earnings in \$

        $2(n-20)$ = Tom's earnings in \$

Remove ( ): $n + (n-20) + 2(n-20) = 120$

           $n + n - 20 + 2n - 40 = 120$

                $4n - 60 = 120$

                   $4n = 180$ $\quad\left\{\begin{array}{l} n - 20 = 25 \\ 2(n-20) = 50 \end{array}\right.$

                    $n = 45$

Ans. John, George and Tom earned \$45, \$25 and \$50 respectively.

5. SOLVING EQUATIONS CONTAINING ONE FRACTION OR FRACTIONS HAVING THE SAME DENOMINATOR

To Solve Equations Having Same Denominator by Clearing of Fractions

Solve: *a*) $\frac{x}{3} + 5 = 2x$ *b*) $\frac{4}{x} - 2 = \frac{8}{x}$

Procedure:

Solutions:

1. Clear of fractions by multiplying both sides of the equation by the denominator:

1. $\frac{x}{3} + 5 = 2x$

Multiply by denominator 3:

M_3 $3(\frac{x}{3} + 5) = 3(2x)$

1. $\frac{4}{x} - 2 = \frac{8}{x}$

Multiply by denominator x:

M_x $x(\frac{4}{x} - 2) = x(\frac{8}{x})$

2. Solve the resulting equation:

             $x + 15 = 6x$ $4 - 2x = 8$

S_x $15 = 5x$ S_4 $-2x = 4$

D_5 $3 = x$ D_{-2} $x = -2$ *Ans.*

Ans. $x = 3$

In (*a*), the denominator 3 is a numerical denominator; in (*b*), the denominator x is a literal denominator, a denominator containing a variable.

5.1 Fractional Equations Having the Same Denominator

Solve:

a) $\frac{3x}{7} - 2 = \frac{x}{7}$

M_7 $7(\frac{3x}{7} - 2) = 7(\frac{x}{7})$

      $3x - 14 = x$

         $2x = 14$

Ans. $x = 7$

b) $\frac{4}{y} = 5 - \frac{1}{y}$

M_y $y(\frac{4}{y}) = y(5 - \frac{1}{y})$

      $4 = 5y - 1$

      $5 = 5y$

Ans. $1 = y$

c) $\frac{5x}{4} - \frac{3}{4} = -12$

M_4 $4(\frac{5x}{4} - \frac{3}{4}) = 4(-12)$

      $5x - 3 = -48$

      $5x = -45$

Ans. $x = -9$

Note. In the solutions of Set 5.1, the reason for the step used to clear of fractions is indicated. Thus, in 5.1(b), the symbol, M_y, denotes that both sides of the equation are multiplied by y. Although the reasons for the remaining steps are not included, they should be supplied by the student. For example, A_1 is the symbol for the reason for the transformation from $4 = 5y - 1$ to $5 = 5y$. Following this, D_5 is the symbol for the reason for the transformation from $5 = 5y$ to $1 = y$.

5.2 Fractional Equations Having Binomial Numerator or Denominator

Find each solution set:

a) $\dfrac{2x+7}{4} = x - \dfrac{3}{4}$

M_4 $4(\dfrac{2x+7}{4}) = 4(x - \dfrac{3}{4})$

$2x + 7 = 4x - 3$

$10 = 2x$

$5 = x$

Ans. {5}

b) $10 = \dfrac{5x}{2x-3}$

$M_{(2x-3)}$ $10(2x-3) = (\dfrac{5x}{2x-3})(2x-3)$

$20x - 30 = 5x$

$15x = 30$

$x = 2$

Ans. {2}

c) $\dfrac{x-3}{x} - 5 = \dfrac{x+7}{x}$

M_x $x(\dfrac{x-3}{x} - 5) = (\dfrac{x+7}{x})x$

$x - 3 - 5x = x + 7$

$-5x = 10$

$x = -2$

Ans. {−2}

6. SOLVING EQUATIONS CONTAINING FRACTIONS HAVING DIFFERENT DENOMINATORS: LEAST COMMON DENOMINATOR (L.C.D.)

The least common denominator (L.C.D.) of two or more numerical fractions is the smallest number divisible by their denominators without remainder. The least common denominator is the least common multiple of the denominators.

Thus, in $\dfrac{1}{2} + \dfrac{x}{3} = \dfrac{7}{4}$, 12 is the **L.C.D.** since 12 is the least number divisible by 2, 3 and 4 without remainder. Greater common denominators of 2, 3 and 4 are 24, 36, 48, etc.

In $\dfrac{1}{5} + \dfrac{2}{x} = \dfrac{11}{5x}$, $5x$ is the **L.C.D.** since $5x$ is the least term divisible by 5, x, and $5x$, without remainder. Greater common denominators of 5, x, and $5x$ are $10x$, $15x$, $20x$, etc.

To Solve Equations Having Different Denominators by Clearing of Fractions

Solve: $\dfrac{x}{2} + \dfrac{x}{3} = 20$

Procedure:

1. Clear of fractions by multiplying both sides of the equation by the **L.C.D.**:

2. Solve the resulting equation:

Solution:

1.   **L.C.D.** = 6

M_6 $6(\dfrac{x}{2} + \dfrac{x}{3}) = 6(20)$

2. $3x + 2x = 120$, $5x = 120$

Ans. $x = 24$

Note that when both sides of an equation are multiplied by the lowest common denominator, the law of distribution applies and, in the process, **each term of the two sides of an equation is multiplied by the L.C.D.**

6.1 Fractional Equations Having Numerical Denominators

Solve:

a) $\dfrac{x}{2} - \dfrac{x}{3} = 5$

L.C.D. = 6

M_6 $6(\dfrac{x}{2} - \dfrac{x}{3}) = 6 \cdot 5$

$3x - 2x = 30$

Ans. $x = 30$

b) $\dfrac{a}{2} - \dfrac{a}{3} - \dfrac{a}{5} = 2$

L.C.D. = 30

M_{30} $30(\dfrac{a}{2} - \dfrac{a}{3} - \dfrac{a}{5}) = 30(2)$

$15a - 10a - 6a = 60$

Ans. $a = -60$

c) $\dfrac{3y}{4} - \dfrac{y}{3} = 10$

L.C.D. = 12

M_{12} $12(\dfrac{3y}{4} - \dfrac{y}{3}) = 12(10)$

$9y - 4y = 120$

$5y = 120$

Ans. $y = 24$

6.2 Fractional Equations Having Literal Denominators

Solve:

$a)$ $\quad \dfrac{10}{x} = \dfrac{25}{3x} - \dfrac{1}{3}$

L.C.D. $= 3x$

M_{3x} $\quad 3x\left(\dfrac{10}{x}\right) = 3x\left(\dfrac{25}{3x} - \dfrac{1}{3}\right)$

$\qquad 30 = 25 - x$

Ans. $\quad x = -5$

$b)$ $\quad \dfrac{8}{a} - 3 = \dfrac{7}{2a}$

L.C.D. $= 2a$

M_{2a} $\quad 2a\left(\dfrac{8}{a} - 3\right) = 2a\left(\dfrac{7}{2a}\right)$

$\qquad 16 - 6a = 7$

Ans. $\quad a = 1\frac{1}{2}$

$c)$ $\quad \dfrac{5}{6} = \dfrac{7}{3x} + 1$

L.C.D. $= 6x$

M_{6x} $\quad 6x\left(\dfrac{5}{6}\right) = 6x\left(\dfrac{7}{3x} + 1\right)$

$\qquad 5x = 14 + 6x$

Ans. $\quad x = -14$

6.3 Fractional Equations Having Binomial Numerators

Find each solution set:

$a)$ $\quad \dfrac{6x+13}{2} + \dfrac{x+3}{3} = \dfrac{5}{6}$

L.C.D. $= 6$

M_6 $\quad 6\left(\dfrac{6x+13}{2}\right) + 6\left(\dfrac{x+3}{3}\right) = 6\left(\dfrac{5}{6}\right)$

$\qquad 18x + 39 + 2x + 6 = 5$

$\qquad\qquad x = -2$

Ans. $\{-2\}$

$b)$ $\quad \dfrac{5y+4}{9} = 2 + \dfrac{2y+4}{6}$

L.C.D. $= 18$

M_{18} $\quad 18\left(\dfrac{5y+4}{9}\right) = 18(2) + 18\left(\dfrac{2y+4}{6}\right)$

$\qquad 10y + 8 = 36 + 6y + 12$

$\qquad\qquad y = 10$

Ans. $\{10\}$

6.4 Fractional Equations Having Binomial Denominators

Solve:

$a)$ $\quad \dfrac{3}{8} = \dfrac{6}{5-y}$

L.C.D. $= 8(5-y)$

$M_{L.C.D.}$ $\quad \left(\dfrac{3}{8}\right)8(5-y) = 8(5-y)\left(\dfrac{6}{5-y}\right)$

$\qquad 3(5-y) = 48$

Ans. $\quad y = -11$

$b)$ $\quad \dfrac{6}{5} + \dfrac{3}{w-3} = \dfrac{9}{5(w-3)}$

L.C.D. $= 5(w-3)$

$M_{L.C.D.}$ $\quad \left(\dfrac{6}{5}\right)(5)(w-3) + 5(w-3)\left(\dfrac{3}{w-3}\right) = \dfrac{9}{5(w-3)}(5)(w-3)$

$\qquad 6(w-3) + 15 = 9$

Ans. $\quad w = 2$

7. SOLVING EQUATIONS CONTAINING DECIMALS

A **decimal** may be written as a fraction whose denominator is 10, 100 or a higher power of 10. Thus, the denominator of .003 or $\dfrac{3}{1000}$ is 1000.

The lowest common denominator (L.C.D.) of two or more decimals is the denominator of the decimal having the greatest number of decimal places. The decimals on both sides of the equation can be eliminated by multiplying by the power of 10 that is the L.C.D.

Thus, in $.15x + 7 = .5x$, the L.C.D. is 100, the denominator of the decimal .15, which has 2 decimal places while .5 only has 1 decimal place. Note in the following model problem, how the equation $.15x + 7 = .5x$ is **cleared of decimals** when both sides of the equation are multiplied by the L.C.D., 100.

To Solve an Equation Having Decimals

Procedure:

1. Clear of decimals by multiplying both sides of the equation by the denominator of the decimal having the greatest number of decimal places:

2. Solve the resulting equation:

Solve: $.15x + 7 = .5x$

Solution:

1. $.15x$ has more decimal places than $.5x$. The denominator of $.15x$ is 100.

M_{100} $\quad 100(.15x+7) = 100(.5x)$

2. $\qquad 15x + 700 = 50x$

Ans. $\qquad x = 20$

In some cases, it may be better not to clear an equation of decimals. Thus, if $3a = .54$, simply divide by 3 to obtain $a = .18$. Or, if $2a - .28 = .44$, then $2a = .72$ and $a = .36$. These are cases where the coefficient of the variable is an integer, not a decimal.

7.1 Equations with One Decimal

First clear each equation of decimals, then solve:

a)	$.3a = 6$	b)	$8 = .05b$	c)	$2.8c = 54 + c$
M_{10}	$10(.3a) = 60$	M_{100}	$100(8) = 100(.05b)$	M_{10}	$10(2.8c) = 10(54+c)$
	$3a = 60$		$800 = 5b$		$28c = 540 + 10c$
Ans.	$a = 20$	*Ans.*	$160 = b$	*Ans.*	$c = 30$

7.2 Solving Equations Without Clearing of Decimals

Find each solution set, without clearing of decimals.

a)	$3a = .6$	b)	$5r - 5 = .05$	c)	$\frac{x}{4} = .28$	d)	$\frac{x}{5} + 2 = 3.5$
D_3	$\frac{3a}{3} = \frac{.6}{3}$	D_5	$\frac{5r}{5} = \frac{5.05}{5}$	M_4	$4(\frac{x}{4}) = 4(.28)$	M_5	$5(\frac{x}{5}) = (1.5)5$
	$a = .2$		$r = 1.01$		$x = 1.12$		$x = 7.5$
Ans. {.2}		*Ans.* {1.01}		*Ans.* {1.12}		*Ans.* {7.5}	

7.3 Equations With Two or More Decimals

Solve. (*Multiply by the denominator of the decimal with the largest number of decimal places.*)

a)	$.05x = 2.5$	b)	$-.9 = .003y$	c)	$.2a = a - .8$	d)	$.5a - 3.5 = .75$
M_{100}	$5x = 250$	M_{1000}	$-900 = 3y$	M_{10}	$2a = 10a - 8$	M_{100}	$50a - 350 = 75$
Ans.	$x = 50$	*Ans.*	$-300 = y$	*Ans.*	$a = 1$	*Ans.*	$a = 8.5$

7.4 Equations Containing Percents

Solve:

a)	25% of $x = 10$	b)	$x + 40\%x = 56$	c)	$x - 16\%x = 420$
	$(25\% = \frac{1}{4})$		$(40\% = .4)$		$(16\% = .16)$
	$\frac{x}{4} = 10$		$x + .4x = 56$		$x - .16x = 420$
Ans.	$x = 40$	*Ans.*	$x = 40$	*Ans.*	$x = 500$

7.5 Equations Containing Decimals and Parentheses

Solve:

a)	$.3(50-x) = 6$	b)	$.8 = .02(x-35)$	c)	$5(x+.8) = -16$
M_{10}	$3(50-x) = 60$	M_{100}	$80 = 2(x-35)$	M_{10}	$50(x+.8) = -160$
	$150 - 3x = 60$		$80 = 2x - 70$		$50x + 40 = -160$
Ans.	$x = 30$	*Ans.*	$75 = x$	*Ans.*	$x = -4$

7.6 More Difficult Decimal Equations

Solve:

a)	$.04x + .03(5000-x) = 190$	b)	$.3(x-200) + .03(1000-x) = 105$
M_{100}	$4x + 3(5000-x) = 19,000$	M_{100}	$30(x-200) + 3(1000-x) = 10,500$
	$4x + 15,000 - 3x = 19,000$		$30x - 6000 + 3000 - 3x = 10,500$
Ans.	$x = 4000$	*Ans.*	$x = 500$

8. SOLVING LITERAL EQUATIONS

Literal equations are equations containing two or more variables.

Thus, $x + y = 20$, $5x = 15a$, and $2x + 3y = 12$ are literal equations.

A formula is a literal equation in which a variable is expressed in terms of the other variables.

Thus, the formulas $RT = D$, $A = \frac{1}{2}bh$, and $p = 2l + 2w$ are literal equations.

To solve a literal equation for a variable, follow the same procedures that are used in solving any equation for a variable.

Thus, to solve $5x = 15a$ for x, divide both sides by 5 to obtain $x = 3a$. Also, to solve the formula $RT = D$, for T, divide both sides by R to obtain $T = \dfrac{D}{R}$.

8.1 Solving Literal Equations Using One Operation

Solve for x:

a) $x - y = 8$
$\mathbf{A}_y$ $\underline{\quad y = y \quad}$
Ans. $x \quad = y + 8$

b) $x + 10 = h$
$\mathbf{S}_{10}$ $\underline{\quad 10 = \quad 10 \quad}$
Ans. $x \quad = h - 10$

c) $ax = b$
$\mathbf{D}_a$ $\dfrac{ax}{a} = \dfrac{b}{a}$
Ans. $x = \dfrac{b}{a}$

d) $\dfrac{x}{a} = b$
$\mathbf{M}_a$ $a\left(\dfrac{x}{a}\right) = a(b)$
Ans. $x = ab$

8.2 Solving for One of the Variables in a Formula

Solve for the variable indicated:

a) $RT = D$

Solve for R:

$\mathbf{D}_T$ $\dfrac{RT}{T} = \dfrac{D}{T}$

Ans. $R = \dfrac{D}{T}$

b) $S = C + P$

Solve for C:

$\mathbf{Tr}$ $S - P = C$

Ans. $S - P = C$

c) $C = \dfrac{5}{9}(F - 32)$

Solve for F:($\mathbf{M}_{9/5}$, first)

$\mathbf{Tr}$ $\dfrac{9}{5}C = F - 32$

Ans. $\dfrac{9}{5}C + 32 = F$

d) $A = \dfrac{1}{2}bh$

Solve for b:($\mathbf{M}_2$, first)

$\mathbf{D}_h$ $2A = bh$

Ans. $\dfrac{2A}{h} = b$

8.3 Solving and Checking Literal Equations

Solve for y and check:

a) $2y - 4a = 8a$
$\quad\quad 2y = 8a + 4a$
$\quad\quad 2y = 12a$
$\quad\quad\ y = 6a$

Check for $y = 6a$:
$2y - 4a = 8a$
$2(6a) - 4a \overset{?}{=} 8a$
$12a - 4a \overset{?}{=} 8a$
$8a = 8a$

b) $2y - 24a = 8y$
$\quad 2y - 8y = 24a$
$\quad\quad -6y = 24a$
$\quad\quad\quad y = -4a$

Check for $y = -4a$:
$2y - 24a = 8y$
$2(-4a) - 24a \overset{?}{=} 8(-4a)$
$-8a - 24a \overset{?}{=} -32a$
$-32a = -32a$

c) $4b + 3y = 12b + y$
$\quad\ 3y - y = 12b - 4b$
$\quad\quad\ 2y = 8b$
$\quad\quad\ \ y = 4b$

Check for $y = 4b$:
$4b + 3y = 12b + y$
$4b + 3(4b) \overset{?}{=} 12b + 4b$
$4b + 12b \overset{?}{=} 16b$
$16b = 16b$

8.4 Solving a Literal Equation for Each Variable

Solve for the letter indicated:

a) $2x = 3y - 4z$
Solve for x:
$\mathbf{D}_2$ $2x = 3y - 4z$

Ans. $x = \dfrac{3y - 4z}{2}$

b) $2x = 3y - 4z$
Solve for y, transposing first:
$\mathbf{D}_3$ $2x + 4z = 3y$

Ans. $\dfrac{2x + 4z}{3} = y$

c) $2x = 3y - 4z$
Solve for z, transposing first:
$\mathbf{D}_4$ $4z = 3y - 2x$

Ans. $z = \dfrac{3y - 2x}{4}$

8.5 Solving More Difficult Literal Equations

Solve for x or y:

a) $3(x-2b) = 9a - 15b$
       $3x - 6b = 9a - 15b$
$\mathbf{D_3}$ $3x = 9a - 9b$
Ans. $x = 3a - 3b$

b) $\dfrac{y}{5} - h = f$

Transpose first:

$\mathbf{M_5}$ $\dfrac{y}{5} = f + h$

Ans. $y = 5f + 5h$

c) $\dfrac{x}{a} - \dfrac{b}{5} = \dfrac{c}{10}$

$\mathbf{L.C.D.} = 10a$

$\mathbf{M_{10a}}$ $10a\left(\dfrac{x}{a} - \dfrac{b}{5}\right) = \left(\dfrac{c}{10}\right)10a$

$\mathbf{Tr}$ $10x - 2ab = ac$
$\mathbf{D_{10}}$ $10x = 2ab + ac$

Ans. $x = \dfrac{2ab + ac}{10}$

9. SOLVING INEQUALITIES OF THE FIRST DEGREE IN ONE VARIABLE

An **inequality** is a sentence stating that two expressions are unequal, or do not have the same value.

Thus, the following are inequalities:

(1) $n + 1 \neq 5$, read, "n plus 1 is not equal to 5"   (3) $3x > 15$, read, "$3x$ is greater than 15"
(2) $2n < 8$, read, "$2n$ is less than 8"

Solving an inequality in one variable is the process of finding the solution set of the values of the variable that satisfy the inequality, provided such values are members of the replacement set or domain of the variable.

Equivalent inequalities are inequalities that have the same solution set.

Thus, $4n - n \neq 12$, $3n \neq 12$, and $n \neq 4$ are equivalent inequalities if the domain of n is the same for each inequality. If n is a whole number, the inequality $4n - n \neq 12$ is solved when it is found that $n \neq 4$, indicating that the answer is "n is any whole number not equal to 4."

COMBINING THE EQUALITY SYMBOL WITH AN INEQUALITY SYMBOL

The equality symbol, $=$, and the inequality symbol, $>$, may be combined into $\geq$.

Thus, $n \geq 10$ is read, "n is either equal to or greater than 10", "n is at least 10" or "the minimum value that n may have is 10".

The equality symbol, $=$, and the inequality symbol, $<$, may be combined into $\leq$.

Thus, $n \leq 20$ is read, "n is either equal to or less than 20", "n is no more than 20" or "the maximum value that n may have is 20".

DOMAIN OR REPLACEMENT SET OF THE VARIABLE IN AN INEQUALITY

If no statement is made concerning the domain or replacement set of a variable in an inequality, the set of real numbers should be assumed to be the replacement set or domain.

PROPERTIES OF INEQUALITIES

1. Order Property

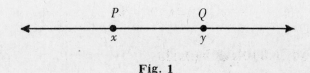

Fig. 1

> On a number line, the coordinate of a point which is to the right of another point is greater than the coordinate of the point to the left.

Thus, on the number line, Fig. 1, since Q is to the right of P, then $y > x$.

2. Transitive Property

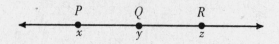

Fig. 2

For any real numbers, x, y, and z, if $z > y$ and $y > x$, then $z > x$.

This property may be stated as follows:

> If the first of three real numbers is greater than the second, and the second is greater than the third, then the first is greater than the third.

The number line, Fig. 2, should be used to picture the transitive property graphically. We see that if R is to the right of Q and Q is to the right of P, then R is to the right of P.

3. Substitution Principle Involving Inequalities

A number or an equivalent expression may be substituted for its equal in any inequality.

Thus, if $x = 10$ and $y < x$, then $y < 10$. Also, if $x = z + 10$ and $y > x$, then $y > z + 10$.

9.1 Inequality Symbols and Properties

Obtain a true statement by replacing the question mark in each with either inequality symbol, $<$ or $>$:

a) If $y > -2$, then $-2 \ ? \ y$ *Ans.* $-2 < y$

b) If $z < y$ and $y < 0$, then $z \ ? \ 0$ *Ans.* $z < 0$, Transitive Property

c) If $y < x$ and $x = -1$, then $-1 \ ? \ y$ *Ans.* $-1 > y$, Substitution Principle

d) If $y \leq x$, either $y = x$ or $y \ ? \ x$ *Ans.* $<$; $\leq$ is a combination of $<$ and $=$

e) If $x < y < z$ and $s < x$, then $s \ ? \ z$ *Ans.* $s < z$, Transitive Property

f) If $x > 1$, then $x^2 \ ? \ x$ *Ans.* $x^2 > x$ for any value of x greater than 1

g) If $x = \frac{1}{2}$, then $x^2 \ ? \ x$ *Ans.* $x^2 < x$ since $\frac{1}{4} < x$. In general, $x^2 < x$ for any value of x between 0 and 1

h) If P, the graph of x, is to the right of Q, the graph of y, and R, the graph of z, is between P and Q, then $y \ ? \ z \ ? \ x$ *Ans.* $y < z < x$, Order and Transitive Properties

9.2 Translating Relationships into Inequalities

Translate into an inequality letting n represent the unknown number:

a) The sum of a number and 10 is greater than 15   *Ans.* $n + 10 > 15$

b) If a number is decreased by 4, the result is less than 8   *Ans.* $n - 4 < 8$

c) 25% of a number is greater than 20   *Ans.* $.25n > 20$ or $\frac{1}{4}n > 20$

d) The product of a number and 3 is at least 12   *Ans.* $3n \geq 12$, "at least" means "equal to or greater than"

e) The quotient of a number and 8 is no more than 6   *Ans.* $\frac{n}{8} \leq 6$, "no more than" means "equal to or less than"

f) If a number is added to one-half of itself, the sum is less than or equal to 10 more than $\frac{1}{4}$ of itself.   *Ans.* $n + \frac{1}{2}n \leq \frac{1}{4}n + 10$

10. RULES FOR SOLVING INEQUALITIES

To solve a given inequality, change the given inequality into an equivalent inequality according to the following six rules:

1. Addition Rule of Inequality

To change an inequality into an equivalent inequality, **add** the same number to both sides and **keep the order** of the inequality.

The number added may be either positive or negative.

2. Subtraction Rule of Inequality

To change an inequality into an equivalent inequality, **subtract** the same number from both sides and **keep the order** of the inequality.

The number subtracted may be either positive or negative.

3. Multiplication by a Positive Number Rule of Inequality

To change an inequality into an equivalent inequality, **multiply** both sides by the same **positive number** and **keep the order** of the inequality.

4. Division by a Positive Number Rule of Inequality

To change an inequality into an equivalent inequality, **divide** both sides by the same **positive number** and **keep the order** of the inequality.

5. Multiplication by a Negative Number Rule of Inequality

To change an inequality into an equivalent inequality, **multiply** both sides by the same **negative number** and **reverse the order** of the inequality.

6. Division by a Negative Number Rule of Inequality

To change an inequality into an equivalent inequality, **divide** both sides by the same **negative number** and **reverse the order** of the inequality.

Note in rules 5 and 6 that the order of the inequality is reversed when both sides of an inequality are either multiplied by a negative number or divided by a negative number. Reversing the order of an inequality means changing from $>$ to $<$ or from $<$ to $>$.

The rules of inequality are simply illustrated by taking two integers, such as 20 and 10, and, on each of these numbers, performing the same operation with a positive number, such as $(+5)$, or a negative number, such as (-5), as follows:

Illustrations of Addition Rule of Inequality

Since $20 > 10$, then $20 + 5 > 10 + 5$; that is $25 > 15$. Also, since, $20 > 10$, then $20 + (-5) > 10 + (-5)$; that is $15 > 5$.

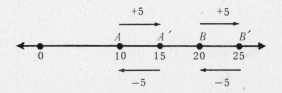

Fig. (a)

Graphic Interpretation of the Addition Rule of Inequality

If points on a number line are shifted an equal distance to the right, the points maintain their respective positions.

Thus, in Fig. (a), B, the graph of 20, is to the right of A, the graph of 10. If A and B are each shifted 5 units to the right, then the new position of B, which is B', is to the right of the new position of A, which is A'.

Illustrations of Subtraction Rule of Inequality

Since $20 > 10$, then $20 - 5 > 10 - 5$; that is $15 > 5$. Also, since $20 > 10$, then $20 - (-5) > 10 - (-5)$; that is $25 > 15$.

Graphic Interpretation of the Subtraction Rule of Inequality

If points on a number line are shifted an equal distance to the left, the points maintain their respective positions.

Thus, in Fig. (a), B', the graph of 25, is to the right of A', the graph of 15. If A' and B' are each shifted 5 units to the left, then the new position of B', which is B, is to the right of the new position of A', which is A.

Illustration of Multiplication by a Positive Number Rule of Inequality

Since $20 > 10$, then $20(5) > 10(5)$; that is, $100 > 50$.

Illustration of Division by a Positive Number Rule of Inequality

Since $20 > 10$, then $\frac{20}{5} > \frac{10}{5}$; that is, $4 > 2$.

Illustration of Multiplication by a Negative Number Rule of Inequality

Since $20 > 10$, then $20(-5) < 10(-5)$; that is $-100 < -50$. (Note the reversed order.)

Illustration of Division by a Negative Number Rule of Inequality

Since $20 > 10$, then $\frac{20}{-5} < \frac{10}{-5}$; that is, $-4 < -2$. (Note the reversed order.)

Keep in Mind

Keep the Order of the Inequality Whenever You Add, Subtract, Multiply by a Positive Number, or Divide by a Positive Number.

Reverse the Order of an Inequality Whenever You Multiply by a Negative Number, or Divide by a Negative Number.

Understanding Why the Order of Inequality Is Reversed When Two Unequal Numbers Are Each Either Multiplied by a Negative Number or Divided by a Negative Number.

Multiplying a real number by a negative number or dividing it by a negative number changes the real number from a positive number to a negative number, or from a negative number to a positive number. In the illustrations previously used, we began with 20 and 10 and the fact that 20 is the greater of the two numbers. When 20 and 10 are either multiplied by -5 or divided by -5, the absolute value of the first result is greater than the absolute value of the second result. However, in the case of negative numbers, it is the number with the greater absolute value that is the smaller number. The student should note what happens in situations involving two negative numbers that are unequal, or two numbers one positive and the other negative.

10.1 Solving Inequalities and Stating the Rules

If x is a real number, solve each and state the inequality rule that applies:

$a)$ $x + 3 < 12$, $b)$ $x - 3 > 12$, $c)$ $3x < 12$, $d)$ $\frac{x}{3} > 12$, $e)$ $-3x < 12$, $f)$ $-\frac{x}{3} > 12$

Solutions:

$a)$
$$x + 3 < 12$$
$$S_3 \quad -3 = -3$$
$$\overline{\qquad\qquad}$$
$$x \quad < 9$$

To change an inequality into an equivalent inequality, subtract the same number from both sides and keep the order of the inequality.

$b)$
$$x - 3 > 12$$
$$A_3 \quad +3 = +3$$
$$\overline{\qquad\qquad}$$
$$x \quad > 15$$

To change an inequality into an equivalent inequality, add the same number to both sides and keep the order of the inequality.

$c)$
$$3x < 12$$
$$D_3 \quad \frac{3x}{3} < \frac{12}{3}$$
$$x < 4$$

To change an inequality into an equivalent inequality, divide both sides by the same positive number and keep the order of the inequality.

$d)$
$$\frac{x}{3} > 12$$
$$M_3 \quad 3(\tfrac{x}{3}) > 3(12)$$
$$x > 36$$

To change an inequality into an equivalent inequality, multiply both sides by the same positive number and keep the order of the inequality.

e) $-3x < 12$ To change an inequality into an equivalent inequality, divide

D_{-3} $\dfrac{-3x}{-3} > \dfrac{12}{-3}$ both sides by the same negative number and **reverse** the order of the inequality.

       $x > -4$

f) $-\dfrac{x}{3} > 12$ To change an inequality into an equivalent inequality, multiply

M_{-3} $-3(-\dfrac{x}{3}) < -3(12)$ both sides by the same negative number and **reverse** the order of the inequality.

     $x < -36$

The symbols A_3, S_3, M_3, and D_3 have been used to indicate that the same operation is performed on both sides of an **equality** using the same number. As we see, they can also indicate that the same operation is performed on both sides of an **inequality** using the same number.

10.2 Solving Inequalities Using Inverse Operations

If n is a real number, solve each and state the needed operation or operations:

a) $n + 4 < 20$ *Ans.* $n < 16$, S_4

b) $n - 4 > 20$ *Ans.* $n > 24$, A_4

c) $4n < 20$ *Ans.* $n < 5$, D_4

d) $-4n < 20$ *Ans.* $n > -5$, D_{-4} and reverse order

e) $\dfrac{n}{4} > 20$ *Ans.* $n > 80$, M_4

f) $-\dfrac{n}{4} < 20$ *Ans.* $n > -80$, M_{-4} and reverse order

g) $-4n \geq 20$ *Ans.* $n \leq -5$, D_{-4} and reverse order

h) $20 \leq -4n$ *Ans.* $-5 \geq n$ or $n \leq -5$, D_{-4} and reverse order

i) $5 + n < 30$ *Ans.* $n < 25$, S_5

j) $5 - n > 30$ *Ans.* $n < 25$: To solve $5 - n > 30$, first S_5 to obtain $-n > 25$, then M_{-1} or D_{-1} to obtain $n < -25$ by reversing the order

k) $30n < 5$ *Ans.* $n < \dfrac{1}{6}$, D_{30}

l) $-5n \leq -30$ *Ans.* $n \geq 6$, D_{-5} and reverse order

m) $2n + 3 < 17$ *Ans.* $n < 7$, First S_3, then D_2

n) $3n - 2 > 16$ *Ans.* $n > 6$, First A_2, then D_3

o) $-\dfrac{1}{2}n + 10 \leq 20$ *Ans.* $n \geq -20$, First S_{10}, keeping the order; then M_{-2} and reverse the order

p) $15 - \dfrac{2}{3}n > -5$ *Ans.* $n < 30$, First S_{15}, keeping the order; then $M_{-3/2}$ and reverse the order.

10.3 Solving and Graphing an Inequality for a Variable Having an Integral Domain

If the domain or replacement set of the variable in each is $\{-3, -2, -1, 0, 1, 2, 3\}$, find and graph the solution set of each inequality:

a) $3x < 3$,   b) $2y \geq -2$,   c) $-\dfrac{1}{2}z \leq -\dfrac{1}{2}$,   d) $-5r + 7 \geq 12$

Solutions:

a) Since $x < 1$, solution set is $\{-3, -2, -1, 0\}$.

b) Since $y \geq -1$, solution set is $\{-1, 0, 1, 2, 3\}$.

c) Since $z \geq 1$, solution set is $\{1, 2, 3\}$.

d) Since $r \leq -1$, solution set is $\{-3, -2, -1\}$.

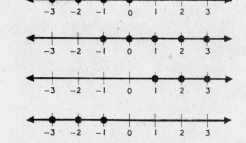

10.4 Solving and Graphing an Inequality for a Variable Having a Real Domain

If the domain of the variable is the set of real numbers, find and graph the solution set of each inequality.

a) $n - 2 > -1$,   b) $2x + 5 < 11$,   c) $\frac{1}{2}y - 1 \leq 2$,   d) $-\frac{1}{4}z \leq 2$,   e) $\frac{2}{3}r - 4 > 14$

Solutions:

a) Since $n > 1$, the required graph is   (1 is not in the solution set.)

Using set-builder notation, the solution set is written $\{n : n > 1,\ n\ \text{is a real number}\}$

b) Since $x < 3$, the required graph is   (3 is not in the solution set.)

In set-builder notation, the solution set is $\{x : x < 3,\ x\ \text{is a real number}\}$.

c) Since $y \leq 6$, the required graph is   (6 is in the solution set.)

In set-builder notation, the solution set is $\{y : y \leq 6,\ y\ \text{is a real number}\}$.

d) Since $z \geq -8$, the required graph is   (-8 is in the solution set.)

In set-builder notation, the solution set is $\{z : z \geq -8,\ z\ \text{is a real number}\}$.

e) Since $r > 27$, the required graph is   (27 is not in the solution set.)

In set-builder notation, the solution set is $\{r : r > 27,\ r\ \text{is a real number}\}$.

10.5 Solving an Inequality Problem Involving a Formula

In the formula $F = \frac{9}{5}C + 32$, C represents the number of degrees Celsius (Centigrade) and F represents the number of degrees Fahrenheit. Find the equivalent Celsius temperature and graph its solution set if during a certain month in town A

a) the maximum temperature is 59°F,   b) the minimum temperature is 50°F.

Solutions:

a) If 59°F is the maximum temperature, then $\frac{9}{5}C + 32 \leq 59$

$$S_{32} \qquad \frac{9}{5}C \leq 27$$

$$M_{5/9} \qquad C \leq \frac{5}{9}(27)\ \text{ Hence, } C \leq 15$$

Since C is a real number, the solution set is $\{C : C \leq 15,\ C\ \text{is a real number}\}$ and the graph of the solution set is

b) Since 50°F is the minimum temperature, then $\frac{9}{5}C + 32 \geq 50$

$$S_{32} \qquad \frac{9}{5}C \geq 18$$

$$M_{5/9} \qquad C \geq \frac{5}{9}(18)\ \text{ Hence, } C \geq 10$$

Since C is a real number, the solution set is $\{C : C \geq 10,\ C\ \text{is a real number}\}$, and the graph of the solution set is

SUPPLEMENTARY PROBLEMS

1. Solve: (1.1)

a) $n + 3 = 11$ *Ans.* $n = 8$ e) $n + .5 = .9$ *Ans.* $n = .4$ i) $2n + 5 = n + 12$ *Ans.* $n = 7$

b) $n + 7 = 20$ *Ans.* $n = 13$ f) $n + 3.4 = 5.1$ *Ans.* $n = 1.7$ j) $n + 18 = 2n + 10$ *Ans.* $n = 8$

c) $12 + n = 30$ *Ans.* $n = 18$ g) $n + 1\frac{1}{2} = 4\frac{1}{2}$ *Ans.* $n = 3$ k) $n^2 + n = n^2 + 15$ *Ans.* $n = 15$

d) $42 = n + 13$ *Ans.* $n = 29$ h) $n + 2\frac{1}{8} = 5\frac{1}{2}$ *Ans.* $n = 3\frac{3}{8}$ l) $2n^2 + 34 = 2n^2 + n$ *Ans.* $n = 34$

2. Solve: (1.2)

a) $x - 9 = 15$ *Ans.* $x = 24$ e) $x - .3 = 1.7$ *Ans.* $x = 2$ i) $8 - x = 0$ *Ans.* $x = 8$

b) $x - 20 = 50$ *Ans.* $x = 70$ f) $x - 5 = 8.3$ *Ans.* $x = 13.3$ j) $10 - x = 3$ *Ans.* $x = 7$

c) $17 = x - 13$ *Ans.* $x = 30$ g) $x - 1\frac{1}{3} = 3\frac{2}{3}$ *Ans.* $x = 5$ k) $10 - x = -4$ *Ans.* $x = 14$

d) $100 = x - 41$ *Ans.* $x = 141$ h) $2\frac{1}{4} = x - 7\frac{1}{4}$ *Ans.* $x = 9\frac{1}{2}$ l) $12 - x^2 = x - x^2$ *Ans.* $x = 12$

3. Solve: (1.3)

a) $3y = 15$ *Ans.* $y = 5$ e) $5y = 6.5$ *Ans.* $y = 1.3$ i) $1\frac{1}{2}y = 1\frac{1}{2}$ *Ans.* $y = 1$

b) $4y = 30$ *Ans.* $y = 7\frac{1}{2}$ f) $.3y = 9$ *Ans.* $y = 30$ j) $2\frac{1}{2}y = 10$ *Ans.* $y = 4$

c) $36 = 12y$ *Ans.* $y = 3$ g) $1.1y = 8.8$ *Ans.* $y = 8$ k) $15 = 1\frac{1}{4}y$ *Ans.* $y = 12$

d) $6y = 3$ *Ans.* $y = \frac{1}{2}$ h) $4 = .4y$ *Ans.* $y = 10$ l) $14 = 2\frac{1}{3}y$ *Ans.* $y = 6$

4. Solve   (1.4)

a) $\frac{a}{4} = 3$ *Ans.* $a = 12$ e) $\frac{1}{3}a = 20$ *Ans.* $a = 60$ i) $\frac{5}{a} = 1$ *Ans.* $a = 5$

b) $\frac{a}{5} = 1$ *Ans.* $a = 5$ f) $\frac{1}{7}a = 12$ *Ans.* $a = 84$ j) $1 = \frac{78}{a}$ *Ans.* $a = 78$

c) $12 = \frac{a}{2}$ *Ans.* $a = 24$ g) $30 = \frac{1}{8}a$ *Ans.* $a = 240$ k) $\frac{a}{.3} = 50$ *Ans.* $a = 15$

d) $25 = \frac{a}{10}$ *Ans.* $a = 250$ h) $5.7 = \frac{1}{10}a$ *Ans.* $a = 57$ l) $200 = \frac{a}{.7}$ *Ans.* $a = 140$

5. Solve: (1.5)

a) $3x + 1 = 13$ *Ans.* $x = 4$ e) $76 = 10x + 6$ *Ans.* $x = 7$ i) $8x + 3\frac{1}{4} = 19\frac{1}{4}$ *Ans.* $x = 2$

b) $5x + 3 = 33$ *Ans.* $x = 6$ f) $45 = 15 + 12x$ *Ans.* $x = 2\frac{1}{2}$ j) $20x + 5\frac{7}{8} = 15\frac{7}{8}$ *Ans.* $x = \frac{1}{2}$

c) $8 + 4x = 44$ *Ans.* $x = 9$ g) $3.4 = 1.4 + 2x$ *Ans.* $x = 1$ k) $3x + 2\frac{1}{4} = 6$ *Ans.* $x = 1\frac{1}{4}$

d) $11 + 7x = 88$ *Ans.* $x = 11$ h) $7.9 = 3.1 + 4x$ *Ans.* $x = 1.2$ l) $4x + 3 = 5\frac{2}{3}$ *Ans.* $x = \frac{2}{3}$

6. Solve (*Use* **A** *and* **D** *or* **A** *and* **M**):   (1.5)

a) $5b - 2 = 33$ *Ans.* $b = 7$ e) $3b - .4 = .8$ *Ans.* $b = .4$ i) $\frac{b}{3} - 5 = 9$ *Ans.* $b = 42$

b) $6b - 8 = 25$ *Ans.* $b = 5\frac{1}{2}$ f) $11b - .34 = .21$ *Ans.* $b = .05$ j) $\frac{b}{6} - 5 = 10$ *Ans.* $b = 90$

c) $89 = 9b - 1$ *Ans.* $b = 10$ g) $7b - 2\frac{1}{2} = 4\frac{1}{2}$ *Ans.* $b = 1$ k) $\frac{1}{4}b - 9 = 12$ *Ans.* $b = 84$

d) $42 = 10b - 3$ *Ans.* $b = 4\frac{1}{2}$ h) $2b - \frac{2}{5} = \frac{4}{5}$ *Ans.* $b = \frac{3}{5}$ l) $20 = \frac{1}{8}b - 11$ *Ans.* $b = 248$

7. Solve (*Use* **M** *and* **D** *or* **A** *and* **S**):   (1.5)

a) $\frac{21}{r} = 3$ *Ans.* $r = 7$ e) $\frac{5.4}{r} = 3$ *Ans.* $r = 1.8$ i) $30 - r = 17$ *Ans.* $r = 13$

b) $\frac{14}{r} = 4$ *Ans.* $r = 3\frac{1}{2}$ f) $.4 = \frac{10}{r}$ *Ans.* $r = 25$ j) $8.4 - r = 5.7$ *Ans.* $r = 2.7$

c) $8 = \frac{24}{r}$ *Ans.* $r = 3$ g) $\frac{5}{r} = 2\frac{1}{2}$ *Ans.* $r = 2$ k) $5.24 = 8.29 - r$ *Ans.* $r = 3.05$

d) $12 = \frac{3}{r}$ *Ans.* $r = \frac{1}{4}$ h) $2\frac{1}{4} = \frac{9}{r}$ *Ans.* $r = 4$ l) $17\frac{3}{4} = 20\frac{1}{4} - r$ *Ans.* $r = 2\frac{1}{2}$

8. Solve:　　　　　　　　　　　　　　　　　　　　　　　　　　　　　　　　(1.6)

a) $6y = 2y + 16$　*Ans.* $y = 4$　　e) $2y + 7y = 72$　*Ans.* $y = 8$　　i) $13y - 4 = 10y + 2$　*Ans.* $y = 2$

b) $10y = 30 + 5y$　*Ans.* $y = 6$　　f) $3y + 5y + 6 = 26$　*Ans.* $y = 2\frac{1}{2}$　　j) $20y + 16 = 30y - 44$　*Ans.* $y = 6$

c) $18 + 2y = 11y$　*Ans.* $y = 2$　　g) $21 = 10y - 4y$　*Ans.* $y = 3\frac{1}{2}$　　k) $2y - 1.7 = y + 1.4$　*Ans.* $y = 3.1$

d) $3y + 40 = 8y$　*Ans.* $y = 8$　　h) $24y - 21y = 14$　*Ans.* $y = 4\frac{2}{3}$　　l) $7y - .8 = 4y - .2$　*Ans.* $y = .2$

9. Find each solution set:　　　　　　　　　　　　　　　　　　　　　　　(1.7)

a) $\frac{1}{5}t = 14$　*Ans.* $\{70\}$　　e) $\frac{1}{3}t + 9 = 14$　*Ans.* $\{15\}$　　i) $24 + \frac{1}{8}t = 31$　*Ans.* $\{56\}$

b) $20 = \frac{1}{10}t$　*Ans.* $\{200\}$　　f) $\frac{1}{4}t - 6 = 8$　*Ans.* $\{56\}$　　j) $17 + \frac{3}{7}t = 29$　*Ans.* $\{28\}$

c) $\frac{2}{5}t = 16$　*Ans.* $\{40\}$　　g) $\frac{2}{5}t + 7 = 13$　*Ans.* $\{15\}$　　k) $40 = \frac{3}{2}t - 11$　*Ans.* $\{34\}$

d) $30 = \frac{6}{7}t$　*Ans.* $\{35\}$　　h) $\frac{3}{7}t - 6 = 6$　*Ans.* $\{28\}$　　l) $\frac{8}{7}t + 9 = \frac{3}{7}t + 39$　*Ans.* $\{42\}$

10. Four times a number, increased by 45, equals seven times the number. Find the number.　(1.8)
Ans. 15

11. Ten times a number, decreased by 7, equals eight times the number, increased by 21.　(1.8)
Find the number.　*Ans.* 14

12. Two-thirds of a number, increased by 10, equals 24. Find the number. *Ans.* 21　(1.8)

13. Solve:　　　　　　　　　　　　　　　　　　　　　　　　　　　　　　　(2.1)

a) $n + 11 = 3$　*Ans.* $n = -8$　　e) $n - 5 = -12$　*Ans.* $n = -7$　　i) $n - 20 = 2n - 3$　*Ans.* $n = -17$

b) $n + 25 = -5$　*Ans.* $n = -30$　　f) $n - .9 = -2$　*Ans.* $n = -1.1$　　j) $2n + 6 = n - 10$　*Ans.* $n = -16$

c) $30 + n = 24$　*Ans.* $n = -6$　　g) $n - 3\frac{1}{3} = -8\frac{1}{3}$　*Ans.* $n = -5$　　k) $-n + 2 = 5$　*Ans.* $n = -3$

d) $40 = n + 70$　*Ans.* $n = -30$　　h) $n - \frac{4}{5} = -8$　*Ans.* $n = -7\frac{1}{5}$　　l) $.34 = .29 - n$　*Ans.* $n = -.05$

14. Solve:　　　　　　　　　　　　　　　　　　　　　　　　　　　　　　　(2.2)

a) $3x = -66$　*Ans.* $x = -22$　　e) $\frac{x}{5} = -4$　*Ans.* $x = -20$　　i) $-7x = 35$　*Ans.* $x = -5$

b) $13x = -130$　*Ans.* $x = -10$　　f) $\frac{x}{2} = -3\frac{1}{2}$　*Ans.* $x = -7$　　j) $-\frac{x}{4} = 120$　*Ans.* $x = -480$

c) $-50 = 15x$　*Ans.* $x = -3\frac{1}{3}$　　g) $-4.8 = \frac{x}{10}$　*Ans.* $x = -48$　　k) $3.1x = -31$　*Ans.* $x = -10$

d) $-7 = 21x$　*Ans.* $x = -\frac{1}{3}$　　h) $-.13 = \frac{x}{6}$　*Ans.* $x = -.78$　　l) $-3\frac{1}{4}x = 130$　*Ans.* $x = -40$

15. Find each solution set:　　　　　　　　　　　　　　　　　　　　　　　(2.3)

a) $2y + 16 = 2$　*Ans.* $\{-7\}$　　e) $6y + 35 = y$　*Ans.* $\{-7\}$　　i) $\frac{40}{y} = -5$　*Ans.* $\{-8\}$

b) $10y + 42 = 37$　*Ans.* $\{-\frac{1}{2}\}$　　f) $8y - 20 = 10y$　*Ans.* $\{-10\}$　　j) $-3 = \frac{18}{y}$　*Ans.* $\{-6\}$

c) $3y - 5 = -17$　*Ans.* $\{-4\}$　　g) $13y = 6y - 84$　*Ans.* $\{-12\}$　　k) $-\frac{20}{y} = 4$　*Ans.* $\{-5\}$

d) $20 + 11y = 9$　*Ans.* $\{-1\}$　　h) $3y = 9y + 78$　*Ans.* $\{-13\}$　　l) $6 = -\frac{3}{y}$　*Ans.* $\{-\frac{1}{2}\}$

16. Solve:　　　　　　　　　　　　　　　　　　　　　　　　　　　　　　　(2.4)

a) $\frac{y}{4} + 6 = 5$　*Ans.* $y = -4$　　d) $\frac{2y}{3} + 7 = -7$　*Ans.* $y = -21$　　g) $y - \frac{1}{2}y = -20$　*Ans.* $y = -40$

b) $8 + \frac{y}{5} = -1$　*Ans.* $y = -45$　　e) $12 + \frac{2y}{5} = -8$　*Ans.* $y = -50$　　h) $y + \frac{2}{3}y = -45$　*Ans.* $y = -27$

c) $30 = 25 - \frac{y}{3}$　*Ans.* $y = -15$　　f) $24 = \frac{7y}{5} + 31$　*Ans.* $y = -5$　　i) $8\frac{1}{2}y + 6 = 7\frac{3}{4}y$　*Ans.* $y = -8$

17. Solve:　　　　　　　　　　　　　　　　　　　　　　　　　　　　　　　(2.5)

a) $4y - 9y + 22 = 3y + 30$　*Ans.* $y = -1$　　c) $2\frac{1}{2}a + 10 = 4\frac{1}{4}a + 52$　*Ans.* $a = -24$

b) $12y - 10 = 8 + 3y - 36$　*Ans.* $y = -2$　　d) $5.4b - 14 = 8b + 38$　*Ans.* $b = -20$

18. The sum of two numbers represented by n and $2n+8$ is -7. Find the numbers. **(2.6)**
Ans. -5 and -2

19. The sum of three numbers represented by x, $3x$ and $3-2x$ is 1. Find the numbers. **(2.6)**
Ans. -1, -3 and 5

20. Solve, using transposition: **(3.1)**

a) $7-2r = 3$ *Ans.* $r = 2$ d) $4s-8 = 16-2s$ *Ans.* $s = 4$ g) $6t+t = 10+11t$ *Ans.* $t = -2\frac{1}{2}$
b) $27 = 30-6r$ *Ans.* $r = \frac{1}{2}$ e) $12+s = 6s+7$ *Ans.* $s = 1$ h) $4t+40-65 = -t$ *Ans.* $t = 5$
c) $10r+37 = -23$ *Ans.* $r = -6$ f) $40-9s = 3s+64$ *Ans.* $s = -2$ i) $20+8t = 40-22$ *Ans.* $t = -\frac{1}{4}$

21. Find each solution set: **(3.2)**

a) $8a + 1 + 3a = 7 + 9a - 12$ *Ans.* $\{-3\}$ b) $n^2 - 6n + 1 = n^2 - 8n - 9$ *Ans.* $\{-5\}$

22. Solve: **(4.1)**

a) $4(x+1) = 20$ *Ans.* $x=4$ e) $6(y-1) = 7y-12$ *Ans.* $y=6$ i) $3(z+1) = 4(6-z)$ *Ans.* $z=3$
b) $3(x-2) = -6$ *Ans.* $x=0$ f) $30-2(y-1) = 38$ *Ans.* $y=-3$ j) $10(2-z) = 4(z-9)$ *Ans.* $z=4$
c) $5(7-x) = 25$ *Ans.* $x=2$ g) $20+8(2-y) = 44$ *Ans.* $y=-1$ k) $6(3z-1) = -7(8+z)$ *Ans.* $z=-2$
d) $42 = 7(2x-1)$ *Ans.* $x=3\frac{1}{2}$ h) $12y - 3 = 5(2y+1)$ *Ans.* $y=4$ l) $2(z+1)-3(4z-2) = 6z$ *Ans.* $z=\frac{1}{2}$

23. Find each solution set: **(4.2)**

a) $3r(2r+4) = 2r(3r+8) - 12$ *Ans.* $\{3\}$ b) $(s+3)(s+5) + s(10-s) = 11s + 1$ *Ans.* $\{-2\}$

24. Find a number if twice the sum of the number and 4 equals 11 more than the number. **(4.3)**
Ans. 3

25. Find a number such that three times the sum of the number and 2 equals four times the number decreased by 3.   *Ans.* 9 **(4.3)**

26. Find a number if 25 minus three times the number equals eight times the difference obtained when 1 is subtracted from the number.   *Ans.* 3 **(4.3)**

27. Three boys earned $60 together. Henry earned $2 less than Ed and Jack earned twice as much as Henry. Find their earnings. **(4.4)**
Ans. Henry, Ed and Jack earned $14.50, $16.50 and $29 respectively.

28. Solve: **(5.1)**

a) $\frac{3x}{4} = 9$ *Ans.* $x = 12$ d) $\frac{12}{x} = -3$ *Ans.* $x = -4$ g) $\frac{y}{3} + 10 = y$ *Ans.* $y = 15$
b) $\frac{2x}{5} + 8 = 6$ *Ans.* $x = -5$ e) $7 = \frac{84}{x}$ *Ans.* $x = 12$ h) $20 - \frac{3y}{5} = y - 12$ *Ans.* $y = 20$
c) $\frac{x}{3} - 5 = 5$ *Ans.* $x = 30$ f) $\frac{10}{x} - 2 = 18$ *Ans.* $x = \frac{1}{2}$ i) $\frac{15}{3y} + 3 = 18$ *Ans.* $y = \frac{1}{3}$

29. Solve: **(5.1)**

a) $\frac{2x}{5} + 6 = \frac{x}{5}$ *Ans.* $x = -30$ c) $\frac{4h}{3} - \frac{5h}{3} = -2$ *Ans.* $h = 6$ e) $\frac{3}{r} = 2 - \frac{7}{r}$ *Ans.* $r = 5$
b) $10 - \frac{x}{7} = \frac{4x}{7}$ *Ans.* $x = 14$ d) $\frac{6h}{5} + 6 = \frac{2h}{5}$ *Ans.* $h = -7\frac{1}{2}$ f) $\frac{1}{r} + 3 = \frac{9}{r} - \frac{2}{r}$ *Ans.* $r = 2$

30. Find each solution set: **(5.2)**

a) $\frac{3x-1}{7} = 2x + 3$ b) $\frac{y}{2y-9} = 2$ c) $\frac{z-6}{5} + z = \frac{4z+16}{5}$

Ans. a) $\{-2\}$ b) $\{6\}$ c) $\{11\}$

31. Solve: $\hspace{8cm}$ **(6.1)**

$a)\ \dfrac{x}{2} - \dfrac{x}{3} = 7$ $Ans.\ x = 42$ $d)\ \dfrac{y}{4} + \dfrac{y}{3} + \dfrac{y}{2} = 26$ $Ans.\ y = 24$ $g)\ \dfrac{3x}{4} - \dfrac{2x}{3} = \dfrac{3}{4}$ $Ans.\ x = 9$

$b)\ \dfrac{x}{5} + \dfrac{x}{6} = 11$ $Ans.\ x = 30$ $e)\ \dfrac{y}{5} + \dfrac{y}{3} - \dfrac{y}{2} = 3$ $Ans.\ y = 90$ $h)\ \dfrac{x}{2} = \dfrac{3x}{7} - 5$ $Ans.\ x = -70$

$c)\ \dfrac{x}{2} = 12 - \dfrac{x}{4}$ $Ans.\ x = 16$ $f)\ 10 + \dfrac{y}{6} = \dfrac{y}{3} - 4$ $Ans.\ y = 84$ $i)\ \dfrac{5x}{2} - \dfrac{2x}{3} = -\dfrac{11}{6}$ $Ans.\ x = -1$

32. Solve: $\hspace{8cm}$ **(6.2)**

$a)\ \dfrac{5}{x} - \dfrac{2}{x} = 3$ $Ans.\ x = 1$ $c)\ \dfrac{1}{x} + \dfrac{1}{2} = \dfrac{5}{x}$ $Ans.\ x = 8$ $e)\ \dfrac{2}{3x} + \dfrac{1}{x} = 5$ $Ans.\ x = \dfrac{1}{3}$

$b)\ \dfrac{7}{a} = 2 + \dfrac{1}{a}$ $Ans.\ a = 3$ $d)\ \dfrac{3}{b} + \dfrac{1}{4} = \dfrac{2}{b}$ $Ans.\ b = -4$ $f)\ \dfrac{3}{4c} = \dfrac{1}{c} - \dfrac{1}{4}$ $Ans.\ c = 1$

33. Solve: $\hspace{8cm}$ **(6.1, 6.2)**

$a)\ \dfrac{r}{6} = \dfrac{1}{2}$ $Ans.\ r = 3$ $d)\ \dfrac{b+3}{b} = \dfrac{2}{5}$ $Ans.\ b = -5$ $g)\ \dfrac{2c+4}{12} = \dfrac{c+4}{7}$ $Ans.\ c = 10$

$b)\ \dfrac{r}{12} = \dfrac{3}{4}$ $Ans.\ r = 9$ $e)\ \dfrac{b+6}{b} = \dfrac{7}{5}$ $Ans.\ b = 15$ $h)\ \dfrac{6c+3}{11} = \dfrac{3c}{5}$ $Ans.\ c = 5$

$c)\ \dfrac{8}{r} = \dfrac{4}{3}$ $Ans.\ r = 6$ $f)\ \dfrac{2b-12}{b} = \dfrac{10}{7}$ $Ans.\ b = 21$ $i)\ \dfrac{c}{10} = \dfrac{c-12}{6}$ $Ans.\ c = 30$

34. Find each solution set: $\hspace{7cm}$ **(6.3)**

$a)\ \dfrac{x-2}{3} - \dfrac{x+1}{4} = 4$ $Ans.\ \{59\}$ $c)\ \dfrac{w-2}{4} - \dfrac{w+4}{3} = -\dfrac{5}{6}$ $Ans.\ \{-12\}$

$b)\ \dfrac{y-3}{5} - 1 = \dfrac{y-5}{4}$ $Ans.\ \{-7\}$ $d)\ 1 - \dfrac{2m-5}{3} = \dfrac{m+3}{2}$ $Ans.\ \{1\}$

35. Solve: $\hspace{8cm}$ **(6.4)**

$a)\ \dfrac{d+8}{d-2} = \dfrac{9}{4}$ $Ans.\ d = 10$ $c)\ \dfrac{8}{y-2} - \dfrac{13}{2} = \dfrac{3}{2y-4}$ $Ans.\ y = 3$

$b)\ \dfrac{4}{x-4} = \dfrac{7}{x+2}$ $Ans.\ x = 12$ $d)\ \dfrac{10}{r-3} + \dfrac{4}{3-r} = 6$ $Ans.\ r = 4$

36. Solve: $\hspace{8cm}$ **(7.1, 7.3)**

$a)\ .5d = 3.5$ $Ans.\ d = 7$ $d)\ 3.1c = .42 + c$ $Ans.\ c = .2$ $g)\ x - 4.2x = .8x - 12$ $Ans.\ x = 3$

$b)\ .05e = 4$ $Ans.\ e = 80$ $e)\ 6d - 10 = 3.5d$ $Ans.\ d = 4$ $h)\ x + .4x + 8 = -20$ $Ans.\ x = -20$

$c)\ 60 = .3f$ $Ans.\ f = 200$ $f)\ 8.6m + 3 = 7.1m$ $Ans.\ m = -2$ $i)\ x - .125x - 1.2 = 19.8$ $Ans.\ x = 24$

37. Solve: $\hspace{8cm}$ **(7.2)**

$a)\ 6a = 3.3$ $Ans.\ a = .55$ $d)\ \dfrac{2}{3}b = 7.8$ $Ans.\ b = 11.7$ $g)\ 4c - 6.6 = c - .18$ $Ans.\ c = 2.14$

$b)\ 7a = 7.217$ $Ans.\ a = 1.031$ $e)\ 8b - 4 = .32$ $Ans.\ b = .54$ $h)\ 3c - 2.6 = c + 5$ $Ans.\ c = 3.8$

$c)\ \dfrac{a}{2} = 12.45$ $Ans.\ a = 24.9$ $f)\ \dfrac{b}{5} + .05 = 1.03$ $Ans.\ b = 4.9$ $i)\ 4c + .8 = c + .44$ $Ans.\ c = -.12$

38. Solve: $\hspace{8cm}$ **(7.4)**

$a)\ 33\dfrac{1}{3}\%$ of $x = 24$ $Ans.\ x = 72$ $d)\ x + 20\%x = 30$ $Ans.\ x = 25$ $g)\ x - 75\%x = 70$ $Ans.\ x = 280$

$b)\ 16\dfrac{2}{3}\%$ of $x = 3.2$ $Ans.\ x = 19.2$ $e)\ 2x + 10\%x = 7$ $Ans.\ x = 3\dfrac{1}{3}$ $h)\ 2x - 50\%x = -9$ $Ans.\ x = -6$

$c)\ 70\%$ of $x = 140$ $Ans.\ x = 200$ $f)\ x = 40.5 - 35\%x$ $Ans.\ x = 30$ $i)\ x + 10 = 4 + 87\dfrac{1}{2}\%x$ $Ans.\ x = -48$

39. Solve: $\hspace{8cm}$ **(7.5, 7.6)**

$a)\ .2(x+5) = 10$ $Ans.\ x = 45$ $e)\ .03y + .02(5000 - y) = 140$ $Ans.\ y = 4000$

$b)\ 4(x - .3) = 12$ $Ans.\ x = 3.3$ $f)\ .05y - .03(600 - y) = 14$ $Ans.\ y = 400$

$c)\ .03(x + 200) = 45$ $Ans.\ x = 1300$ $g)\ .1(1000 - x) + .07(2000 - x) = 104$ $Ans.\ x = 800$

$d)\ 50 - .05(x - 100) = 20$ $Ans.\ x = 700$ $h)\ 250 - .3(x + 100) = .5(600 - x) - 40$ $Ans.\ x = 200$

40. Solve for x: (8.1)

a) $x - b = 3b$

b) $x - 5a = 20$

c) $x + 10c = c + 8$

d) $ax = -10a$

e) $bx = b^3$

f) $2cx = -8cd$

g) $\dfrac{x}{a} = 10b$

h) $\dfrac{x}{4b} = \dfrac{b}{2}$

i) $a + b = \dfrac{x}{3}$

Ans.
a) $x = 4b$
b) $x = 5a + 20$
c) $x = -9c + 8$

d) $x = -10$
e) $x = b^2$
f) $x = -4d$

g) $x = 10ab$
h) $x = 2b^2$
i) $x = 3a + 3b$

41. Solve for the variable indicated: (8.2)

a) $LW = A$ for L

b) $RP = I$ for P

c) $P = S - C$ for S

d) $A = \frac{1}{2}bh$ for h

e) $V = \frac{1}{3}Bh$ for B

f) $S = 2\pi rh$ for r

g) $A = \frac{1}{2}h(b + b')$ for h

h) $s = \frac{1}{2}at^2$ for a

i) $F = \frac{9}{5}C + 32$ for C

Ans.
a) $L = \dfrac{A}{W}$

b) $P = \dfrac{I}{R}$

c) $S = P + C$

d) $h = \dfrac{2A}{b}$

e) $B = \dfrac{3V}{h}$

f) $r = \dfrac{S}{2\pi h}$

g) $h = \dfrac{2A}{b + b'}$

h) $a = \dfrac{2s}{t^2}$

i) $C = \dfrac{5}{9}(F - 32)$

42. Solve for x or y: (8.3)

a) $2x = 6a + 22a$

b) $3y - a = -10a$

c) $\dfrac{x}{4} + b = -b$

d) $ax - 3a = 5a$

e) $\dfrac{x}{3} + b = 7b$

f) $\dfrac{2x}{3} - 4c = 10c$

g) $ay - 6b = 3ay$

h) $\dfrac{y}{m} + 3m = 4m$

i) $\dfrac{y}{r} - 5 = r + 2$

Ans.
a) $x = 14a$

b) $y = -3a$

c) $x = -8b$

d) $x = 8$

e) $x = 18b$

f) $x = 21c$

g) $y = -\dfrac{3b}{a}$

h) $y = m^2$

i) $y = r^2 + 7r$

43. Solve for the variable indicated: (8.4)

a) $x - 10 = y$ for x

b) $2y = 6x + 8$ for y

c) $x + 2y = 20$ for x

d) $2x + 3y = 10$ for y

e) $2x + 3y = 12$ for x

f) $\dfrac{x}{2} + 8 = y$ for x

g) $x + y = z$ for x

h) $\dfrac{x}{3} - 2y = 3z$ for x

i) $ax - by = cz$ for x

Ans.
a) $x = y + 10$

b) $y = 3x + 4$

c) $x = 20 - 2y$

d) $y = \dfrac{10 - 2x}{3}$

e) $x = \dfrac{12 - 3y}{2}$

f) $x = 2y - 16$

g) $x = z - y$

h) $x = 6y + 9z$

i) $x = \dfrac{by + cz}{a}$

44. Solve for x or y: (8.5)

a) $5(x + a) = 10(x - 2a)$ *Ans.* $x = 5a$

b) $\dfrac{x}{3} + b = c - 4b$ *Ans.* $x = 3c - 15b$

c) $\dfrac{x}{12} = \dfrac{a}{6} + b$ *Ans.* $x = 2a + 12b$

d) $\dfrac{x}{6} - \dfrac{a}{3} = \dfrac{b}{2}$ *Ans.* $x = 2a + 3b$

e) $3(5 - y) = 7(y - b)$ *Ans.* $y = \dfrac{7b + 15}{10}$

f) $\dfrac{y}{3} = \dfrac{y}{4} + c$ *Ans.* $y = 12c$

45. Obtain a true statement by replacing the question mark in each with either inequality   **(9.1)**
symbol, $<$ and $>$:

    a) If $x < -3$, then -3 ? x

    b) If $a > 5$ and $5 > b$, then a ? b

    c) If $y > z$ and $z = 2\frac{1}{2}$, then y ? $2\frac{1}{2}$

    d) If $y \leq x$, either $y = x$ or y ? x

    e) If $a > b > c$ and $a < x$, then x ? c

    f) If $0 < x < 1$, then x^2 ? x

    g) If $|x| > 1$, then x ? x^2

    h) If P is to the right of Q, then x, the coordinate of P, ? y, the coordinate of Q

    i) If $x < y$ and A, the graph of z, is to the right of B, the graph of y, then z ? x

Ans. a) $>$ *b*) $>$ *c*) $>$ *d*) $<$ *e*) $>$ *f*) $<$ *g*) $<$ *h*) $>$ *i*) $>$

46. Translate into an inequality letting n represent the unknown number: **(9.2)**

    a) If a number is increased by 5, the resulting sum is equal to or less than 12

    b) If 20 is divided by a number, the resulting quotient is greater than 2

    c) Twice the sum of a number and 3 is no more than 14

    d) The product of a number and 4 is at least 16

    e) 75% of a number decreased by 8 is less than 10

    f) If one-half of a number is subtracted from four times the number, the difference is less than the number increased by 2.

Ans. a) $x + 5 \leq 12$ *c*) $2(n+3) \leq 14$ *e*) $.75n - 8 < 10$ or $\frac{3}{4}n - 8 < 10$

    b) $\frac{20}{n} > 2$ *d*) $4n \geq 16$ *f*) $4n - \frac{1}{2}n < n + 2$

47. If x is a real number, solve each and state the inequality rule that applies: **(10.1)**

    a) $x - 5 > 15$ *e*) $-5x > 15$ *h*) $-\frac{x}{5} < 15$

    b) $x + 5 < 15$ *f*) $15x > -5$ *i*) $\frac{x}{15} > -5$

    c) $5x < 15$ *g*) $\frac{x}{5} > 15$

    d) $15x > 5$ *j*) $-5 < -\frac{x}{15}$

Ans. The rules in each case are abbreviated, using "keep" and "reverse" to indicate how the order of the inequality is affected, and using the initial letters of the operation to be applied.

    a) $x > 20$, A_5 and keep   *g*) $x > 75$, M_5 and keep

    b) $x < 10$, S_5 and keep   *h*) $x > -75$, M_{-5} and reverse

    c) $x < 3$, D_5 and keep   *i*) $x > -75$, M_{15} and keep

    d) $x < \frac{1}{3}$, D_{15} and keep   *j*) $75 > x$, M_{-15} and reverse; or, first change to

    e) $x < -3$, D_{-5} and reverse $-\frac{x}{15} > -5$. Then M_{-15} and reverse to obtain $x < 75$.

    f) $x > -\frac{1}{3}$, D_{15} and keep

48. If n is a real number, solve each and state the needed operations: **(10.2)**

    a) $n - 3 < 10$ *Ans.* $n < 13$, A_3 and keep

    b) $n + 5 \leq -3$ *Ans.* $n \leq -8$, S_5 and keep

    c) $5n \geq 30$ *Ans.* $n \geq 6$, D_5 and keep

    d) $-10n < 5$ *Ans.* $n > -\frac{1}{2}$, D_{-10} and reverse

    e) $\frac{n}{7} < 2$ *Ans.* $n < 14$, M_7 and keep

    f) $-\frac{n}{2} \geq 7$ *Ans.* $n \leq -14$, M_{-2} and reverse

    g) $-\frac{1}{2} > \frac{n}{4}$ *Ans.* $-2 > n$ or $n < -2$, M_4 and keep

    h) $8 - n < 2$ *Ans.* $n > 6$; first, S_8 and keep the order to obtain $-n < -6$, then M_{-1} and reverse the order to obtain the answer.

    i) $10 + n \leq 5$ *Ans.* $n \leq -5$, S_{10} and keep

j) $2n - 4 < 12$ *Ans.* $n < 8$, A_4, then D_2, keeping the order each time.

k) $\frac{1}{2}n + 5 > 3$ *Ans.* $n > -4$, S_5, then M_2, keeping the order each time.

l) $12n - n > 70 + n$ *Ans.* $n > 7$, first, S_n and combine to obtain $10n > 70$, then D_{10} and keep to obtain the answer.

m) $3n + 5 < 2n + 20$ *Ans.* $n < 15$, S_{2n+5} and keep the order to obtain the answer.

n) $14 - 2n > n - 1$ *Ans.* $n < 5$, S_{14+n} and keep the order, then D_{-3} and reverse to obtain the answer.

o) $\frac{2}{3}n - 10 \leq -4$ *Ans.* $n \leq 9$, A_{10} and $M_{3/2}$, keeping the order each time.

p) $-\frac{3}{4}n + 12 > 24$ *Ans.* $n < -16$, first, S_{12} and keep, then $M_{-4/3}$ and reverse the order to obtain the answer.

49. If the domain or replacement set of the variable in each is $\{-2, -1, 0, 1, 2, 3, 4, 5\}$ **(10.3)** find and graph the solution set of each inequality:

  a) $\frac{1}{2}x > 1$,   *b*) $-2x \geq 2$,   *c*) $3x - 2x \leq 2 - x$,   *d*) $\frac{2x}{3} + 7 > 8$

Ans. *a*) Since $x > 2$, solution set is $\{3, 4, 5\}$.

  b) Since $x \leq -1$, solution set is $\{-2, -1\}$.

  c) Since $x \leq 1$, solution set is $\{-2, -1, 0, 1\}$.

  d) Since $x > \frac{3}{2}$, solution set is $\{2, 3, 4, 5\}$.

50. If the domain of the variable is the set of real numbers, find and graph the solution set   **(10.4)** of each inequality:

  a) $n + 3 < 1$,   *b*) $3x - 4 > 8$,   *c*) $8 + \frac{1}{2}y \leq 6$,   *d*) $-\frac{1}{2}w \leq 1$,   *e*) $16 - 3z > 10$

Ans. *a*) Since $n < -2$, the required graph is   (−2 is not in the set.)
  In set builder notation, the solution set is $\{n : n < -2, n \text{ is a real number}\}$.

  b) Since $x > 4$, the required graph is   (4 is not in the set.)
  In set-builder notation, the solution set is $\{x : x > 4, x \text{ is a real number}\}$.

  c) Since $y \leq -4$, the required graph is   (4 is in the set.)
  In set-builder notation, the solution set is $\{y : y \leq -4, y \text{ is a real number}\}$.

  d) Since $w \geq -2$, the required graph is   (−2 is in the set.)
  In set-builder notation, the solution set is $\{w : w \geq -2, w \text{ is a real number}\}$.

  e) Since $z < 2$, the required graph is   (2 is not in the set.)
  In set-builder notation, the solution set is $\{z : z > 2, z \text{ is a real number}\}$.

51. In the formula $F = \frac{9}{5}C + 32$, F and C represent the number of degrees Fahrenheit and Celsius (centigrade) respectively. Find the equivalent Celsius temperature and graph its solution set if during a certain month in town G,   **(10.5)**

  a) the minimum temperature is $77°F$ *b*) the maximum temperature is $-13°F$

Ans. *a*) $C \geq 25$

  b) $C \leq -25$

Chapter 6

Geometry and Formulas

1. UNDERSTANDING GEOMETRY

A. Understanding the Basic Terms of Geometry

The word **geometry** is derived from the Greek words **geos** meaning earth and **metron** meaning measure. The ancient Egyptians, Chinese, Babylonians, Romans and Greeks found geometry essential for surveying, navigation, and astronomy. The Greeks used geometry to develop logical reasoning by systematizing geometric facts and establishing logical relationships among these facts. Today, geometry is of the greatest importance in aviation and space travel.

The basic terms of geometry are point, line, surface, and solid. These terms begin the process of definition and underlie the definitions of all other geometric terms.

Point

A point has position only. It has no length, width, or thickness.

A point is represented by a dot. Keep in mind however that the dot represents a point but is not a point, just as a dot on a map may represent a locality but is not the locality. A dot, unlike a point, has size.

A point is designated by a capital letter next to the dot, thus: ·P

A point is represented also by the tip of a needle.

Line

A line has length but has no width or thickness.

A line may be represented by the path of a piece of chalk on the blackboard or by a stretched rubber band.

A line is designated by the capital letters of any two of its points or by a small letter, thus:

A line may be straight, curved, or a combination of these. To understand how lines differ, think of a line as being generated by a moving point.

A **straight line**, such as ⟶ , is generated by a point moving in the same direction.

A **curved line**, such as ⌒ , is generated by a point moving in a continuously changing direction.

A **broken line**, such as ∕\⁄ , is a combination of straight lines.

A straight line is unlimited in extent. It may be extended in either direction indefinitely.

A straight line is the shortest line between two points. Two straight lines intersect in a point.

A straight line is represented by the edge of a ruler.

Surface

A surface has length and width but no thickness. It may be represented by a blackboard, a side of a box or the outside of a sphere; these are representations of a surface but are not surfaces.

A **plane surface** or a **plane** is a surface such that a straight line connecting any two of its points lies entirely in it. A plane is a flat surface and may be represented by the surface of a flat mirror or the top of a desk.

Plane Geometry is the geometry that deals with plane figures that may be drawn on a plane surface.

Solids

A **solid** is an enclosed portion of space bounded by plane and curved surfaces.

Thus, the **pyramid** △ , the **cube** ▱ , the **cone** △ , the **cylinder** ⌷ and the **sphere** ◯ are solids.

B. Understanding Lines and Angles

The Number Line, Graphs, and Coordinates

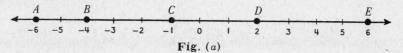

Fig. (*a*)

Recall that the number line is called the **real number line** because there is a one-to-one correspondence between the set of points on the number line and the set of real numbers. To each point on the number line, there is one and only one real number that can be paired with it; and to each real number, there is one and only one point on the number line. On the number line, a point is the graph of a real number and, in turn, a real number is the coordinate of a point.

Thus, in Fig. (*a*), *B* is the graph of −4, and −4 is the coordinate of *B*.

Line Segment

Fig. (*b*)   **Fig.** (*c*)

A **line segment** is a part of a line between two points. A line segment is defined as the set of points lying between two endpoints, including the endpoints.

The notation $\overline{AB}$ denotes the line segment between points *A* and *B*. $\overline{AB}$ is the set of points between *A* and *B* and also the endpoints *A* and *B*.

The **length of a line segment** is the distance between its endpoints. This distance is the measure of the line segment, the number of units in the line segment.

The notation *AB* denotes the measure or length of $\overline{AB}$.

Thus, in Fig. (*a*), *DE* = 4.

Rule. The measure of a line segment is the absolute value of the difference between the coordinates of its endpoints. Hence, the measure of a line segment is always positive.

Thus, in Fig. (*a*), $DE = |6 - 2| = 4$, $\quad CD = |2 - (-1)| = 3$, and $AB = |-4 - (-6)| = 2$.

Equal line segments are segments having the same measure.

Thus, if *PQ* = 5 and *ST* = 5, then *PQ* = *ST*.

The **midpoint of a line segment** is the point that divides the line segment into two equal line segments.

Thus, in Fig. (*a*), *C* is the midpoint of $\overline{BD}$ since *BC* = *CD*.

A **ray** is the set of a point (the endpoint) and all the points of a line extending in one direction from the endpoint. The notation $\overrightarrow{AB}$ denotes the ray whose endpoint is *A* and which passes through *B*, Fig. (*b*); and the notation $\overrightarrow{BA}$ denotes the ray whose endpoint is *B* and which passes through *A*, Fig. (*c*).

Rule. One and only one straight line can be drawn through any two points.

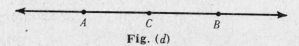

Fig. (*d*)

Thus, one and only one straight line can be drawn through *A* and *B*. The line, Fig. (*d*), drawn through *A* and *B* is said to be "determined" by *A* and *B*. The notation for the line determined by *A* and *B* is $\overleftrightarrow{AB}$.

The notation $\overline{ACB}$ denotes the line segment $\overline{AB}$ with point *C* lying between *A* and *B*.

Summary of Line Notation

$\overline{AB}$ denotes the line segment between points A and B. AB denotes the length or measure of line segment $\overline{AB}$.

$\overleftrightarrow{AB}$ denotes the line determined by A and B.

$\overrightarrow{AB}$ denotes the ray having endpoint A and passing through B; $\overrightarrow{BA}$ denotes the ray having endpoint B and passing through A.

$\overline{ACB}$ denotes line segment $\overline{AB}$ with C between A and B.

Understanding Angle

An **angle** is the figure formed by two rays having the same endpoint.

Thus, angle A is formed by rays $\overrightarrow{AB}$ and $\overrightarrow{AC}$ having endpoint A.

Angle A, Fig. (e), may be designated as $\angle A$, $\angle a$, $\angle BAC$ or $\angle CAB$. Note that three letters may be used to designate an angle. The letter of the endpoint must be the middle letter of the three.

Each of the rays of an angle is one of its **sides**. The common endpoint is called the **vertex** of the angle.

The **measure of an angle** is the number of degrees in the angle. The measure of an angle depends on the extent to which one side of the angle must be rotated or turned about the vertex until the turned side meets the other side.

Thus the protractor in Fig. (f) shows that the measure of $\angle A$ is $60°$. If $\overrightarrow{AC}$ were rotated about the vertex A until it met $\overrightarrow{AB}$, the amount of turn would be $60°$.

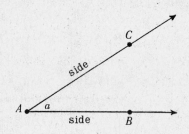

Fig. (e)

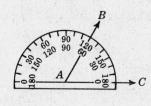

Fig. (f)

Rule. The measure in degrees of an angle whose vertex is at the center of a protractor is the absolute value of the difference between the coordinates of the points where the sides of the angle intersect the circular number line of the protractor.

Thus, in Fig. (f), the measure of angle $A = |60-0|$ or $|120-180|$. Hence, $\angle A = 60°$.

Note. Although the measure of angle A may be denoted by "$m\angle A$", we shall use "$\angle A$" instead to avoid a symbol having two letters. Thus the context will govern whether "$\angle A$" means angle A or the measure of angle A.

Equal angles are angles having the same measure.

Thus, if the measure of angles A and B is $90°$, then $\angle A = \angle B$.

The measure of an angle is **not** changed if the sides of the angle are made larger or smaller.

Thus, the measure of $\angle B$ is unchanged when rays $\overrightarrow{BA}$ and $\overrightarrow{BC}$ are changed in length, Fig. (g).

No matter how large or small a clock is, the angle formed by its hands at 3 o'clock is $90°$, as shown in Fig. (h).

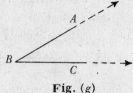

Fig. (g)

Fig. (h)

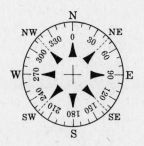

The Navy Compass, shown to the right, is read clockwise from 0° to 360°, beginning with North. A rotation from N to E is a quarter turn or 90°, that from NE to E is an eighth turn or 45°.

Kinds of Angles:

1. Acute Angle — An acute angle is an angle whose measure is more than 0° and less than 90°, Fig. (*i*).

Thus, 0° is less than $a°$ and $a°$ is less than 90°; this is denoted by $0 < a < 90$.

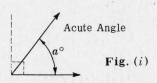

Acute Angle
$a°$
Fig. (*i*)

2. Right Angle — A right angle is an angle whose measure is 90°, Fig. (*j*).

Thus, rt. $\angle A = 90°$. The square corner denotes a right angle.

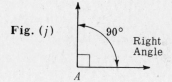

Fig. (*j*)   90°
Right Angle
A

3. Obtuse Angle — An obtuse angle is an angle whose measure is more than 90° and less than 180°, Fig. (*k*).

Thus, 90° is less than $b°$ and $b°$ is less than 180°; this is denoted by $90 < b < 180$.

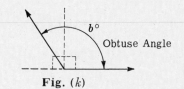

$b°$
Obtuse Angle
Fig. (*k*)

4. Straight Angle — A straight angle is an angle whose measure is 180°, Fig. (*l*).

Thus, st. $\angle B = 180°$. Note that the sides of a straight angle lie in the same straight line. However, do not confuse a straight angle with a straight line!

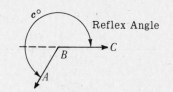

180°   Straight Angle
A B C
Fig. (*l*)

5. Reflex Angle — A reflex angle is an angle whose measure is more than 180° and less than 360°, Fig. (*m*).

Thus, 180° is less than $c°$ and $c°$ is less than 360°; this is symbolized by $180 < c < 360$.

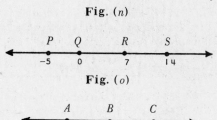

$c°$ Reflex Angle
B C
A
Fig. (*m*)

1.1 Geometry on a Number Line: Notation

State the meaning of each of the following, Fig. (*n*):

a) PQ,   *b*) $\overrightarrow{QR}$ *c*) $\overline{RS}$ *d*) $\overline{QRS}$ *e*) $\overleftrightarrow{QR}$ *f*) $\overrightarrow{SQ}$

Ans. *a*) measure or length of segment $\overline{PQ}$

b) ray having endpoint Q and passing through R

c) line segment having endpoints R and S

d) line segment $\overline{QS}$ with R between Q and S

e) line passing through or determined by Q and R

f) ray having endpoint S and passing through Q

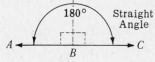

P Q R S
Fig. (*n*)

1.2 Finding the Measures of Line Segments

In Fig. (*o*), find

a) PQ,   *b*) QS,   *c*) PR,   *d*) $PQ + RS$,   *e*) 10 PS

In Fig.(*p*), if a, b, and c are the respective coordinates of A, B, and C, find

f) AB if $a = -5$ and $b = 5$,   *g*) BC if $b = 12$ and $c = 25$,

h) AC if $a = -3$ and $c = 15$.

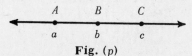

P Q R S
-5 0 7 14
Fig. (*o*)

A B C
a b c
Fig. (*p*)

Ans. (The measure of a line segment is the absolute value of the difference between the coordinates of its endpoints.) Each answer is underlined.

a) $0 - (-5) = \underline{5}$ d) $PQ + RS = 5 + 7 = \underline{12}$ g) $25 - 12 = 13$

b) 14   e) $10(19) = \underline{190}$ h) $15 - (-3) = \underline{18}$

c) $7 - (-5) = \underline{12}$ f) $5 - (-5) = \underline{10}$

1.3 Finding the Measures of Angles

On the inner scale of the protractor, Fig. (*q*), *a* is the co-ordinate of *A* and *b* is the coordinate of *B*. *x*, *y*, and *z* are the measures of angles.

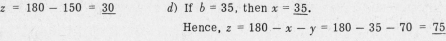

    a) Find *y* if $a = 120$ and $b = 40$,

    b) Find *z* if $a = 150$,

    c) Find *x* if $b = 52$,

    d) Find *z* if $y = 70$ and $b = 35$

Fig. (*q*)

Solutions: Each answer is underlined.

a) $y = 120 - 40 = \underline{80}$ c) $x = 52 - 0 = \underline{52}$

b) $z = 180 - 150 = \underline{30}$ d) If $b = 35$, then $x = \underline{35}$.

Hence, $z = 180 - x - y = 180 - 35 - 70 = \underline{75}$

C. Understanding Polygons and Circles

Understanding Polygons in General

A **polygon** is a closed figure in a plane (flat surface) bounded by straight line segments, called sides.

Names of Polygon According to the Number of Sides

No. of Sides	Polygon		No. of Sides	Polygon
3	Triangle		8	Octagon
4	Quadrilateral		10	Decagon
5	Pentagon		12	Dodecagon
6	Hexagon		*n*	*n*-gon

An **equilateral polygon** is a polygon having equal sides.
    Thus, a square is an equilateral polygon.

An **equiangular polygon** is a polygon having equal angles.
    Thus, a rectangle is an equiangular polygon.

A **regular polygon** is an equilateral and equiangular polygon.
    Thus, a regular pentagon is a 5-sided equilateral and equiangular polygon.

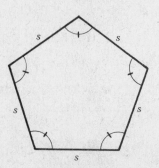

Regular Pentagon

Symbols for Equal Sides and Equal Angles

Using the same letter for sides indicates they are equal. Equal angles may be shown by using arcs crossed by the same number of strokes, as in the adjacent diagram.

Understanding Circles

A **circle** is the set of points in a plane at a fixed distance, called the radius, from a fixed point, called the center.

The **circumference** of a circle is the length of the circle.

An **arc** is a part of a circle.

A **radius** is a line segment joining the center of a circle to a point on the circle. All radii of a circle are equal.

A **chord** is a line segment joining any two points of a circle.

A **diameter** is a chord through the center of a circle. A diameter is the largest chord. It is twice the length of a radius.

A **sector** is a figure bounded by an arc of a circle and the two radii to the ends of the arc.

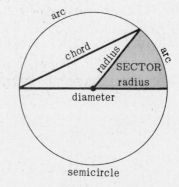

D. Understanding Triangles and Quadrilaterals

1. An **equilateral triangle** has three equal sides.
   It also has three equal angles, each 60°.

2. An **isosceles triangle** has at least two equal sides.
   It also has at least two equal angles. The equal angles shown lie along the base (b) and are called the base angles.

3. A **scalene triangle** has no equal sides.

4. A **right triangle** has one right angle.
   Its **hypotenuse** is opposite the right angle.
   Its **legs** (or **arms**) are the other two sides.
   The symbol for the right angle is a square corner.

5. An **obtuse triangle** has one obtuse angle (more than 90° and less than 180°).

6. An **acute triangle** has all acute angles (less than 90°).

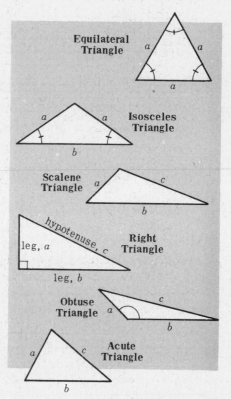

Understanding Quadrilaterals

1. A **parallelogram** has two pairs of parallel sides.
   Its opposite sides and its opposite angles are equal. The distance between the two bases is h. This distance is at right angles to both bases.

2. A **rhombus** has four equal sides. Its opposite angles are equal. It is an equilateral parallelogram.

3. A **rectangle** has four right angles. Its bases (b) and its heights (h) are equal. It is an equiangular parallelogram.

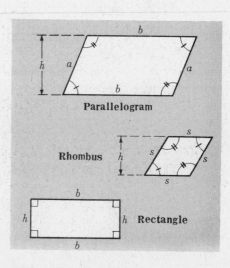

4. A **square** has four equal sides and four right angles. It is an equilateral and equiangular parallelogram. A **square unit** is a square whose side is 1 unit. Thus, a square foot is a square whose side is 1 foot.

5. A **trapezoid** has one and only one pair of parallel sides. The unequal bases are represented by b and b'.

6. An **isosceles trapezoid** has two equal legs (nonparallel sides). Note the equal angles.

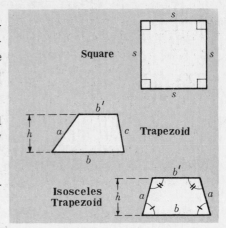

E. Understanding Solids

A **polyhedron** is a solid bounded only by plane surfaces called faces. Thus, the pyramid and cube are polyhedrons. The cone, cylinder and sphere are not polyhedrons since each has a curved surface. The faces of a polyhedron are its bounding polygons. The edges of a polyhedron are the sides of its faces.

A **prism** is a polyhedron two of whose faces are parallel polygons and whose remaining faces are parallelograms. The bases of a prism are its parallel polygons. These may have any number of sides. The lateral (side) faces are its parallelograms. The distance between the two bases is h. This line is at right angles to each base.

    A **right prism** is a prism whose lateral faces are rectangles. The distance, h, is the height of any of the lateral faces.

A **rectangular solid** (box) is a prism bounded by six rectangles. The rectangular solid can be formed from the pattern of six rectangles folded along the dotted lines. The length (l), the width (w) and the height (h) are its dimensions.

A **cube** is a rectangular solid bounded by six squares. The cube can be formed from the pattern of six squares folded along the dotted lines. Each equal dimension is represented by e in the diagram.

    A **cubic unit** is a cube whose edge is 1 unit. Thus, a cubic inch is a cube whose edge is 1 inch.

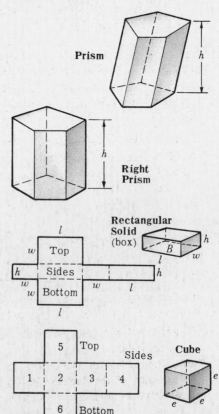

A **pyramid** is a polyhedron whose base is a polygon and whose other faces meet at a point, its vertex. The base (B) may have any number of sides. However, the other faces must be triangles. The distance from the vertex to the base is equal to the altitude or height (h), a line from the vertex at right angles to the base.

A **regular pyramid** is a pyramid whose base is a regular polygon and whose altitude joins the vertex and the center of the base.

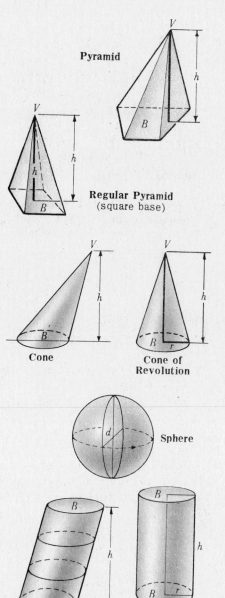

A **circular cone** is a solid whose base is a circle and whose lateral surface comes to a point. (*A circular cone will be referred to as a cone.*)

A **cone of revolution** is formed by revolving a right triangle about one of its legs. This leg becomes the altitude or height (h) of the cone and the other becomes the radius (r) of the base.

A **sphere** is a solid such that every point on its surface is at a fixed distance, its radius, from the same point, its center.

A sphere is formed by revolving a semicircle about its diameter.

A **circular cylinder** is a solid whose bases are parallel circles of the same radius. Any cross-section parallel to the bases is also a circle. (*A circular cylinder will be referred to as a cylinder.*)

A **cylinder of revolution** is formed by revolving a rectangle about one of its two dimensions. This dimension becomes the height (h) of the cylinder and the other becomes the radius (r) of the base.

2. FORMULAS FOR PERIMETERS AND CIRCUMFERENCES: LINEAR MEASURE

A **formula** is an equation in which a variable is expressed in terms of other variables.

Thus, in the formula, $s = c + p$, the variable s is expressed in terms of c and p.

In perimeter formulas, the perimeter is in the same unit as the dimensions. Thus, if the side of a square is 3 yards, the perimeter is 12 yards.

The **perimeter of a polygon** is the sum of the lengths of its sides.

Thus, the perimeter (p) of the triangle shown is the sum of the lengths of its three sides; or simply, the sum of its sides; that is,

$$p = a + b + c$$

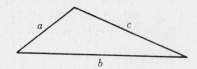

Note. In a rule or sentence related to a formula, the word "side" is understood to mean "length of a side".

The **circumference** of a circle is the length of the circle. For any circle, the circumference (c) is π times the diameter (d); that is, $c = \pi d$. The value of π, using 5 digits, is 3.1416. If less accuracy is needed, 3.142, 3.14 or $\frac{22}{7}$ may be used.

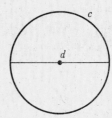

2.1 Perimeter Formulas for Triangles and Quadrilaterals

State the formula for the perimeter (p) of each, using the letters shown on pages 121 and 122:

a) equilateral triangle   *Ans.* $p = 3a$ *d*) square   *Ans.* $p = 4s$
b) isosceles triangle   *Ans.* $p = 2a + b$ *e*) rectangle   *Ans.* $p = 2b + 2h$
c) scalene triangle   *Ans.* $p = a + b + c$ *f*) obtuse triangle *Ans.* $p = a + b + c$

2.2 Perimeter Formulas for Polygons

State the name of the equilateral polygon to which each perimeter formula applies:

a) $p = 3s$ *Ans.* equilateral triangle   *c*) $p = 10s$ *Ans.* equilateral decagon
b) $p = 4s$ *Ans.* square or rhombus   *d*) $p = 12s$ *Ans.* equilateral dodecagon

2.3 Finding a Side of an Equilateral Polygon

If each of the following polygons has a perimeter of 36 in., find a side:

a) square   *b*) equilateral   *c*) equilateral   *d*) equilateral
                            triangle   hexagon   decagon

Solutions:

a) $p = 4s$ *b*) $p = 3s$ *c*) $p = 6s$ *d*) $p = 10s$
       $36 = 4s$ $36 = 3s$ $36 = 6s$ $36 = 10s$
        $9 = s$ $12 = s$ $6 = s$ $3.6 = s$
Ans. 9 in.   *Ans.* 12 in.   *Ans.* 6 in.   *Ans.* 3.6 in.

2.4 Finding Perimeters of Regular Polygons

Find the perimeter of

a) an equilateral triangle   *b*) a square with a side   *c*) a regular hexagon with a
     with a side of 5 in.   of $4\frac{1}{2}$ ft.   side of 2 yd. 1 ft.

Solutions:

a)   *b*)   *c*)

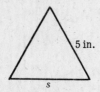   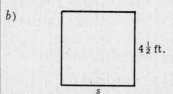   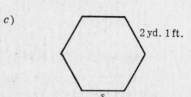

$p = 3s$ $p = 4s$ $p = 6s$
Let s = no. of in. in side = 5   Let s = no. of ft. in side = $4\frac{1}{2}$ Let s = no. of yd. in 1 side = $2\frac{1}{3}$
$p = 3(5) = 15$ $p = 4(4\frac{1}{2}) = 18$ $p = 6(2\frac{1}{3}) = 14$
Ans. 15 in.   *Ans.* 18 ft.   *Ans.* 14 yd. or 42 ft.

2.5 Finding Perimeters of Quadrilaterals

Find the perimeter of

a) a rectangle with sides of 4 ft. and $1\frac{1}{2}$ ft.   *b*) a parallelogram with sides of 4 yd. and 2 ft.

Solutions:

a)

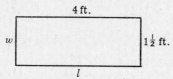

$$p = 2l + 2w$$
Let l = no. of ft. in length = 4
and w = no. of ft. in width = $1\frac{1}{2}$
$$p = 2(4) + 2(1\frac{1}{2}) = 11$$
Ans. 11 ft.

b)

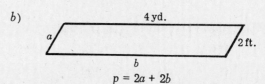

$$p = 2a + 2b$$
Let a = no. of yd. in 1 side = $\frac{2}{3}$
and b = no. of yd. in other side = 4
$$p = 2(\frac{2}{3}) + 2(4) = 9\frac{1}{3}$$
Ans. $9\frac{1}{3}$ yd. or 28 ft.

2.6 Finding the Perimeter of a Rectangle

If l, w and p are in inches, find the perimeter of the rectangle shown if

a) $l = 10$, $w = 3$ *b*) $l = 3\frac{1}{2}$, $w = 4\frac{1}{4}$ *c*) $l = 3.1$, $w = 2.6$

Solutions:

a) $p = 2l + 2w$
$p = 2(10) + 2(3)$
$p = 26$
Ans. 26 in.

b) $p = 2l + 2w$
$p = 2(3\frac{1}{2}) + 2(4\frac{1}{4})$
$p = 15\frac{1}{2}$
Ans. $15\frac{1}{2}$ in.

c) $p = 2l + 2w$
$p = 2(3.1) + 2(2.6)$
$p = 11.4$
Ans. 11.4 in.

2.7 Finding the Length or Width of a Rectangle

For a rectangle, if l, w and p are in ft., find

a) the length if $p = 20$, $w = 3$
b) the width if $p = 27$, $l = 5\frac{1}{2}$
c) the width if $p = 40$ and $l = w + 5$
d) the length if $p = 30$ and $w = 3l$

Solutions:

a) $p = 2l + 2w$
$20 = 2l + 6$
$7 = l$
Ans. 7 ft.

b) $p = 2l + 2w$
$27 = 2(5\frac{1}{2}) + 2w$
$8 = w$
Ans. 8 ft.

c) $p = 2l + 2w$
$40 = 2(w+5) + 2w$
$7\frac{1}{2} = w$
Ans. $7\frac{1}{2}$ ft.

d) $p = 2l + 2w$
$30 = 2l + 2(3l)$
$3\frac{3}{4} = l$
Ans. $3\frac{3}{4}$ ft.

2.8 Perimeter of an Isosceles Triangle

For the isosceles triangle shown, if a, b and p are in inches find

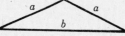

a) the perimeter if $a = 10$ and $b = 12$
b) the base if $p = 25$ and $a = 8$
c) the base if $p = 33$ and $a = b - 3$
d) an equal side if $p = 35$ and $b = 1.5a$

Solutions:

a) $p = 2a + b$
$p = 2(10) + 12$
$p = 32$
Ans. 32 in.

b) $p = 2a + b$
$25 = 2(8) + b$
$9 = b$
Ans. 9 in.

c) $p = 2a + b$
$33 = 2(b-3) + b$
$13 = b$
Ans. 13 in.

d) $p = 2a + b$
$35 = 2a + 1.5a$
$10 = a$
Ans. 10 in.

2.9 Circumference and Arc Formulas

For any circle, state a formula which relates

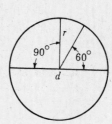

a) the diameter (d) and radius (r)   *Ans.* $d = 2r$
b) the circumference (c) and the diameter (d)   *Ans.* $c = \pi d$
c) the circumference (c) and the radius (r)   *Ans.* $c = 2\pi r$
d) the circumference (c) and an arc of 90°(a)   *Ans.* $c = 4a$
e) an arc of 60°(a') and the radius (r)   *Ans.* $a' = \frac{\pi r}{3}$
   (Read a' as "a-prime".)

2.10 Circumference of a Circle

For a circle, if r, d and c are in ft., find, using $\pi = 3.14$,

a) the circumference if $r = 5$ c) the radius if $c = 942$
b) a 90° arc if $d = 8$ d) the diameter if $c = 1570$

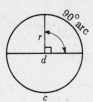

Solutions:

a) $c = 2\pi r$
   $= 2(3.14)5$
   $= 31.4$
Ans. 31.4 ft.

b) 90° arc $= \dfrac{c}{4} = \dfrac{\pi d}{4}$
   $= \dfrac{(3.14)8}{4}$
   $= 6.28$
Ans. 6.28 ft.

c) $c = 2\pi r$
   $942 = 2(3.14)r$
   $150 = r$
Ans. 150 ft.

d) $c = \pi d$
   $1570 = 3.14\,d$
   $500 = d$
Ans. 500 ft.

2.11 Perimeters of Combined Figures

State the formula for the perimeter, p, for each figure:

(sq.= square, *each curved figure is a semicircle*)

a)
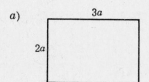

b)
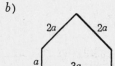

c)
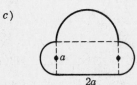

d)
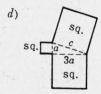

e)
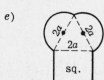

f)
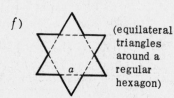

(equilateral triangles around a regular hexagon)

Ans. a) $p = 10a$
   d) $p = 12a + 3c$

b) $p = 9a$
e) $p = 6a + 2\pi a$

c) $p = 2a + 2\pi a$
f) $p = 12a$

3. FORMULAS FOR AREAS: SQUARE MEASURE

A **square unit** is a square whose side is 1 unit. Thus, a square inch is a square whose side is 1 inch.

The **area of a circle or polygon** is the number of square units contained in the region bounded by the circle or polygon. Thus, the area of a rectangle 5 units long and 4 units wide contains 20 square units.

In area formulas, the area is in **square units**, the unit being the same as that used for the dimensions. Thus, if the side of a square is 3 yards, its area is 9 square yards.

1 Square Inch

1 inch

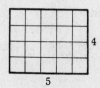

Area Formulas (using A for the area of the figure):

1. **Rectangle:** $A = bh$

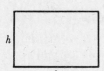

2. **Parallelogram:** $A = bh$

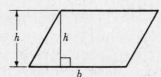

3. **Triangle:** $A = \dfrac{bh}{2}$

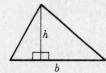

4. **Square:** $A = s^2$

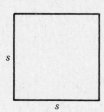

5. **Trapezoid:** $A = \dfrac{h}{2}(b+b')$

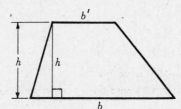

6. **Circle:** $A = \pi r^2$. Also, $A = \dfrac{\pi d^2}{4}$

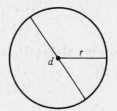

Area Formulas for Solids (using T for the total area of the solid):

1. Total area of the six squares of a **cube:**
$$T = 6e^2$$

$A = e^2$ for each face.

2. Total area of the six rectangles of a **rectangular solid:** $\qquad T = 2lw + 2lh + 2wh$

$A = lw$ for top or bottom faces
$A = lh$ for front or back faces
$A = wh$ for left or right faces

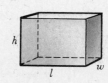

3. Total area of a **sphere:**

$A = 4\pi r^2$

4. Total area of a **cylinder of revolution:**

$T = 2\pi rh + 2\pi r^2$
$T = 2\pi r(r+h)$

3.1 Relations Among Square Units

Find the area (A) of (*Hint*: *A square unit is a square whose side is 1 unit.*)
a) a square foot in square inches,
b) a square yard in square feet,
c) a square meter in square centimeters.

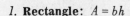
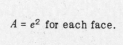

Solutions:

a) $\qquad A = s^2$
Since 1 ft. = 12 in.,
$\qquad A = 12^2 = 144$
Ans. 1 sq. ft. = 144 sq. in.

b) $\qquad A = s^2$
Since 1 yd. = 3 ft.,
$\qquad A = 3^2 = 9$
Ans. 1 sq. yd. = 9 sq. ft.

c) $\qquad A = s^2$
Since 1 meter = 100 cm.,
$\qquad A = 100^2 = 10,000$
Ans. 1 sq. meter = 10,000 sq. cm.

3.2 Finding the Area of Squares

Find the area of a square (A) in sq. ft. whose side is

a) 6 in. b) 6 ft. c) 6 yd. d) 6 rd.

Solutions: (*To find area in sq. ft., express side in ft.*)

a) $A = s^2$	b) $A = s^2$	c) $A = s^2$	d) $A = s^2$
Since 6 in. $= \frac{1}{2}$ ft.,	$A = 6^2$	Since 6 yd. $= 18$ ft.,	Since 6 rd. $= 6(16\frac{1}{2})$ or 99 ft.,
$A = (\frac{1}{2})^2 = \frac{1}{4}$	$A = 36$	$A = 18^2 = 324$	$A = 99^2 = 9801$
Ans. $\frac{1}{4}$ sq. ft.	*Ans.* 36 sq. ft.	*Ans.* 324 sq. ft.	*Ans.* 9801 sq. ft.

3.3 Finding Areas

Find the area of

a) a rectangle with sides of 4 ft. and $2\frac{1}{2}$ ft.,

b) a parallelogram with a base of 5.8 in. and a height of 2.3 in.,

c) a triangle with a base of 4 ft. and an altitude to the base of 3 ft. 6 in.

Solutions:

a)

$h = 2\frac{1}{2}$, $b = 4$

$A = bh$
$A = 4(2\frac{1}{2}) = 10$
Ans. 10 sq. ft.

b)

$h = 2.3$, $b = 5.8$

$A = bh$
$A = (5.8)(2.3) = 13.34$
Ans. 13.34 sq. in.

c)

$h = 3\frac{1}{2}$, $b = 4$

$A = \frac{1}{2}bh$
$A = \frac{1}{2}(4)(3\frac{1}{2}) = 7$
Ans. 7 sq. ft.

3.4 Area of Circle Formulas

For a circle, state a formula which relates

a) the area (A) and the radius (r)   *Ans.* $A = \pi r^2$

b) the area (A) and the diameter (d)   *Ans.* $A = \dfrac{\pi d^2}{4}$

c) the area (A) and a sector of $90°$ (S)   *Ans.* $A = 4S$

d) a sector of $60°$ (S') and the area (A)   *Ans.* $S' = \dfrac{A}{6}$

e) a sector of $40°$ (S'') and the radius (r)   *Ans.* $S'' = \dfrac{\pi r^2}{9}$
(Read S'' as "S-double prime".)

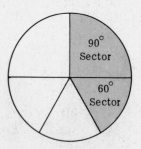

3.5 Area of a Circle

For a circle, if r and d are in inches, find, *to the nearest integer*, the area of

a) the circle if $r = 20$ c) a $90°$ sector if $r = 4$

b) the circle if $d = 10$ d) a $30°$ sector if $d = 12.2$

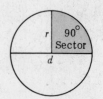

Solutions: Let $\pi = 3.14$.

a) $A = \pi r^2$	b) $A = \pi r^2$	c) $A = \pi r^2$	d) $A = \pi r^2$
$A = 3.14(20^2)$	$A = 3.14(5^2)$	$A = (3.14)4^2$	$A = (3.14)(6.1^2)$
$= 3.14(400)$	$= 3.14(25)$	$90°$ sector $= \frac{1}{4}(3.14)(16)$	$30°$ sector $= \frac{1}{12}(3.14)(37.21)$
$= 1256$	$= 78.5$	$= 12.56$	$= 9.7366$
Ans. 1256 sq. in.	*Ans.* 79 sq. in.	*Ans.* 13 sq. in.	*Ans.* 10 sq. in.

3.6 Formulas for Combined Areas

State the formula for the area (A) of each shaded figure:

a)

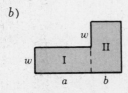

b)

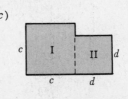

c)

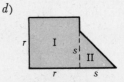

d)

Solutions: (*Abbreviations used are* rect. *for* rectangle, sq. *for* square *and* $\triangle$ *for* triangle.)

a) $A = \text{rect.I} + \text{rect.II}$

Ans. $A = aw + bw$

b) $A = \text{rect.I} + \text{rect.II}$

Ans. $A = aw + 2bw$

c) $A = \text{sq.I} + \text{sq.II}$

Ans. $A = c^2 + d^2$

d) $A = \text{sq.I} + \triangle\text{II}$

Ans. $A = r^2 + \dfrac{s^2}{2}$

3.7 Formulas for Reduced Areas

State the formula for the area (A) of each shaded figure:

a)

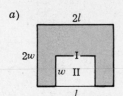

b)

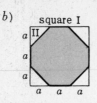

c)

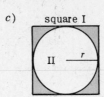

d)

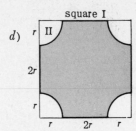

Solutions: ($\odot$ is used for circle.)

a) $A = \text{rect.I} - \text{rect.II}$

$A = 4lw - lw$

Ans. $A = 3lw$

b) $A = \text{sq.I} - 4\triangle\text{II}$

$A = (3a)^2 - 4\left(\dfrac{a^2}{2}\right)$

Ans. $A = 7a^2$

c) $A = \text{sq.I} - \odot\text{II}$

$A = (2r)^2 - \pi r^2$

Ans. $A = 4r^2 - \pi r^2$

d) $A = \text{sq.I} - 4 \text{ sector II}$

$A = (4r)^2 - 4\left(\dfrac{\pi r^2}{4}\right)$

Ans. $A = 16r^2 - \pi r^2$

3.8 Finding Total Areas of Solids

Find, to the nearest integer, the total area of

a) a cube with an edge of 5 in.

b) a rectangular solid with dimensions of 10 ft., 7 ft. and $4\frac{1}{2}$ ft.

c) a sphere with a radius of 1.1 yd.

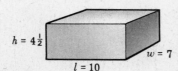

Solutions:

a) $T = 6e^2$

$T = 6(5^2)$

$= 150$

Ans. 150 sq. in.

b) $T = 2lw + 2lh + 2wh$

$T = 2(10)(7) + 2(10)(4\frac{1}{2}) + 2(7)(4\frac{1}{2})$

$= 293$

Ans. 293 sq. ft.

c) $T = 4\pi r^2$

$T = 4(3.14)(1.1^2)$

$= 15.1976$

Ans. 15 sq. yd.

4. FORMULAS FOR VOLUMES: CUBIC MEASURE

A **cubic unit** is a cube whose edge is 1 unit. Thus, a cubic inch is a cube whose side is 1 inch.

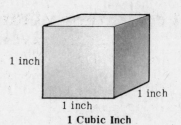

1 inch

1 inch

1 inch

1 Cubic Inch

The **volume of a solid** is the number of cubic units that it contains. Thus, a box 5 units long, 3 units wide and 4 units high has a volume of 60 cubic units; that is, it has a capacity or space large enough to contain 60 cubes, 1 unit on a side.

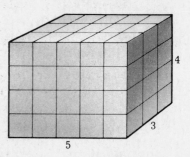

4

3

5

In volume formulas, the volume is in **cubic units**, the unit being the same as that used for the dimensions. Thus, if the edge of a cube is 3 yards, its volume is 27 cubic yards.

Volume Formulas (using V for the volume of the solid, B for the area of a base and h for the distance between the bases or between the vertex and a base):

1. **Rectangular Solid:** $V = lwh$

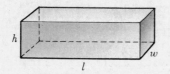

h w l

3. **Cylinder:** $V = Bh$ or $V = \pi r^2 h$

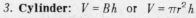
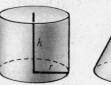

h r h r

2. **Prism:** $V = Bh$

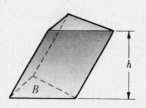

h B h B

4. **Cube:** $V = e^3$

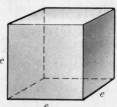

e e e

5. **Pyramid:** $V = \frac{1}{3}Bh$

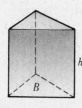

h B h B

6. **Cone:** $V = \frac{1}{3}Bh$ or $V = \frac{1}{3}\pi r^2 h$

h r h

7. **Sphere:** $V = \frac{4}{3}\pi r^3$

r r

4.1 Relations Among Cubic Units

Find the volume V of (*Hint: A cubic unit is a cube whose edge is 1 unit.*)

a) a cubic foot in cubic inches
b) a cubic yard in cubic feet
c) a liter (cubic decimeter) in cubic centimeters.

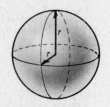

1 Cubic Unit

1 unit

1 unit

1 unit

Solutions:

a) $V = e^3$

Since 1 ft. = 12 in.,

     $V = 12^3 = 1728$

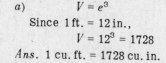
Ans. 1 cu. ft. = 1728 cu. in.

b) $V = e^3$

Since 1 yd. = 3 ft.,

     $V = 3^3 = 27$

Ans. 1 cu. yd. = 27 cu. ft.

c) $V = e^3$

Since 1 dm. = 10 cm.,

     $V = 10^3 = 1000$

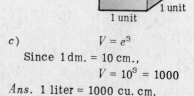
Ans. 1 liter = 1000 cu. cm.

4.2 Finding Volumes of Cubes

Find the volume of a cube (V) in cu. ft. whose edge is a) 4 in., b) 4 ft., c) 4 yd., d) 4 rd.

Solutions: (To find volume in cu. ft., express side in ft.)

a) $V = e^3$
Since 4 in. $= \frac{1}{3}$ ft.,
$\quad V = (\frac{1}{3})^3 = \frac{1}{27}$
Ans. $\frac{1}{27}$ cu. ft.

b) $V = e^3$
$\quad V = 4^3 = 64$
Ans. 64 cu. ft.

c) $V = e^3$
Since 4 yd. $= 12$ ft.,
$\quad V = 12^3 = 1728$
Ans. 1728 cu. ft.

d) $V = e^3$
Since 4 rd. $= 4(16\frac{1}{2})$ or 66 ft.
$\quad V = 66^3 = 287{,}496$
Ans. 287,496 cu. ft.

4.3 Finding Volumes of Rectangular Solid, Prism and Pyramid

Find the volume of

a) a rectangular solid having a length of 6 in., a width of 4 in. and a height of 1 ft.

b) a prism having a height of 15 yd. and a triangular base of 120 sq. ft.

c) a pyramid having a height of 8 yd. and a square base whose side is $4\frac{1}{2}$ yd.

Solutions:

a) $V = lwh$
$\quad V = 6(4)(12) = 288$
Ans. 288 cu. in.

b) $V = Bh$
$\quad V = 120(45) = 5400$
Ans. 5400 cu. ft. or 200 cu. yd.

c) $V = \frac{1}{3}Bh$
$\quad V = \frac{1}{3}(\frac{9}{2})^2(8) = 54$
Ans. 54 cu. yd.

4.4 Finding Volumes of Sphere, Cylinder and Cone

Find the volume, to the nearest integer, of

a) a sphere with a radius of 10 in.

b) a cylinder with a height of 4 yd. and a base whose radius is 2 ft.

c) a cone with a height of 2 ft. and a base whose radius is 2 yd.

Solutions: (Let $\pi = 3.14$)

a) $V = \frac{4}{3}\pi r^3$
$\quad = \frac{4}{3}(3.14)10^3$
$\quad \doteq 4186\frac{2}{3}$
Ans. 4187 cu. in.

b) $V = \pi r^2 h$
$\quad = (3.14)(2^2)12$
$\quad = 150.72$
Ans. 151 cu. ft.

c) $V = \frac{1}{3}\pi r^2 h$
$\quad = \frac{1}{3}(3.14)(6^2)(2)$
$\quad = 75.36$
Ans. 75 cu. ft.

4.5 Deriving Formulas from V = Bh

From $V = Bh$, the volume formula for a prism or cylinder, derive the volume formulas for each of the following:

a) **Rectangular Solid**
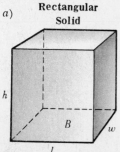

b) **Cube**
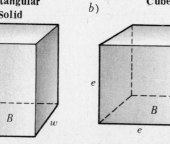

c) **Cylinder of Revolution**
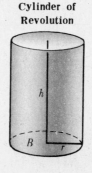

d) **Right Prism with a Trapezoid for a Base**
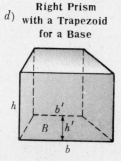

Solutions:

a) $V = Bh$
Since $B = lw$,
$\quad V = (lw)h$
Ans. $V = lwh$

b) $V = Bh$
Since $B = e^2$,
and $h = e$,
$\quad V = (e^2)e$
Ans. $V = e^3$

c) $V = Bh$
Since $B = \pi r^2$,
$\quad V = (\pi r^2)h$
Ans. $V = \pi r^2 h$

d) $V = Bh$
Since $B = \frac{h'}{2}(b+b')$,
$\quad V = \frac{h'}{2}(b+b')h$
Ans. $V = \frac{hh'}{2}(b+b')$

4.6 Formulas for Combined Volumes

State the formula for the volume of each solid:

a)

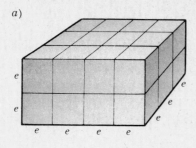

b)

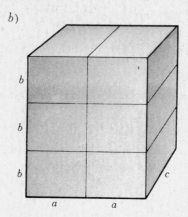

c)

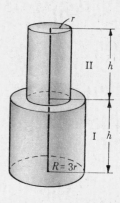

Solutions:

a) $V = lwh$
    Now, $l = 4e$, $w = 3e$, $h = 2e$

    Hence, $V = (4e)(3e)(2e)$
    Ans. $V = 24e^3$

b) $V = lwh$
    Now, $l = 2a$, $w = c$, $h = 3b$

    Hence, $V = (2a)(c)(3b)$
    Ans. $V = 6abc$

c) $V = \text{cyl.I} + \text{cyl.II}$
         $V = \pi R^2 h + \pi r^2 h$

    Now, $R = 3r$
    Hence, $V = \pi(3r)^2 h + \pi r^2 h$
    Ans. $V = 10\,\pi r^2 h$

5. DERIVING FORMULAS

To Derive a Formula for Related Quantities

Derive a formula relating the **distance** (D) traveled in a **time** (T) at a **rate of speed** (R).

Procedure:

1. **Obtain sets of values** for these quantities, using convenient numbers:

2. **Make a table of values** for those sets of values:

Solution:

1. **Sets of Values:**
    At 50 mph for 2 hr, 100 mi. will be traveled.
    At 25 mph for 10 hr, 250 mi. will be traveled.
    At 40 mph for 3 hr, 120 mi. will be traveled.

2. **Table of Values:** (*Place units above quantities.*)

(mph)	(hr.)	(mi.)
Rate (R)	**Time** (T)	**Distance** (D)
50	2	$50 \cdot 2 \ = 100$
25	10	$25 \cdot 10 = 250$
40	3	$40 \cdot 3 \ = 120$

3. **State the rule** that follows:

4. **State the formula** that expresses the rule:

3. **Rule:** The product of the rate and time equals the distance.

4. **Formula:**
        $RT = D$

Note: If D is in mi. and T in hr., then R must be in mi. per hr. (mph);
    or, if D is in ft. and T in sec., then R must be in ft. per sec. (fps).
    Rate *must be in* **distance** *units per* **time** *unit.*

Obtaining Formulas from a More General Formula

A formula, such as $RT = D$, relates **three** quantities: time, rate and distance. Each of these quantities may vary in value; that is, they may have many values. However, in a problem, situation or discussion, one of these quantities may have a fixed or unchanging value. When such is the case, this constant value may be used to obtain a formula relating the other **two** quantities.

Thus, $D = RT$ leads to $D = 30T$ if the rate of speed is fixed at 30 mph or 30 feet per min. Or, $D = RT$ leads to $D = 3R$ when the time of travel is fixed at 3 hr. or 3 min.

5.1 Deriving a Coin Formula

Derive a formula for the number of nickels (n) equivalent to q quarters:
(equivalent *means equal in value*)

Solution:

1. Sets of values: 2. Table of Values:

	No. of Quarters (q)	No. of Nickels (n)
2 quarters equal 10 nickels	2	$5 \cdot 2$ or 10
4 quarters equal 20 nickels	4	$5 \cdot 4$ or 20
10 quarters equal 50 nickels	10	$5 \cdot 10$ or 50
q quarters equal $5q$ nickels	q	$5q$

3. **Rule:** The number of nickels equivalent to a number of quarters is five times that number.

4. **Formula:** $n = 5q$ *Ans.*

5.2 Deriving a Coin Formula

Derive a formula for the value in cents (c) of d dimes and n nickels.

Solution:

1. Sets of values: 2. Table of Values:

	No. of Dimes (d)	No. of Nickels (n)	(cents) Value of Dimes & Nickels (c)
In 3 dimes and 4 nickels, there are 50¢.	3	4	$10 \cdot 3 + 5 \cdot 4$ or 50
In 4 dimes and 2 nickels, there are 50¢.	4	2	$10 \cdot 4 + 5 \cdot 2$ or 50
In 5 dimes and 3 nickels, there are 65¢.	5	3	$10 \cdot 5 + 5 \cdot 3$ or 65
In d dimes and n nickels, there are $(10d+5n)$¢.	d	n	$10d + 5n$

3. **Rule:** The value in cents of dimes and nickels is ten times the number of dimes plus five times the number of nickels.

4. **Formula:** $c = 10d + 5n$ *Ans.*

5.3 Deriving Coin Formulas

Derive a formula for each relationship:

a) For the number of pennies (p) equivalent to q quarters.   *Ans.* $p = 25q$
b) For the number of nickels (n) equivalent to d dimes.   *Ans.* $n = 2d$
c) For the number of quarters (q) equivalent to D dollars.   *Ans.* $q = 4D$
d) For the number of pennies (p) equivalent to n nickels and q quarters.   *Ans.* $p = 5n + 25q$
e) For the number of nickels (n) equivalent to q quarters and d dimes.   *Ans.* $n = 5q + 2d$

5.4 Deriving Time Formulas

Derive a formula for each relationship:

a) For the number of seconds (s) in m minutes.   *Ans.* $s = 60m$

b) For the number of hours (h) in d days.   *Ans.* $h = 24d$

c) For the number of weeks (w) in d days.   *Ans.* $w = \frac{d}{7}$

d) For the number of days (d) in w weeks and 5 days.   *Ans.* $d = 7w + 5$

e) For the number of minutes (m) in h hours and 30 sec. *Ans.* $m = 60h + \frac{1}{2}$

5.5 Deriving Length Formulas

Derive a formula for each relationship:

a) For the number of in. (i) in f feet.   *Ans.* $i = 12f$

b) For the number of ft. (f) in y yards.   *Ans.* $f = 3y$

c) For the number of yd. (y) in i inches.   *Ans.* $y = \frac{i}{36}$

d) For the number of ft. (f) in m miles and 50 yd.   *Ans.* $f = 5280m + 150$

5.6 Obtaining Formulas from $D = RT$

From $D = RT$, derive a formula for each relationship:

a) For the distance in mi. and time in hr. when the rate is 35 mph.   *Ans.* $D = 35T$

b) For the distance in ft. and the time in sec. when sound travels at 1100 ft. per sec.   *Ans.* $D = 1100T$

c) For the distance in mi. and the time in sec. when light travels at 186,000 mi. per sec.   *Ans.* $D = 186,000T$

d) For the distance in mi. and the rate in mph when the time of travel is 1 hr. and 30 min.   *Ans.* $D = 1\frac{1}{2}R$

e) For the rate in mph and the time in hr. when the distance traveled is 125 mi.   *Ans.* $125 = RT$

6. TRANSFORMING FORMULAS

The **subject of a formula** is the variable that is expressed in terms of the other variables. Thus, in $p = 4s$, p is the subject of the formula.

Transforming a formula is the process of changing the subject.

Thus, $p = 4s$ becomes $\frac{p}{4} = s$ when both sides are divided by 4. In the transforming of the formula, the subject has changed from p to s.

In solving a formula for a variable, the formula is transformed in order that the variable be made the subject.

Thus, to solve $D = 5T$ for T, transform it into $T = \frac{D}{5}$.

Use Inverse Operations to Transform Formulas, as follows:

1. Use **division** to undo **multiplication**.

   Thus, $c = 25q$ becomes

   $\frac{c}{25} = q$ by division.

2. Use **multiplication** to undo **division**.

   Thus, $w = \frac{d}{7}$ becomes

   $7w = d$ by multiplication.

3. Use **subtraction** to undo **addition**.

   Thus, $S = P + C$ becomes

   $S - P = C$ by subtraction.

4. Use **addition** to undo **subtraction**.

   Thus, $S = C - L$ becomes

   $S + L = C$ by addition

Formulas may be transformed by transposing terms. In transposing a term, change its sign. Thus, $a + b = 180$ becomes $a = 180 - b$ when $+b$ is transposed. Actually, $+b$ has been subtracted from both sides to undo addition.

6.1 Transformations Requiring Division

Solve for the variable indicated:

a) $D = RT$ for R | b) $D = RT$ for T | c) $V = LWH$ for L | d) $c = 10d$ for d | e) $C = 2\pi r$ for r

Solutions:

a) $\quad D = RT$ | b) $\quad D = RT$ | c) $\quad V = LWH$ | d) $\quad c = 10d$ | e) $\quad C = 2\pi r$

$\mathbf{D}_T \quad \dfrac{D}{T} = \dfrac{RT}{T}$ | $\mathbf{D}_R \quad \dfrac{D}{R} = \dfrac{RT}{R}$ | $\mathbf{D}_{WH} \quad \dfrac{V}{WH} = \dfrac{LWH}{WH}$ | $\mathbf{D}_{10} \quad \dfrac{c}{10} = \dfrac{10d}{10}$ | $\mathbf{D}_{2\pi} \quad \dfrac{C}{2\pi} = \dfrac{2\pi r}{2\pi}$

Ans. $\dfrac{D}{T} = R$ | Ans. $\dfrac{D}{R} = T$ | Ans. $\dfrac{V}{WH} = L$ | Ans. $\dfrac{c}{10} = d$ | Ans. $\dfrac{C}{2\pi} = r$

6.2 Transformations Requiring Multiplication

Solve for the variable indicated:

a) $\dfrac{i}{12} = f$ for i | b) $f = \dfrac{n}{d}$ for n | c) $\dfrac{V}{LW} = H$ for V | d) $\dfrac{b}{2} = \dfrac{A}{h}$ for A

Solutions:

a) $\quad \dfrac{i}{12} = f$ | b) $\quad f = \dfrac{n}{d}$ | c) $\quad \dfrac{V}{LW} = H$ | d) $\quad \dfrac{b}{2} = \dfrac{A}{h}$

$\mathbf{M}_{12} \quad 12\left(\dfrac{i}{12}\right) = 12f$ | $\mathbf{M}_d \quad fd = d\left(\dfrac{n}{d}\right)$ | $\mathbf{M}_{LW} \quad LW\left(\dfrac{V}{LW}\right) = LWH$ | $\mathbf{M}_h \quad \left(\dfrac{b}{2}\right)h = \left(\dfrac{A}{h}\right)h$

Ans. $\quad i = 12f$ | Ans. $fd = n$ | Ans. $\quad V = LWH$ | Ans. $\dfrac{bh}{2} = A$

6.3 Transformations Requiring Addition or Subtraction

(Transposing is the result of adding or subtracting.)

Solve for the variable indicated:

a) $a + b = 90$ for a | b) $a = b - 180$ for b | c) $a + c = b + 100d$ for b | d) $a - b - 25 = c$ for a

Solutions:

a) $a + b = 90$ | b) $a = b - 180$ | c) $a + c = b + 100d$ | d) $a - b - 25 = c$

Transpose b: | **Transpose -180:** | **Transpose $100d$:** | **Transpose $-b - 25$:**

Ans. $a = 90 - b$ | Ans. $a + 180 = b$ | Ans. $a + c - 100d = b$ | Ans. $a = b + c + 25$

6.4 Transformations Requiring Two Operations

Solve for the variable indicated:

a) $P = 2a + b$ for a | b) $c = 10d + 25q$ for q | c) $F = \frac{9}{5}C + 32$ for C | d) $V = \frac{1}{3}Bh$ for B

Solutions:

a) $P = 2a + b$ | b) $c = 10d + 25q$ | c) $F = \frac{9}{5}C + 32$ | d) $V = \frac{1}{3}Bh$

Transpose b: | **Transpose $10d$:** | **Transpose 32:** | $\mathbf{M}_3 \quad 3V = 3\left(\frac{1}{3}Bh\right)$

$\mathbf{D}_2 \quad P - b = 2a$ | $\mathbf{D}_{25} \quad c - 10d = 25q$ | $\mathbf{M}_{5/9} \quad F - 32 = \frac{5}{9}C$ | $\mathbf{D}_h \quad 3V = Bh$

Ans. $\dfrac{P - b}{2} = a$ | Ans. $\dfrac{c - 10d}{25} = q$ | Ans. $\dfrac{5}{9}(F - 32) = C$ | Ans. $\dfrac{3V}{h} = B$

6.5 More Difficult Transformations

Solve for the variable indicated:

a) $A = \dfrac{h}{2}(b + b')$ for h | b) $S = \dfrac{n}{2}(a + l)$ for a | c) $l = a + (n - 1)d$ for n

Solutions:

a)
$$A = \frac{h}{2}(b+b')$$
M₂ $2A = 2(\frac{h}{2})(b+b')$

D₍b+b'₎ $\frac{2A}{b+b'} = \frac{h(b+b')}{b+b'}$

Ans. $\frac{2A}{b+b'} = h$

b) **M₂** $S = \frac{n}{2}(a+l)$

Dₙ $2S = n(a+l)$

$\frac{2S}{n} = a+l$

Transpose +*l*:

Ans. $\frac{2S}{n} - l = a$

c) $l = a + (n-1)d$

Transpose *a*:

D_d_ $l-a = (n-1)d$

$\frac{l-a}{d} = n-1$

Transpose −1:

Ans. $\frac{l-a}{d} + 1 = n$

7. FINDING THE VALUE OF A VARIABLE IN A FORMULA

To Find the Value of a Variable That is the Subject of a Formula

The value of a variable in a formula may be found if values are given for the other variables. By substitution, replace the other variables by their given values, and then solve for the subject; that is, evaluate the numerical expression that results.

Thus, in $A = bh$ if $b = 10$ and $h = 5$, then $A = 10(5)$ or 50.

To Find the Value of a Variable That is Not the Subject of a Formula

When a variable is to be found and it is not the subject of a formula, two methods may be used:

Method 1. **Substitute first**, then solve.
Method 2. **Transform the formula first** to make the variable to be found the subject of the formula, then substitute, and then solve.

Thus, in $p = 3s$ if $p = 27$, the value of s may be found

(1) by substituting first: $27 = 3s$, $s = 9$

or (2) by transforming first: transform $p = 3s$ into $s = \frac{p}{3}$.   Then $s = \frac{27}{3}$ or 9.

7.1 To Find the Value of a Variable That is the Subject of a Formula

Find the value of the indicated variable in each:

a) Find V if $V = lwh$ and $l = 10$, $w = 2$, $h = 3.2$
b) Find S if $S = \frac{n}{2}(a+l)$ and $n = 8$, $a = 5$, $l = 12$
c) Find A if $A = p + prt$ and $p = 800$, $r = .04$, $t = 3$
d) Find S if $S = \frac{1}{2}gt^2$ and $g = 32$, $t = 5$

Solutions:

a) $V = lwh$
$V = 10(2)(3.2)$
Ans. $V = 64$

b) $S = \frac{n}{2}(a+l)$
$S = \frac{8}{2}(5+12)$
Ans. $S = 68$

c) $A = p + prt$
$A = 800 + 800(.04)3$
Ans. $A = 896$

d) $S = \frac{1}{2}gt^2$
$S = \frac{1}{2} \cdot 32 \cdot 5^2$
Ans. $S = 400$

7.2 To Find the Value of a Variable That Is Not the Subject of a Formula

Find the value of the indicated variable in each:

a) Find h if $A = bh$,
$b = 13$ and $A = 156$.

b) Find a if $p = 2a+b$,
$b = 20$ and $p = 74$.

c) Find h if $V = \frac{1}{3}Bh$,
$B = 240$ and $V = 960$.

Solutions:

(1) By substitution first:
$A = bh$
$156 = 13h$
Ans. $12 = h$

(1) By substitution first:
$p = 2a + b$
$74 = 2a + 20$
Ans. $27 = a$

(1) By substitution first:
$V = \frac{1}{3}Bh$
$960 = \frac{1}{3}(240)h$
Ans. $12 = h$

(2) By transformation first:
$A = bh$
Transform: $\frac{A}{b} = h$
Substitute: $\frac{156}{13} = h$
Ans. $12 = h$

(2) By transformation first:
$p = 2a + b$
Transform: $\frac{p-b}{2} = a$
Substitute: $\frac{74-20}{2} = a$
Ans. $27 = a$

(2) By transformation first:
$V = \frac{1}{3}Bh$
Transform: $\frac{3V}{B} = h$
Substitute: $\frac{3(960)}{240} = h$
Ans. $12 = h$

7.3 More Difficult Evaluations Using Transformations

Find each variable: *a)* Find h if $V = \pi r^2 h$, $\pi = 3.14$, $V = 9420$ and $r = 10$.

b) Find t if $A = p + prt$, $A = 864$, $p = 800$ and $r = 2$.

Solutions:

a) $$V = \pi r^2 h$$

Transform: $$\frac{V}{\pi r^2} = h$$

Substitute: $$\frac{9420}{(3.14)(100)} = h$$

$$\frac{9420}{314} = h$$

Ans. $$30 = h$$

b) $$A = p + prt$$

Transform: $$\frac{A - p}{pr} = t$$

Substitute: $$\frac{864 - 800}{800(2)} = t$$

$$\frac{64}{1600} = t$$

Ans. $$.04 = t$$

7.4 Finding an Unknown in a Problem

A train takes 3 hours and 15 minutes to go a distance of 247 miles. Find its average speed.

Solution: Here, $D = RT$, $T = 3\frac{1}{4}$ hr. and $D = 247$. To find R:

(1) By substitution first:

$$247 = \frac{13}{4}R$$

$\text{M}_{4/13}$ $$\frac{4}{13} \cdot \overset{19}{\cancel{247}} = R$$

$$76 = R$$

(2) By transformation first:

$$D = RT$$

Transform: $$\frac{D}{T} = R$$

$$247 \div \frac{13}{4} = R$$

$$247 \cdot \frac{4}{13} = R$$

Ans. Average rate is 76 mph

SUPPLEMENTARY PROBLEMS

1. In Fig. (*a*), state the meaning of each: **(1.1)**

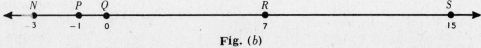

Fig. (*a*)

a) $\overline{AB}$,   *b)* AB,   *c)* $\overline{ABC}$,   *d)* $\overrightarrow{AC}$,   *e)* $\overrightarrow{BA}$,   *f)* $\overleftrightarrow{AC}$,   *g)* $AB + BC$

Ans. a) line segment $\overline{AB}$,

b) measure or length of line segment $\overline{AB}$,

c) line segment $\overline{AC}$ with point C lying between A and C,

d) ray with endpoint A and passing through C,

e) ray with endpoint B and passing through A,

f) line passing through or determined by points A and C,

g) the sum of the lengths of $\overline{AB}$ and $\overline{BC}$.

2. In Fig. (*b*), find each: **(1.2)**

Fig. (*b*)

a) NP,   *d)* RS,   *g)* NS,   *j)* $2NQ + 3QR$,

b) PQ,   *e)* NQ,   *h)* $NQ + QR$,   *k)* $3PR - 2RS$.

c) QR,   *f)* PR,   *i)* $NP + PR$,

Ans. (Rule: The measure of a line segment is the absolute value of the difference between the coordinates of its endpoints.)

a) 2,   *b)* 1,   *c)* 7,   *d)* 8,   *e)* 3,   *f)* 8,   *g)* 18,   *h)* 10,   *i)* 10,   *j)* 27,   *k)* 8

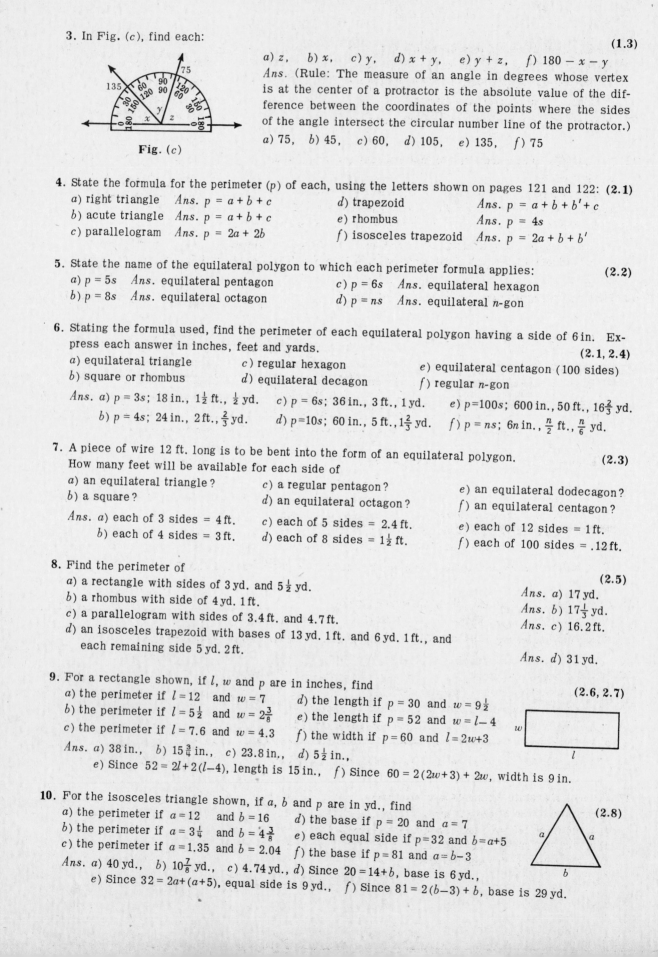

3. In Fig. (c), find each: **(1.3)**

a) z,   b) x,   c) y,   d) x + y,   e) y + z,   f) 180 − x − y

Ans. (Rule: The measure of an angle in degrees whose vertex is at the center of a protractor is the absolute value of the difference between the coordinates of the points where the sides of the angle intersect the circular number line of the protractor.)

a) 75,   b) 45,   c) 60,   d) 105,   e) 135,   f) 75

Fig. (c)

4. State the formula for the perimeter (p) of each, using the letters shown on pages 121 and 122: **(2.1)**

a) right triangle   *Ans.* $p = a + b + c$ d) trapezoid   *Ans.* $p = a + b + b' + c$

b) acute triangle   *Ans.* $p = a + b + c$ e) rhombus   *Ans.* $p = 4s$

c) parallelogram   *Ans.* $p = 2a + 2b$ f) isosceles trapezoid   *Ans.* $p = 2a + b + b'$

5. State the name of the equilateral polygon to which each perimeter formula applies: **(2.2)**

a) $p = 5s$ *Ans.* equilateral pentagon   c) $p = 6s$ *Ans.* equilateral hexagon

b) $p = 8s$ *Ans.* equilateral octagon   d) $p = ns$ *Ans.* equilateral n-gon

6. Stating the formula used, find the perimeter of each equilateral polygon having a side of 6 in. Express each answer in inches, feet and yards. **(2.1, 2.4)**

a) equilateral triangle   c) regular hexagon   e) equilateral centagon (100 sides)

b) square or rhombus   d) equilateral decagon   f) regular n-gon

Ans. a) $p = 3s$; 18 in., $1\frac{1}{2}$ ft., $\frac{1}{2}$ yd.   c) $p = 6s$; 36 in., 3 ft., 1 yd.   e) $p = 100s$; 600 in., 50 ft., $16\frac{2}{3}$ yd.

b) $p = 4s$; 24 in., 2 ft., $\frac{2}{3}$ yd.   d) $p = 10s$; 60 in., 5 ft., $1\frac{2}{3}$ yd.   f) $p = ns$; $6n$ in., $\frac{n}{2}$ ft., $\frac{n}{6}$ yd.

7. A piece of wire 12 ft. long is to be bent into the form of an equilateral polygon. How many feet will be available for each side of **(2.3)**

a) an equilateral triangle?   c) a regular pentagon?   e) an equilateral dodecagon?

b) a square?   d) an equilateral octagon?   f) an equilateral centagon?

Ans. a) each of 3 sides = 4 ft.   c) each of 5 sides = 2.4 ft.   e) each of 12 sides = 1 ft.

b) each of 4 sides = 3 ft.   d) each of 8 sides = $1\frac{1}{2}$ ft.   f) each of 100 sides = .12 ft.

8. Find the perimeter of **(2.5)**

a) a rectangle with sides of 3 yd. and $5\frac{1}{2}$ yd.

b) a rhombus with side of 4 yd. 1 ft.

c) a parallelogram with sides of 3.4 ft. and 4.7 ft.

d) an isosceles trapezoid with bases of 13 yd. 1 ft. and 6 yd. 1 ft., and each remaining side 5 yd. 2 ft.

Ans. a) 17 yd.

Ans. b) $17\frac{1}{3}$ yd.

Ans. c) 16.2 ft.

Ans. d) 31 yd.

9. For a rectangle shown, if l, w and p are in inches, find **(2.6, 2.7)**

a) the perimeter if $l = 12$ and $w = 7$ d) the length if $p = 30$ and $w = 9\frac{1}{2}$

b) the perimeter if $l = 5\frac{1}{2}$ and $w = 2\frac{3}{8}$ e) the length if $p = 52$ and $w = l - 4$

c) the perimeter if $l = 7.6$ and $w = 4.3$ f) the width if $p = 60$ and $l = 2w + 3$

Ans. a) 38 in.,   b) $15\frac{3}{4}$ in.,   c) 23.8 in.,   d) $5\frac{1}{2}$ in.,

e) Since $52 = 2l + 2(l-4)$, length is 15 in.,   f) Since $60 = 2(2w+3) + 2w$, width is 9 in.

10. For the isosceles triangle shown, if a, b and p are in yd., find **(2.8)**

a) the perimeter if $a = 12$ and $b = 16$ d) the base if $p = 20$ and $a = 7$

b) the perimeter if $a = 3\frac{1}{4}$ and $b = 4\frac{3}{8}$ e) each equal side if $p = 32$ and $b = a + 5$

c) the perimeter if $a = 1.35$ and $b = 2.04$ f) the base if $p = 81$ and $a = b - 3$

Ans. a) 40 yd.,   b) $10\frac{7}{8}$ yd.,   c) 4.74 yd.,   d) Since $20 = 14 + b$, base is 6 yd.,

e) Since $32 = 2a + (a+5)$, equal side is 9 yd.,   f) Since $81 = 2(b-3) + b$, base is 29 yd.

11. For any circle, state a formula which relates   (2.9)

    a) the circumference (*c*) and an arc of 45° (*a*)   *Ans. a*) $c = 8a$

    b) the semi-circumference (*s*) and the radius (*r*)   *Ans. b*) $s = \pi r$

    c) an arc of 120° (*a'*) and the diameter (*d*)   *Ans. c*) $a' = \dfrac{\pi d}{3}$

    d) an arc of 20° (*a''*) and semi-circumference (*s*)   *Ans. d*) $a'' = \dfrac{s}{9}$

12. For a circle, if *r*, *d* and *c* (*c* = circumference) are in mi., find,   (2.10)

    using $\pi = 3.14$,

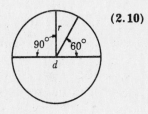

    a) circumference if $r = 6$ *d*) radius if $c = 157$

    b) semi-circumference if $d = 20$ *e*) diameter if $c = 314$

    c) 60° arc if $r = 12$ *f*) radius, if a 90° arc = 9.42 mi.

    Ans. a) 37.68 mi.,   *b*) 31.4 mi.,   *c*) 12.56 mi.,   *d*) 25 mi.,   *e*) 100 mi.,

        f) Since 90° arc = $\frac{1}{4}$ of circumference, $9.42 = \frac{1}{4} \times 2(3.14)r$. Radius is 6 mi.

13. State the formula for the perimeter of each figure: (2.11)

    a)   *b*)   *c*)

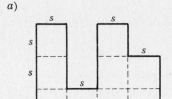 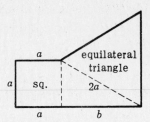 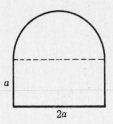

    Ans. a) $p = 18s$ *b*) $p = 7a + b$ *c*) $4a + \pi a$

14. Find the area of   (3.1)

    a) a square yard in square inches

    b) a square rod in square yards (1 rd. = $5\frac{1}{2}$ yd.)

    c) a square rod in square feet (1 rd. = $16\frac{1}{2}$ ft.)

    Ans. a) 36^2 or 1296 sq. in.,   *b*) $(5\frac{1}{2})^2$ or $30\frac{1}{4}$ sq. yd.,   *c*) $(16\frac{1}{2})^2$ or $272\frac{1}{4}$ sq. ft.

15. Find the area of a square in sq. in. whose side is   (3.2)

    a) 5 in.   *b*) $6\frac{1}{2}$ in.   *c*) 7.2 in.   *d*) 1 ft. 3 in.   *e*) 1.3 ft.

    Ans. a) 25 sq. in.,   *b*) $42\frac{1}{4}$ sq. in.,   *c*) 51.84 sq. in.,   *d*) 225 sq. in.,   *e*) 243.36 sq. in.

16. Find the area in sq. ft. of   (3.3)

    a) a rectangle with sides of $8\frac{1}{2}$ ft. and 12 ft.

    b) a parallelogram with a base of $5\frac{1}{2}$ ft. and an altitude of 4 ft.

    c) a triangle with a base of 10.4 ft. and an altitude of 8 ft.

    d) a trapezoid with bases of 6 ft. and 4 ft. and an altitude of $3\frac{1}{2}$ ft. ($A = \frac{h}{2}(b + b')$)

    Ans. a) 102 sq. ft.,   *b*) 22 sq. ft.,   *c*) 41.6 sq. ft.,   *d*) $17\frac{1}{2}$ sq. ft.

17. For a circle, state a formula which relates   (3.4)

    a) the area of the circle (*A*) and a sector of 60° (*S*)

    b) a sector of 120° (*S'*) and the area of the circle (*A*)

    c) a sector of 90° (*S''*) and the radius (*r*)

    d) a sector of 90° (*S''*) and the diameter (*d*).

    Ans. a) $A = 6S$,   *b*) $S' = \dfrac{A}{3}$,   *c*) $S'' = \dfrac{\pi r^2}{4}$,   *d*) $S'' = \frac{1}{4}\left(\dfrac{\pi d^2}{4}\right) = \dfrac{\pi d^2}{16}$

18. Find, in terms of π and to the nearest integer, using $\pi = 3.14$, the area of   **(3.5)**
  a) a circle whose radius is 30 in.   *Ans.* 900 π or 2826 sq. in.
  b) a circle whose diameter is 18 in.   *Ans.* 81 π or 254 sq. in.
  c) a semi circle whose radius is 14 ft.   *Ans.* 98 π or 308 sq. ft.
  d) a 45° sector whose radius is 12 yd.   *Ans.* 18 π or 57 sq. yd.

19. State the formula for the area (A) of each shaded figure :   **(3.6, 3.7)**

a)

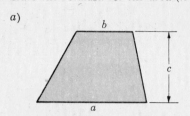

b)

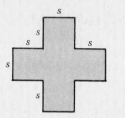

c)

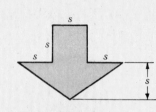

d)

e)

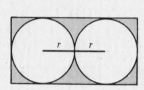

f)

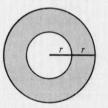

Ans. a) $A = \dfrac{c}{2}(a+b)$ *b)* $A = 5s^2$ *c)* $A = s^2 + 1\frac{1}{2}s^2$ or $2\frac{1}{2}s^2$

  d) $A = \pi r^2 + 2r^2$ *e)* $A = 8r^2 - 2\pi r^2$ *f)* $A = 4\pi r^2 - \pi r^2$ or $3\pi r^2$

20. Find, to the nearest integer, using $\pi = 3.14$, the total area of   **(3.8)**
  a) a cube with an edge of 7 yd.
  b) a rectangular solid with dimensions of 8 ft., $6\frac{1}{2}$ ft. and 14 ft.
  c) a sphere with a radius of 30 in.
  d) a cylinder of revolution with a radius of 10 rd. and a height of $4\frac{1}{2}$ rd. [*Hint.* Use $T = 2\pi r(r+h)$]
  Ans. a) $6(7^2)$ or 294 sq. yd.,   *b)* $2(8)(6\frac{1}{2}) + 2(8)(14) + 2(6\frac{1}{2})(14)$ or 510 sq. ft.,
       c) $4(3.14)30^2$ or 11,304 sq. in.,   *d)* $2(3.14)(10)(10 + 4\frac{1}{2})$ or 911 sq. rd.

21. Find the volume of   **(4.1)**
  a) a cubic yard in cubic inches
  b) a cubic rod in cubic yards
  c) a cubic meter in cubic centimeters (1 meter = 100 cm.).
  Ans. a) 36^3 or 46,656 cu. in.,   *b)* $(5\frac{1}{2})^3$ or $166\frac{3}{8}$ cu. yd.,   *c)* 100^3 or 1,000,000 cu. cm.

22. Find, to the nearest cubic inch, the volume of a cube whose edge is   **(4.2)**
       a) 3 in.   *b)* $4\frac{1}{2}$ in.   *c)* 7.5 in.   *d)* .3 ft.   *e)* 1 ft. 2 in.
  Ans. a) 27 cu. in.,   *b)* 91 cu. in.,   *c)* 422 cu. in.,   *d)* 47 cu. in.,   *e)* 2744 cu. in.

23. Find, to the nearest integer, the volume of   **(4.3)**
  a) a rectangular solid whose length is 3 in., width $8\frac{1}{2}$ in. and height 8 in.
  b) a prism having a height of 2 ft. and a square base whose side is 3 yd.
  c) a pyramid having a height of 2 yd. and a base whose area is 6.4 sq. ft.
  Ans. a) $3(8\frac{1}{2})(8)$ or 204 cu. in.,   *b)* $2(9)(9)$ or 162 cu. ft.,   *c)* $\frac{1}{3}(6)(6.4)$ or 13 cu. ft.

24. Find, to the nearest integer, the volume of   **(4.4)**

   a) a sphere with a radius of 6 in.

   b) a cylinder having a height of 10 ft. and a base whose radius is 2 yd.

   c) a cone having a height of 3 yd. and a base whose radius is 1.4 ft.

   a) $\frac{4}{3}(3.14) 6^3$ or 904.32 b) $(3.14)(6^2)10$ or 1130.4 c) $\frac{1}{3}(3.14)(1.4^2)(9)$ or 18.4632

   Ans. 904 cu. in.   *Ans.* 1130 cu. ft.   *Ans.* 18 cu. ft.

25. From $V = \frac{1}{3}Bh$, the volume formula for a pyramid or cone, derive volume formulas for each of the   **(4.5)**
following:

a) b) c) d)

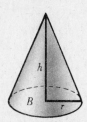   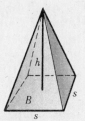   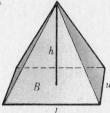   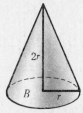

   Cone   **Pyramid with a**   **Pyramid with a**   **Cone where**
                       Square Base   **Rectangular Base**   **$h = 2r$**

a) $V = \frac{1}{3}Bh$ b) $V = \frac{1}{3}Bh$ c) $V = \frac{1}{3}Bh$ d) $V = \frac{1}{3}Bh$

   Since $B = \pi r^2$,   Since $B = s^2$,   Since $B = lw$,   Since $B = \pi r^2$

   $V = \frac{1}{3}(\pi r^2) h$ $V = \frac{1}{3}(s^2) h$ $V = \frac{1}{3}(lw) h$ and $h = 2r$,

Ans. $V = \frac{1}{3}\pi r^2 h$ *Ans.* $V = \frac{1}{3}s^2 h$ *Ans.* $V = \frac{1}{3}lwh$ $V = \frac{1}{3}(\pi r^2)(2r)$

                                                                         Ans. $V = \frac{2}{3}\pi r^3$

26. State a formula for the volume of each solid: **(4.6)**

a) b) c)

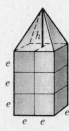   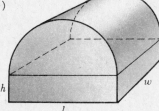   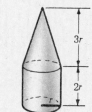

a) $(2e)(3e) e + \frac{1}{3}(2e^2) h$ b) $lwh + \frac{1}{2}\cdot\pi(\frac{l}{2})^2 w$ c) $\pi r^2(2r) + \frac{1}{3}\pi r^2(3r)$

Ans. $6e^3 + \dfrac{2e^2 h}{3}$ *Ans.* $lwh + \dfrac{\pi l^2 w}{8}$ *Ans.* $3\pi r^3$

27. Derive a formula for each relationship: **(5.1)**

   a) the no. of pennies (p) equivalent to d dimes

   b) the no. of dimes (d) equivalent to p pennies

   c) the no. of nickels (n) equivalent to D dollars

   d) the no. of half dollars (h) equivalent to q quarters

   e) the no. of quarters (q) equivalent to d dimes.

   Ans. a) $p = 10d$, b) $d = \dfrac{p}{10}$, c) $n = 20D$, d) $h = \frac{1}{2}q$, e) $q = \frac{2}{5}d$ or $\dfrac{2d}{5}$

28. Derive a formula for each relationship: (5.2, 5.3)
a) the value in cents (c) of d dimes and q quarters
b) the value in cents (c) of n nickels and D dollars
c) the no. of nickels (n) equivalent to d dimes and h half dollars
d) the no. of dimes (d) equivalent to n nickels and p pennies
e) the no. of quarters (q) equivalent to D dollars and n nickels.

Ans. a) $c = 10d + 25q$, b) $c = 5n + 100D$, c) $n = 2d + 10h$, d) $d = \frac{n}{2} + \frac{p}{10}$, e) $q = 4D + \frac{n}{5}$

29. Derive a formula for each relationship: (5.4)
a) the no. of sec. (s) in h hr. c) the no. of hr. (h) in w wk.
b) the no. of hr. (h) in m min. d) the no. of da. (d) in M mo. of 30 days.
   e) the no. of da. (d) in M mo. of 30 days, w wk. and 5 da.
   f) the no. of min. (m) in h hr. and 30 sec.
   g) the no. of da. (d) in y yr. of 365 da. and 3 weeks.

Ans. a) $s = 3600h$, b) $h = \frac{m}{60}$, c) $h = 168w$, d) $d = 30M$, e) $d = 30M + 7w + 5$,
f) $m = 60h + \frac{1}{2}$, g) $d = 365y + 21$

30. Derive a formula for each relationship: (5.5)
a) the no. of in. (i) in y yd. c) the no. of yd. (y) in r rd.
b) the no. of yd. (y) in f ft. d) the no. of mi. (m) in f ft.
   e) the no. of meters (m) in c centimeters. (1 meter = 100 cm.)
   f) the no. of centimeters (c) in d decimeters. (1 decimeter = 10 cm.)
Ans. a) $i = 36y$, b) $y = \frac{f}{3}$, c) $y = 5\frac{1}{2}r$, d) $m = \frac{f}{5280}$, e) $m = \frac{c}{100}$, f) $c = 10d$

31. From $D = RT$, obtain a formula for each relationship: (5.6)
a) distance in mi. and rate in mph for a time of 5 hr.
b) distance in mi. and rate in mph for a time of 30 min.
c) time in hr. and rate in mph for a distance of 25 mi.
d) time in sec. and rate in ft. per sec. for a distance of 100 yd.
e) distance in ft. and time in min. for a rate of 20 ft. per min.
f) distance in ft. and time in min. for a rate of 20 ft. per sec.
Ans. a) $D = 5R$, b) $D = \frac{1}{2}R$, c) $RT = 25$, d) $RT = 300$, e) $D = 20T$,
f) $D = 1200T$ (20 ft. per sec = 1200 ft. per min.)

32. Solve for the variable indicated: (6.1)
a) $d = 2r$ for r e) $c = \pi d$ for d i) $V = LWH$ for H
b) $p = 5s$ for s f) $c = \pi d$ for π j) $V = 2\pi r^2 h$ for h
c) $D = 30T$ for T g) $NP = C$ for N k) $9C = 5(F - 32)$ for C
d) $25W = A$ for W h) $I = PR$ for R l) $2A = h(b + b')$ for h
Ans. a) $\frac{d}{2} = r$ c) $\frac{D}{30} = T$ e) $\frac{c}{\pi} = d$ g) $N = \frac{C}{P}$ i) $\frac{V}{LW} = H$ k) $C = \frac{5(F-32)}{9}$
b) $\frac{p}{5} = s$ d) $W = \frac{A}{25}$ f) $\pi = \frac{c}{d}$ h) $\frac{I}{P} = R$ j) $\frac{V}{2\pi r^2} = h$ l) $\frac{2A}{b+b'} = h$

33. Solve for the variable indicated: (6.2)
a) $\frac{p}{10} = s$ for p e) $\pi = \frac{c}{2r}$ for c i) $\frac{V}{3LW} = H$ for V
b) $R = \frac{D}{15}$ for D f) $\frac{M}{D} = F$ for M j) $\frac{T}{14RS} = \frac{1}{2}$ for T
c) $W = \frac{A}{8}$ for A g) $P = \frac{A}{2F}$ for A k) $\frac{L}{KA} = V^2$ for L
d) $w = \frac{d}{7}$ for d h) $\frac{T}{Q} = 5R$ for T l) $\frac{V}{\pi r^2} = \frac{h}{3}$ for V
Ans. a) $p = 10s$ c) $8W = A$ e) $2\pi r = c$ g) $2PF = A$ i) $V = 3LWH$ k) $L = KAV^2$
b) $15R = D$ d) $7w = d$ f) $M = FD$ h) $T = 5RQ$ j) $T = 7RS$ l) $V = \frac{\pi r^2 h}{3}$

34. Solve for the variable indicated: $\qquad$ **(6.3)**

a) $a + b = 60$ for a d) $3m = 4n + p$ for p g) $5a + b = c - d$ for b

b) $3c + g = 85$ for g e) $10r = s - 5t$ for s h) $5a - 4c = 3e + f$ for f

c) $h - 10r = l$ for h f) $4g + h - 12 = j$ for h i) $\frac{b}{2} - 10 + c = 100p$ for c

Ans. a) $a = 60 - b$ c) $h = l + 10r$ e) $10r + 5t = s$ g) $b = c - d - 5a$

b) $g = 85 - 3c$ d) $3m - 4n = p$ f) $h = j + 12 - 4g$ h) $5a - 4c - 3e = f$ i) $c = 100p + 10 - \frac{b}{2}$

35. Solve for the indicated variable: $\qquad$ **(6.4)**

a) $4P - 3R = 40$ for P d) $A = \frac{1}{2}bh$ for b g) $\frac{R}{2} - 4S = T$ for R

b) $36 - 5i = 12f$ for i e) $V = \frac{1}{3}\pi r^2 h$ for h h) $8h - \frac{k}{5} = 12$ for k

c) $\frac{P}{2} + R = S$ for P f) $A = \frac{1}{2}h(b + b')$ for h i) $20p - \frac{2}{3}q = 8t$ for q

Ans. a) $P = \frac{3R + 40}{4}$ d) $\frac{2A}{h} = b$ g) $R = 8S + 2T$

b) $\frac{36 - 12f}{5} = i$ e) $\frac{3V}{\pi r^2} = h$ h) $5(8h - 12) = k$ or $40h - 60 = k$

c) $P = 2S - 2R$ f) $\frac{2A}{b + b'} = h$ i) $\frac{3}{2}(20p - 8t) = q$

or $30p - 12t = q$

36. Solve for the indicated variable: $\qquad$ **(6.5)**

a) $l = a + (n-1)d$ for d b) $S = \frac{n}{2}(a + l)$ for l c) $F = \frac{9}{5}C + 32$ for C

Ans. a) $\frac{l - a}{n - 1} = d$ b) $l = \frac{2s}{n} - a$ or $\frac{2s - an}{n}$ c) $\frac{5}{9}(F - 32) = C$

37. Find the value of the indicated variable in each: $\qquad$ **(7.1)**

a) Find I if $I = prt$ and $p = 3000$, $r = .05$, $t = 2$.   Ans. a) 300

b) Find t if $t = \frac{I}{pr}$ and $I = 40$, $p = 2000$, $r = .01$.   Ans. b) 2

c) Find F if $F = \frac{9}{5}C + 32$ and $C = 55$.   Ans. c) 131

d) Find F if $F = \frac{9}{5}C + 32$ and $C = -40$.   Ans. d) -40

e) Find C if $C = \frac{5}{9}(F - 32)$ and $F = 212$.   Ans. e) 100

f) Find S if $S = \frac{1}{2}gt^2$ and $g = 32$, $t = 8$.   Ans. f) 1024

g) Find g if $g = \frac{2S}{t^2}$ and $S = 800$, $t = 10$.   Ans. g) 16

h) Find S if $S = \frac{a - lr}{1 - r}$ and $a = 5$, $l = 40$, $r = -1$.   Ans. h) $22\frac{1}{2}$

38. Find the value of the indicated variable in each: $\qquad$ **(7.2, 7.3)**

a) Find R if $D = RT$ and $D = 30$, $T = 4$.   Ans. a) $7\frac{1}{2}$

b) Find b if $A = bh$ and $A = 22$, $h = 2.2$.   Ans. b) 10

c) Find a if $P = 2a + b$ and $P = 12$, $b = 3$.   Ans. c) $4\frac{1}{2}$

d) Find w if $P = 2l + 2w$ and $P = 68$, $l = 21$.   Ans. d) 13

e) Find c if $p = a + 2b + c$ and $p = 33$, $a = 11$, $b = 3\frac{1}{2}$.   Ans. e) 15

f) Find h if $2A = h(b + b')$ and $A = 70$, $b = 3.3$, $b' = 6.7$.   Ans. f) 14

g) Find B if $V = \frac{1}{3}Bh$ and $V = 480$, $h = 12$.   Ans. g) 120

h) Find a if $l = a + (n-1)d$ and $l = 140$, $n = 8$, $d = 3$.   Ans. h) 119

39. a) A train takes 5 hours and 20 minutes to go a distance of 304 miles. Find its average speed.

Ans. 57 mph $(R = \frac{D}{T})$

$\qquad$ **(7.4)**

b) A rectangle has a perimeter of 2 yd. and a length of 22 in. Find its width.   Ans. 14 in.

Chapter 7

Coordinate Geometry: Graphing Linear Equations and Linear Inequalities

1. UNDERSTANDING COORDINATE PLANES

Reviewing Number Lines

A **number line** is a line on which distances from a point are numbered in equal units, positively in one direction and negatively in the other.

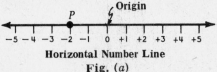

Horizontal Number Line
Fig. (a)

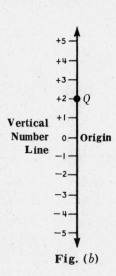

Fig. (b)

The **origin** is the zero point from which distances are numbered.

Note on the horizontal number line, Fig. (a), how positive numbers are to the **right** of the origin, while on the vertical number line, Fig. (b), positive numbers are **above** the origin.

The coordinate of a point on a number line is its directed distance from the origin; that is, its direction and distance from the origin.

Thus, the coordinate of P on the horizontal number line, Fig. (a), is −2, which indicates that P is a distance of 2 units to the left of the origin; while the coordinate of Q on the vertical number line, Fig. (b), is +2, which indicates that Q is a distance of 2 units above the origin.

Forming a Coordinate Plane by Combining Number Lines

The coordinate plane, Fig. (c), is formed by combining two number lines at right angles to each other so that their zero points coincide at the origin, O. The coordinate plane is called the Cartesian plane in honor of the French mathematician René Descartes. (A plane may be regarded as a flat surface extending indefinitely in any direction.)

The horizontal number line is usually called the x-axis. Note that there is an arrowhead at the right end. This arrowhead points in the positive direction.

The vertical number line is usually called the y-axis. Note that there is an arrowhead at the top. This arrowhead points in the positive direction.

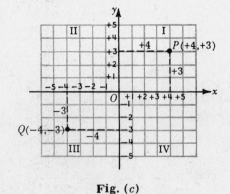

Fig. (c)

> In a coordinate plane, a point is the graph of an **ordered pair of coordinates**, both of which are real numbers.
> Each coordinate is a **directed distance** from the origin.

(Recall that on a number line, a point is the graph of a single real number coordinate.)

Thus, in Fig. (c), point Q is the graph of the ordered pair (−4, −3), each of these real numbers being a directed distance. The direction is indicated by the sign of the coordinate and the distance by the absolute value of the coordinate.

144

(1) The x-**coordinate of a point** is its directed distance from the y-axis. The x-coordinate is called the **abscissa** of the point.

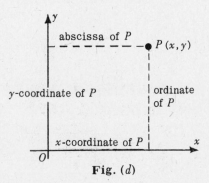

Fig. (d)

Thus, in Fig. (c), the abscissa of P is +4, and the abscissa of Q is −4.

Note, in Fig. (d), that the abscissa of P equals its x-coordinate.

(2) The y-**coordinate** of a point is its directed distance from the x-axis. The y-coordinate is called the **ordinate** of the point.

Thus, in Fig. (c), the ordinate of P is +3, and the ordinate of Q is −3.

Note in Fig. (d), that the ordinate of P equals its y-coordinate.

In stating the coordinates of a point, there is common agreement that the x-coordinate precedes the y-coordinate, just as x in the alphabet precedes y. Since there is an order to follow, the coordinates are written in parentheses as an **ordered pair**.

Thus, in Fig. (c), the coordinates of P are written (+4,+3) or simply, (4,3).

In Fig. (d), note that the ordered pair (x, y) is the general ordered pair of any point, P. You may think of the general ordered pair, (x, y), as (abscissa, ordinate).

The quadrants of a coordinate plane are the four sections out off by the axes. Note in Fig. (c) how these four quadrants are numbered I, II, III, and IV in a counterclockwise direction.

Comparing a Map and a Coordinate Plane

A map is a special kind of coordinate plane. Each position on a map, such as the map of Graphtown, Fig. (e), is located using a street number and an avenue number. Similarly, each point on a coordinate plane, Fig. (f), is located using an x-number and a y-number. Note that the points, B, M, L, S, and T on the coordinate plane, Fig. (f), correspond to the position of the bank, museum, library, school, and town hall on the map, Fig. (e).

Note how quadrant I corresponds to the northeast map section, quadrant II to the northwest, quadrant III to the southwest, and quadrant IV to the southeast.

Use the map and coordinate plane in exercises 1.1 and 1.2.

MAP OF GRAPHTOWN

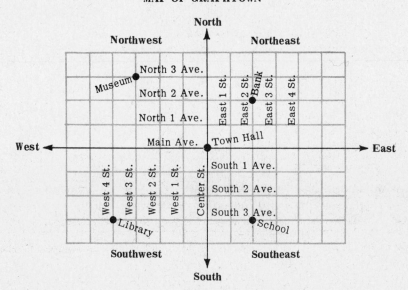

Fig. (e)

COORDINATE PLANE

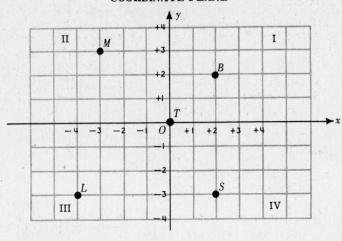

Fig.(f)

1.1 Locating Points on a Coordinate Plane

In Fig. (f), locate each point, placing the x-coordinate before the y-coordinate:

	Point	Coordinates (Ans.)		Point	Coordinates (Ans.)
a)	B	(+2,+2) or (2,2)	d)	L	(−4,−3)
b)	M	(−3,+3) or (−3,3)	e)	S	(+2,−3) or (2,−3)
c)	T	(0,0), the origin			

1.2 Locating Positions on a Map

In Fig. (e), of Graphtown, locate the position of each indicated building, placing the street before the avenue.

	Building	Position (Ans.)		Building	Position (Ans.)
a)	Bank	(E 2 St., N 2 Ave.)	d)	Library	(W 4 St., S 3 Ave.)
b)	Museum	(W 3 St., N 3 Ave.)	e)	School	(E 2 St., S 3 Ave.)
c)	Townhall	(Center St., Main Ave.)			

1.3 Coordinates of Points in the Four Quadrants

State the signs of the coordinates of

a) any point A in I
b) any point B in II
c) any point C in III
d) any point D in IV.

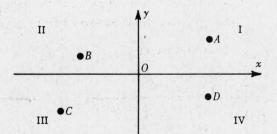

Ans.   a) A : (+,+)   c) C : (−,−)
       b) B : (−,+)   d) D : (+,−)

1.4 Coordinates of Points Between the Quadrants

State the zero value of one coordinate and the sign of the other for

a) any point P between I and II
b) any point Q between II and III
c) any point R between III and IV
d) any point S between IV and I.

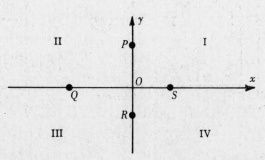

Ans.   a) P : (0,+)   c) R : (0,−)
       b) Q : (−,0)   d) S : (+,0)

1.5 Graphing a Quadrilateral

If $A(3,1)$, $B(-5,1)$, $C(-5,-3)$ and $D(3,-3)$ are the vertices of the rectangle shown, find its perimeter and area.

Solution:

The base and the height of the rectangle $ABCD$ are 8 and 4. Hence the perimeter is 24 units and the area is 32 sq. units.   *Ans.* 24,32

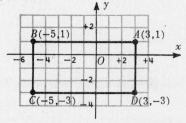

1.6 Graphing a Triangle

If $A(4\frac{1}{2},-2)$, $B(-2\frac{1}{2},-2)$ and $C(1,5)$ are the vertices of the triangle shown, find its area.

Solution:

The base, $BA=7$. The height, $CD=7$.
Since $A=\frac{1}{2}bh$, $A=\frac{1}{2}(7)(7)=24\frac{1}{2}$.   *Ans.* $24\frac{1}{2}$

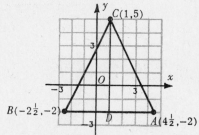

2. GRAPH OF AN EQUATION IN ONE VARIABLE: LINES PARALLEL TO AN AXIS

Note on the map of Graphtown, Fig. (g), that the avenues are parallel to Main Avenue and the streets are parallel to Center Street. The hospital is at the intersection of North 3rd Avenue and East 5th Street. Similarly, on the coordinate plane, Fig. (h), point $H(5, 3)$ is at the intersection of two lines, each of which is parallel to one of the axes. Note that these two lines are labeled "$x = 5$" and "$y = 3$". We shall refer to these lines as the line $x = 5$ and the line $y = 3$.

On the line $x = 5$, the x-coordinate of each point is a constant, 5. However, the y-coordinate of a point on the line, $x = 5$, may be any real number. Hence, in general, $(5, y)$ is the ordered pair of a point on the line $x = 5$.

On the line $y = 3$, the y-coordinate of each point is a constant, 3. However, the x-coordinate of a point on the line $y = 3$ may be any real number. Hence, in general, $(x, 3)$ is the ordered pair of a point on the line $y = 3$.

Note in Fig. (h) that (5, 3) is the ordered pair of point H.

The ordered pair (5, 3) indicates that H is the intersection of two lines $x = 5$ and $y = 3$. The ordered pair (2, −3) indicates that the graph of the ordered pair (2, −3) is the intersection of the lines $x = 2$ and $y = -3$. In general, the ordered pair of a point indicates that the point is the intersection of two lines that are parallel to the axes.

Using Fig. (i), we shall show how to **graph** or **plot the graph** of an ordered pair of real num-

Map of Graphtown

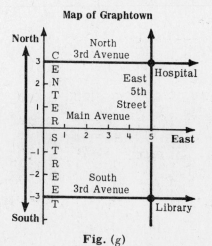

Fig. (g)

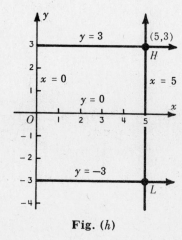

Fig. (h)

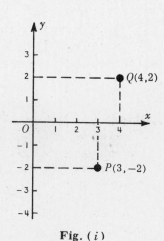

Fig. (i)

bers, such as (3, −2). First, a vertical line is drawn through the graph of 3 on the x-axis. Then, a horizontal line is drawn through the graph of −2 on the y-axis. The point of intersection, P, of the vertical line, $x = 3$, and the horizontal line, $y = -2$, is the graph of (3, −2). This method illustrates the following rule:

Rule 1. For each ordered pair of real numbers, there is one and only one point of the coordinate plane.

On the other hand, we can begin with a point such as Q and determine its ordered pair. This can be done by drawing two lines through Q, one vertical and the other horizontal, as shown. Since the vertical line passes through the graph of 4 on the x-axis, its equation is $x = 4$. Since the horizontal line passes through the graph of 2 on the y-axis, its equation is $y = 2$. Hence, the ordered pair of Q is (4, 2). This method illustrates the following rule:

Rule 2. For each point of the coordinate plane, there is one and only one ordered pair of real numbers.

The following important principle combines the ideas in rule 1 and rule 2:

> There is a one-to-one correspondence between the set of all points of a coordinate plane and the set of all ordered pairs of real numbers.

Recall the one-to-one correspondence between the set of all points of a number line and the set of real numbers. This is a correspondence in one dimension while the new rule above is a correspondence in two dimensions.

Rule 3. The graph of a first degree equation in only one variable is either the x-axis, the y-axis or a line parallel to one of the axes. Thus, as shown in Fig. (j):

(1) The graph of $y = 0$ is the x-axis and the graph of $x = 0$ is the y-axis.

(2) The graphs of $y = 3$ and $y = -3$ are lines parallel to the x-axis.

(3) The graphs of $x = 4$ and $x = -4$ are lines parallel to the y-axis.

Note. The coordinates of any point of intersection of two such lines are obtainable from the equations of these lines. Thus, (4,3) is the intersection of $x = 4$ and $y = 3$.

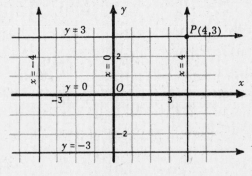

Fig. (j)

2.1 Lines Which Are the Graphs of Equations in One Variable

In the coordinate plane, Fig. (k), state the line which is the graph of:

a) $x = 0$ e) $y = 2$
b) $y = 0$ f) $y = -1$
c) $x = 4$ g) $y = 5$
d) $x = -2$

Ans. a) y-axis   e) line (b)
b) x-axis   f) line (a)
c) line (e) g) line (c)
d) line (d)

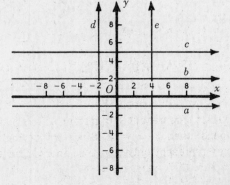

Fig. (k)

2.2 Graphing Equations of the First Degree in One Variable

Using a separate set of axes for each, graph

a) $x = -4$, $x = 0$, $x = 2\frac{1}{2}$ 　　　　　　　　　*b*) $y = 3\frac{1}{2}$, $y = 0$, $y = -4$

Solutions: (*Each graph is an axis or a line parallel to an axis.*)

a) Graphs of $x = -4$ and $x = 2\frac{1}{2}$ are parallel to *y*-axis. Graph of $x = 0$ is the *y*-axis.

b) Graphs of $y = 3\frac{1}{2}$ and $y = -4$ are parallel to *x*-axis. Graph of $y = 0$ is the *x*-axis.

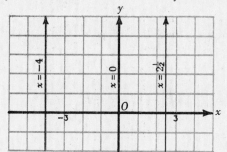　　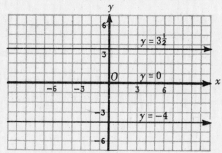

2.3 Describing a Line Which Is the Graph of an Equation in One Variable

Describe fully the line whose equation is

a) $x = 0$, 　*b*) $y = 0$, 　*c*) $x = 3$, 　*d*) $x = -2$, 　*e*) $y = 1$, 　*f*) $y = -15$, 　*g*) $x = 4\frac{1}{2}$, 　*h*) $y = -3.5$

Ans. *a*) *y*-axis

　　b) *x*-axis,

　　c) parallel to the *y*-axis and 3 units to the right of it,

　　d) parallel to the *y*-axis and 2 units to the left of it,

　　e) parallel to the *x*-axis and 1 unit above it,

　　f) parallel to the *x*-axis and 15 units below it,

　　g) parallel to the *y*-axis and $4\frac{1}{2}$ units to the right of it, or midway between the lines $x = 4$ and $x = 5$,

　　h) parallel to the *x*-axis and 3.5 units below it, or midway between the lines $y = -3$ and $y = -4$.

2.4 Ordered Pairs of Points of Intersection of Lines Parallel to the Axes

a) State the equations of the lines parallel to the axes if the ordered pair of their intersection is

　　　(1) $(5, -3)$, 　(2) $(-4, 0)$, 　(3) $(0, -2.5)$

b) State the ordered pair of the intersection of

　　(1) the lines, $x = 4$ and $y = -7$, 　　(3) the line $y = -4.5$ and the *y*-axis,

　　(2) the line $x = -6$ and the *x*-axis, 　　(4) the *x*-axis and the *y*-axis.

Ans. *a*) (1) $x = 5$ and $y = -3$, 　(2) $x = -4$ and $y = 0$, the *x*-axis, 　(3) $y = -2.5$ and $x = 0$, the *y*-axis.

　　b) (1) $(4, -7)$, 　(2) $(-6, 0)$, 　(3) $(0, -4.5)$, 　(4) $(0, 0)$

3. GRAPHS OF AN EQUATION IN TWO VARIABLES

A box contains only red pens and white pens. If you are asked to select any five pens from the box, in how many ways can this selection be made?

If we let *x* represent the number of red pens that are selected and let *y* represent the number of white pens, then $x + y = 5$. Since a fraction of a pen is not a plausible answer, the variables *x* and *y* may represent only whole numbers. Hence, we shall use the set of whole numbers as the replacement set. The equation $x + y = 5$ is either a true statement or a false statement when both variables are replaced by whole numbers. Note in the following table and in the set of ordered pairs, the six combinations of whole numbers that will lead to a true statement:

$$S = \{(5,0), (4,1), (3,2), (2,3), (1,4), (0.5)\}$$

x	y
5	0
4	1
3	2
2	3
1	4
0	5

Each of the ordered pairs in set S is a **solution** of the equation $x + y = 5$. The set S is the **solution set** of the equation $x + y = 5$ when the replacement set is the set of whole numbers.

The graph of the solution set, S, is the set of six points shown in Fig. (l) with their ordered pairs. Keep in mind that the variables x and y represent only whole numbers when they represent a number of pens. However, if x and y represent any real numbers, then the graph of $x + y = 5$ is a continuous line as shown in Fig. (m). This line extends indefinitely in each direction. Note that the six points of Fig. (l) are points of the line, $x + y = 5$, in Fig. (m).

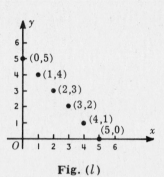

Fig. (l)

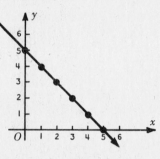

Fig. (m)

The equation $x + y = 5$ is an illustration of an equation of the first degree in two variables, according to the following definition:

An **equation of the first degree** in two variables is one which can be transformed into an equivalent equation of the form $ax + by = c$ where a, b, and c are real numbers, $a \neq 0$ and $b \neq 0$.

Thus, $2x + 3y = 12$ and $y = \frac{1}{2}x + 15$ are equations of the first degree in two variables but $3xy = 15$ is not since the variables x and y are not in separate terms.

Rule. If the replacement set of the variables is the set of real numbers, the graph of a first degree equation in two variables is a straight line. Hence, such equations are **linear equations**.

Thus, if the replacement set is the set of real numbers, the graphs of the equations $x + y = 6$, $2x + 3y = 12$ and $y = \frac{1}{2}x - 3$ are straight lines.

3.1 Varying the Replacement Set in the Graphing of an Equation in Two Variables

A committee of students is to be chosen from a group of 8, 4 of whom are boys and the other 4 are girls.
a) In how many ways can a total of 4 students be selected?
b) In how many ways can a selection be made in which the number of boys equals the number of girls?
c) Graph the possible selections that can be made in (a) and (b) and show how the graph can be used to determine the number of ways in which a selection of 4 students can be made so that there is an equal number of boys and girls.
d) Indicate how the graphs made in (c) would change if the replacement set were the set of real numbers.

Solution:
a) Let x = the number of boys and y = the number of girls.
Then since the total is 4, $x + y = 4$.
The 5 possible combinations for the first selection are listed by roster in set S:

$$S = \{(0,4), (1,3), (2,2), (3,1), (4,0)\}$$

b) Since the number of boys equals the number of girls, $x = y$.
The 4 possible combinations for the second selection are listed by roster in set T:

$$T = \{(1,1), (2,2), (3,3), (4,4)\}$$

c) The graphs of $x + y = 4$ and $x = y$ for the given replacement set are shown in Fig. (*n*).

The graph of $x + y = 4$ is the set of 5 points, whose ordered pairs are members of S, and the graph of $x = y$ is the set of 4 points, whose ordered pairs are members of T. The only ordered pair in common is (2,2), whose graph is point P. This shows that there is only one way in which both selections can be made.

d) Figure (*o*) shows the graphs of $x + y = 4$ and $x = y$ for a replacement set of real numbers. Note that the graphs are continuous lines rather than a limited set of points.

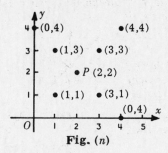

Fig. (*n*)

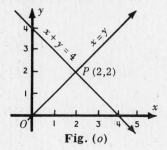

Fig. (*o*)

4. GRAPHING LINEAR EQUATIONS

A **linear equation** is an equation whose graph is a straight line. Note "line" in linear.

In graph problems assume the following:

1. The set of real numbers is the replacement set of the variables when no replacement set is indicated.

2. "ordered pairs" means ordered pairs of coordinates of points.

3. "table of coordinates" means a table of ordered pairs of coordinates.

Rule 1. If a point is **on the graph** of an equation, its coordinates **satisfy** the equation. Thus, $x = 1$ and $y = 4$, the coordinates of P on the graph of $y = x + 3$, satisfy the equation $y = x + 3$.

Rule 2. If a point is **not on the graph** of an equation, its coordinates **do not satisfy** the equation.

Thus, $x = 3$ and $y = 4$, the coordinates of B which is not on the graph of $y = x + 3$, do not satisfy the equation $y = x + 3$.

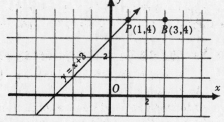

To Graph a Linear Equation

Procedure:

1. **Make a table of coordinates for three ordered pairs**, as follows: Let x have convenient values such as 2, 0 and −2. Substitute each of these for x and find the corresponding value of y.

2. **Plot the points and draw the straight line joining them:**

   Note. If correct, two points determine a line. The third point serves as a check point to ensure correctness.

Graph: $y = x + 4$

Solution:

1. **Table of Coordinate Values:**

   Since $y = x + 4$,

	Point	Coordinates (x,y)
(*1*) if $x = 2$, $y = 2 + 4 = 6 \rightarrow$	A	(2,6)
(*2*) if $x = 0$, $y = 0 + 4 = 4 \rightarrow$	B	(0,4)
(*3*) if $x = -2$, $y = -2 + 4 = 2 \rightarrow$	C	(−2,2)

2. **Join the Plotted Points:**

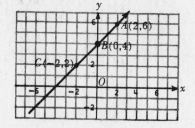

An intercept of a graph is the directed distance from the origin to the point where the graph crosses either axis.

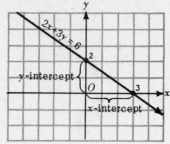

(1) The *x*-intercept of a graph is the *x*-coordinate for the point where the graph crosses the *x*-axis. At this point, $y = 0$.

Thus, for $2x + 3y = 6$, the *x*-intercept = 3.

(2) The *y*-intercept of a graph is the *y*-coordinate for the point where the graph crosses the *y*-axis. At this point, $x = 0$.

Thus, for $2x + 3y = 6$, the *y*-intercept = 2.

To Graph a Linear Equation Using Intercepts
Procedure:

1. **Make a table of coordinates, as follows:**

a) Let $x = 0$ to obtain the *y*-intercept.
b) Let $y = 0$ to obtain the *x*-intercept.
c) Obtain a third or check point, using any convenient value for either unknown.

2. **Plot the points and join them with a straight line:**

Graph: $2x + 3y = 6$
Solution:

1. Table of Coordinates:

Point	Coordinates (x, y)
A	(0, 2)
B	(3, 0)
C	(−3, 4)

a) If $x = 0$, $y = 2$.
b) If $y = 0$, $x = 3$.
c) If $x = −3$, $y = 4$.

2. Join the Plotted Points:

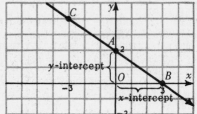

4.1 Making Tables of Coordinates

Complete the table of coordinates:

a) $y = 2x - 3$

	(x, y)
(1)	(−2, ?)
(2)	(0, ?)
(3)	(2, ?)

b) $x = 3y + 1$

	(x, y)
(1)	(?, −2)
(2)	(?, 0)
(3)	(?, 2)

(Vertically Arranged Tables)

c) $x + 2y = 10$

	(1)	(2)	(3)
x	?	?	?
y	−2	0	2

d) $y = 3$

	(1)	(2)	(3)
x	−2	0	2
y	?	?	?

(Horizontally Arranged Tables)

Solutions:

a)

	(x, y)
(1)	(−2, −7)
(2)	(0, −3)
(3)	(2, 1)

b)

	(x, y)
(1)	(−5, −2)
(2)	(1, 0)
(3)	(7, 2)

c)

	(1)	(2)	(3)
x	14	10	6
y	−2	0	2

d)

	(1)	(2)	(3)
x	−2	0	2
y	3	3	3

(y = 3 for all values of x.)

4.2 Rule 1. Coordinates of Any Point on a Line

$A(4, 3)$ and $B(-5, 6)$ are on the graph of $x + 3y = 13$. Show that their coordinates satisfy the equation.

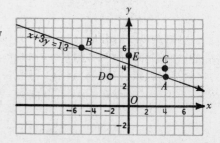

Solution: *(Substitute to test each ordered pair)*

Test for $A(4, 3)$:

$$x + 3y \overset{?}{=} 13$$
$$4 + 3(3) \overset{?}{=} 13$$
$$13 = 13$$

Test for $B(-5, 6)$:

$$x + 3y \overset{?}{=} 13$$
$$-5 + 3(6) \overset{?}{=} 13$$
$$13 = 13$$

4.3 Rule 2. Coordinates of Any Point Not on a Line

$C(4,4)$, $D(-2,3)$ and $E(0,5\frac{1}{3})$ are not on the graph of $x+3y=13$ used in **4.2** Show that their coordinates do not satisfy the equation.

Solutions: (*Substitute to test each ordered pair*)

Test for $C(4,4)$:

$$x + 3y = 13$$
$$4 + 3(4) \overset{?}{=} 13$$
$$4 + 12 \overset{?}{=} 13$$
$$16 \neq 13$$

Test for $D(-2,3)$:

$$x + 3y = 13$$
$$-2 + 3(3) \overset{?}{=} 13$$
$$-2 + 9 \overset{?}{=} 13$$
$$7 \neq 13$$

Test for $E(0,5\frac{1}{3})$:

$$x + 3y = 13$$
$$0 + 3(5\frac{1}{3}) \overset{?}{=} 13$$
$$16 \neq 13$$

4.4 Intercepts and Points of Intersection

The graphs of $3x+2y=6$, $x+2y=-2$ and $2y-3x=6$ are shown in the adjoining diagram. Find:

a) the x and y-intercepts of each line

b) the coordinates of their points of intersection

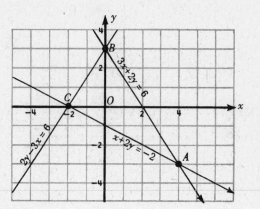

Solutions:

a)

	(Let $y=0$) x-intercept	(Let $x=0$) y-intercept
$3x+2y=6$	2	3
$x+2y=-2$	-2	-1
$2y-3x=6$	-2	3

b) $A(4,-3)$ is the point of intersection of $3x+2y=6$ and $x+2y=-2$.

$B(0,3)$ is the point of intersection of $3x+2y=6$ and $2y-3x=6$.

$C(-2,0)$ is the point of intersection of $x+2y=-2$ and $2y-3x=6$.

4.5 Graphing Linear Equations

Using the same set of axes, graph:

a) $y=\frac{x}{2}$ and $y=5-x$

b) $y=\frac{x-2}{2}$ and $y=3$

Procedure:

1. Make a table of coordinates:

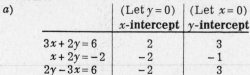

Point	(x,y)
A	$(-2,-1)$
B	$(0,0)$
C	$(2,1)$

Point	(x,y)
D	$(-2,7)$
E	$(0,5)$
F	$(2,3)$

	G	H	I
x	-2	0	2
y	-2	-1	0

	J	K	L
x	-2	0	2
y	3	3	3

2. Join the plotted points:

(a)

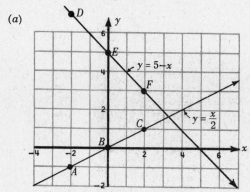

(b)

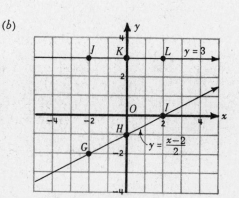

4.6 Graphing Linear Equations, Using Intercepts

Graph, using intercepts: *a*) $2x + 5y = 10$ | *b*) $3x - 4y = 6$

Procedure: **Solutions:**

1. Make a table of coordinates.

Point	(x,y)
A	$(0,2)$
B	$(5,0)$
C	$(2\frac{1}{2},1)$

Point	(x,y)
D	$(0,-1\frac{1}{2})$
E	$(2,0)$
F	$(4,1\frac{1}{2})$

   a) Let $x = 0$ to find *y*-intercept:
   b) Let $y = 0$ to find *x*-intercept:
   c) Obtain a check point:

2. Join the plotted points:

(*a*)

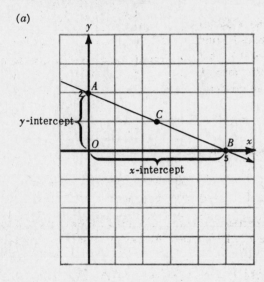

(*b*)

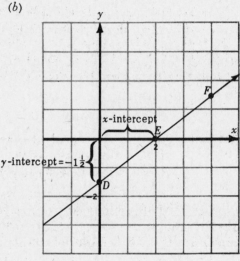

5. SLOPE OF A LINE

Understanding Slope of a Line

    To determine the slope of a road, engineers divide the "rise" of the road by its "run". Since the rise of the road means the vertical distance climbed and the run of the road is the horizontal distance covered, then the slope of road *A*, Fig. (*a*), is 40% and the slope of road *B*, Fig. (*b*), is 20%, calculated as follows:

$$\text{Slope of road } A = \frac{\text{rise}}{\text{run}} = \frac{40}{100} = 40\% \qquad \text{Slope of road } B = \frac{\text{rise}}{\text{run}} = \frac{20}{100} = 20\%$$

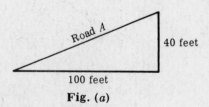

Fig. (*a*)

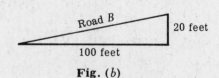

Fig. (*b*)

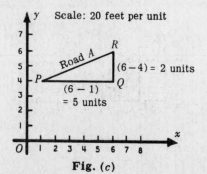

Fig. (*c*)

    On the engineer's graph chart, Fig. (*c*), a scale of 20 feet per unit is used. On this chart, the slope of road *A* is the slope of $\overline{PR}$, which can be found by dividing RQ by PQ, thus:

$$\text{Slope of } \overline{PR} = \frac{RQ}{PQ} = \frac{6-4}{6-1} = \frac{2}{5}$$

    Hence, slope of road A = slope of $\overline{PR} = \frac{2}{5} = 40\%$.

    Note that the slope of $\overline{PR}$ is the quotient of two differences.

Finding the slope of a road is an application of the general rule for finding the slope of any line in a coordinate plane. In Fig. (d), line $\overleftrightarrow{PR}$ joins $P(x_1, y_1)$. with $R(x_2, y_2)$. The slope of $\overleftrightarrow{PR}$ is found by means of Rule 1:

Rule 1. If a line passes through $P(x_1, y_1)$ and $R(x_2, y_2)$, then

$$\boxed{\text{Slope of } \overleftrightarrow{PR} = \frac{y_2 - y_1}{x_2 - x_1}}$$

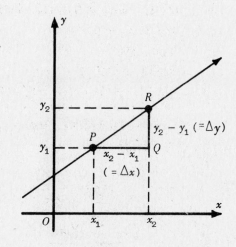

Fig. (d)

In the rule, $y_2 - y_1$ is the difference of the y-coordinates, and $x_2 - x_1$ is the difference of the x-coordinates. If the symbol "Δy" denotes $y_2 - y_1$ and the symbol "Δx" denotes $x_2 - x_1$, rule 1 can be stated in a simpler form. In the following delta form, the slope of a line is represented by m:

Delta Form of Slope Definition

$$\boxed{m = \text{Slope of } \overleftrightarrow{PR} = \frac{\Delta y}{\Delta x}}$$

Δy means $y_2 - y_1$.

Δx means $x_2 - x_1$.

Δ, the fourth letter of the Greek alphabet, corresponds to d, the fourth letter of the English alphabet. Read Δy as "delta y" and Δx as "delta x". If you think of "delta y" as "y-difference", you will see why "Δy" is used to replace "$y_2 - y_1$".

Thus, if a line passes through $P(2,5)$ and $R(4,11)$, then the slope of the line, $m = \frac{11 - 5}{4 - 2} = \frac{6}{2} = 3$. Also, if a line passes through $A(1,6)$ and $B(5,5)$, its slope, $m = \frac{5 - 6}{5 - 1} = \frac{-1}{4} = -\frac{1}{4}$.

Kinds of Slopes

The slope of a line may be positive, negative, zero, or the line may have no slope. Rule 2 to 5 consider each of the four possible situations.

Rule 2. The slope of a line is **positive** if the line rises from left to right.

Thus, in Fig. (e), $\overleftrightarrow{PQ}$ rises from left to right in passing through $P(1,1)$ and $Q(5,4)$. Note that Δy and Δx, the differences, are both positive. Hence, the quotient of these differences is positive.

$$\text{Slope of } \overleftrightarrow{PQ} = \frac{4 - 1}{5 - 1} = \frac{3}{4}$$

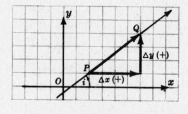

Fig. (e)

Observe in Fig. (e) that the angle made by the line and the positive direction of the x-axis, $\angle i$, is an acute angle.

Rule 3. The slope of a line is **negative** if the line falls from left to right.

Thus, in Fig. (f), $\overleftrightarrow{PQ}$ falls from left to right in passing through $P(1,3)$ and $Q(4,1)$. Note that Δy, the y-difference is negative and Δx, the x-difference, is positive. Hence, the quotient of these differences is negative.

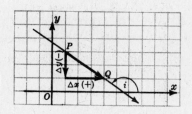

Fig. (f)

$$\text{Slope of } \overleftrightarrow{PQ} = \frac{1-3}{4-1} = \frac{-2}{3} = -\frac{2}{3}.$$

Observe in Fig. (f) that the angle made by the line and the positive direction of the x-axis, $\angle i$, is an obtuse angle.

Rule 4. The slope of a line is **zero** if the line is parallel to the x-axis.

Thus, in Fig. (g), $\overleftrightarrow{PQ}$, which passes through $P(2,2)$ and $Q(6,2)$, is parallel to the x-axis. Note that the Δy, the y-difference, is 0 and Δx, the x-difference, is positive. Hence, the quotient of these differences is zero.

$$\text{Slope of } \overleftrightarrow{PQ} = \frac{2-2}{6-2} = \frac{0}{4} = 0$$

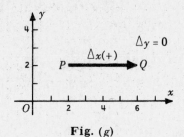

Fig. (g)

Rule 5. A line parallel to the y-axis has **no** slope.

Thus, in Fig. (h), $\overleftrightarrow{PQ}$, which passes through $P(2,1)$ and $Q(2,4)$, is parallel to the y-axis. Note that Δy, the y-difference, is positive and Δx, the x-difference is 0. Hence, the denominator of the quotient, $\frac{y}{x}$, is zero and the division by zero is impossible. In this case, there is **no** slope.

$$\text{Slope of } \overleftrightarrow{PQ} = \frac{4-1}{2-2} = \frac{3}{0} \quad \text{(Division is impossible)}$$

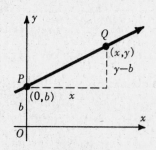

Fig. (h)

Observe in Fig. (h) that the angle made by the line with the x-axis is a right angle.

Rule 6. If a line has a y-intercept, b, and a slope, m, then the line is the graph of an equation of the form $y = mx + b$.

In Fig. (i), since b is the y-intercept, the line intersects the y-axis at $P(0,b)$. If Q is any other point on the line, the coordinates (x,y) may be used as the ordered pair of Q.

$$\text{Slope of } \overleftrightarrow{PQ} = \frac{y\text{-difference}}{x\text{-difference}} = \frac{y-b}{x-0} = m$$

Hence, $\frac{y-b}{x} = m$. Therefore, $y = mx + b$.

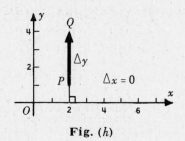

Fig. (i)

Thus, if the y-intercept of a line is 3 and its slope is 2, an equation of the line is $y = 2x + 3$.

Rule 7. If the equation of a line is in the form $y = mx + b$, then its slope is m and its y-intercept is b.

---

m = **Slope of a line whose equation is** $y = mx + b$

Thus, in Fig. (j), each of the lines has a y-intercept of 2. The slope of the line $y = 3x + 2$ is 3, the slope of the line $y = \frac{1}{3}x + 2$ is $\frac{1}{3}$, the slope of the line, $y = -\frac{1}{3}x + 2$ is $-\frac{1}{3}$ and the slope of the line, $y = -3x + 2$ is -3.

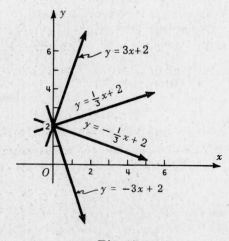

Fig. (j)

5.1 Applying Rule 1: Slope of line $= \dfrac{y_2 - y_1}{x_2 - x_1} = \dfrac{\Delta y}{\Delta x}$

Graph and find the slope of the line through
a) (0,0) and (2,4),   b) (−2,−1) and (4,3).

Procedure:

Solutions:

1. **Plot** the points and draw the line which passes through them.

1. 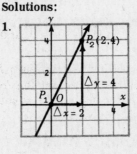   1.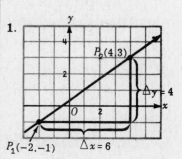

2. Find Δy and Δx, the corresponding differences of y and x:

2. $P_2(2,4) \rightarrow x_2 = 2,\ y_2 = 4$
$P_1(0,0) \rightarrow x_1 = 0,\ y_1 = 0$
$\Delta x = 2,\ \Delta y = 4$

2. $P_2(4,3) \rightarrow x_2 = 4,\quad y_2 = 3$
$P_1(-2,-1) \rightarrow x_1 = -2,\ y_1 = -1$
$\Delta x = 6,\quad \Delta y = 4$

3. Find slope of line $= \dfrac{\Delta y}{\Delta x}$:

3. Slope of $\overrightarrow{P_1 P_2}$
$= \dfrac{\Delta y}{\Delta x} = \dfrac{4}{2} = 2$
Ans. 2

3. Slope of $\overrightarrow{P_1 P_2}$
$= \dfrac{\Delta y}{\Delta x} = \dfrac{4}{6} = \dfrac{2}{3}$
Ans. $\dfrac{2}{3}$

5.2 Determining the Slope of a Line by Inspection: Rules 2 to 5

In Fig. (k), indicate which of the lines shown have
1) a positive slope
2) a negative slope
3) zero slope
4) no slope

Ans. 1) (b) and (f) have a positive slope. These lines rise from left to right, Rule 2
2) (d) and (g) have a negative slope. These lines fall from left to right, Rule 3
3) (c) and (e) have a zero slope. These lines are parallel to the x-axis, Rule 4
4) (a) has no slope. This line is parallel to the y-axis, Rule 5

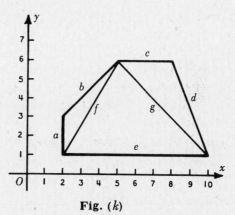

Fig. (k)

Note. It is left to the student to find the slopes of these lines to check each of the answers. Slope of (a) $= \dfrac{2}{0}$ (no slope); slope of (b) = 1 (positive); slope of (c) $= \dfrac{0}{3} = 0$; slope of (d) $= \dfrac{-5}{2} = -\dfrac{5}{2}$ (negative); slope of (e) $= \dfrac{0}{8} = 0$; slope of (f) $= \dfrac{5}{3}$ (positive); and slope of (g) $= \dfrac{-5}{5} = -1$ (negative).

5.3 Stating the Equation of a Line Given Its Slope and y-intercept: Rule 6

State the equation of a line whose slope and y-intercept are respectively:
a) 2 and $\tfrac{1}{2}$,   b) $\tfrac{1}{2}$ and 2,   c) −2 and $\tfrac{1}{2}$,   d) $\tfrac{1}{2}$ and 0,   e) 0 and $-\tfrac{1}{2}$,   f) −2 and $-\tfrac{1}{2}$

Ans. a) $y = 2x + \tfrac{1}{2}$ or $2y = 4x + 1$
b) $y = \tfrac{1}{2}x + 2$ or $2y = x + 4$
c) $y = -2x + \tfrac{1}{2}$ or $2y = -4x + 1$

d) $y = \tfrac{1}{2}x$ or $2y = x$
e) $y = -\tfrac{1}{2}$ or $2y = -1$
f) $y = -2x - \tfrac{1}{2}$ or $2y = -4x - 1$

5.4 Stating the Slope and y-intercept of a Line Given Its Equation: Rule 7

Find the slope of the line whose equation is
a) $2y = 6x - 8$, | b) $3y - 4x = 15$.

Procedure: | **Solutions:**

1. **Transform** equation into the form, $y = mx + b$:

1. D_2 $2y = 6x - 8$	1. Tr $3y - 4x = 15$
$y = 3x - 4$	D_3 $3y = 4x + 15$
	$y = \frac{4}{3}x + 5$

2. **Find slope** of line $= m$, the coefficient of x:

2. Slope $= 3$. | 2. Slope $= \frac{4}{3}$.
Ans. 3 | Ans. $\frac{4}{3}$

6. DERIVING A LINEAR EQUATION FROM A TABLE OF VALUES

Deriving a Simple Linear Equation By Inspection

A simple linear equation such as $y = x + 3$ involves only one operation. Any y-value equals **3 added to** its corresponding x-value. Note this in the following table of values for $y = x + 3$:

y	-7	0	3	4	6	13
x	-10	-3	0	1	3	10

A simple equation can be derived from a table of values by inspection. Once the single operation is found, the equation follows. For example, suppose we are given the table

y	4	8	16	40
x	1	2	4	10

An inspection shows that any y-value equals 4 times its corresponding x-value. Hence, its equation is $y = 4x$.

Deriving a Linear Equation by the Ratio Method

How can we derive a linear equation when two operations are involved as in the case of $y = 4x + 2$? Here any y-value equals 2 added to four times its corresponding x-value.

Examine the following table of values for $y = 4x + 2$ and notice that as x increases 1, y increases 4; as x increases 2, y increases 8 and finally as x decreases 1, y decreases 4.

Change in y $+4$ $+8$ -4

y	6	10	18	14
x	1	2	4	3

Change in x $+1$ $+2$ -1

Compare each change in y (above the table) with the corresponding change in x (below the table). Notice that any y-change or y-difference equals 4 times the corresponding x-change or x-difference. From this, we may conclude that the equation is of the form $y = 4x + b$. The value of b may now be found. To find b, substitute any tabular pair of values for x and y in $y = 4x + b$.

Thus, in $y = 4x + b$, substitute $x = 1$ and $y = 6$.
$6 = 4(1) + b$
$2 = b$ Since $b = 2$, the equation is $y = 4x + 2$.

Rule. If a linear equation has the form $y = mx + b$, the value of m can be obtained from a table using the ratio of the y-difference to the corresponding x-difference; that is,

$$m = \frac{y\text{-difference}}{x\text{-difference}} = \frac{\text{difference of two } y\text{-values}}{\text{corresponding difference of two } x\text{-values}}$$

(Think of $\underline{m}$ as the $\underline{\text{multiplier}}$ of x in $y = \underline{m}x + b$.)

6.1 Deriving Simple Linear Equations by Inspection

Derive the linear equation for each table:

a)

y	3	4	10
x	1	2	8

b)

y	2	0	−4
x	5	3	−1

c)

y	7	21	70
x	1	3	10

d)

y	2	5	9
x	6	15	27

Solutions:

a) Since each y-value is 2 more than its corresponding x-value, $y = x + 2$. *Ans.*

b) Since each y-value is 3 less than its corresponding x-value, $y = x - 3$. *Ans.*

c) Since each y-value is 7 times its corresponding x-value, $y = 7x$. *Ans.*

d) Since each y-value is one-third of its corresponding x-value, $y = \frac{x}{3}$. *Ans.*

6.2 Deriving a Linear Equation of Form $y = mx + b$ by Ratio Method

Derive the linear equation for each table:

a)

y	1	4	10
x	0	1	3

b)

y	−12	−2	18
x	−2	0	4

Procedure:

1. Find m:

$$m = \frac{y\text{-difference}}{x\text{-difference}}$$

2. Find b:
Substitute any tabular
pair of values in
$$y = mx + b$$

3. Form equation
$$y = mx + b$$

Solutions:

1.
$$m = \frac{+3}{+1} = \frac{+6}{+2} = 3$$

2. Since $m = 3$, $y = 3x + b$.
Substitute $x = 0$, $y = 1$
in $y = 3x + b$
$$1 = 3(0) + b$$
$$1 = b$$

3. $y = 3x + 1$ *Ans.*

1.
$$m = \frac{+10}{+2} = \frac{+20}{+4} = 5$$

2. Since $m = 5$, $y = 5x + b$.
Substitute $y = 18$, $x = 4$
in $y = 5x + b$
$$18 = 5(4) + b$$
$$-2 = b$$

3. $y = 5x - 2$ *Ans.*

7. GRAPHING INEQUALITIES

Dividing a Number Line into Two Half-Lines

Rule 1. A point on the number line divides the number line into two half-lines.

(The point of division is not on either of the half-lines.)

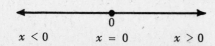

Number Line Divided by the Origin

Fig. (a)

Number Line Divided by the Graph of 3

Fig. (b)

Thus, the origin, $x = 0$, divides the number line, Fig. (a), into two half-lines; the half-line which is the graph of the positive numbers, $x > 0$, and the half-line which is the graph of the negative numbers, $x < 0$.

Thus, the graph of 3 divides the number line into two half-lines; the half-line which is the graph of the numbers greater than 3, $x > 3$, and the half-line which is the graph of the numbers less than 3, $x < 3$.

Dividing a Coordinate Plane into Two Half-Planes

Rule 2. A line on the coordinate plane divides the plane into two half-planes.

(The line of division is not on either of the half-planes.)

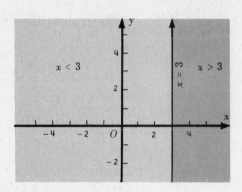

Fig. (c)

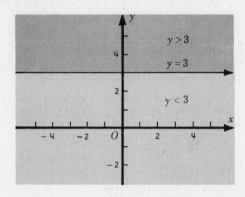

Fig. (d)

Thus, the line, $x = 3$, divides the coordinate plane, Fig. (c), into two half-planes; the half-plane which is the graph of the ordered pairs whose x-coordinate is greater than 3, $x > 3$; and the half-plane which is the graph of the ordered pairs whose x-coordinate is less than 3, $x < 3$.

Thus, the line, $y = 3$, divides the coordinate plane, Fig. (d), into two half-planes; the half-plane which is the graph of the ordered pairs whose y-coordinate is greater than 3, $y > 3$; and the half-plane which is the graph of the ordered pairs whose y-coordinate is less than 3, $y < 3$.

Rule 3. The line that is the graph of $y = mx + b$, where m and b are constants, divides the coordinate plane into two half-planes such that the half-plane above the line $y = mx + b$ is the graph of the inequality $y > mx + b$, and the half-plane below the line $y = mx + b$ is the graph of the inequality $y < mx + b$.

Thus, the line $y = 2x + 1$, Fig. (e), divides the coordinate plane into two half-planes; the half-plane that is the graph of the inequality $y > 2x + 1$ and is **above** the line; and the half-plane that is the graph of the inequality $y < 2x + 1$ and is **below** the line.

Note. If there is any doubt with regard to the pairing of a half-plane with an inequality, a simple test may be made by testing a single convenient point, such as $A(2,0)$. The y-coordinate, 0, is **less** than twice the x-coordinate, 2, plus 1. Hence, the point A must lie in the half-plane, $y < 2x + 1$. Verify this in Fig. (e).

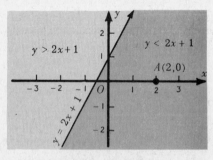

Fig. (e)

Graphing Inequalities in the Coordinate Plane

a) Graph $y \geq 2x - 2$.

Solution:

a) 1. Graph $y = 2x - 2$, by drawing a **full** line through the graphs of the x-intercept, 1, and the y-intercept, -2.
Note. The line is drawn full because it is part of the graph $y \geq 2x - 2$.

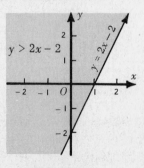

Fig. (f)

b) Graph $y < 2x - 2$.

Solution:

b) 1. Graph $y = 2x - 2$, by drawing a **dotted** line through the graphs of the x-intercept, 1, and the y-intercept, -2.
Note. The line is drawn dashed because it is **not** part of the graph of $y < 2x - 2$.

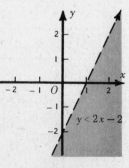

Fig. (g)

2. Graph $y > 2x - 2$ by using rule 3. The graph of $y > 2x - 2$ is the shaded half-plane **above** the line, $y = 2x - 2$.

3. The sentence, $y \geq 2x - 2$, is a combination of the inequality, $y > 2x - 2$, and the equation, $y = 2x - 2$. Hence, the graph of $y \geq 2x - 2$ is a combination of the half-plane $y > 2x - 2$, which is shaded, and the line, $y = 2x - 2$, which is in full.

2. Graph $y < 2x - 2$ by using rule 3. The graph of $y < 2x - 2$ is the shaded half-plane **below** the line, $y = 2x - 2$.

3. The inequality, $y < 2x - 2$, does **not** include the equation $y = 2x - 2$. Hence, the required graph is the shaded half-plane.

7.1 Graphing Inequalities on a Number Line

On a number line, graph each inequality:

a) $x \geq 0$ *b)* $x > 2$ *c)* $x < -2$ *d)* $x \geq -2$

Solutions:

(a)
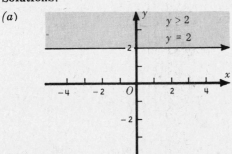
Graph of "x is equal to or greater than 0".

(b)
Graph of "x is greater than 2".

(c)
Graph of "x is less than -2".

(d)
Graph of "x is greater than or equal to -2".

7.2 Graphing Inequalities in a Coordinate Plane: Rule 2

In a coordinate plane, draw the graph of each inequality for real numbers x and y:

a) $y \geq 2$ *b)* $y \leq -2$ *c)* $x > 1$ *d)* $x < -2$

Solutions:

(a)
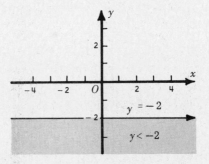

(b)

The graph of $y \geq 2$ includes the shaded half-plane above the line, $y = 2$, and also the line which is drawn in full.

The graph of $y \leq -2$ includes the shaded half-plane below the line, $y = -2$, and also the line which is drawn in full.

(c)
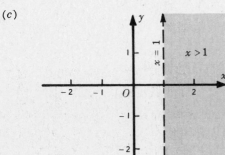

(d)
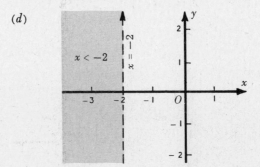

The graph of $x > 1$ is the shaded half-plane, to the right of the line, $x = 1$. The graph does not include the line which is not drawn in full.

The graph of $x < -2$ is the shaded half-plane to the left of the line, $x = -2$. The graph does not include the line which is not drawn in full.

7.3 Graphing Inequalities in a Coordinate Plane: Rule 3

In a coordinate plane, graph each inequality for real numbers x and y:

a) $y < x$,   b) $y + x > 2$,   c) $y \geq 2x - 2$,   d) $2y \leq x - 2$

(a)

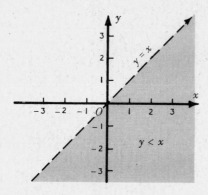

The graph of $y < x$ is the shaded half-plane **below** the line $y = x$. The graph does not include the line which is not drawn in full.

(b) First, transform into $y > -x + 2$, by subtracting x from each side.

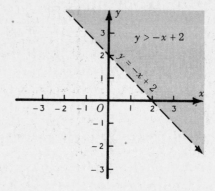

The graph of $y > -x + 2$ is the shaded half-plane **above** the line $y = -x + 2$. The graph does not include the line which is not drawn in full.

(c)

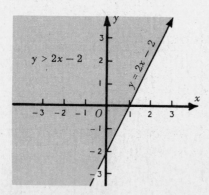

The graph of $y \geq 2x - 2$ includes the shaded half-plane **above** the line, $y = 2x - 2$, and also the line which is drawn in full.

(d) First, transform into $y \leq \frac{1}{2}x - 1$ by dividing both sides by 2.

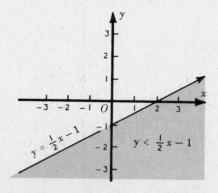

The graph of $y \leq \frac{1}{2}x - 1$ includes the shaded half-plane **below** the line, $y = \frac{1}{2}x - 1$, and also the line which is drawn in full.

SUPPLEMENTARY PROBLEMS

1. State the coordinates of each lettered point on the graph.   **(1.1)**
Ans.
$A(3,0)$
$B(4,3)$
$C(3,4)$
$D(0,2)$
$E(-2,4)$
$F(-4,2)$
$G(-1,0)$
$H(-3\tfrac{1}{2},-2)$
$I(-2,-3)$
$J(0,-4)$
$K(1\tfrac{1}{2},-2\tfrac{1}{2})$
$L(4,-2\tfrac{1}{2})$

3. Plot each point: $A(2,3)$, $B(-3,3)$, $C(-3,-2)$, $D(2,-2)$. Find the perimeter and area of the square $ABCD$.   **(1.5)**
Ans. Perimeter of square formed is 20 units, its area is 25 square units.

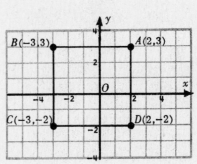

2. Plot each point and locate it with reference to quadrants I to IV: **(1.3, 1.4)**

$A(-2,-3)$	$C(0,-1)$	$E(3,-4)$	$G(0,3)$
$B(-3,2)$	$D(-3,0)$	$F(1\tfrac{1}{2},2\tfrac{1}{2})$	$H(3\tfrac{1}{2},0)$

Ans.

F is in I
B is in II
A is in III
E is in IV
G is between
    I and II
D is between
    II and III
C is between
    III and IV
H is between
    IV and I

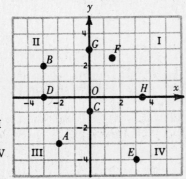

4. Plot each point: $A(4,3)$, $B(-1,3)$, $C(-3,-3)$, $D(2,-3)$. Find the area of parallelogram $ABCD$ and triangle BCD.   **(1.5, 1.6)**
Ans. Area of parallelogram =
    $bh = 5(6)$ or 30 sq. units
Area of $\triangle BCD$ =
    $\tfrac{1}{2}bh = \tfrac{1}{2}(30) = 15$ sq. units

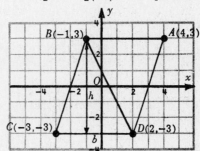

5. In the coordinate plane, state the lettered line which is the graph of each equation: **(2.1)**

  a) $x = 0$,
  b) $y = 0$,
  c) $x = 2$,
  d) $x = -2\tfrac{1}{2}$,
  e) $y = -3$,
  f) $y = 1$

Ans. a) y-axis, line *(d)*,
    b) x-axis, line *(c)*,
    c) line *(b)*,
    d) line *(f)*,
    e) line *(g)*,
    f) line *(a)*

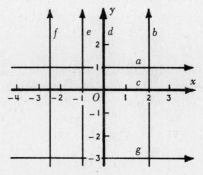

6. Using one set of axes, graph each line and state the coordinates of their nine points of intersection: $x = 1\frac{1}{2}$, $x = 0$, $x = -3$, $y = 5$, $y = 0$, $y = -2\frac{1}{2}$.   **(2.2)**

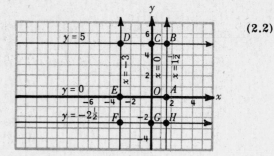

Ans. The points of intersection are

$A(1\frac{1}{2},0)$	$D(-3,5)$	$G(0,-2\frac{1}{2})$
$B(1\frac{1}{2},5)$	$E(-3,0)$	$H(1\frac{1}{2},-2\frac{1}{2})$
$C(0,5)$	$F(-3,-2\frac{1}{2})$	$O(0,0)$

7. Describe fully the line whose equation is

a) $x = 0$,   b) $y = 0$,   c) $x = -1\frac{1}{2}$,   d) $x = 3.5$,   e) $y = -3$,   f) $y = 15$.   **(2.3)**

Ans. a) y-axis

b) x-axis

c) parallel to the y-axis and $1\frac{1}{2}$ units to the left of it

d) parallel to the y-axis and $3\frac{1}{2}$ units to the right of it

e) parallel to the x-axis and 3 units below it

f) parallel to the x-axis and 15 units above it

8.   a) State the equations of the lines parallel to the axes if the ordered pair of their   **(2.4)**
intersection is

(1) $(6,-2)$ (2) $(0, 3\frac{1}{2})$ (3) $(-1\frac{1}{4},0)$ (4) $(-4, -1)$

b) State the ordered pair of the intersection of

(1) the lines $x = 5$ and $y = 0$,   (3) the lines $x = -7\frac{1}{4}$ and $y = 25$.

(2) the lines $x = 0$ and $y = -4\frac{1}{2}$,

Ans. a) (1) $x = 6$, $y = -2$,   (2) $x = 0$, $y = 3\frac{1}{2}$,   (3) $x = -1\frac{1}{4}$, $y = 0$,   (4) $x = -4$, $y = -1$.

b) (1) $(5,0)$,   (2) $(0, -4\frac{1}{2})$,   (3) $(-7\frac{1}{4}, 25)$.

9. A group of volunteers is to be chosen from a group of 10, 5 of whom are boys and the   **(3.1)**
other 5 are girls.

a) In how many ways can a total of 5 volunteers be selected?

b) In how many ways can a selection be made in which the number of boys is one more than the number of girls?

c) Graph the possible selections that can be made in (a) and (b) and show how the graph can be used to determine the number of ways in which a selection of 5 volunteers can be made so that the number of boys is one more than the number of girls.

d) Indicate how the graphs would change in (c) if the replacement set were the set of real numbers.

Ans. a) Let x = the number of boys and y = the number of girls. Then $x + y = 5$. The 6 possible combinations for the first selection are listed by roster in set A:

$$A = \{(0,5), (1,4), (2,3), (3,2), (4,1), (5,0)\}$$

b) Since the number of boys is one more than the number of girls, $x = y + 1$. The 4 possible combinations for the second selection are listed by roster in set B:

$$B = \{(5,4), (4,3), (3,2) (2,1)\}$$

c) The graph of $x + y = 5$ is the set of 6 points whose ordered pairs are members of A, and the graph of $x = y + 1$ is the set of 4 points, whose ordered pairs are members of B. The only ordered pair in common is $(3,2)$, whose graph is point P. This shows that there is only one way in which both selections can be made.

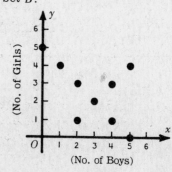

d) For a replacement set of real numbers, the graphs of $x + y = 5$ and $x = y + 1$ are continuous lines rather than a limited number of points.

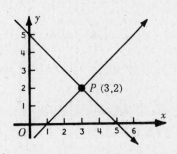

(4.1)

10. Complete the table of coordinates:

a) $y = 3x - 2$

	(x,y)
(1)	(−2, ?)
(2)	(0, ?)
(3)	(2, ?)

b) $x = 2y + 5$

	(x, y)
(1)	(?, −2)
(2)	(?, 0)
(3)	(?, 2)

c) $2x + y = 12$

	(1)	(2)	(3)
x	−2	0	2
y	?	?	?

d) $x = 7\frac{1}{2}$

	(1)	(2)	(3)
x	?	?	?
y	−2	0	2

Vertically Arranged Tables

Horizontally Arranged Tables

Ans. a)

	(x, y)
(1)	(−2, −8)
(2)	(0, −2)
(3)	(2, 4)

b)

	(x, y)
(1)	(1, −2)
(2)	(5, 0)
(3)	(9, 2)

c)

	(1)	(2)	(3)
x	−2	0	2
y	16	12	8

d)

	(1)	(2)	(3)
x	$7\frac{1}{2}$	$7\frac{1}{2}$	$7\frac{1}{2}$
y	−2	0	2

$(x = 7\frac{1}{2}$ for all values of y.)

---

11. Locate $A(1,0)$ and $B(2,-4)$ on the graph of $y + 4x = 4$ and show that their coordinates satisfy the equation. Also, show that $C(2,2)$ and $D(-1,3)$ are not on the graph of $y + 4x = 4$ and show that their coordinates do not satisfy the equation.

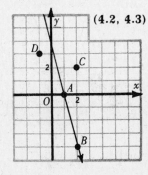

(4.2, 4.3)

Ans.

Test $A(1,0)$	Test $B(2,-4)$	Test $C(2,2)$	Test $D(-1,3)$
$y + 4x = 4$	$y + 4x = 4$	$y + 4x = 4$	$y + 4x = 4$
$0 + 4(1) \overset{?}{=} 4$	$-4 + 4(2) \overset{?}{=} 4$	$2 + 4(2) \overset{?}{=} 4$	$3 + 4(-1) \overset{?}{=} 4$
$4 = 4$	$4 = 4$	$10 \neq 4$	$-1 \neq 4$
A is on graph	B is on graph	C is not on graph	D is not on graph

---

12. The graphs of $2y - x = 6$, $2y - x = 2$ and $2y = 3x - 2$ are shown in the adjacent figure. Find
a) the x- and y-intercepts of each line,
b) the coordinates of any point of intersection common to two graphs.

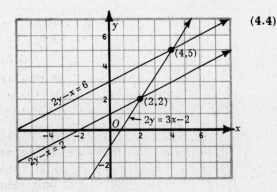

(4.4)

Ans. a)

equation	(Let $y = 0$.) x-intercept	(Let $x = 0$.) y-intercept
$2y - x = 6$	−6	3
$2y - x = 2$	−2	1
$2y = 3x - 2$	$\frac{2}{3}$	−1

b) (2,2) is the point of intersection of $2y - x = 2$ and $2y = 3x - 2$.
(4,5) is the point of intersection of $2y - x = 6$ and $2y = 3x - 2$.
Since $2y - x = 2$ and $2y - x = 6$ are parallel, they have no point of intersection.

13. Graph each equation after completing each table of coordinates: **(4.5)**

a) $y = -4$

	(x,y)
A	$(-2,?)$
B	$(0,?)$
C	$(2,?)$

b) $y = 2x$

	(x,y)
D	$(-2,?)$
E	$(0,?)$
F	$(2,?)$

c) $x = 2y + 3$

	(x,y)
G	$(?,-1)$
H	$(?,0)$
I	$(?,1)$

Ans. a)

	(x,y)
A	$(-2,-4)$
B	$(0,-4)$
C	$(2,-4)$

Ans. b)

	(x,y)
D	$(-2,-4)$
E	$(0,0)$
F	$(2,4)$

Ans. c)

	(x,y)
G	$(1,-1)$
H	$(3,0)$
I	$(5,1)$

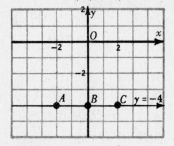
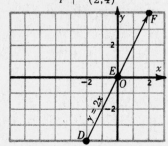
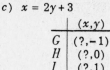
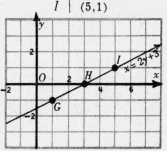

14. Graph each equation, using intercepts: **(4.6)**

a) $3x + 2y = 6$

Ans. a)

	(x,y)
A	$(0,3)$
B	$(2,0)$
C	$(4,-3)$

b) $4y - 3x = 6$

Ans. b)

	(x,y)
D	$(0,1\frac{1}{2})$
E	$(-2,0)$
F	$(2,3)$

c) $\dfrac{x}{4} + \dfrac{y}{3} = 1$

Ans. c)

	(x,y)
G	$(0,3)$
H	$(4,0)$
I	$(-4,6)$

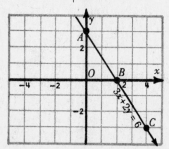
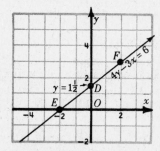
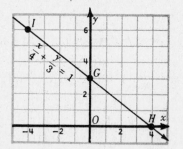

15. Find the slope of the line through **(5.1)**

a) $(0,0)$ and $(6,15)$
b) $(2,3)$ and $(6,15)$

c) $(3,-4)$ and $(5,6)$
d) $(-2,-3)$ and $(2,1)$

e) $(8,10)$ and $(0,-2)$
f) $(-1,2)$ and $(5,14)$

a) $\dfrac{15-0}{6-0} = \dfrac{15}{6}$ *Ans.* $\dfrac{5}{2}$

b) $\dfrac{15-3}{6-2} = \dfrac{12}{4}$ *Ans.* 3

c) $\dfrac{6-(-4)}{5-3} = \dfrac{10}{2}$ *Ans.* 5

d) $\dfrac{1-(-3)}{2-(-2)} = \dfrac{4}{4}$ *Ans.* 1

e) $\dfrac{-2-10}{0-8} = \dfrac{-12}{-8}$ *Ans.* $\dfrac{3}{2}$

f) $\dfrac{14-2}{5-(-1)} = \dfrac{12}{6}$ *Ans.* 2

16. Which of the lines in the coordinate plane have: **(5.2)**

1) a positive slope,   3) zero slope,
2) a negative slope,   4) no slope.

Ans. 1) (e), (g), and (h) have a positive slope,
2) (a), (f), and (d) have a negative slope,
3) (b) has a zero slope,
4) (c) has no slope.

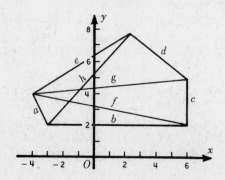

17. State the equation of a line whose slope and y-intercept are respectively: **(5.3)**

a) 4 and $\frac{1}{4}$,   e) 0 and 4,

b) $\frac{1}{4}$ and 4,   f) $\frac{1}{2}$ and 0,

c) -4 and $-\frac{1}{2}$,   g) 0 and $-\frac{1}{2}$,

d) 4 and 0,   h) -4 and $-\frac{1}{2}$.

Ans a) $y = 4x + \frac{1}{4}$ or $4y = 16x + 1$,   e) $y = 4$,

b) $y = \frac{1}{4}x + 4$ or $4y = x + 16$,   f) $y = \frac{1}{2}x$ or $2y = x$,

c) $y = -4x - \frac{1}{2}$ or $2y + 8x = -1$,   g) $y = -\frac{1}{2}$ or $2y = -1$,

d) $y = 4x$,   h) $y = -4x - \frac{1}{2}$ or $2y + 8x = -1$

18. Find the slope of the line whose equation is   **(5.4)**

a) $y = 3x - 4$ d) $2y = 6x - 10$ g) $\frac{y}{2} = x - 3$

b) $y = 5x$ e) $3y = 21 - 6x$ h) $\frac{y}{3} + 2x = 8$

c) $y = 5$ f) $4y - 3x = 16$ i) $x - \frac{2}{3}y = 12$

a) $y = 3x - 4$ *Ans.* 3   d) $y = 3x - 5$ *Ans.* 3   g) $y = 2x - 6$ *Ans.* 2

b) $y = 5x + 0$ *Ans.* 5   e) $y = -2x + 7$ *Ans.* -2 h) $y = -6x + 24$ *Ans.* -6

c) $y = 0x + 5$ *Ans.* 0   f) $y = \frac{3}{4}x + 4$ *Ans.* $\frac{3}{4}$ i) $y = \frac{3}{2}x - 18$ *Ans.* $\frac{3}{2}$

19. Derive the linear equation for each table: **(6.1)**

a)
y	5	8	9
x	2	5	6

b)
y	-4	-6	-10
x	-2	-3	-5

c)
y	-8	-7	-3
x	0	1	5

d)
y	-1	1	4
x	-3	3	12

e)
y	2	2	2
x	7	-7	20

f)
y	4	2	0
x	3	5	7

g)
p	6	9	15
q	8	12	20

h)
r	$4\frac{1}{2}$	$\frac{1}{2}$	-2
s	$1\frac{1}{2}$	$-2\frac{1}{2}$	-5

Ans. a) $y = x + 3$ b) $y = 2x$ c) $y = x - 8$ d) $y = \frac{x}{3}$

e) $y = 2$ f) $x + y = 7$ g) $p = \frac{3}{4}q$ h) $r = s + 3$

20. Derive the linear equation for each table: **(6.2)**

a)
y	-1	1	5
x	0	1	3

b)
y	-1	3	15
x	-1	0	3

c)
y	4	3	-2
x	-1	0	5

d)
p	8	0	-4
q	0	4	6

e)
y	2	8	14
x	-2	0	2

f)
y	-19	-4	6
x	-3	0	2

g)
y	6	0	-2
x	0	3	4

h)
s	1	3	7
t	-4	0	8

i)
y	7	16	28
x	1	4	8

j)
y	27	13	-1
x	5	3	1

k)
y	7	-2	-14
x	-1	2	6

l)
a	5	7	11
b	6	9	15

Ans. a) $y = 2x - 1$ b) $y = 4x + 3$ c) $y = -x + 3$ d) $p = -2q + 8$

e) $y = 3x + 8$ f) $y = 5x - 4$ g) $y = -2x + 6$ h) $s = \frac{1}{2}t + 3$

i) $y = 3x + 4$ j) $y = 7x - 8$ k) $y = -3x + 4$ l) $a = \frac{2}{3}b + 1$

21. On a number line, graph each inequality for a real number x: (7.1)

a) $x > -1$,   b) $x \geq 3$,   c) $x \leq -1$,   d) $x < 7$

Ans.

a) Graph of $x > -1$ (-1 is not in the graph.)

b) Graph of $x \geq 3$ (3 is in the graph.)

c) Graph of $x \leq -1$ (-1 is in the graph.)

d) Graph of $x < 7$ (7 is not in the graph.)

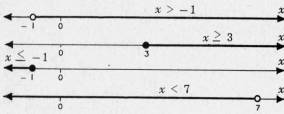

22. In a coordinate plane, draw the graph of each inequality for real numbers x and y: (7.2)

a) $y < 1$,   b) $y \geq -1$,   c) $x \leq 1$,   d) $x > -2$

Ans.

a) The graph of $y < 1$ is the shaded half-plane **below** the line $y = 1$. The graph does not include the line which is not drawn in full.

b) The graph of $y \geq -1$ includes the shaded half-plane **above** the line, $y = -1$, and also the line which is drawn in full.

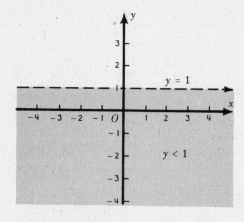

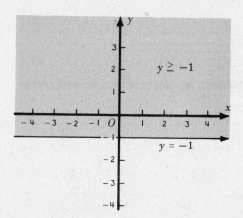

c) The graph of $x \leq 1$ includes the shaded half-plane to the left of the line, $x = 1$, and also the line which is drawn in full.

d) The graph of $x > -2$ is the shaded half-plane to the right of the line, $x = -2$. The graph does not include the line which is not drawn in full.

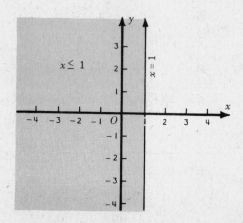

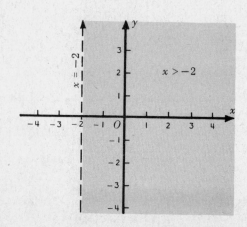

23. In a coordinate plane, draw the graph of each inequality for real numbers x and y: **(7.3)**

a) $y < 2x$,   b) $y > -x$,   c) $y \geq -2x + 2$,   d) $y \leq 2x - 1$

Ans.

a) The graph of $y < 2x$ is the shaded half-plane **below** the line, $y = 2x$. The graph does not include the line which is not drawn in full.

b) The graph of $y > -x$ is the shaded half-plane **above** the line $y > -x$. The graph does not include the line which is not drawn in full.

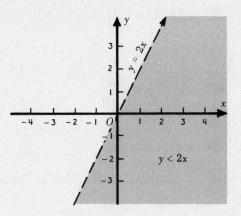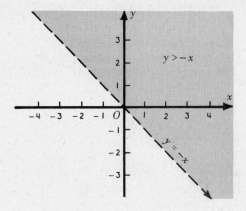

c) The graph of $y \geq -2x + 2$ includes the shaded half-plane **above** the line, $y = -2x + 2$, and also the line which is drawn in full.

d) The graph of $y \leq 2x - 1$ includes the shaded half-plane **below** the line, $y = 2x - 1$, and also the line which is drawn in full.

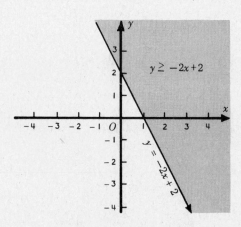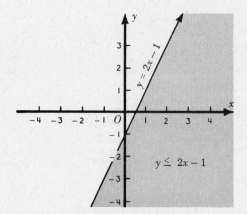

Chapter 8

Systems of Linear Equations and Linear Inequalities In Two Variables

1. SOLVING GRAPHICALLY A SYSTEM OF LINEAR EQUATIONS IN TWO VARIABLES

We have found that the graph of a linear equation in two variables is a straight line. Figures (a), (b), and (c) picture graphically the three possible relations that may exist between two linear equations.

1. In Fig. (a), the graphs of the two equations, $y = x + 4$ and $x + y = 10$, have **one and only one point in common**. When the graphs of two linear equations intersect, the equations are called **consistent equations**. The intersection point indicates the common solution of both equations. Since the intersection point is (3,7), the solution set of both equations is $\{(3,7)\}$, a set containing a single ordered pair. The common solution is $x = 3$, $y = 7$.

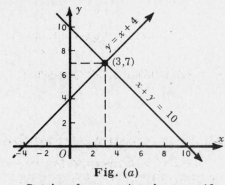

Fig. (a)

Graphs of $y = x + 4$ and $x + y = 10$

CONSISTENT EQUATIONS

The two linear equations $y = x + 4$ and $x + y = 10$ place on the variables x and y two conditions or limitations which must hold at the same time. For this reason, these equations are members of a system of **simultaneous linear equations** or simply a **system of linear equations**. In a system of consistent equations, the graphs of the two equations are straight lines which have unequal slopes and intersect in one point.

2. In Fig. (b) below, the graphs of the equations, $x + y = 5$ and $x + y = 3$, have no point in common. When the graphs of two linear equations are **parallel**, the equations are called **inconsistent equations**. Since there is no intersection point, the solution set is the empty set and there is no common solution. An inspection of the equations shows why there is no common solution since $x + y$ cannot have a value of 5 and at the same time have another value of 3.

In a system of inconsistent equations, the graphs of two equations are parallel lines which have equal slopes.

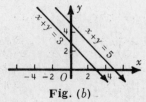

Fig. (b)

Graphs of $x + y = 5$ and $x + y = 3$

INCONSISTENT EQUATIONS

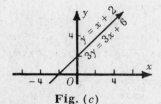

Fig. (c)

Graphs of $y = x + 2$ and $3y = 3x + 6$

DEPENDENT EQUATIONS

3. In Fig. (c) above, the graphs of the two equations $y = x + 2$ and $3y = 3x + 6$ **coincide**. When the graphs of two linear equations coincide, the two lines have all their points in common and are called **dependent equations**. In this case, the equations are also equivalent equations since the equations have the same solution set. Either of two dependent equations can be transformed into the other by using the rules of equality. Note that multiplying each side by 3 transforms $y = x + 2$ into $3y = 3x + 6$. In turn, by dividing each side by 3, the equation $3y = 3x + 6$ is transformable into $y = x + 2$.

In a system of dependent equations, the same line is the graph of each equation. Hence, any solution of one equation is a solution of the other.

To Solve a Pair of Linear Equations Graphically

Solve $x + 2y = 7$ and $y = 2x + 1$ graphically and check their common solution.

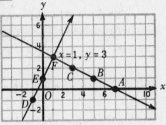

Procedure:

1. Graph each equation, using the same set of axes:

2. Find the common solution:

3. Check the values found:

Solution:

1. $x + 2y = 7$ $\qquad$ $y = 2x + 1$

(x, y)	(x, y)
$A(7, 0)$	$D(-1, -1)$
$B(5, 1)$	$E(0, 1)$
$C(3, 2)$	$F(1, 3)$

2. Since the point of intersection is $(1, 3)$, the common solution is $x = 1$, $y = 3$. The solution set is $\{(1, 3)\}$.

3. Check, using $x = 1$ and $y = 3$:

$$x + 2y = 7 \qquad\qquad y = 2x + 1$$
$$1 + 6 \overset{?}{=} 7 \qquad\qquad 3 \overset{?}{=} 2 + 1$$
$$7 = 7 \qquad\qquad 3 = 3$$

1.1 Finding Common Solutions Graphically

From the graphs of $3y + x = 5$, $x + y = 3$ and $y = x + 3$ shown, find the common solution of

a) $3y + x = 5$ and $x + y = 3$,
b) $3y + x = 5$ and $y = x + 3$,
c) $x + y = 3$ and $y = x + 3$.

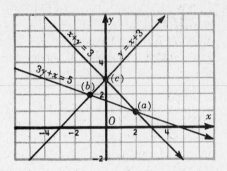

Solutions:

The common solution of each pair of equations is found by using the ordered pair of their point of intersection.

Ans. a) $(2, 1)$ $\qquad$ b) $(-1, 2)$ $\qquad$ c) $(0, 3)$

1.2 Consistent Equations and Their Graphic Solution

Solve each system of equations graphically:

a) $\begin{cases} y = 3 \\ x = 4 \end{cases}$

b) $\begin{cases} y = 1 \\ y = x - 2 \end{cases}$

c) $\begin{cases} x + y = 8 \\ y = x + 6 \end{cases}$

Solutions:

Graph of $y = 3$ is a line parallel to x-axis	Graph of $x = 4$ is a line parallel to y-axis

Graph of $y = 1$ is a line parallel to x-axis	$y = x - 2$
	(x, y)
	$(-2, -4)$
	$(0, -2)$
	$(2, 0)$

$x + y = 8$	$y = x + 6$
(x, y)	(x, y)
$(0, 8)$	$(-2, 4)$
$(2, 6)$	$(0, 6)$
$(4, 4)$	$(2, 8)$

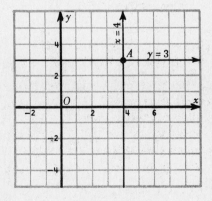

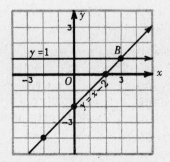

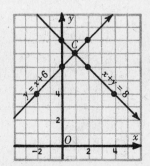

Using intersection point A, $x=4$, $y=3$	Using intersection point B, $x=3$, $y=1$	Using intersection point C, $x=1$, $y=7$
Ans. The solution is (4,3) or solution set is {(4,3)}.	*Ans*. The solution is (3,1) or solution set is {(3,1)}.	*Ans*. The solution is (1,7) or solution set is {(1,7)}.

1.3 Inconsistent Equations

Show graphically that there is no common solution for the following pair of equations:

$$x + y = 4, \quad 2x = 6 - 2y$$

Solution:

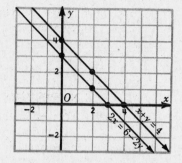

$$x + y = 4, \quad 2x = 6 - 2y$$

(x,y)	(x,y)
(0,4)	(0,3)
(4,0)	(3,0)
(2,2)	(2,1)

The graphs are parallel lines. Hence, the equations are inconsistent and there is no common solution.

1.4 Dependent Equations

For the equations $x - 2y = 2$ and $2x = 4y + 4$, show graphically that any pair of values satisfying one equation satisfies the other equation also.

Solution:

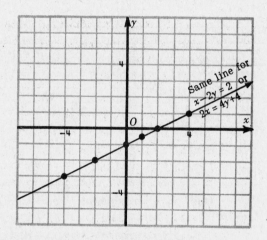

$x - 2y = 2$	$2x = 4y + 4$
(x,y)	(x,y)
(0,−1)	(−2,−2)
(2,0)	(−4,−3)
(4,1)	(1,−½)

The same line is the graph of the two equations. Hence, any ordered pair satisfying one equation satisfies the other also.

2. SOLVING A SYSTEM OF EQUATIONS BY ADDITION OR SUBTRACTION

To Solve a System of Equations by Adding or Subtracting

Solve: (*1*) $3x - 7 = y$
(*2*) $4x - 5y = 2$

Procedure:

1. **Arrange** so that like terms are in the same column:

2. **Multiply** so that the coefficients of one of the variables will have the same absolute value:

3. **To eliminate the variable** whose coefficients have the same absolute value:
   a) **Add** if their signs are **unlike**,
   b) **Subtract** if their signs are **like**.

Solution:

1. **Arrange:** (*1*) $3x - 7 = y \longrightarrow 3x - y = 7$
   (*2*) $\qquad\qquad\qquad 4x - 5y = 2$

2. **Multiply:**
   $M_5 \quad 3x - y = 7 \longrightarrow 15x - 5y = 35$

3. **Eliminate** y:

$$
\begin{array}{rl}
15x - 5y &= 35 \\
\text{Subtract:} \quad 4x - 5y &= 2 \\
\hline
11x \quad\quad &= 33
\end{array}
$$

4. Find the remaining variable by solving the resulting equation:

4. Find x: $\qquad$ D_{11} $\qquad$ $11x = 33$
$$x = 3$$

5. Find the other variable by substituting the value found in any equation having both variables.

5. Find y: $\qquad\qquad\qquad 4x - 5y = 2$

Substitute 3 for x: $\quad 4(3) - 5y = 2$
$$y = 2$$

Ans. The common solution is (3,2).

6. Check the common solution in each of the original equations:

6. Check for $x = 3$, $y = 2$:

(1)	$3x - 7 = y$	(2)	$4x - 5y = 2$
	$3(3) - 7 \overset{?}{=} 2$		$4(3) - 5(2) \overset{?}{=} 2$
	$2 = 2$		$2 = 2$

2.1 Using Addition or Subtraction to Eliminate One Variable

Add or subtract to eliminate one variable, then find the value of remaining variable.

$$a\begin{cases} 5x + 3y = 19 \\ x + 3y = 11 \end{cases} \quad b)\begin{cases} 10x + 4y = 58 \\ 13x - 4y = 57 \end{cases} \quad c)\begin{cases} 10y = 38 - 6x \\ 12y = 48 - 6x \end{cases} \quad d)\begin{cases} 3x + 10 = 5y \\ 7x + 20 = -5y \end{cases}$$

Solutions:

a) By subt., $4x = 8$ | b) By adding, $23x = 115$ | c) By subt., $-2y = -10$ | d) By adding, $10x + 30 = 0$

Ans. $\qquad x = 2$ | *Ans.* $\qquad x = 5$ | *Ans.* $\qquad y = 5$ | *Ans.* $\qquad x = -3$

2.2 Solutions Not Requiring Multiplication

Solve by addition or subtraction and check:

a) (1) $5x + 3y = 17$
$\quad (2)$ $\quad x + 3y = 1$

b) (1) $10x + 4y = 20$
$\quad (2)$ $13x - 4y = -66$

Solutions:

a) $\qquad$ By subtracting, $4x = 16$
$$x = 4$$

Subst. 4 for x in $x + 3y = 1$
$$4 + 3y = 1$$
$$y = -1$$

Ans. $x = 4$, $y = -1$

Check for $x = 4$, $y = -1$:

(1) $5x + 3y = 17$	(2) $x + 3y = 1$
$20 - 3 \overset{?}{=} 17$	$4 - 3 \overset{?}{=} 1$
$17 = 17$	$1 = 1$

b) $\qquad$ By adding, $23x = -46$
$$x = -2$$

Subst. -2 for x in $10x + 4y = 20$
$$-20 + 4y = 20$$
$$y = 10$$

Ans. $x = -2$, $y = 10$

Check for $x = -2$, $y = 10$

(1) $10x + 4y = 20$	(2) $13x - 4y = -66$
$-20 + 40 \overset{?}{=} 20$	$-26 - 40 \overset{?}{=} -66$
$20 = 20$	$-66 = -66$

2.3 Solutions Requiring Multiplication

Find each solution set by addition or subtraction:

a) (1) $13x - 4y = 57$
$\quad (2)$ $\quad 5x + 2y = 29$

b) (1) $3r - 5s = 19$
$\quad (2)$ $2r - 4s = 16$

Solutions: [In (a) one multiplication is needed, in (b) two are needed.]

a) (1) $\qquad\qquad 13x - 4y = 57$
$\quad (2)$ M_2 $\; 5x + 2y = 29 \rightarrow \underline{10x + 4y = 58}$

By adding, $\quad 23x \quad = 115$
$$x = 5$$

Subst. 5 for x in $5x + 2y = 29$
$$25 + 2y = 29$$
$$y = 2$$

$x = 5$, $y = 2$ $\quad$ *Ans.* {(5,2)}

b) (1) M_2 $\; 3r - 5s = 19 \rightarrow 6r - 10s = 38$
$\quad (2)$ M_3 $\; 2r - 4s = 16 \rightarrow \underline{6r - 12s = 48}$

By subtracting, $\qquad 2s = -10$
$$s = -5$$

Subst. -5 for s in $3r - 5s = 19$
$$3r + 25 = 19$$
$$r = -2$$

$s = -5$, $r = -2$ $\quad$ *Ans.* {(−5,−2)}

2.4 Solutions Requiring Rearrangements of Terms

Rearrange, then find the solution set by addition or subtraction:

a) (1) $2x + y = 16$
 (2) $\quad y = 25 - 5x$

b) (1) $3(x-2) = 8y + 1$
 (2) $8(y+1) = 4x - 4$

Procedure:

Solutions:

1. Rearrange:

(1) $2x + y = 16$
(2) $\underline{5x + y = 25}$

(1) $\quad 3x - 8y = 7$
(2) $\underline{-4x + 8y = -12}$

2. Add or subtract:

By subtr., $-3x = -9$
$\qquad\qquad x = 3$

By adding, $-x = -5$
$\qquad\qquad x = 5$

3. Substitute:

Subst. 3 for x in
$\qquad 2x + y = 16$
$\qquad 6 + y = 16$
$\qquad\qquad y = 10$
$\qquad x = 3,\ y = 10$
$Ans.\ \{(3,10)\}$

Subst. 5 for x in
$\qquad 3(x-2) = 8y + 1$
$\qquad\qquad 9 = 8y + 1$
$\qquad\qquad 1 = y$
$\qquad x = 5,\ y = 1$
$Ans.\ \{(5,1)\}$

2.5 Solving Systems of Equations Involving Fractions

Solve by addition or subtraction:

a) (1) $\frac{1}{2}x + \frac{1}{4}y = 5$
 (2) $\frac{1}{2}x - \frac{3}{4}y = -3$

Solutions:

(1) $\frac{1}{2}x + \frac{1}{4}y = 5$
(2) $\underline{\frac{1}{2}x - \frac{3}{4}y = -3}$

By subtracting, $y = 8$
Subst. 8 for y in $\quad \frac{1}{2}x + \frac{1}{4}y = 5$
$\qquad\qquad\qquad \frac{1}{2}x + 2 = 5$
$\qquad\qquad\qquad\qquad x = 6$

$Ans.\ x = 6,\ y = 8$

b) (1) $\quad \frac{a}{b} + 5 = -\frac{4}{b}$
 (2) $-2a - 3b = -6$

(1) $M_b \quad \frac{a}{b} + 5 = -\frac{4}{b}$
$\quad M_2 \quad a + 5b = -4$
$\qquad\qquad 2a + 10b = -8$
(2) $\quad \underline{-2a - 3b = -6}$
By adding, $\qquad 7b = -14, \quad b = -2$
Subst. -2 for b in $-2a - 3b = -6$
$\qquad\qquad\qquad\qquad -2a + 6 = -6$
$Ans.\ a = 6,\ b = -2$

2.6 Solving Systems of Equations Involving Decimals

Find each solution set by addition or subtraction:

a) (1) $\quad .3x = .6y$
 (2) $x + 6y = 8000$

Solutions:

(1) $M_{10} \quad .3x = .6y$
Rearrange $\quad 3x = 6y$
$\qquad\qquad 3x - 6y = 0$
(2) $\qquad x + 6y = 8000$

By adding, $4x = 8000, \quad x = 2000$
Subst. 2000 for x in $\ x + 6y = 8000$
$\qquad\qquad\qquad 2000 + 6y = 8000$
$\qquad x = 2000,\ y = 1000$

$Ans.\ \{(2,000,\ 1000)\}$

b) (1) $\quad .2x = .05y + 75$
 (2) $3x - 5y = 700$

(1) $M_{100} \qquad .2x = .05y + 75$
Rearrange $\qquad 20x = 5y + 7500$
$\qquad\qquad 20x - 5y = 7500$
(2) $\qquad 3x - 5y = 700$

By subtracting, $17x = 6800, \quad x = 400$
Subst. 400 for x in $3x - 5y = 700$
$\qquad\qquad\qquad 1200 - 5y = 700$
$\qquad x = 400,\ y = 100$

$Ans.\ \{(400,\ 100)\}$

3. SOLVING A SYSTEM OF EQUATIONS BY SUBSTITUTION

<u>To Solve a System of Equations by Substitution</u>

Solve: $\begin{array}{l} (1)\ \ x - 2y\ =\ 7 \\ (2)\ \ 3x + y\ =\ 35 \end{array}$

<u>Procedure:</u>

1. Express one variable in terms of the other by transforming one of the equations: **

2. In the other equation, **substitute** for the first variable the expression containing the other variable:

3. Find the remaining variable by solving the resulting equation:

4. Find the other variable by substituting the value found in any equation having both variables:

5. Check the common solution in each of the original equations:

Solution:

1. Express x **in terms** of y:

$(1)\ \ x - 2y\ =\ 7 \longrightarrow x\ =\ 2y + 7$

2. Substitute for x:

Subst. $(2y + 7)$ for x in $\ 3x + y\ =\ 35$

$3(2y + 7) + y\ =\ 35$

3. Find y:

$\begin{array}{r} 6y + 21 + y\ =\ 35 \\ 7y\ =\ 14 \\ y\ =\ 2 \end{array}$

4. Find x: Subst. 2 for y in $\ x\ =\ 2y + 7$

$\begin{array}{r} x\ =\ 4 + 7 \\ x\ =\ 11 \end{array}$

5. Check for $x = 11,\ y = 2$:

$(1) \qquad x - 2y \overset{?}{=} 7 \qquad \Big| \quad (2) \qquad 3x + y \overset{?}{=} 35$
$\qquad\quad 11 - 2(2) \overset{?}{=} 7 \qquad \Big| \qquad\quad 3(11) + 2 \overset{?}{=} 35$
$\qquad\qquad\qquad\quad 7 = 7 \qquad \Big| \qquad\qquad\qquad 35 = 35$

**Do this after studying the equations to determine which transformation provides the easier expression for one of the variables.

3.1 Using Substitution to Eliminate One Unknown

Substitute to eliminate one variable then find the value of the remaining variable.

$a)\ \begin{cases} y = 4x \\ 3x + y = 21 \end{cases}$

$a)$ Subst. $4x$ for y in $\ 3x + y = 21$

$\qquad\qquad\qquad\quad 3x + 4x = 21$

$\qquad\qquad\qquad\quad 7x = 21, \quad x = 3 \ \ Ans.$

$b)\ \begin{cases} x = y + 8 \\ x + 3y = 48 \end{cases}$

$b)$ Subst. $(y + 8)$ for x in $\ x + 3y = 48$

$\qquad\qquad\qquad\quad (y + 8) + 3y = 48$

$\qquad\qquad\qquad\quad 4y = 40, \quad y = 10 \ \ Ans.$

$c)\ \begin{cases} x = \frac{y}{2} \\ 4x = y + 6 \end{cases}$

$c)$ Subst. $\frac{y}{2}$ for x in $\ 4x = y + 6$

$\qquad\qquad\qquad\quad 4(\frac{y}{2}) = y + 6$

$\qquad\qquad\qquad\quad 2y = y + 6, \quad y = 6 \ \ Ans.$

$d)\ \begin{cases} y = 3x + 2 \\ 2y - 5x = 7 \end{cases}$

$d)$ Subst. $(3x + 2)$ for y in $\ 2y - 5x = 7$

$\qquad\qquad\qquad\quad 2(3x + 2) - 5x = 7,$

$\qquad\qquad\qquad\quad 6x + 4 - 5x = 7, \quad x = 3 \ \ Ans.$

3.2 Substitution Solutions Requiring Transformation

Solve by substitution:

$a)\ \ (1)\ \ 2x = 3y + 14$
$\qquad (2)\ \ x - y = 10$

Solutions:

Rearrange $(2) \rightarrow x = y + 10$

Subst. $y + 10$ for x in $\ 2x = 3y + 14$

$\qquad\qquad 2(y + 10) = 3y + 14$

$\qquad\qquad 2y + 20 = 3y + 14$

$\qquad\qquad\qquad\quad y = 6$

Since $\ x = y + 10, \ x = 6 + 10 = 16.$

Ans. $x = 16, \ y = 6$

$b)\ \ (1)\ \ y - 2x = 9$
$\qquad (2)\ \ 5x = 3y - 26$

Rearrange $(1) \rightarrow y = 2x + 9$

Subst. $2x + 9$ for y in $\ 5x = 3y - 26$

$\qquad\qquad\qquad 5x = 3(2x + 9) - 26$

$\qquad\qquad\qquad 5x = 6x + 27 - 26$

$\qquad\qquad\qquad x = -1$

Since $\ y = 2x + 9, \ y = -2 + 9 = 7$

Ans. $x = -1, \ y = 7$

3.3 Solving Systems of Equations Involving Fractions or Decimals

Find the solution set of each by substitution:

$a)$ (1) $a = 3b$

(2) $\dfrac{b+5}{3} = 15 - a$

Solutions:

M_3 $\dfrac{b+5}{3} = 15 - a$

Subst. $3b$ for a in

$b + 5 = 45 - 3a$

$b + 5 = 45 - 9b$

$b = 4$

Since $a = 3b$, $a = 3(4) = 12$.

Ans. $\{12, \ 4\}$

$b)$ (1) $x = 7 - y$

(2) $\dfrac{x}{3} = \dfrac{4-y}{2}$

M_6 $\dfrac{x}{3} = \dfrac{4-y}{2}$

Subst. $7 - y$ for x in

$2x = 12 - 3y$

$14 - 2y = 12 - 3y$

$y = -2$

Since $x = 7 - y$, $x = 7 + 2 = 9$.

Ans. $\{(9, \ -2)\}$

$c)$ (1) $y = 2000 - x$

(2) $.3x = \dfrac{y}{2} - 40$

M_{10} $.3x = \dfrac{y}{2} - 40$

Subst. $2000 - x$ for y in

$3x = 5y - 400$

$3x = 5(2000 - x) - 400$

$x = 1200$

Since $y = 2000 - x$, $y = 800$.

Ans. $\{(1200, \ 800)\}$

4. COMPOUND SENTENCES: UNION AND INTERSECTION OF SETS

Compound sentences are formed by joining separate sentences into a single sentence. The words **and** and **or** may be used as connectives to form the compound sentence.

Thus, "I sing **and** I write" is a compound sentence; also, "I sing **or** I write" is a compound sentence.

A **conjunction** is a compound sentence formed by joining separate sentences into a single sentence using the connective **and**.

Thus, a conjunction may be a system of linear equations, such as $\begin{cases} x + y = 10 \\ x - y = 4 \end{cases}$, read, "the system, $x + y = 10$ **and** $x - y = 4$." Note the use of a single brace before the system to indicate the combining of the two equations into one system. A conjunction may also be a system of linear inequalities such as $\begin{cases} x + y > 10 \\ x - y < 4 \end{cases}$, or a system combining an equality with an inequality, such as $\begin{cases} x + y = 10 \\ x - y < 4 \end{cases}$.

A **disjunction** is a compound sentence formed by joining separate sentences into a single sentence using the connective **or**.

Thus, a **disjunction** may be an equation involving absolute values, such as $|x| = 5$. The equation $|x| = 5$ means "$x = 5$ **or** $x = -5$".

When Is a Conjunction or a Disjunction a True Statement?

The conjunction, "I sing **and** I write" is true only if I am both singing and writing. However, the disjunction, "I sing **or** I write" is true if I am either singing or writing or doing both.

In general, a conjunction of two sentences is a true statement if and only if both sentences are true statements.

An illustration of a conjunction is the system $\begin{cases} x + y = 10 \\ x - y = 4 \end{cases}$. If x and y are real numbers, the system is true only for $(7,3)$, the common solution that is true for both equations.

In general, a disjunction of two sentences is a true statement if and only if one or the other or both of two sentences is a true statement.

An illustration of a disjunction is the absolute value equation, $|x - 1| = 2$. This equation is true if either $x - 1 = 2$ or $x - 1 = -2$. There is no common solution of both equations. The solution set is $\{3, -1\}$. The first number 3 satisfies the first equation, $x - 1 = 2$, and the second number, -1, satisfies the second equation, $x - 1 = -2$.

Intersection and Union Sets

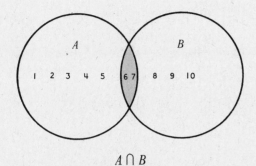

$A \cap B$

Intersection Set (shaded)
Fig. (a)

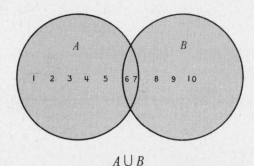

$A \cup B$

Union Set (shaded)
Fig. (b)

The **intersection set** of two sets is the set that contains only those members that are in both sets. Note the idea of conjunction involved in the intersection set. Thus, if $A = \{1,2,3,4,5,6,7\}$ and $B = \{6,7,8,9,10\}$, then their intersection set, denoted by $A \cap B = \{6,7\}$, shaded in Fig. (a). Read $A \cap B$ as "A intersection B".

The **union set** of two sets is the set that contains those members that are either in one set, the other, or both. Note the idea of disjunction involved in the union set. Thus, the union set of A and B, denoted by $A \cup B = \{1,2,3,4,5,6,7,8,9,10\}$, shaded in Fig.(b). Read $A \cup B$ as "A union B".

4.1 Conjunctions and Disjunctions in Systems and Absolute Value Equations

Insert "and" or "or" to make each sentence a true statement:

a) The system $\begin{cases} x = y \\ y = 2x + 4 \end{cases}$ is true only for the ordered pair which makes $x = y$ true ? $y = 2x + 4$ true.

b) The system $\begin{cases} x > 2 \\ y \geq x + 1 \end{cases}$ is true only for the ordered pairs which make $x > 2$ true ? $y \geq x + 1$ true.

c) The absolute value equation $|x - 4| = 7$ is true only for the ordered pairs which make $x - 4 = 7$? $x - 4 = -7$

Ans. a) and. The system of equations is a conjunction,
b) and. The system of inequalities is a conjunction,
c) or.   The absolute value equation is a disjunction.

4.2 Intersection Sets and Union Sets

Determine the intersection set and the union set of the sets in each:

a) $A = \{1, 2, 3\}$ and $B = \{2, 3, 4\}$
b) $A = \{(1,2), (2,2), (2,3)\}$ and $B = \{(1,3), (2,2)\}$
c) $A = \{1, 3, 5, \ldots, 15, 17, 19\}$ and $B = \{3, 6, 9, \ldots, 15, 18, 21\}$
d) $A = \{\text{odd integers}\}$ and $B = \{\text{even integers}\}$
e) $A = \{\text{natural numbers}\}$ and $B = \{\text{whole numbers}\}$.

Ans. a) Intersection set, $A \cap B = \{2, 3\}$ and union set $A \cup B = \{1, 2, 3, 4\}$
b) $A \cap B = \{(2,2)\}$ and $A \cup B = \{(1,2), (2,2), (1,3), (2,3)\}$
c) $A \cap B = \{3, 9, 15, 21\}$ and $A \cup B = \{1, 3, 5, 6, 7, 9, 11, 12, 13, 15, 17, 18, 19, 21\}$
d) $A \cap B = \emptyset$, the empty set and $A \cup B = \{\text{integers}\}$
e) $A \cap B = \{\text{natural numbers}\}$ and $A \cup B = \{\text{whole numbers}\}$.

Illustrative Solution:

In (d), since there is no integer that can be both odd and also even, the intersection set is an empty set. Each integer in the set of integers is either an odd integer or an even integer. Hence, the set of integers is the union set that includes each odd integer and also each even integer.

5. SOLVING A SYSTEM OF LINEAR INEQUALITIES GRAPHICALLY

If x and y are real numbers, the system of linear inequalities $\begin{cases} x > 2 \\ y < -2 \end{cases}$ is true only for those ordered pairs that satisfy both of the inequalities. Note in Fig. (a) the shaded half-plane that contains the graphs of the ordered pairs that satisfy the first inequality, $x > 2$, and the shaded half-plane that contains the graphs of the ordered pairs that satisfy the second inequality, $y < -2$. The only ordered pairs that satisfy both inequalities are those whose graphs lie in the cross-hatched region, S, where both half-planes intersect.

Since the equations $x = 2$ and $y = -2$ are not in the given system, the graphs of these equations are drawn as dashed lines and not as full lines.

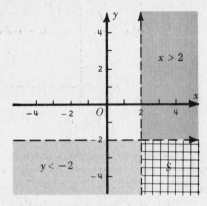

Fig. (a)

5.1 Solving a System of Linear Inequalities Graphically

a) On the same set of axes, graph the solution set of the system of inequalities,

$$\begin{cases} y \geq x \\ y \leq 2 \end{cases}$$

b) Name an ordered pair in the solution set of the given system.

c) Name an ordered pair in the solution set of $y \geq x$ but not in the solution set of $y \leq 2$.

d) Name an ordered pair that is not in the solution set of either inequality.

Solution:

a) Graph the solution set as follows:

1. The graph of $y \geq x$ includes both the shaded half-plane $y > x$ which is above the line, $y = x$, and also the line itself. See Fig. (b).

2. The graph of $y \leq 2$ includes both the shaded half-plane below the line, $y = 2$, and also the line itself.

3. The intersection of the two graphs obtained in steps 1 and 2 is the graph of the solution set of the given system of inequalities. This intersection includes the cross-hatched region, S, which is the intersection of both shaded half-planes and also the lines, $y = x$ and $y = 2$.

b) Examples are (0,1), (−2,0), and ($\frac{1}{2}$, 1).

c) Examples are (2,3) and (0,3).

d) Examples are (4,3) and (3, $3\frac{1}{2}$).

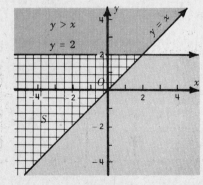

Fig. (b)

6. GRAPHING EQUATIONS INVOLVING ABSOLUTE VALUES

In each of the problems in this section, assume that the replacement set of each variable or variables is the set of real numbers.

To Graph an Equation in One Variable Involving an Absolute Value

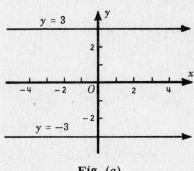

Fig. (a)

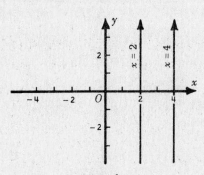

Fig. (b)

The absolute value equation $|y| = 3$ means $y = 3$ or $y = -3$. The graph of $|y| = 3$, Fig. (a), consists of two lines, $y = 3$ and $y = -3$, parallel to the x-axis. The solution set of $|y| = 3$ is the set of ordered pairs that satisfy $y = 3$ **or** satisfy $y = -3$.

The absolute value equation $|x - 3| = 1$ means $x - 3 = 1$ or $x - 3 = -1$. The graph of $|x - 3| = 1$, Fig. (b), consists of two lines, $x = 2$ **and** $x = 4$. The solution set of $|x - 3| = 1$ is the set of ordered pairs that satisfy $x - 3 = 1$ **or** $x - 3 = -1$.

To Graph an Equation in Two Variables Involving Absolute Values

Procedure:

1. Prepare a table of ordered pairs:

Graph $y = |x|$.

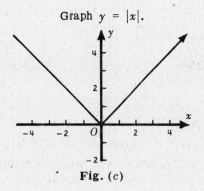

y	5	4	3	2	1	0	1	2	3	4	5
x	-5	-4	-3	-2	-1	0	1	2	3	4	5

2. Plot the points for the ordered pairs and join them, as shown in Fig. (c).

The graph of $y = |x|$ consists of two lines meeting at the origin. Since the values of y may only be positive or zero, the lines, except for the origin, lie above the x-axis.

Fig. (c)

6.1 Graphing Equations in One Variable Involving an Absolute Value

Graph each equation:

a) $|x| = 2$,   b) $|x + 1| = 2$,   c) $|y - 2| = 1$

Solutions:

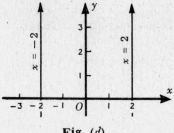

Fig. (d)

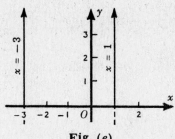

Fig. (e)

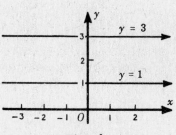

Fig. (f)

a) The graph of $|x| = 2$ consists of two lines, $x = 2$ and $x = -2$, Fig. (*d*). The solution set of $|x| = 2$ is the set of ordered pairs that satisfy either $x = 2$ **or** $x = -2$.

b) The graph of $|x + 1| = 2$ consists of two lines, $x = 1$ and $x = -3$, Fig. (*e*). The solution set of $|x + 1| = 2$ is the set of ordered pairs that satisfy either $x + 1 = 2$ or $x + 1 = -2$.

c) The graph of $|y - 2| = 1$ consists of two lines, $y = 3$ and $y = -3$, Fig. (*f*). The solution set of $|y - 2| = 1$ is the set of ordered pairs that satisfy either $y - 2 = 1$ or $y - 2 = -1$.

6.2 Graphing Equations in Two Variables Involving Absolute Values

Graph each of the following:

a) $x = |y|$,   *b*) $y = |x| - 1$,   *c*) $|x| + |y| = 3$

Solutions:

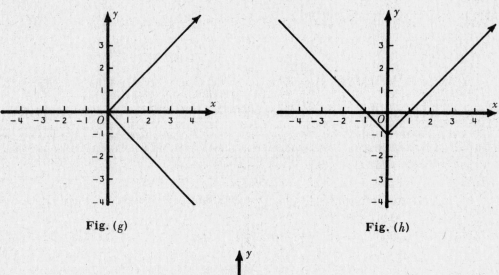

Fig. (*g*)   Fig. (*h*)

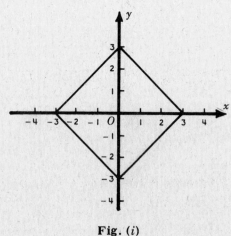

Fig. (*i*)

a) The graph of $x = |y|$ consists of two lines meeting at the origin, Fig. (*g*). Since the values of x may only be zero or positive, the lines, except for the origin, lie to the right of the y-axis.

b) The graph of $y = |x| -1$ consists of two lines meeting at $(0,-1)$ on the y-axis, Fig. (*h*). Since $|x| \geq 0$, then y cannot have a value that is less than -1.

c) The graph of $|x| + |y| = 3$ is the set of four lines constituting the sides of a square, Fig. (*i*). Since both $|x|$ and $|y|$ are positive, either $|x|$ is less than or equal to 3, or $|y|$ is less than or equal to 3.

SUPPLEMENTARY PROBLEMS

1. From the graph of $3x + 4y = 12$, $4y + 7x = 12$ and $3x + 4y = -4$, find common solutions to any two of the given equations.

    Ans. The common solution of $3x + 4y = 12$ and $4y + 7x = 12$ is $x = 0$, $y = 3$. The common solution of $3x + 4y = -4$ and $4y + 7x = 12$ is $x = 4$, $y = -4$. Since $3x + 4y = 12$ and $3x + 4y = -4$ are parallel, there is no common solution.

(1.1)

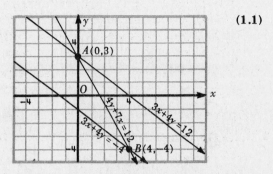

2. Solve each system of equations graphically: **(1.2)**

    a) $\begin{cases} y = -2 \\ x = 3\frac{1}{2} \end{cases}$ *b)* $\begin{cases} y = 4 \\ x + y = 2 \end{cases}$ *c)* $\begin{cases} 3x + 4y = -6 \\ y = 3 - 3x \end{cases}$

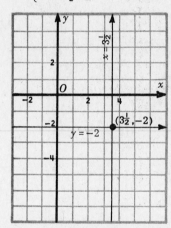 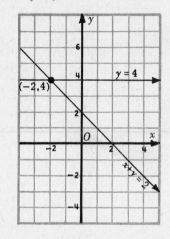 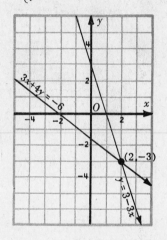

Ans. $x = 3\frac{1}{2}$, $y = -2$ *Ans.* $x = -2$, $y = 4$ *Ans.* $x = 2$, $y = -3$

Solution set is $\{(3\frac{1}{2}, -2)\}$ Solution set is $\{(-2, 4)\}$ Solution set is $\{(2, -3)\}$

3. Graph each equation and determine which equations have no common solution.   **(1.3)**

    a) $2x + 3y = 6$
           $5x + 3y = 6$
           $2x + 3y = -3$

                                b) $y + 2x = 0$
                                       $2y - 3x = 6$
                                       $y = 3 - 2x$

Ans.   *Ans.*

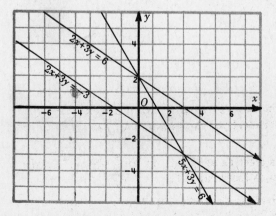

    $2x + 3y = 6$ and $2x + 3y = -3$ have no common solution. $y = 3 - 2x$ and $y + 2x = 0$ have no common solution.

4. Graph each equation and determine which equations are such that any pair of values satisfying one equation satisfies the other also: **(1.4)**

a) $2y - x = 2$
$\quad y + 2x = 6$
$\quad 3x = 6y - 6$

Ans.

b) $2y = x - 4$
$\quad x + 4y = 4$
$\quad 8y = 8 - 2x$

Ans.

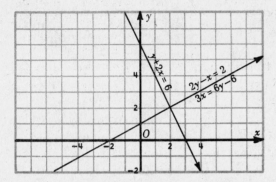

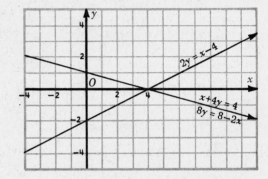

The graph of $2y - x = 2$ and $3x = 6y - 6$ is the same line. A pair of values satisfying one equation satisfies the other.

The graph of $x + 4y = 4$ and $8y = 8 - 2x$ is the same line. A pair of values satisfying one equation satisfies the other.

5. Add or subtract to eliminate one variable then find the value of the remaining variable. **(2.1)**

a) $\begin{cases} 3x - y = 21 \\ 2x + y = 4 \end{cases}$

c) $\begin{cases} m + 4n = 6 \\ m - 2n = 18 \end{cases}$

e) $\begin{cases} 8r = 11 - 5s \\ 5r = 15 + 5s \end{cases}$

b) $\begin{cases} 7a + b = 22 \\ 5a + b = 14 \end{cases}$

d) $\begin{cases} 3k + 5p = 9 \\ 3k - p = -9 \end{cases}$

f) $\begin{cases} -10u = 2v + 30 \\ -u = -2v + 14 \end{cases}$

a) (Add, $5x = 25$) *Ans.* $x = 5$
b) (Subt., $2a = 8$) *Ans.* $a = 4$

c) (Subt., $6n = -12$) *Ans.* $n = -2$
d) (Subt., $6p = 18$) *Ans.* $p = 3$

e) (Add, $13r = 26$) *Ans.* $r = 2$
f) (Add, $-11u = 44$) *Ans.* $u = -4$

6. Solve by addition or subtraction: **(2.2)**

a) $\begin{cases} 7a + t = 42 \\ 3a - t = 8 \end{cases}$

c) $\begin{cases} 2a + 5s = 44 \\ 6a - 5s = -8 \end{cases}$

e) $\begin{cases} 8r - 1 = 3t \\ 8r + 1 = 9t \end{cases}$

b) $\begin{cases} 4r - 2s = -14 \\ 4r - 5s = -32 \end{cases}$

d) $\begin{cases} 7c - 3d = 23 \\ -2c - 3d = 5 \end{cases}$

f) $\begin{cases} -7g = 31 - 2h \\ -17g = 17 + 2h \end{cases}$

a) (Add) *Ans.* $a = 5$, $t = 7$
b) (Subt.) *Ans.* $r = -\frac{1}{2}$, $s = 6$

c) (Add) *Ans.* $a = 4\frac{1}{2}$, $s = 7$
d) (Subt.) *Ans.* $c = 2$, $d = -3$

e) (Subt.) *Ans.* $r = \frac{1}{4}$, $t = \frac{1}{3}$
f) (Add) *Ans.* $g = -2$, $h = 8\frac{1}{2}$

7. Solve by addition or subtraction: **(2.3a)**
(One multiplication is needed before adding or subtracting.)

a) *(1)* $2x - y = 5$
$\quad$ *(2)* $3x + 3y = 21$

c) *(1)* $3c + 5d = 11$
$\quad$ *(2)* $2c - d = 16$

e) *(1)* $3h - 4j = 13$
$\quad$ *(2)* $-6h + 3j = -21$

b) *(1)* $A + 4B = 18$
$\quad$ *(2)* $5A + 3B = 5$

d) *(1)* $7r = 5s + 15$
$\quad$ *(2)* $2r = s + 9$

f) *(1)* $6t = 3v + 63$
$\quad$ *(2)* $5t = 9v + 85$

a) (M_3 in eq.*1* and add)
$\quad$ *Ans.* $x = 4$, $y = 3$

c) (M_5 in eq.*2* and add)
$\quad$ *Ans.* $c = 7$, $d = -2$

e) (M_2 in eq.*1* and add)
$\quad$ *Ans.* $h = 3$, $j = -1$

b) (M_5 in eq.*1* and subt.)
$\quad$ *Ans.* $A = -2$, $B = 5$

d) (M_5 in eq.*2* and subt.)
$\quad$ *Ans.* $r = 10$, $s = 11$

f) (M_3 in eq.*1* and subt.)
$\quad$ *Ans.* $t = 8$, $v = -5$

8. Find each solution set by addition or subtraction: (2.3b)

(Two multiplications are needed before adding or subtracting.)

a) (1) $3x + 5y = 11$
    (2) $4x - 3y = 5$

c) (1) $8a + 3b = 13$
    (2) $3a + 2b = 11$

e) (1) $-3m + 4p = -6$
    (2) $5m - 6p = 8$

b) (1) $5t - 2s = 17$
    (2) $8t + 5s = 19$

d) (1) $6c + 12b = 7$
    (2) $8c - 15b = -1$

f) (1) $7r + 11s = 35$
    (2) $6r - 12s = 30$

a) (M_4 in eq. 1, M_3 in eq. 2
    and subtract)

$x = 2, \; y = 1$

Ans. $\{(2, 1)\}$

c) (M_2 in eq. 1, M_3 in eq. 2
    and subtract)

$a = -1, \; b = 7$

Ans. $\{(-1, 7)\}$

e) (M_3 in eq. 1, M_2 in eq. 2
    and add)

$m = -2, \; p = -3$

Ans. $\{(-2, -3)\}$

b) (M_5 in eq. 1, M_2 in eq. 2
    and add)

$t = 3, \; s = -1$

Ans. $\{(3, -1)\}$

d) (M_4 in eq. 1, M_3 in eq. 2
    and subtract)

$c = \frac{1}{2}, \; b = \frac{1}{3}$

Ans. $\{(\frac{1}{2}, \frac{1}{3})\}$

f) (M_6 in eq. 1, M_7 in eq. 2
    and subtract)

$r = 5, \; s = 0$

Ans. $\{(5,0)\}$

---

9. Rearrange; then find the solution set by addition or subtraction: (2.4)

a) $\begin{cases} 3x - y = 17 \\ y = 8 - 2x \end{cases}$

c) $\begin{cases} 9 = 8p - 5q \\ 10 + 7q = 6p \end{cases}$

e) $\begin{cases} 12r - 3s = 3 \\ 3(r-1) = s - 4 \end{cases}$

b) $\begin{cases} 2y - 7x = 2 \\ 3x = 14 - y \end{cases}$

d) $\begin{cases} 10C - 9D = 18 \\ 6D + 2C = 1 \end{cases}$

f) $\begin{cases} 4(W+3) = 3Z + 7 \\ 2(Z-5) = W + 5 \end{cases}$

a) $x = 5, \; y = -2$; Ans. $\{(5,-2)\}$ c) $p = \frac{1}{2}, \; q = -1$; Ans. $\{(\frac{1}{2}, -1)\}$ e) $r = 2, \; s = 7$; Ans. $\{(2,7)\}$

b) $x = 2, \; y = 8$;   Ans. $\{(2,8)\}$ d) $C = \frac{3}{2}, \; D = -\frac{1}{3}$; Ans. $\{(\frac{3}{2}, -\frac{1}{3})\}$ f) $W = 7, \; Z = 11$; Ans. $\{(7,11)\}$

---

10. Solve by addition or subtraction: (2.5)

a) $\begin{cases} \frac{1}{2}c + \frac{1}{2}d = 4 \\ \frac{1}{2}c - \frac{1}{2}d = -2 \end{cases}$

c) $\begin{cases} 3K - \frac{1}{3}N = 11 \\ 2K + \frac{1}{3}N = 4 \end{cases}$

e) $\begin{cases} 3r - 2p = 32 \\ \frac{r}{5} + 3p = -1 \end{cases}$

b) $\begin{cases} \frac{4}{5}r - \frac{1}{4}s = 11 \\ \frac{3}{5}r - \frac{1}{4}s = 8 \end{cases}$

d) $\begin{cases} x - y = 17 \\ \frac{4}{3}x + \frac{3}{2}y = 0 \end{cases}$

f) $\begin{cases} \frac{3b}{a} - 4 = \frac{3}{a} \\ \frac{5a}{b} + 2 = \frac{25}{b} \end{cases}$

Ans. a) $c = 2, \; d = 6$ b) $r = 15, \; s = 4$ c) $K = 3, \; N = -6$ d) $x = 9, \; y = -8$ e) $r = 10, \; p = -1$ f) $a = 3, \; b = 5$

---

11. Find each solution set by addition or subtraction: (2.6)

a) $\begin{cases} 3x - y = 500 \\ .7x + .2y = 550 \end{cases}$

c) $\begin{cases} y = 4x - 100 \\ .06y = .05x + 32 \end{cases}$

e) $\begin{cases} .8R - .7T = 140 \\ .03R + .05T = 51 \end{cases}$

b) $\begin{cases} a - 2b = 500 \\ .03a + .02b = 51 \end{cases}$

d) $\begin{cases} .03C + .04D = 44 \\ .04C + .02D = 42 \end{cases}$

f) $\begin{cases} .05(W+2000) = .03(Y+3000) \\ W = \frac{Y}{2} + 500 \end{cases}$

Ans. a) $x = 500, \; y = 1000$
    $\{(500,1000)\}$

c) $y = 700, \; x = 200$
    $\{(700, 200)\}$

e) $R = 700, \; T = 600$
    $\{(700, 600)\}$

b) $a = 1400, \; b = 450$
    $\{(1400, 450)\}$

d) $C = 800, \; D = 500$
    $\{(800, 200)\}$

f) $W = 4000, \; Y = 7000$
    $\{(4000, 7000)\}$

---

12. Substitute to eliminate one variable, then find the value of the remaining variable: (3.1)

a) $\begin{cases} y = 2x \\ 7x - y = 35 \end{cases}$

d) $\begin{cases} r = 4t - 1 \\ 6t + r = 79 \end{cases}$

g) $\begin{cases} a = 9 - 3b \\ 7b + 5a = 33 \end{cases}$

b) $\begin{cases} a = b + 2 \\ 3a + 4b = 20 \end{cases}$

e) $\begin{cases} 3p = 27 - q \\ 2q = 3p \end{cases}$

h) $\begin{cases} 3d - 2g = 27 \\ d = 4 - g \end{cases}$

c) $\begin{cases} R = \frac{S}{3} \\ 3R + 2S = 36 \end{cases}$

f) $\begin{cases} 5y - 9x = -24 \\ 5y = 11x \end{cases}$

i) $\begin{cases} s = \frac{t}{3} - 1 \\ 6s + t = 21 \end{cases}$

a) (Subst. $2x$ for y)
   Ans. $x = 7$

b) (Subst. $b + 2$ for a)
   Ans. $b = 2$

c) (Subst. $\frac{S}{3}$ for R)
   Ans. $S = 12$

d) (Subst. $4t - 1$ for r)
   Ans. $t = 8$

e) (Subst. $2q$ for $3p$)
   Ans. $q = 9$

f) (Subst. $11x$ for $5y$)
   Ans. $x = -12$

g) (Subst. $9 - 3b$ for a)
   Ans. $b = 1\frac{1}{2}$

h) (Subst. $4 - g$ for d)
   Ans. $g = -3$

i) (Subst. $\frac{t}{3} - 1$ for s)
   Ans. $t = 9$

13. Solve by substitution: **(3.2)**

a) $\begin{cases} x - y = 12 \\ 3x = 1 - 4y \end{cases}$

b) $\begin{cases} 5A - 8B = 8 \\ B + A = 12 \end{cases}$

c) $\begin{cases} r - 3s = 11 \\ 5s + 30 = 4r \end{cases}$

d) $\begin{cases} p = 2(r - 5) \\ 4p + 40 = 8r \end{cases}$

e) $\begin{cases} 6a = 7c + 7 \\ 7c - a = 28 \end{cases}$

f) $\begin{cases} h - 5 = \frac{d}{3} \\ 3h - 2d = -6 \end{cases}$

a) (Subst. $y + 12$ for x)
   Ans. $x = 7$, $y = -5$

b) (Subst. $12 - B$ for A)
   Ans. $A = 8$, $B = 4$

c) (Subst. $3s + 11$ for r)
   Ans. $r = 5$, $s = -2$

d) (Subst. $2r - 10$ for p)
   Ans. $p = -12$, $r = -1$

e) (Subst. $7c - 28$ for a)
   Ans. $a = 7$, $c = 5$

f) (Subst. $\frac{d}{3} + 5$ for h)
   Ans. $h = 12$, $d = 21$

14. Find the solution set of each by substitution: **(3.3)**

a) $\begin{cases} x - 9b = 0 \\ \frac{x}{3} = 2b + \frac{1}{3} \end{cases}$

b) $\begin{cases} r + 5 = 2s \\ \frac{4s + 1}{5} = 3r - 3 \end{cases}$

c) $\begin{cases} \frac{c}{2} + \frac{d}{3} = 9 \\ c = 4d + 4 \end{cases}$

d) $\begin{cases} h + 10m = 900 \\ .4h = -2m + 300 \end{cases}$

a) (Subst. $9b$ for x)
   Ans. $b = \frac{1}{3}$, $x = 3$
   $\{(\frac{1}{3}, 3)\}$

b) (Subst. $2s - 5$ for r)
   Ans. $s = 3\frac{1}{2}$, $r = 2$
   $\{(3\frac{1}{2}, 2)\}$

c) (Subst. $4d + 4$ for c)
   Ans. $c = 16$, $d = 3$
   $\{(16,3)\}$

d) (Subst. $900 - 10m$ for h)
   Ans. $h = 600$, $m = 30$
   $\{(600,30)\}$

15. Insert **and** or **or** to make each sentence a true statement: **(4.1)**

a) The system $\begin{cases} x = 2y \\ x + y = 6 \end{cases}$ is true only for the ordered pair which makes $x = 2y$ true

? $x + y = 6$ true.

b) The system $\begin{cases} x > 2y \\ y \le 2x - 3 \end{cases}$ is true only for the ordered pairs which make $x > 2y$ true

? $y \ge 2x - 3$ true.

c) The absolute value equation $|x + 2| = 5$ is true only for the ordered pairs which make
$x + 2 = 5$? $x + 2 = -5$ true.

Ans. a) and,   b) and,   c) or

16. Determine the intersection set and the union set of the sets in each: **(4.2)**

a) $C = \{2, 4, 6, 8\}$ and $D = \{1, 2, 3, 4, 5\}$

b) $E = \{2, 4, 6, \ldots, 20, 22, 24\}$ and $F = \{1, 3, 5, \ldots, 19, 21, 23\}$

c) $G = \{(1,1), (2,2), (3,3), (4,4)\}$ and $H = \{(1, 2), (2,2), (2, 3), (3,3)\}$

d) $K = \{\frac{1}{2}, 1\frac{1}{2}, 2\frac{1}{2}, 3\frac{1}{2}, 4\frac{1}{2}, \ldots\}$ and $N = \{\text{natural numbers}\}$.

Ans. a) Intersection set, $C \cap D = \{2, 4\}$ and union set, $C \cup D = \{1, 2, 3, 4, 5, 6, 8\}$

    b) $E \cap F = \emptyset$, $E \cup F = \{1, 2, 3, \ldots, 22, 23, 24\}$

    c) $G \cap H = \{(2,2), (3,3)\}$, $G \cup H = \{(1,1), (1,2), (2,2), (2,3), (3,3), (4,4)\}$

    d) $K \cap N = \emptyset$, $K \cup N = \{\frac{1}{2}, 1, 1\frac{1}{2}, 2, 2\frac{1}{2}, 3, 3\frac{1}{2}, \ldots\}$

17. On the same set of axes, graph the solution set of each system of inequalities and   **(5.1)**
name an ordered pair in the solution set of the system:

a) $\begin{cases} x \le -2 \\ y < -x \end{cases}$,

b) $\begin{cases} y > x + 2 \\ y < -2x + 4 \end{cases}$,

c) $\begin{cases} x + y \le 3 \\ y < x - 2 \end{cases}$,

d) $\begin{cases} y \ge -x + 2 \\ y > \frac{1}{2}x \end{cases}$

Ans. a) In Fig. (*a*), the graph of the solution set of the given system includes the cross-hatched region, S, which is the intersection of the shaded half-planes, $x < -2$ and $y < -x$, and also the line, $x = -2$.

Examples of ordered pairs in the system are

$$(-3,0), (-2,1), (-4,1)$$

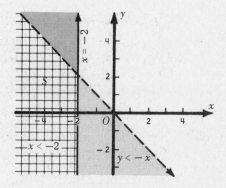

Fig. (*a*)

b) In Fig. (*b*), the graph of the solution set of the given system is the cross-hatched region, S, which is the intersection of the shaded half-planes, $y > x + 2$ and $y < -2x + 4$. The region does not include the lines $y = x + 2$ and $y = -2x + 4$, which are not drawn in full.

Examples of ordered pairs in the system are

$$(-3,0), (0,3), \text{ and } (-4,-1)$$

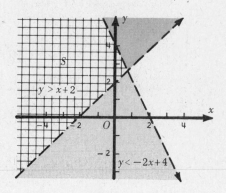

Fig. (*b*)

c) In Fig. (*c*), the graph of the solution set of the given system includes the cross-hatched region, S, which is the intersection of the shaded half-planes, $x + y < 3$ and $y < x - 2$, and also the line $x + y = 3$. The graph does not include the line, $y = x - 2$ which is not drawn in full.

Examples of ordered pairs in the system are

$$(2\tfrac{1}{2}, 0), (3,0), \text{ and } (2,-2)$$

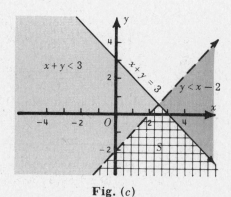

Fig. (*c*)

d) In Fig. (*d*), the graph of the solution set of the given system includes the cross-hatched region, S, which is the intersection of the shaded half-planes, $y > \tfrac{1}{2}x$ and $y > -x + 2$, and also the line, $y = -x + 2$. The graph does not include the line, $y = \tfrac{1}{2}x$ which is not drawn in full.

Examples of ordered pairs in the system are

$$(2,2), (0,3) \text{ and } (3,5)$$

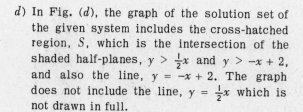

Fig. (*d*)

18. Graph each equation: **(6.1)**

$a)$ $|y| = 3$, $\quad$ $b)$ $|x - 3| = 1$, $\quad$ $c)$ $|y + 3| = 1$

Ans. $a)$ The graph of $|y| = 3$ consists of two lines, $y = 3$ and $y = -3$, Fig. (a).

$\quad$ $b)$ The graph of $|x - 3| = 1$ consists of two lines $x = 4$ and $x = 2$, Fig. (b).

$\quad$ $c)$ The graph of $|y + 3| = 1$ consists of two lines $y = -2$ and $y = -4$, Fig. (c).

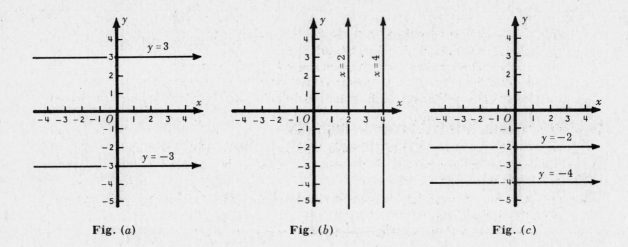

Fig. (a) $\qquad\qquad$ Fig. (b) $\qquad\qquad$ Fig. (c)

19. Graph each equation: **(6.2)**

$a)$ $y = -|x|$, $\quad$ $b)$ $x = |y| - 2$, $\quad$ $c)$ $|x + y| = 3$

Ans. $a)$ In Fig. (d), the graph of $y = -|x|$ consists of two lines meeting at the origin. Except for the origin, the lines lie below the x-axis since y is 0 or negative.

$\quad$ $b)$ In Fig. (e), the graph of $x = |y| - 2$ consists of two lines meeting at $(-2,0)$ on the x-axis. Since $|y| \geq 0$, then x cannot have a value less than -2.

$\quad$ $c)$ In Fig. (f), the graph of $|x + y| = 3$ consists of two lines, $x + y = 3$ and $x + y = -3$, which are parallel to each other.

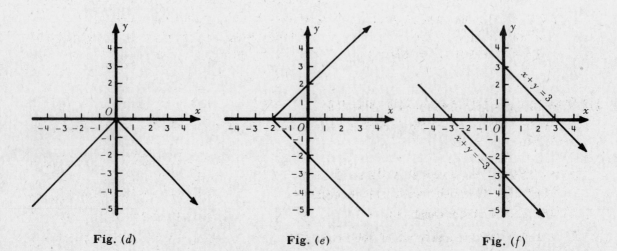

Fig. (d) $\qquad\qquad$ Fig. (e) $\qquad\qquad$ Fig. (f)

Chapter 9

Problem-Solving

The four steps of **problem-solving** are as follows:
1. **Representation** of unknowns by variables.
2. **Translation** of relationships among unknowns into equations.
3. **Solution** of equations to find the values of the unknowns.
4. **Check or verification** of the values found to see if they satisfy the original problem.

1. NUMBER PROBLEMS HAVING ONE UNKNOWN

In number problems having one unknown a single relationship involving the unknown is needed. After the unknown is represented by a variable such as n or x, this relationship is used to obtain an equation.

The value of the unknown is found by solving the equation. However, the value found must be checked in the original problem.

Do not check in any equation; the equation may be incorrect!

To Solve a Number Problem Having One Unknown

Solve: Twice a certain number, increased by 10, equals 32. Find the number.

Procedure:

1. **Represent** the unknown by a variable.

2. **Translate** the relationship about the unknown into an equation:

3. **Solve** the equation:

4. **Check** the value found in the original problem:
(Do not check in any equation!)

Solution:

1. **Representation:** Let n = the number.

2. **Translation:**
Twice a certain number, increased by 10, equals 32.
$$2n \qquad + \quad 10 \qquad = \quad 32$$

3. **Solution:** $2n = 22$ or $n = 11$. *Ans.* The number is 11.

4. **Check:** Does 11 satisfy the statement,
"Twice the number, increased by 10, equals 32."?
If it does, then $2(11) + 10 \overset{?}{=} 32$
$$32 = 32$$

1.1 Translation of Statements into Equations

Using n to represent the unknown, express each sentence as an equation; then, find the unknown:

	Equations	Value of n
a) If a number is decreased by 5, the result is 28.	*Ans.* $n - 5 = 28$	$n = 33$
b) Three times a number, increased by 8, equals 41.	*Ans.* $3n + 8 = 41$	$n = 11$
c) Two-fifths a number equals 18.	*Ans.* $\frac{2n}{5} = 18$	$n = 45$
d) A number added to one-fourth of itself equals 45.	*Ans.* $n + \frac{n}{4} = 45$	$n = 36$
e) When eight times a number is diminished by 20, the remainder is 28.	*Ans.* $8n - 20 = 28$	$n = 6$
f) 10 exceeds one-fourth of a number by 3.	*Ans.* $10 - \frac{n}{4} = 3$	$n = 28$

1.2 Verification or Check in Original Statement

Check each statement:

a) Does 20 check in "one-fifth of the number, increased by 3, is 7"?

Check: $\frac{20}{5} + 3 \overset{?}{=} 7$, $4 + 3 \overset{?}{=} 7$, $7 = 7$ *Ans.* Yes

b) Does 3 check in "seven times a number, less 12, is 9"?

Check: $7(3) - 12 \overset{?}{=} 9$, $21 - 12 \overset{?}{=} 9$, $9 = 9$ *Ans.* Yes

c) Does 24 check in "three-fourths of the number, decreased by 10, equals 8"?

Check: $\frac{3}{4}(24) - 10 \overset{?}{=} 8$, $18 - 10 \overset{?}{=} 8$, $8 = 8$ *Ans.* Yes

d) Does 21 check in "five times the sum of the number and 8 is three times the number, less 2"?

Check: $5(21 + 8) \overset{?}{=} 3(21) - 2$, $5(29) \overset{?}{=} 63 - 2$, $145 \neq 61$ *Ans.* No

1.3 Complete Solutions of Number Problems

a) Find a number such that three times the number, decreased by 5, equals 19.

b) What number added to 40 is the same as five times the number?

c) If eleven times a number is increased by 10, the result is fourteen times the number, less 5. Find the number.

Solutions:

a) Let n = the number.

$3n - 5 = 19$

$3n = 24$, $\underline{n = 8}$

Ans. The number is 8.

Check:

Does 8 check in "three times the number, decreased by 5, equals 19"?

$24 - 5 \overset{?}{=} 19$, $19 = 19$

b) Let n = the number.

$n + 40 = 5n$

$40 = 4n$, $\underline{n = 10}$

Ans. The number is 10.

Does 10 check in "the number added to 40 is five times the number"?

$40 + 10 \overset{?}{=} 50$, $50 = 50$

c) Let n = the number.

$11n + 10 \overset{?}{=} 14n - 5$

$15 = 3n$, $\underline{n = 5}$

Ans. The number is 5.

Does 5 check in "eleven times the number, increased by 10, is fourteen times the number, less 5"?

$55 + 10 \overset{?}{=} 70 - 5$, $65 = 65$

2. NUMBER PROBLEMS HAVING TWO UNKNOWNS

In number problems having two unknowns, two relationships concerning the unknowns are needed. Such problems may be solved by either of two methods:

Method 1.   Using One Variable and Obtaining One Equation

One of the relationships is used to represent the two unknowns in terms of one variable. The other relationship is then used to obtain a single equation.

Method 2.   Using Two Variables and Obtaining Two Equations

Each of the unknowns is represented by a different variable. Each of the two relationships is then used to obtain a separate equation.

The value found for the unknown by either method must be checked in the **original problem**.

Do not check in any equation or equations since they may be incorrect!

To Solve a Number Problem Having Two Unknowns

Solve: One positive number is twice another. The larger is 10 more than the smaller. Find the numbers.

Procedure, using one letter:

1. **Represent** one of the unknowns by a variable. Represent the other unknown in terms of the variable using one of the relationships.

2. **Translate** the other relationship into an equation:

3. **Solve** the equation:

4. **Check** the values found in the **original problem:**

Solution: Method 1.

1. **Representation:** Let s = the smaller number.
   Then $2s$ = the larger number, since the larger is twice the smaller.

2. **Translation:** The larger is 10 more than the smaller.
$$2s \quad = \quad s + 10$$

3. **Solution:** $2s - s = 10$, $s = 10$ and $2s = 20$

Ans. The numbers are 20 and 10.

4. **Check:** Are the numbers 20 and 10?

One number is twice another.	The larger is 10 more than the smaller.
Hence, $20 \overset{?}{=} 2(10)$	Hence, $20 \overset{?}{=} 10 + 10$
$20 = 20$	$20 = 20$

Procedure, using two letters:

1. **Represent** each of the two unknowns by a different variable:

2. **Translate** each relationship into a separate equation:

3. **Solve** both equations:

4. **Check** in the **original problem:**

Solution: Method 2.

1. **Representation:** Let l = the larger number, and s = the smaller number.

2. **Translation:** One number is twice another.
$$l \quad = \quad 2s$$

The larger is 10 more than the smaller.
$$l \quad = \quad s + 10$$

3. **Solution:** Substitute $2s$ for l in $l = s + 10$,
$$2s = s + 10, \quad s = 10.$$
Since $l = 2s$, $l = 20$.

Ans. The numbers are 20 and 10.

4. **Check:** (Same as check for Method 1.)

2.1 Representing Two Unknowns Using One Variable

If n represents a number, represent another number that is

a) five more than n	*Ans.* $n + 5$	f) the product of n and 15	*Ans.* $15n$
b) ten less than n	*Ans.* $n - 10$	g) the quotient of n and 3	*Ans.* $\frac{n}{3}$
c) five times as large as n	*Ans.* $5n$	h) 3 more than twice n	*Ans.* $2n + 3$
d) one-fifth of n	*Ans.* $\frac{n}{5}$	i) 80 reduced by six times n	*Ans.* $80 - 6n$
e) the sum of twice n and 8	*Ans.* $2n + 8$	j) ten less than the product of n and 5.	*Ans.* $5n - 10$

2.2 Using One Equation for Two Unknowns

Express each sentence as an equation; then, find the numbers.

a) Two numbers are represented by n and $(n+5)$. Their sum is 3 less than three times the smaller.

Ans. $n + (n+5) = 3n - 3$, $n = 8$
Numbers are 8 and 13.

b) Two numbers are represented by n and $(20-n)$. The first is three times the second.

Ans. $n = 3(20-n)$, $n = 15$
Numbers are 15 and 5.

c) Two numbers are represented by n and $(3n-2)$. The second number is twice the first number, less 6.

Ans. $(3n-2) = 2n - 6$, $n = -4$
Numbers are -4 and -14.

d) Two numbers are represented by n and $6n$. Ten times the first exceeds the second by 18.

Ans. $10n - 6n = 18$, $n = 4\frac{1}{2}$
Numbers are $4\frac{1}{2}$ and 27.

2.3 Using Two Equations for Two Unknowns

Using s for the smaller number and l for the larger, obtain two equations for each problem; then find l and s.

a) The sum of two numbers is 15.
Their difference is 8.

b) The sum of the larger and 8 is three times the smaller.
The larger reduced by 10 equals twice the smaller.

c) Separate 40 into two parts such that the larger exceeds twice the smaller by 52.

Ans. a) $l + s = 15$ $\quad l = 11\frac{1}{2},\ s = 3\frac{1}{2}$
$\ l - s = 8$

b) $l + 8 = 3s$ $\quad l = 46,\ s = 18$
$\ l - 10 = 2s$

c) $l + s = 40$ $\quad l = 44,\ s = -4$
$\ l - 2s = 52$

2.4 Complete Solution of Number Problem Having Two Unknowns

The larger of two numbers is three times the smaller. Their sum is 8 more than twice the smaller. Find the numbers.

Solution:

Method 1

1. Representation, using one variable:

Let s = smaller number
$3s$ = larger number, since larger is three times as large.

2. Translation, using one equation:

Their sum is 8 more than twice the smaller.
$3s + s = 2s + 8$

3. Solution:

$$4s = 2s + 8, \quad 2s = 8$$
$$s = 4 \text{ and } 3s = 12$$

Ans. Numbers are 12 and 4.

4. Check: (*Do this in the original problem.*)

Method 2

1. Representation, using two variables:

Let s = smaller number
l = larger number

2. Translation, using two equations:

Larger is three times the smaller.
$(1)\ l\ =3s$

Their sum is 8 more than twice the smaller.
$(2)\ l + s\ =2s + 8$

3. Solution: Substitute $3s$ for l in (2):
$3s + s = 2s + 8, \quad 2s = 8$
$s = 4 \text{ and } l = 3s = 12$

Ans. Numbers are 12 and 4.

4. Check: (*Do this in the original problem.*)

3. CONSECUTIVE INTEGER PROBLEMS

The members of the set of integers, I, are the positive integers, zero, and the negative integers:

$$I = \{\ldots, -6, -5, -4, -3, -2, -1, 0, 1, 2, 3, 4, 5, 6, \ldots\}$$

The members of the set of integers, I, may be divided into two sets; the set of even integers and the set of odd integers, as follows:

$$I = \{\ldots, -6, -4, -2, 0, 2, 4, 6, \ldots\} \cup \{\ldots, -5, -3, -1, 1, 3, 5, \ldots\}$$

Each consecutive integer problem involves a set of consecutive integers, a set of consecutive even integers or a set of consecutive odd integers. Each such set involves integers arranged in **increasing order** from left to right.

TABLE OF INTEGERS

	Consecutive Integers	Consecutive Even Integers	Consecutive Odd Integers
Illustrations	4, 5, 6, 7 −4, −3, −2, −1	4, 6, 8, 10 −4, −2, 0, 2	5, 7, 9, 11 −5, −3, −1, 1
Kinds of Integers	**Odd or Even**	**Even Only**	**Odd Only**
Differ by	1	2	2
Representation of First Consecutive No. of Second Consecutive No. of Third Consecutive No.	n $n+1$ $n+2$	n $n+2$ $n+4$	n $n+2$ $n+4$

Note. In the table, n represents the first number of a set. However, n may be used to represent any other number in the set. Thus, a set of three consecutive integers may be represented by $n-1$, n and $n+1$.

3.1 Representation Using n for First Integer

Using n for the first integer, represent

Representation

a) three consecutive integers and their sum, *Ans.* a) n, $n+1$, $n+2$ Sum = $3n+3$
b) three consecutive even integers and their sum, *Ans.* b) n, $n+2$, $n+4$ Sum = $3n+6$
c) three consecutive odd integers and their sum, *Ans.* c) n, $n+2$, $n+4$ Sum = $3n+6$
d) four consecutive integers and their sum. *Ans.* d) n, $n+1$, $n+2$, $n+3$ Sum = $4n+6$

3.2 Representation Using n for Middle Integer

Using n for the middle integer, represent

Representation

a) three consecutive integers and their sum, *Ans.* a) $n-1$, n, $n+1$ Sum = $3n$
b) three consecutive even integers and their sum, *Ans.* b) $n-2$, n, $n+2$ Sum = $3n$
c) five consecutive odd integers and their sum. *Ans.* c) $n-4$, $n-2$, n, $n+2$, $n+4$ Sum = $5n$

3.3 Translation in Consecutive Integer Problems

Using n, $n+1$ and $n+2$ for three consecutive integers, express each sentence as an equation; then, find the integers.

Equations | **Integers**

a) Their sum is 21. *Ans.* a) $3n+3 = 21$ | 6, 7, 8
b) The sum of the first two is 7 more than the third. *Ans.* b) $2n+1 = (n+2)+7$ | 8. 9, 10
c) The sum of the second and third is 2 less than three times the first. *Ans.* c) $2n+3 = 3n-2$ | 5, 6, 7
d) The third added to twice the first is 12 more than twice the second. *Ans.* d) $2n+(n+2) = 2(n+1)+12$ | 12, 13, 14

3.4 Translation in Consecutive Even Integer Problems

Using n, $n+2$ and $n+4$ for three consecutive even integers, express each sentence as an equation; then, find the integers.

	Equations	Integers
a) Their sum is 42.	Ans. a) $3n + 6 = 42$	12, 14, 16
b) The second is half the first.	Ans. b) $n + 2 = \frac{n}{2}$	$-4, -2, 0$
c) The first equals the sum of the second and third.	Ans. c) $n = 2n + 6$	$-6, -4, -2$

3.5 Complete Solutions of an Integer Problem

Find five consecutive odd integers whose sum is 45.

Solutions:

Method 1	Method 2
Represent the five consecutive odd integers, using n, $n+2$, $n+4$, $n+6$ and $n+8$.	Represent the five consecutive odd integers, using $n-4$, $n-2$, n, $n+2$ and $n+4$.
Then, their sum = $5n + 20 = 45$.	Then, their sum = $5n = 45$.
$5n = 25$, $n = 5$ (the first)	$n = 9$ (the third)
Ans. 5, 7, 9, 11, 13	Ans. 5, 7, 9, 11, 13

4. AGE PROBLEMS

Rule 1. To find a person's future age a number of years hence, **add** that number of years to his present age.

Thus, in 10 yr., a person 17 yr. old will be $17 + 10$ or 27 yr. old.

Rule 2. To find a person's past age a number of years ago, **subtract** that number of years from his present age.

Thus, 10 yr. ago, a person 17 yr. old was $17 - 10$ or 7 yr. old.

4.1 Representing Ages on Basis of Present Age

Represent the age of a person in years

a) 10 yr. hence if his present age is x yr.	Ans. a) $x + 10$
b) 10 yr. ago if his present age is x yr.	Ans. b) $x - 10$
c) in y yr. if his present age is 40 yr.	Ans. c) $40 + y$
d) y yr. ago if his present age is 40 yr.	Ans. d) $40 - y$
e) y yr. ago if his present age is p yr.	Ans. e) $p - y$

4.2 Representing Ages

Find or represent the age of a person in years –

(In answer, the expression in parentheses is present age.)

a) 5 yr. hence if he was 20 yr. old 10 yr. ago.	Ans. a) $(20+10) + 5 = 35$
b) y yr. hence if he was 30 yr. old 5 yr. ago.	Ans. b) $(30+5) + y = y + 35$
c) 5 yr. ago if he will be 20 yr. old in y yr.	Ans. c) $(20-y) - 5 = 15 - y$

4.3 Using One Equation for Two Unknowns in Age Problems

Using $4S$ and S to represent the present ages of a father and his son, express each sentence as an equation; then, find their present ages.

		Equations	Ages Now
a) In 14 yr., the father will be twice as old as his son will be then.		*Ans. a)* $4S+14 = 2(S+14)$ $S = 7$	28, 7
b) In 5 yr., the father will be 21 yr. older than twice the age of his son now.		*Ans. b)* $4S+5 = 2S+21$ $S = 8$	32, 8
c) 3 yr. ago, the father was five times as old as his son was then.		*Ans. c)* $4S-3 = 5(S-3)$ $S = 12$	48, 12

4.4 Using Two Equations for Two Unknowns in Age Problems

Obtain two equations for each problem, using F and S to represent the present ages of a father and son, respectively; then, find their present ages.

	Equations	Ages Now
a) The sum of their present ages is 40. The father is 20 yr. older than the son.	*Ans. a)* (1) $F + S = 40$ (2) $F = S + 20$	30, 10
b) The sum of their present ages is 50. In 5 yr., the father will be three times as old as the son will be then.	*Ans. b)* (1) $F + S = 50$ (2) $F + 5 = 3(S+5)$	40, 10
c) In 8 yr., the father will be twice as old as his son will be then. 3 yr. ago, the father was three times as old as his son was then.	*Ans. c)* (1) $F + 8 = 2(S+8)$ (2) $F - 3 = 3(S-3)$	36, 14

4.5 Complete Solution of an Age Problem: Two Methods

A father is now 20 yr. older than his son. In 8 yr., the father's age will be 5 yr. more than twice the son's age then. Find their present ages.

Solutions:

Method 1, using two variables

Let F = father's present age
S = son's present age
Then (1) $F = S + 20$
(2) $F + 8 = 2(S+8) + 5$
Substitute $S+20$ for F in (2):
$(S+20) + 8 = 2(S+8) + 5$, $S = 7$

Method 2, using one variable

Let S = son's present age
and $S+20$ = father's present age
Then $(S+20) + 8 = 2(S+8) + 5$
$S + 28 = 2S + 16 + 5$
$7 = S$

Ans. 27 yr. and 7 yr.

5. RATIO PROBLEMS

Ratios are used to compare quantities by division.
The ratio of two quantities expressed in the same unit is the first divided by the second. Thus, the ratio of 10 ft. to 5 ft. is 10 ft. ÷ 5 ft., which equals 2.

Ways of Expressing a Ratio

A ratio can be expressed in the following ways:

1. Using a colon, 3:4 .
2. Using "to", 3 to 4 .
3. As a common fraction, $\frac{3}{4}$.
4. As a decimal fraction, .75 .
5. As a percent, 75% .

General Principles of Ratios

1. To find the ratios between quantities, the quantities must have the same unit.

> Thus, to find the ratio of 1 foot to 4 inches, first change the foot to 12 inches. Then, take the ratio of 12 inches to 4 inches. The result is a ratio of 3 to 1, or 3.

2. A ratio is an abstract number; that is, a number without a unit of measure.

> Thus, the ratio of $7 to $10 = 7 : 10 = .7. The common unit of $ must be removed.

> **Rule 1.** To obtain a ratio of two quantities having the same unit of measure, eliminate the unit of measure.

Thus, the ratio of $7 to $10 = $\frac{7}{10}$ = .7.

(Think of $7 as $7 \times \$1$ and $10 as $10 \times \$1$. Hence, $\frac{7 \times \$1}{10 \times \$1} = \frac{7}{10}$, by the elimination of the common factor, $1.)

3. **To simplify a ratio:**

> *a*) Eliminate any fractions contained in the ratio.
>
> Thus, the ratio of $2\frac{1}{2} : \frac{1}{2} = \frac{5}{2} \div \frac{1}{2} = \frac{5}{2}(2) = 5$ or $5:1$.
>
> *b*) Reduce the ratio to lowest terms:

> **Rule 2. To reduce a ratio to lowest terms,** eliminate any common factor that the terms, numerator and denominator, may have.

Thus, the ratio of 20 to 30 = $\frac{20}{30} = \frac{2(10)}{3(10)} = \frac{2}{3}$ or $2:3$.

We may write in ratio form: $20:30 = 2(10):3(10) = 2:3$.

4. The ratios of three or more quantities may be expressed as a **continued ratio.** This is simply an enlarged ratio statement.

> Thus, the ratio of $2 to $3 to $5 is the continued ratio, $2:3:5$. This enlarged ratio is a combination of three separate ratios. These are $2:3$, $3:5$ and $2:5$, as shown:

$$\overset{\displaystyle 2:5}{\underset{\displaystyle 2:3 \quad 3:5}{2 \ : \ 3 \ : \ 5}}$$

A continued ratio such as 20 to 30 to 50 may be reduced to lowest terms by using rule 2, as follows:

$20:30:50 = 2(10):3(10):5(10) = 2:3:5$ by the elimination of the common factor, 10.

To Find the Ratio of Two Quantities Having Different Units of Measure

Find the ratio of 2 years to 3 months.

Procedure: **Solution:**

1. Express each quantity in the same unit: $\frac{2 \text{ yr.}}{3 \text{ mo.}} = \frac{24 \text{ mo.}}{3 \text{ mo.}}$

2. Eliminate the common unit of measure, using rule 1: $= \frac{24}{3}$

3. Reduce to lowest terms, using rule 2: $= \frac{3(8)}{3(1)} = \frac{8}{1}$ or 8 *Ans.*

5.1 Ratio of Two Quantities Having the Same Unit: Rule 1

Express each ratio in lowest terms:

a) \$15 to \$3 $Ans.\ a)\ \frac{15}{3} = 5$ e) \$2.50 to \$1.50 $Ans.\ e)\ \frac{2.50}{1.50} = \frac{5}{3}$

b) 15 lb. to 3 lb. $Ans.\ b)\ \frac{15}{3} = 5$ f) \$1.25 to \$5 $Ans.\ f)\ \frac{1.25}{5} = \frac{1}{4}$

c) 3 oz. to 15 oz. $Ans.\ c)\ \frac{3}{15} = \frac{1}{5}$ g) $2\frac{1}{2}$ d. to 2 d. $Ans.\ g)\ 2\frac{1}{2} \div 2 = \frac{5}{4}$

d) 24 sec. to 18 sec. $Ans.\ d)\ \frac{24}{18} = \frac{4}{3}$ h) $2\frac{1}{4}$ yr. to $\frac{1}{4}$ yr. $Ans.\ h)\ 2\frac{1}{4} \div \frac{1}{4} = 9$

5.2 Ratio of Two Quantities with Different Units

Express each ratio in lowest terms:

	Change to Same Unit	**Ratio**
a) 2 yr. to 3 mo.	a) 24 mo. to 3 mo.	$\frac{24}{3} = 8$ $Ans.$
b) 80¢ to \$3.20	b) 80¢ to 320¢	$\frac{80}{320} = \frac{1}{4}$ $Ans.$
c) $1\frac{2}{3}$ yd. to 2 ft.	c) 5 ft. to 2 ft.	$\frac{5}{2} = 2\frac{1}{2}$ $Ans.$
d) 50 mph to 1 mi. per min.	d) 50 mph to 60 mph	$\frac{50}{60} = \frac{5}{6}$ $Ans.$

5.3 Continued Ratio of Three Quantities

Express each continued ratio in lowest terms:

	Change to Same Unit	**Continued Ratio**
a) 1 gal. to 2 qt. to 2 pt.	a) 8 pt. to 4 pt. to 2 pt.	$8:4:2 = 4:2:1$ $Ans.$
b) 1 ton to 1 lb. to 8 oz.	b) 2000 lb. to 1 lb. to $\frac{1}{2}$ lb.	$2000:1:\frac{1}{2} = 4000:2:1$
c) \$1 to 1 quarter to 2 dimes	c) 100¢ to 25¢ to 20¢	$100:25:20 = 20:5:4$
d) 30 sec. to 2 min. to 1 hr.	d) 30 sec. to 120 sec. to 3600 sec.	$30:120:3600 = 1:4:120$

5.4 Reducing a Ratio to Lowest Terms: Simplifying a Ratio: Rule 2

Express each ratio in lowest terms:

a) 50 to 60 $Ans.\ \frac{50}{60} = \frac{5}{6}$ e) $1\frac{3}{4}$ to 7 $Ans.\ \frac{7}{4} \div 7 = \frac{1}{4}$

b) 70 to 55 $Ans.\ \frac{70}{55} = \frac{14}{11}$ f) 12 to $\frac{3}{8}$ $Ans.\ 12 \div \frac{3}{8} = 32$

c) 175 to 75 $Ans.\ \frac{175}{75} = \frac{7}{3}$ g) $7\frac{1}{6}$ to $1\frac{1}{3}$ $Ans.\ \frac{43}{6} \div \frac{4}{3} = \frac{43}{8}$

d) 6.3 to .9 $Ans.\ \frac{6.3}{.9} = 7$ h) 80% to 30% $Ans.\ \frac{80\%}{30\%} = \frac{8}{3}$

5.5 Reducing a Ratio Containing Variables to Lowest Terms: Rule 2

Express each ratio in lowest terms:

a) $2x$ to $5x$ $Ans.\ \frac{2x}{5x} = \frac{2}{5}$ d) $4ab$ to $3ab$ $Ans.\ \frac{4ab}{3ab} = \frac{4}{3}$

b) $3a$ to $6b$ $Ans.\ \frac{3a}{6b} = \frac{a}{2b}$ e) $5s^2$ to s^3 $Ans.\ \frac{5s^2}{s^3} = \frac{5}{s}$

c) πD to πd $Ans.\ \frac{\pi D}{\pi d} = \frac{D}{d}$ f) x to $5x$ to $7x$ $Ans.\ x:5x:7x = 1:5:7$

5.6 Representation of Numbers in a Fixed Ratio

Using x as their common factor, represent the numbers and their sum if

		Numbers	Sum
a) two numbers have a ratio of 4 to 3		Ans. $4x$ and $3x$	$7x$
b) two numbers have a ratio of 7 to 1		Ans. $7x$ and x	$8x$
c) three numbers have a ratio of $4:3:1$		Ans. $4x$, $3x$ and x	$8x$
d) three numbers have a ratio of $2:5:8$		Ans. $2x$, $5x$ and $8x$	$15x$
e) five numbers have a ratio of $8:5:3:2:1$		Ans. $8x$, $5x$, $3x$, $2x$ and x	$19x$

5.7 Ratio in Number Problems

If two numbers in the ratio of $5:3$ are represented by $5x$ and $3x$, express each sentence as an equation; then, find x and the numbers.

	Equations	Value of x	Numbers
a) The sum of the numbers is 88.	Ans. a) $8x = 88$	$x = 11$	55 and 33
b) The difference of the numbers is 4.	Ans. b) $2x = 4$	$x = 2$	10 and 6
c) Twice the larger added to three times the smaller is 57.	Ans. c) $10x + 9x = 57$	$x = 3$	15 and 9
d) Three times the smaller equals the larger increased by 20.	Ans. d) $9x = 5x + 20$	$x = 5$	25 and 15

5.8 Ratio in a Triangle Problem

The sides of a triangle are in the ratio of $2:3:4$. If the perimeter of the triangle is 45 in., find each side.

Solution:

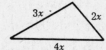

Let $2x$, $3x$, and $4x$ represent the sides in inches.
Then the perimeter, $9x = 45$;
$\underline{x = 5}$, $2x = 10$, $3x = 15$, $4x = 20$.   Ans. 10 in., 15 in., 20 in.

5.9 Ratio in a Money Problem

Will has $3\frac{1}{2}$ times as much money as Lester. If Will gives Lester a quarter, they will then have the same amount. How much did each have?

Solution:

Since the ratio of their money, $3\frac{1}{2}$ to 1, is $7:2$,
let $7x$ = Will's money in ¢ and $2x$ = Lester's money in ¢.
Then, $7x - 25 = 2x + 25$, and $\underline{x = 10}$, $7x = 70$, $2x = 20$.

Ans. 70¢ and 20¢

5.10 Ratio in a Will Problem

In his will, a man left his wife $20,000 and his son $12,000. Upon his death, his estate amounted to only $16,400. If the court divides the estate in the ratio of the bequests in the will, what should each receive?

Solution:

The ratio of $20,000 to $12,000 is $5:3$.
Let $5x$ = the wife's share in $ and $3x$ = the son's share in $.
Then, $8x = 16,400$, and $\underline{x = 2050}$, $5x = 10,250$, $3x = 6150$.

Ans. $10,250 and $6150

6. ANGLE PROBLEMS

The **measure of an angle** is the number of degrees in the angle.

Thus, the measure of angle A is 60 if 60 is the number of degrees in the angle.

In problems involving angles, when reference is made to an angle in a numerical context, the word "**angle**" means "the number of degrees in the angle" or "the measure of the angle in degrees."

Equal angles are angles having the same measure.

Thus, in triangle ABC, if $\angle A = 70°$ and $\angle B = 70°$, then $\angle A = \angle B$.

Pairs of Angles:

(1) Adjacent Angles	**(2) Complementary Angles**	**(3) Supplementary Angles**
Adjacent angles are two angles having the same vertex and a common side between them.	Complementary angles are two angles the sum of whose measures is 90°.	Supplementary angles are two angles the sum of whose measures is 180°.

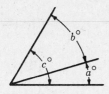   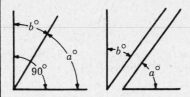 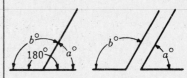

Fig. 1   Fig. 2   Fig. 3   Fig. 4   Fig. 5

Rule 1. If an angle of $c°$ consists of two adjacent angles of $a°$ and $b°$, as in Fig. 1, then

$$a + b = c$$

Thus, if $a = 25$ and $b = 32$, then $c = 25 + 32 = 57$.

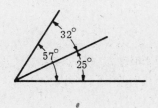

Rule 2. If two complementary angles contain $a°$ and $b°$, then

$$a + b = 90$$

Thus, 70 and 20 are the measures of complementary angles.

Complementary angles may be adjacent as in Fig. 2, or non-adjacent as in Fig. 3.

Either of two complementary angles is the complement of the other. If a and b are the measures of two complementary angles,

$$\text{then } b = 90 - a$$
$$\text{and } a = 90 - b$$

Rule 3. If two supplementary angles contain $a°$ and $b°$, then

$$a + b = 180$$

Thus, 70 and 110 are the measures of supplementary angles.

Supplementary angles may be adjacent as in Fig. 4, or non-adjacent as in Fig. 5.

Either of two supplementary angles is the supplement of the other. If a and b are the measures of two supplementary angles,

$$\text{then } b = 180 - a$$
$$\text{and } a = 180 - b$$

(4) Angles of any Triangle	**(5) Angles of a Right Triangle**	**(6) Angles of Isosceles Triangle**
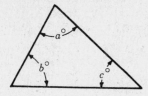	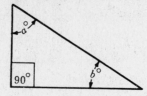	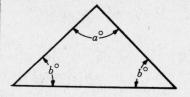
Fig. 6	Fig. 7	Fig. 8

Rule 4. The sum of the angles of any triangle equals 180°.

Thus, if the angles of a triangle contain $a°$, $b°$ and $c°$ as in Fig. 6, then

$$a + b + c = 180$$

Rule 5. The sum of the acute angles of a right triangle equals 90°.

Thus, if the acute angles of a right triangle as in Fig. 7, contain $a°$ and $b°$, then

$$a + b = 90$$

Rule 6. The angles opposite the equal sides of an isosceles triangle are equal.

Thus, if the equal angles of an isosceles triangle contain $b°$ and the third angle $a°$, as in Fig. 8, then

$$a + 2b = 180$$

6.1 Using One Equation for Two Unknowns in Angle Problems

If two angles in the ratio of 3 to 2 are represented by $3x$ and $2x$, express each sentence as an equation; then find x and the angles.

	Equation	x	Angles
a) The angles are adjacent and form an angle of 40°.	Ans. $3x + 2x = 40$	8	24°, 16°
b) The angles are complementary.	Ans. $3x + 2x = 90$	18	54°, 36°
c) The angles are supplementary.	Ans. $3x + 2x = 180$	36	108°, 72°
d) The larger angle is 28° less than twice the smaller.	Ans. $3x = 4x - 28$	28	84°, 56°
e) The smaller is 40° more than one-third of the larger.	Ans. $2x = \frac{3x}{3} + 40$	40	120°, 80°
f) The angles are two angles of a triangle whose third angle is 70°.	Ans. $3x + 2x + 70 = 180$	22	66°, 44°
g) The angles are the acute angles of a right triangle.	Ans. $3x + 2x = 90$	18	54°, 36°
h) The first angle is one of the two equal angles of an isosceles triangle and the other is the remaining angle.	Ans. $3x + 3x + 2x = 180$	$22\frac{1}{2}$	$67\frac{1}{2}°$, 45°

6.2 Using Two Equations for Two Unknowns in Angle Problems

If two angles are represented by a and b, obtain two equations for each problem; then find the angles.

	Equations	Angles
a) The angles are adjacent forming an angle of 88°. One is 36° more than the other.	Ans. $a + b = 88$ $a = b + 36$	62°, 26°
b) The angles are complementary. One is twice as large as the other.	Ans. $a + b = 90$ $a = 2b$	60°, 30°
c) The angles are supplementary. One is 60° less than twice the other.	Ans. $a + b = 180$ $a = 2b - 60$	100°, 80°
d) The angles are two angles of a triangle whose third angle is 40°. The difference of the angles is 24°	Ans. $a + b = 140$ $a - b = 24$	82°, 58°
e) The first angle is one of the two equal angles of an isosceles triangle and the other is the remaining angle. The second angle is three times the first.	Ans. $2a + b = 180$ $b = 3a$	36°, 108°

6.3 Three Angles Having a Fixed Ratio

If three angles in the ratio of 4:3:2 are represented by $4x$, $3x$ and $2x$, express each sentence as an equation; then find x and the angles.

	Equation	x	Angles
a) The first and second are adjacent and form an angle of 84°.	Ans. $4x+3x = 84$	12	48°, 36°, 24°
b) The second and third are complementary.	Ans. $3x+2x = 90$	18	72°, 54°, 36°
c) The first and third are supplementary.	Ans. $4x+2x = 180$	30	120°, 90°, 60°
d) The angles are the three angles of a triangle.	Ans. $4x+3x+2x = 180$	20	80°, 60°, 40°
e) The sum of the first and second is 27° more than twice the third.	Ans. $4x+3x = 4x+27$	9	36°, 27°, 18°
f) The first and third are acute angles of a right triangle.	Ans. $4x+2x = 90$	15	60°, 45°, 30°

6.4 Supplementary Angles Problem

The number of degrees in each of two supplementary angles are consecutive odd integers. Find each angle.

Solution: Let n and $n+2$ = the no. of degrees in each of the angles.
Then $2n+2 = 180$, $\underline{n = 89}$.   *Ans.* 89°, 91°

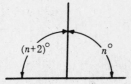

6.5 Sum of Angles of a Triangle Problem

In a triangle, one angle exceeds another by 12°. The third angle is 4° less than the sum of the other two. Find the angles.

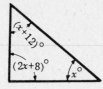

Solution: Let x = the no. of degrees in one angle
$x+12$ = the no. of degrees in the second
$2x+8$ = the no. of degrees in the third,   since $x+(x+12)-4 = 2x+8$.

Then their sum $4x+20 = 180$, and
$\underline{x = 40}$, $x+12 = 52$, $2x+8 = 88$.   *Ans.* 40°, 52°, 88°

7. PERIMETER PROBLEMS

The **length or the measure of a side of a polygon** is the number of linear units in the side.

Thus, the measure in inches of a side of 6 inches is 6; the measure in feet of the same side of 6 inches is $\frac{1}{2}$.

In problems involving sides, when reference is made to a side in a numerical context, the word "side" means "the number of linear units in the side" or "the length or measure of the side".

Equal sides are sides having the same measure.

Thus, in triangle ABC, if $AB = 10$ and $BC = 10$, then $AB = BC$.

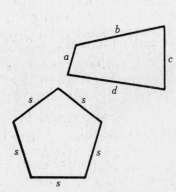

The **perimeter of a polygon** is the sum of its sides.
Thus, for a quadrilateral as shown, if p = the perimeter,
$$p = a+b+c+d$$

The perimeter of a regular polygon equals the product of one side and the number of sides.
Thus, for a regular pentagon, if p = the perimeter,
$$p = 5s$$

7.1 One-Equation Method: Perimeter of Rectangle

The width and length of a particular rectangle are represented by w and $2w + 2$, respectively. Express each sentence as an equation; then find w and the dimensions of the rectangle:

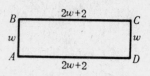

	Equation	w	Width, Length
a) The perimeter is 76 ft.	*Ans.* $6w + 4 = 76$	12	12 ft., 26 ft.
b) The semi-perimeter (half-perimeter) is 56 in.	*Ans.* $3w + 2 = 56$	18	18 in., 38 in.
c) The sum of three sides not including BC is 82 yd.	*Ans.* $4w + 2 = 82$	20	20 yd., 42 yd.
d) A rectangle having each dimension 3 rods less than those of the one shown has a perimeter of 28 rods.	*Ans.* $2(2w-1) + 2(w-3) = 28$	6	6 rd., 14 rd.

7.2 Two-Equation Method: Perimeter of Triangle

The base of a triangle is 20. If x and y represent the remaining sides, obtain two equations for each problem; then find AB and BC.

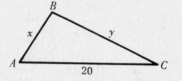

	Equations	AB, BC
a) The perimeter is 50. BC is twice AB.	*Ans.* $x + y + 20 = 50$ $y = 2x$	10, 20
b) The sum of AB and BC is 25. BC is 15 less than three times AB.	*Ans.* $x + y = 25$ $y = 3x - 15$	10, 15
c) AB is 4 more than half of BC. The difference of BC and AB is 2.	*Ans.* $x = \frac{y}{2} + 4$ $y - x = 2$	10, 12

7.3 One-Equation Method: Perimeter of Trapezoid

In a trapezoid having equal sides, the bases and sides are represented as shown in the adjoining figure. Express each sentence as an equation; then find x and the length of each base.

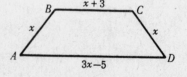

	Equation	x	BC, AD
a) The perimeter is 70 yd.	*Ans.* $6x - 2 = 70$	12	15 yd., 31 yd.
b) The combined length of the upper and lower bases is 36 in.	*Ans.* $4x - 2 = 36$	$9\frac{1}{2}$	$12\frac{1}{2}$ in., $23\frac{1}{2}$ in.
c) The sum of three sides not including the upper base is 65 ft.	*Ans.* $5x - 5 = 65$	14	17 ft., 37 ft.
d) The perimeter of the trapezoid exceeds the perimeter of a square having BC as a side by 10 rd.	*Ans.* $6x - 2 = 4(x+3) + 10$	12	15 rd., 31 rd.

7.4 Perimeter of a Quadrilateral: Ratio of Sides

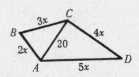

The sides of a quadrilateral in the ratio of $2:3:4:5$ are represented by $2x$, $3x$, $4x$ and $5x$, as shown in the adjoining figure. Express each sentence as an equation; then find x and AB.

	Equation	x	AB
a) The perimeter is 98 ft.	*Ans.* $14x = 98$	7	14 ft.
b) The largest side is 8 in. less than the sum of the other three sides.	*Ans.* $5x = 9x - 8$	2	4 in.
c) The sum of twice the smaller side and the other sides is 84 mi.	*Ans.* $2(2x) + 12x = 84$	$5\frac{1}{4}$	$10\frac{1}{2}$ mi.
d) The perimeter of the quadrilateral is 22 rd. more than that of a square having a side 4 rd. less than BC.	*Ans.* $14x = 4(3x - 4) + 22$	3	6 rd.
e) The perimeter of triangle ACD exceeds that of triangle ABC by 18 yd.	*Ans.* $9x + 20 = (5x + 20) + 18$	$4\frac{1}{2}$	9 yd.

7.5 Perimeter of an Isosceles Triangle

In an isosceles triangle, the ratio of one of the equal sides to the base is $4:3$. A piece of wire 55 inches long is to be used to make a wire model of it. Find the base and the side.

Solution: Let $4x$ = each equal side in in. and $3x$ = base in in.

Hence, $4x + 4x + 3x = 55$, $11x = 55$,

$\underline{x = 5}$, $3x = 15$, $4x = 20$.   *Ans.* 15 in. and 20 in.

8. COIN AND STAMP PROBLEMS

The total value (T) of a number of coins or stamps of the same kind equals the number (N) of the coins or stamps multiplied by the value (V) of one of the coins or stamps.

Formula: $T = NV$

Thus, 8 nickels have a total value in cents of $8(5) = 40$.

20 3-cent stamps have a total value in cents of $20(3) = 60$.

Note: In $T = NV$, T and V must have the same unit of money; that is, if V is in dollars, then T must be in dollars.

8.1 Finding Total Values

Find the total value *in cents* of each of the following:

a) 3 nickels and 5 dimes.   *Ans. a*) $3(5) + 5(10) = 65$

b) q quarters and 7 nickels.   *Ans. b*) $25q + 7(5) = 25q + 35$

c) 8 2-cent and t 3-cent stamps.   *Ans. c*) $8(2) + 3t = 3t + 16$

d) x 4-cent and $(x+5)$ 6-cent stamps.   *Ans. d*) $4x + 6(x+5) = 10x + 30$

8.2 Representation in Coin or Stamp Problems

Write the expression that represents the total value *in cents* of each; then simplify it:

	Representation	In Simplified Form
a) n dimes and $(n+3)$ quarters.	*Ans. a*) $10n + 25(n+3)$	$35n + 75$
b) n nickels and $(2n-3)$ half-dollars.	*Ans. b*) $5n + 50(2n-3)$	$105n - 150$
c) n 2-cent and $2n$ $1\frac{1}{2}$-cent stamps.	*Ans. c*) $2n + 2n(1\frac{1}{2})$	$5n$
d) n 6-cent and $(3n-10)$ 12-cent stamps.	*Ans. d*) $6n + 12(3n-10)$	$42n - 120$

8.3 Using One Equation in Coin or Stamp Problems

Express each sentence as an equation; then find n and the number of each coin or stamp.

a) The total value of n dimes and $2n$ nickels is $\$2.40$.

b) The total value of n nickels and $(n-3)$ quarters is $\$7.65$.

c) The value of $(n+5)$ dimes is three times n nickels.

d) The value of n 2-cent and $(n+3)$ 3-cent stamps is 2¢ more than $(n-1)$ 6¢ stamps.

Ans.	Equations	n	Number of Each Coin or Stamp
a)	$10n + 5(2n) = 240$	12	12 dimes and 24 nickels
b)	$5n + 25(n-3) = 765$	28	28 nickels and 25 quarters
c)	$10(n+5) = 3(5n)$	10	10 nickels and 15 dimes
d)	$2n + 3(n+3) = 6(n-1) + 2$	13	13 2-cent, 16 3-cent and 12 6-cent stamps

8.4 Using Two Equations in Coin or Stamp Problems

Using x for the value in ¢ of the first kind of coin and y for the value in ¢ of the second, obtain two equations for each problem; then find the kind of coins.

Equations

a) The value of 5 of the first kind and 6 of the second is 85¢. Each second coin has twice the value of each first.

Ans. a) $5x + 6y = 85$
$y = 2x$
$x = 5,\qquad y = 10$
NICKELS and DIMES

b) The value of 4 of the first kind is 85¢ less than 5 of the second. The value of 2 of the first kind and 4 of the second is $\$1.20$.

Ans. b) $\quad 4x = 5y - 85$
$2x + 4y = 120$
$x = 10,\qquad y = 25$
DIMES and QUARTERS

8.5 Complete Solution of a Coin Problem

In his coin bank, Joe has three times as many quarters as nickels. If the value of the quarters is $\$5.60$ more than the value of the nickels, how many of each kind does he have?

Solution: Let n = the number of nickels. $\qquad NV = T$

	Number of Coins	Value of Each in (¢)	Total Value in ¢
nickels	n	5	$5n$
quarters	$3n$	25	$75n$

The value of the quarters is $\$5.60$ more than the value of the nickels.

$75n = 5n + 560,\qquad \underline{n = 8},\ 3n = 24.\qquad$ *Ans.* 8 nickels, 24 quarters

8.6 Complete Solution of a Change Problem

Is it possible to change a $\$10$ bill into an equal number of half-dollars, quarters and dimes?

Solution: Let the no. of half-dollars, the no. of quarters and the no. of dimes, each be represented by n. The combined value is $\$10$.

Then, $\quad 10n + 25n + 50n = 1000,\quad 85n = 1000,\quad \underline{n = 11\tfrac{13}{17}}$

Ans. Impossible; the number of coins must be a whole number.

8.7 Complete Solution of a Fares Problem

On a trip, the fare for each adult was 50¢ and for each child 25¢. The number of passengers was 30 and the total paid was $12.25. How many adults and children were there?

Solution: Let a = the no. of adults   and c = the no. of children.

Then, $50a + 25c = 1225$

$a + c = 30$

Solving, $a = 19$, $c = 11$.   *Ans.* 19 adults, 11 children

9. COST AND MIXTURE PROBLEMS

The total value (T) of a number of units of the same kind equals the number (N) of the units multiplied by the value (V) of one of the units.

Formula: $T = NV$

Thus, the total value in cents of 5 books at 15¢ a book = 5(15) or 75.

The total value in cents of 6 tickets at 50¢ each and 5 tickets at 25¢ each = 6(50)+5(25) or 425.

Coin or Stamp Problems

The coin or stamp problems previously considered, are special cases of mixture problems. Stamps and coins may be "mixed" as coffees, teas, nuts and other items are mixed.

Cost Problems

When $T = NV$ is applied to a cost problem, the formula $C = NP$ should be used as follows:

$$C = NP \begin{cases} C = \text{total cost of number of units of a kind} \\ N = \text{number of such units} \\ P = \text{price of each unit purchased} \end{cases}$$

Thus, the cost in cents of 5 pencils at 8¢ a pencil = 5(8) or 40.

9.1 Representation in Mixture Problems: $T = NV$

Write the expression that represents the total value in *cents*; then simplify it:

	Representation	In Simplified Form
a) n lb. of coffee valued at 90¢ a lb. and $(n+3)$ lb. of coffee valued at $1.05 a lb.	*Ans. a*) $90n + 105(n+3)$	$195n + 315$
b) 3 lb. of tea valued at $1.50 per lb. and n lb. of tea valued at $1.75 per lb.	*Ans. b*) $3(150) + 175n$	$175n + 450$
c) n stamps valued at 35¢ each and $(20-n)$ stamps valued at 50¢ each.	*Ans. c*) $35n + 50(20-n)$	$1000 - 15n$
d) d dozen pencils at $1.30 a dozen and 3 dozen pencils at 60¢ a dozen.	*Ans. d*) $130d + 3(60)$	$130d + 180$

9.2 Representation in Cost Problems

Write the expression that represents the total cost in *dollars*; then simplify it:

	Representation	In Simplified Form
a) 10 tables priced at $5 apiece and n tables at $7.50 apiece.	*Ans. a*) $5(10) + 7.50n$	$7.5n + 50$
b) n lb. of candy priced at 65¢ a lb. and $(30-n)$ lb. of candy at $1.45 a lb.	*Ans. b*) $.65n + 1.45(30-n)$	$43.5 - .8n$
c) q qt. of cream at 35¢ a qt. and $(2q+3)$ qt. of cream at 42¢ a qt.	*Ans. c*) $.35q + .42(2q+3)$	$1.19q + 1.26$

9.3 Translation in Value and Cost Problems

Express each sentence as an equation; then find n and the number of each kind.

	Equation
a) The cost of n lb. of coffee at 95¢ a lb. and $(25-n)$ lb. of coffee at $1.10 a lb. is $26.00.	*Ans.* $95n + 110(25-n) = 2600$, $n = 10$ 10 lb. at 95¢ and 15 lb. at $1.10
b) The value of 40 tickets at 75¢ each and n tickets at $1.35 each is $40.80.	*Ans.* $40(75) + 135n = 4080$, $n = 8$ 8 tickets at $1.35
c) The cost of n lb. of cookies at 80¢ a lb. and $(2n-3)$ lb. of cookies at $1.60 a lb. is $15.20.	*Ans.* $80n + 160(2n-3) = 1520$, $n = 5$ 5 lb. at 80¢ and 7 lb. at $1.60
d) The value of n dollar bills, $(n+10)$ five-dollar bills and $(3n-2)$ ten-dollar bills is $174.	*Ans.* In dollars: $n + 5(n+10) + 10(3n-2) = 174$, $n = 4$ 4 $1 bills, 14 $5 bills, 10 $10 bills

9.4 Complete Solution: Coffee-Blending Problem

A coffee merchant blended coffee worth $.93 a lb. with coffee worth $1.20 a lb. The mixture of 30 lb. was valued by him at $1.02 a lb. How many lb. of each grade of coffee did he use?

Solutions:

Method 1, using one variable

	Value per lb. (¢)	No. of lb.	Total Value (¢)
cheaper	93	x	$93x$
better	120	$30-x$	$120(30-x)$
mixture	102	30	3060

$93x + 120(30-x) = 3060$
$93x + 3600 - 120x = 3060$
$x = 20$, $30 - x = 10$

Ans. 20 lb. of $.93¢ coffee and 10 lb. of $1.20 coffee

Method 2, using two variables

	Value per lb. (¢)	No. of lb.	Total Value (¢)
cheaper	93	x	$93x$
better	120	y	$120y$
mixture	102	30	3060

$93x + 120y = 3060$
M_{93} $x + y = 30$

$93x + 120y = 3060$
$93x + 93y = 2790$

Subtract: $27y = 270$
$y = 10$, $x = 20$

9.5 Complete Solution: Ticket-Selling Problem

At a game, tickets were bought at 30¢, 50¢ and 75¢ each. The number of 50¢ tickets was three times the number of 30¢ tickets and ten less than the number at 75¢. The receipts amounted to $88.50. How many of each were sold?

Solution:

Let n = the number of tickets at 30¢ each
$3n$ = the number of tickets at 50¢ each
$3n + 10$ = the number of tickets at 75¢ each.

Hence, $30n + 50(3n) + 75(3n+10) = 8850$
$30n + 150n + 225n + 750 = 8850$ or $405n = 8100$
$n = 20$, $3n = 60$, $3n + 10 = 70$ *Ans.* 20 at 30¢,   60 at 50¢,   70 at 75¢

10. INVESTMENT OR INTEREST PROBLEMS

Annual interest (I) equals the principal (P) multiplied by the rate of interest (R) per year.

Formula: $I = PR$

Thus, the annual interest from $200 at 6% per year is $(200)(.06)$ or $12.

Note. Unless otherwise stated, the rate of interest is the rate per yr.; that is, "5%" means "5% per yr.".

10.1 Representation in Interest Problems: $I = PR$

Write the expression that represents the annual interest in dollars earned by each principal; then simplify it.

		Representation	In Simplified Form
a)	\$2000 at 4% and \$(P+200) at 3%.	Ans. .04(2000) + .03(P+200)	.03P + 86
b)	\$P at 2% and \$2P at 5½%.	Ans. .02P + .05½(2P)	.13P
c)	\$P at 3% and \$(2P−400) at 6%.	Ans. .03P + .06(2P−400)	.15P − 24
d)	\$P at 7%, \$2P at 5% and \$3P at 3%.	Ans. .07P + .05(2P) + .03(3P)	.26P

10.2 Translation in an Interest Problem

Express each sentence as an equation; then solve and state each principal.

		Equation
a)	The total annual income from \$500 at 4% and \$P at 5% is \$55.	Ans. a) .04(500) + .05P = 55, P = 700 \$700 at 5%
b)	The total annual income from \$P at 3% and \$(5000−P) at 2% is \$120.	Ans. b) .03P + .02(5000−P) = 120, P = 2000 \$2000 at 3% and \$3000 at 2%
c)	The annual interest from \$P at 3% equals that from \$(P−2000) at 5%.	Ans. c) .03P = .05(P−2000), P = 5000 \$5000 at 3% and \$3000 at 5%
d)	The annual interest from \$2P at 5% exceeds that from \$3P at 3% by \$25.	Ans. d) .05(2P) = .03(3P) + 25, P = 2500 \$5000 at 5% and \$7500 at 3%
e)	The total annual interest from \$P at 6%, \$2P at 5% and \$(2P−300) at 4% is \$180.	Ans. e) .06P + .05(2P) + .04(2P−300) = 180, P = 800 \$800 at 6%, \$1600 at 5%, \$1300 at 4%

10.3 Complete Solution: Ratio in an Interest Problem

Mr. White invested two sums of money in the ratio of 5:3. The first sum was invested at 4% and the second at 2%. The annual interest from the first exceeds that of the second by \$56. How much was each investment?

Solution: Since the ratio is 5:3, let $5x$ = first investment in \$
and $3x$ = second investment in \$.

	(\$) Principal	Rate of Interest	Annual Interest (\$)
First Investment	$5x$	.04	.04($5x$)
Second Investment	$3x$	.02	.02($3x$)

$.04(5x) = .02(3x) + 56$
$.20x = .06x + 56$
$x = 400, 5x = 2000, 3x = 1200$

Ans. \$2000 at 4%, \$1200 at 2%

10.4 Alternate Methods in an Investment Problem

Mr. White invested $8000, part at 5% and the rest at 2%. The yearly income from the 5% investment exceeded that from the 2% investment by $85. Find the investment at each rate.

Solutions:

Method 1, using one variable

	($) Principal	Rate of Interest	Annual Interest ($)
1st	x	.05	$.05x$
2nd	$(8000-x)$	.02	$.02(8000-x)$

M_{100}
$$.05x - .02(8000-x) = 85$$
$$5x - 2(8000-x) = 8500$$
$$5x - 16,000 + 2x = 8500$$
$$7x = 24,500$$
$$\underline{x = 3500}, \quad 8000 - x = 4500$$

Method 2, using two variables

	($) Principal	Rate of Interest	Annual Interest ($)
1st	x	.05	$.05x$
2nd	y	.02	$.02y$

M_2 　　　　$x + y = 8000$

M_{100} 　$.05x - .02y = 85$

$$2x + 2y = 16,000$$
Add: 　$5x - 2y = \underline{8,500}$
$$7x = 24,500$$
$$\underline{x = 3500}, \quad y = 4500$$

Ans. $3500 at 5%, $4500 at 2%

10.5 Alternate Methods in a Profit and Loss Investment Problem

Mr. Brown invested a total of $4000. On part of this he earned 4%. On the remainder he lost 3%. Combining his earnings and losses, he found his annual income to be $55. Find the amounts at each rate.

Solutions:

Method 1, using one variable

	($) Principal	Rate of Interest	Annual Interest ($)
1st	x	.04	$.04x$
2nd	$4000-x$	$-.03$	$-.03(4000-x)$

M_{100}
$$.04x - .03(4000-x) = 55$$
$$4x - 3(4000-x) = 5500$$
$$7x - 12,000 = 5500$$
$$\underline{x = 2500}, \quad 4000 - x = 1500$$

Method 2, using two variables

	($) Principal	Rate of Interest	Annual Interest ($)
1st	x	.04	$.04x$
2nd	y	$-.03$	$-.03y$

M_3 　　　$x + y = 4000 \rightarrow 3x + 3y = 12,000$

M_{100} $.04x - .03y = 55 \longrightarrow \underline{4x - 3y = 5,500}$
$$7x = 17,500$$
$$\underline{x = 2500}, \quad y = 1500$$

Ans. Earnings on $2500 at 4%, losses on $1500 at 3%.

10.6 Complete Solution: Adding a Third Investment

Mr. Black has $3000 invested at 3% and $1000 at 4%. How much must he invest at 6% so that his annual income will be 5% of the entire investment?

Solution:

Let x = the principal to be added at 6%; then
$4000 + x$ = the entire principal at 5%.

$$.03(3000) + .04(1000) + .06x = .05(4000+x)$$
$$90 + 40 + .06x = 200 + .05x$$
$$\underline{x = 7000} \quad Ans. \ \$7000 \text{ at } 6\%$$

11. MOTION PROBLEMS

The distance (D) traveled equals the rate of speed (R) multiplied by the time spent traveling (T).

Formula: $D = RT$ **Other Forms:** $R = \dfrac{D}{T}$, $T = \dfrac{D}{R}$

Thus, the distance traveled in 5 hr. at a rate of 30 mph is 150 mi.,
     and the distance traveled in 5 sec. at a rate of 30 ft. per sec. is 150 ft.

Note. In using $D = RT$, units for rate, time and distance must be in agreement.
     Thus, if the rate is in miles per hour (mph), use miles for distance and hours for time.

Uniform and Average Rates of Speed

Unless otherwise stated "rate of speed" or simply "rate" may be taken to mean **(1)** uniform rate of speed or **(2)** average rate of speed.

(1) A uniform rate of speed is an unchanging or fixed rate of speed for each unit of time.
     Thus, a uniform rate of 40 mph for 3 hr. means that 40 mi. was covered during each of the 3 hours.

(2) An average rate of speed is a rate that is the average per unit of time for changing rates of speed.
     Thus, an average rate of 40 mph for 3 hr. may mean the average rate in a situation where 30 mi. was covered during the first hr., 40 mi. during the second hr. and 50 mi. during the third hr.

11.1 Representation of Distance: $D = RT$

Write the expression that represents the distance in miles traveled; then simplify it:

		Representation	In Simplified Form
a) In 5 hr. at 20 mph and in 6 hr. more at R mph.		$Ans.$ $5(20)+6R$	$6R + 100$
b) In 6 hr. at 45 mph and in T hr. more at 50 mph.		$Ans.$ $6(45) + 50T$	$50T + 270$
c) In T hr. at 40 mph and in $(10-T)$ hr. more at 30 mph.		$Ans.$ $40T+30(10-T)$	$10T + 300$
d) In 2 hr. at R mph and in 30 min. more at 20 mph.		$Ans.$ $2R + \frac{1}{2}(20)$	$2R + 10$
e) In 4 hr. at R mph and in 8 hr. more at $(R+10)$ mph.		$Ans.$ $4R + 8(R+10)$	$12R + 80$
f) In 5 min. at R mi. per min. and in 1 hr. more at 3 mi. per min.		$Ans.$ $5R + 60(3)$	$5R + 180$

11.2 Representation of Time: $T = \dfrac{D}{R}$

Write the expression that represents the time *in hr.* needed to travel; then simplify it:

		Representation	In Simplified Form
a) 100 mi. at 20 mph and 80 mi. farther at R mph.		$Ans.$ a) $\dfrac{100}{20} + \dfrac{80}{R}$	$5 + \dfrac{80}{R}$
b) 120 mi. at 30 mph and D mi. farther at 20 mph.		$Ans.$ b) $\dfrac{120}{30} + \dfrac{D}{20}$	$4 + \dfrac{D}{20}$
c) 60 mi. at R mph and 80 mi. farther at 2 mi. per min.		$Ans.$ c) $\dfrac{60}{R} + \dfrac{80}{120}$	$\dfrac{60}{R} + \dfrac{2}{3}$

11.3 Separation Situation:

Two travelers start from the same place at the same time and travel **in opposite directions**.

Two planes leave the same airport at the same time and fly in opposite directions. The speed of the faster plane is 100 mph faster than the slower one. At the end of 5 hr., they are 2000 miles apart. Find the rate of each plane.

Solutions:

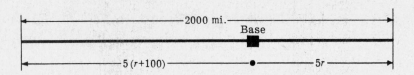

ALTERNATE   METHODS   OF   SOLUTION

Method 1

	(mph) Rate	(hr.) Time	D (mi.) Distance
faster plane	$r + 100$	5	$5(r+100)$
slower plane	r	5	$5r$

The sum of the distances equals 2000 mi.

$$5r + 5(r+100) = 2000$$
$$5r + 5r + 500 = 2000$$
$$10r = 1500$$

$$r = 150, \quad r + 100 = 250.$$

Ans. The rates are 150 mph and 250 mph.

Method 2

(mph) Rate of Separation	(hr.) Time of Separation	(mi.) Distance of Separation
R	5	2000

Here, R is the rate at which the two planes are separating from each other!

$$5R = 2000, \quad R = 400$$

Hence, the rate of separation is 400 mph.

Since 400 mph is the sum of both rates

$$r + (r+100) = 400$$
$$r = 150, \quad r + 100 = 250$$

11.4 Separation Situations:

In each of the following, *two travelers start from the same place at the same time and travel in* **opposite directions**. Using the variable indicated, express each sentence as an equation; then solve and find each quantity represented.

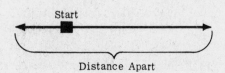

a) After 5 hr., both are 300 mi. apart, one going 40 mph faster. Find the rate of the slower, using R in mph.

b) At speeds of 40 mph and 20 mph, both travel until they are 420 mi. apart. Find time of each, using T in hr.

c) At speeds in the ratio of 7:3, both are 360 mi. apart at the end of 3 hr. Find their repective rates in mph, using $7x$ and $3x$ for these.

Ans. a) $5R + 5(R+40) = 300$, $R=10$
Slower rate is 10 mph.

Ans. b) $40T + 20T = 420$, $T = 7$
Time for each is 7 hr.

Ans. c) $3(7x) + 3(3x) = 360$, $x = 12$
Faster rate is 84 mph.
Slower rate is 36 mph.

11.5 Closure Situation:

Two travelers start from distant points at the same time and travel toward each other until they meet.

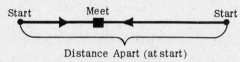

Distance Apart (at start)

A car leaves Albany en route to New York at the same time that another car leaves New York for Albany. The car from Albany travels at an average rate of 40 mph, while the other averages 20 mph. If Albany and New York are 150 mi. apart, how soon will the cars meet and how far will each have traveled?

Solutions:

ALTERNATE METHODS OF SOLUTION

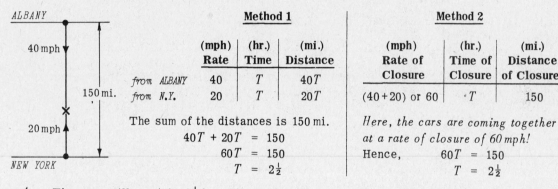

	(mph) Rate	(hr.) Time	(mi.) Distance
from ALBANY	40	T	$40T$
from N.Y.	20	T	$20T$

Method 1

The sum of the distances is 150 mi.
$$40T + 20T = 150$$
$$60T = 150$$
$$T = 2\tfrac{1}{2}$$

(mph) Rate of Closure	(hr.) Time of Closure	(mi.) Distance of Closure
(40+20) or 60	T	150

Method 2

Here, the cars are coming together at a rate of closure of 60 mph!

Hence,
$$60T = 150$$
$$T = 2\tfrac{1}{2}$$

Ans. The cars will meet in $2\tfrac{1}{2}$ hr. The Albany car will have traveled 100 miles and the New York car 50 miles.

11.6 Closure Situations:

In each of the following, *two travelers start from distant places at the same time and travel toward each other until they meet.*

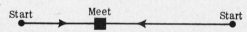

Using the variable indicated, express each sentence as an equation; then solve and find each quantity represented:

a) Starting 600 mi. apart, they meet in 10 hr., one traveling 20 mph faster. Find the rate of the slower in mph, using R for this.

b) Starting 420 mi. apart, they travel at rates of 27 mph and 33 mph. Find the time of each in hr., using T for this.

c) Starting 560 mi. apart, they travel for 4 hr., one rate being four times the other. Find the rate of the slower in mph, using R for this.

d) Starting 480 mi. apart, they travel at rates in the ratio of 4:3. They meet in 5 hr. The slower is delayed for 1 hr. along the way. Find the rates of speed in mph, using $4x$ and $3x$ for these.

Ans. a) $10R + 10(R+20) = 600$, $R = 20$
Slower rate is 20 mph.

Ans. b) $27T + 33T = 420$, $T = 7$
Time for each is 7 hr.

Ans. c) $4R + 4(4R) = 560$, $R = 28$
Slower rate is 28 mph.

Ans. d) $4(3x) + 5(4x) = 480$, $x = 15$
Slower rate is 45 mph.
Faster rate is 60 mph.

11.7 Round Trip Situation

A traveler travels out and back to the starting place along the same road.

Henry drove from his home to Boston and back again along the same road in a total of 10 hr. His average rate going was 20 mph while his average rate on the return trip was 30 mph. How long did he take in each direction and what distance did he cover each way?

Solutions:

ALTERNATE   METHODS   OF   SOLUTION

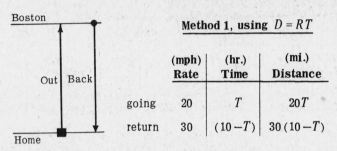

Method 1, using $D = RT$

	(mph) Rate	(hr.) Time	(mi.) Distance
going	20	T	$20T$
return	30	$(10-T)$	$30(10-T)$

The distance out equals the distance back.

$$20T = 30(10-T)$$
$$20T = 300 - 30T$$
$$50T = 300$$
$$T = 6, \quad 10-T = 4$$

Method 2, using $T = \dfrac{D}{R}$

	(mph) Rate	(hr.) Time	(mi.) Distance
going	20	$\dfrac{D}{20}$	D
return	30	$\dfrac{D}{30}$	D

The total time is 10 hr.

$$\mathbf{M_{60}} \quad \frac{D}{20} + \frac{D}{30} = 10 \qquad \mathbf{L.C.D = 60}$$
$$3D + 2D = 600, \quad 5D = 600$$
$$D = 120$$

Ans. Henry took 6 hr. going and 4 hr. back in going 120 mi. each way.

1.8 Round Trip Situations:

In each situation, *a traveler travels out and back to the starting place along the same road.*

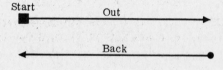

Using the variable indicated, express each sentence as an equation; then solve and find each quantity represented.

a) A traveler required a total of 12 hr. on a round trip, averaging 20 mph out and 30 mph back. Find the time in hr. going, using T for this.

Ans. a) $20T = 30(12-T)$, $T = 7.2$
Time out was 7.2 hr.

b) A traveler took 2 hr. more to travel back than to go out, averaging 50 mph out and 45 mph back. Find the time in hr. going, using T for this.

Ans. b) $50T = 45(T+2)$, $T = 18$
Time out was 18 hr.

c) A traveler traveled to his destination at an average rate of 25 mph. By traveling at 5 mph faster, he took 30 minutes less to return. Find his time in hr. going out, using T for this.

Ans. c) $25T = 30(T-\frac{1}{2})$, $T = 3$
Time out was 3 hr.

d) After taking 5 hr. going out, a traveler came back in 3 hr. at a rate that was 20 mph faster. Find the average rate going in mph, using R for this.

Ans. d) $5R = 3(R+20)$, $R = 30$
Rate out was 30 mph.

e) After taking 5 hr. going out, a traveler came back in 3 hr. at a rate that was 20 mph faster. Find the distance either way in mi., using D for this.

Ans. e) $\dfrac{D}{3} = \dfrac{D}{5} + 20$, $D = 150$
Each distance was 150 mi.

11.9 Gain or Overtake Situation:

After a traveler has begun his trip, a second one starts from the same place and, going in the same direction, overtakes the first.

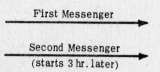

A messenger going at 30 mph has been gone for 3 hr. Another messenger, sent to overtake him, travels at 50 mph. How long will it take the second messenger to overtake the first and what distance will he cover?

Solutions:

ALTERNATE METHODS OF SOLUTION

	Method 1				**Method 2**		
	(mph) Rate	(hr.) Time	(mi.) Distance		(mph) Rate of Gain	(hr.) Time of Gain	(mi.) Distance to Gain
First	30	$T+3$	$30(T+3)$		(50−30) or 20	T	3(30) or 90
Second	50	T	$50T$				

The distances are equal.

$$30(T+3) = 50T$$
$$30T + 90 = 50T, \quad 90 = 20T$$
$$4\tfrac{1}{2} = T$$

Here the second messenger is gaining at the rate of 20 mph. The first has a head start of 90 mi. since he started 3 hr. earlier and his rate was 30 mph.

$$20T = 90$$
$$T = 4\tfrac{1}{2}$$

Ans. To overtake the first, the second messenger must take $4\tfrac{1}{2}$ hr. and cover 225 mi.

11.10 Gain or Overtake Situations:

In each of the following, *after a traveler has begun his trip, a second traveler starts from the same place and, going in the same direction, overtakes the first.*

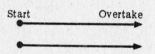

Using the variable indicated, express each sentence as an equation; then solve and find each quantity represented.

a) Their speeds are 20 mph and 40 mph. The second starts 3 hr. later. Find the time of the second in hr., using T for this.

Ans. a) $20(T+3) = 40T$, $T = 3$
Time of second is 3 hr.

b) The second starts 3 hr. later and travels 6 mi. an hr. faster to overtake the first in 8 hr. Find the rate of the first in mph, using R for this.

Ans. b) $11R = 8(R+6)$, $R = 16$
Rate of first is 16 mph.

c) The second travels 9 mph slower than twice the speed of the first and starts out $2\tfrac{1}{2}$ hr. later, overtaking in 4 hr. Find the rate of the first in mph, using R for this.

Ans. c) $6\tfrac{1}{2}R = 4(2R-9)$, $R = 24$
Rate of first is 24 mph.

12. WORK PROBLEMS

The work accomplished (W) equals the rate of work (R) multiplied by the time of work (T).

Formula: $W = RT$ Other Forms: $R = \dfrac{W}{T}$ $T = \dfrac{W}{R}$

Thus, typing at the rate of 60 words per minute, then in 3 minutes a typist can type 180 words. Also, working at the rate of $\tfrac{1}{5}$ of a job per day, then in 3 days a worker will complete $\tfrac{3}{5}$ of the job.

In general, if a worker requires r days to do a job and works at it for d days, then the part of the job done is $\dfrac{d}{r}$.

Thus, if A requires 5 days to do a job and works at it for 2 days, then the part of the job done is $\frac{2}{5}$.

Note. In work problems, unless otherwise indicated, assume that the workers and machines operate at a fixed rate of work.

In the case of workers working together, add the parts of the job completed to determine the total work accomplished. If the job is completed, then the sum of the parts is 1.

Thus, if A does $\frac{5}{8}$ of a job and, at the same time, B does $\frac{3}{8}$ of the job, then together they have completed $\frac{3}{8} + \frac{5}{8}$ or 1 job.

12.1 Representation of Rate of Work: $R = \frac{W}{T}$

Write the expression that represents the rate of work per unit of time in each case.
  a) Write the expression for the rate of typing if 360 words are typed in
      (1) 10 minutes, (2) 5 minutes, (3) m minutes,
  b) Write the expression for the rate of manufacturing if t toys are produced in
      (1) 2 days, (2) $2\frac{1}{2}$ days, (3) d days,
  c) Write the expression for the rate of work if 1 job requires
      (1) 5 hours, (2) $\frac{1}{2}$ hour, (3) h hours.

Ans. a) (1) $\frac{360}{10}$ or 36 words per minute,   (2) $\frac{360}{5}$ or 72 words per minute,

        (3) $\frac{360}{m}$ words per minute

  b) (1) $\frac{t}{2}$ toys per day,   (2) $\frac{t}{2\frac{1}{2}}$ or $\frac{2t}{5}$ toys per day,   (3) $\frac{t}{d}$ toys per day.

  c) (1) $\frac{1}{5}$ job per hour,   (2) $\frac{1}{\frac{1}{2}}$ or 2 jobs per hour,   (3) $\frac{1}{h}$ jobs per hour.

12.2 Determining the Part of a Job Accomplished by Workers Working Together

In each case, determine the part of the job accomplished by the two workers working together or by the two pipes filling the pool together:
  a) Joe who can do the job in 15 minutes alone works for 5 minutes and George who can do the job in 20 minutes alone works for 10 minutes.
  b) A and B work together for 4 days painting the side of a house. Working alone, A requires 16 days; working alone, B needs 8 days.
  c) Separately the larger of two pipes can fill a pool in 3 hours, while separately, the smaller requires 9 hours. Both pipes are left open for 2 hours together.

Solutions:
  a) Joe does $\frac{5}{15}$ or $\frac{1}{3}$ while George does $\frac{10}{20}$ or $\frac{1}{2}$. Together, they do $\frac{1}{3} + \frac{1}{2} = \frac{5}{6}$. *Ans.*
  b) A does $\frac{4}{16}$ or $\frac{1}{4}$ while B does $\frac{4}{8}$ or $\frac{1}{2}$. Together, they do $\frac{1}{4} + \frac{1}{2} = \frac{3}{4}$. *Ans.*
  c) The larger pipe fills $\frac{2}{3}$ of the pool and the smaller fills $\frac{2}{9}$. Together, they fill $\frac{2}{3} + \frac{2}{9} = \frac{8}{9}$ of the pool. *Ans.* $\frac{8}{9}$.

12.3 Translation and Solution in Work Problems

Express each sentence as an equation; then solve and find the value of each represented quantity:
  a) A can mow a lawn in 4 hours alone and B can mow the same lawn in t hours alone. Together, they can complete the mowing in 3 hours.
  b) Three pipes are used to fill a tank. The times required by each of the pipes to fill the pool separately are 4 minutes, 8 minutes, and 12 minutes. Together, the three pipes require m minutes.
  c) Jim can plaster a wall in 12 hours working alone. Mark works at one-half the speed of of Jim. Together, they can complete the job in h hours.

Solutions:

a) Since A mows $\frac{3}{4}$ of the lawn and B mows $\frac{3}{t}$ of the lawn, then $\frac{3}{4} + \frac{3}{t} = 1$.

Clear of fractions by multiplying both sides by $4t$: $4t\left(\frac{3}{4}\right) + 4t\left(\frac{3}{t}\right) = 4t$

$$3t + 12 = 4t$$
$$12 = 4t - 3t, \; t = 12$$

Hence, B can mow the lawn in 12 hours.

Check: Can the mowing be completed in 3 hours?

A does $\frac{3}{4}$ and B does $\frac{3}{12}$ or $\frac{1}{4}$. Hence, $\frac{3}{4} + \frac{1}{4} = 1$, $1 = 1$. Yes.

b) In one minute, the pipes working separately can fill $\frac{1}{4}$ of the tank, $\frac{1}{8}$ of the tank, and $\frac{1}{12}$ of the tank. Since the tank is filled in m minutes, then $\frac{m}{4} + \frac{m}{8} + \frac{m}{12} = 1$. Multiply both sides by 24 to obtain $6m + 3m + 2m = 24$.

$$\text{Hence,}\; 11m = 24, \; m = \frac{24}{11}$$

Hence, working together the pipes require $2\frac{2}{11}$ minutes.

c) Mark needs twice as much time to plaster the wall; that is, Mark requires 24 hours.

Hence, $\frac{h}{12} + \frac{h}{24} = 1$. Multiplying both sides by 24: $2h + h = 24$
$$3h = 24, \; h = 8$$

Therefore, working together, Jim and Mark need 8 hours.

13. COMBINATION PROBLEMS

Combination problems such as those included here are solved best by means of simultaneous equations. In each of these problems, it is especially important to keep in mind that a letter may represent a number only.

Thus, s may stand for the *number* of shirts, the *number* of dollars in the price of a shirt, the *number* of cents in the cost of laundering a shirt; but s may not stand for "shirts".

13.1 Cost Problems: Combining Prices or Numbers

a) Mr. Jones bought 5 shirts and 4 hats for $39. Later, at the same prices, he bought 4 shirts and 2 hats for $24. Find the price of each.

b) Mr. Dodge paid $65 for a number of shirts at $5 apiece and a number of hats at $10 each. Had the shirts been $10 each and the hats $5 apiece, he would have paid $55. Find the number of shirts and the number of hats purchased.

Solution:

a) Let s = price of one shirt in $
  h = price of one hat in $.

Then, $5s + 4h = 39$
$4s + 2h = 24$.

Solving, $s = 3$ and $h = 6$.

Ans. The prices were $3 per shirt and $6 per hat.

Solution:

b) Let s = no. of shirts
  h = no. of hats.

Then, $5s + 10h = 65$
$10s + 5h = 55$.

Solving, $s = 3$ and $h = 5$.

Ans. The number of shirts was 3 and the number of hats was 5.

13.2 Motion Problems: Combining Rates or Times

a) Mr. Ford covered 310 mi. by traveling for 4 hr. at one speed and then for 5 hr. at another. Had he gone 5 hr. at the first speed and 4 hr. at the second, he would have gone 320 mi. Find the two rates.

Solution:

a) Let r = first rate in mph
R = second rate in mph.

$$4r + 5R = 310$$
$$5r + 4R = 320.$$

Solving, $r = 40$ and $R = 30$.

Ans. The rates were 40 mph and 30 mph.

b) By going 20 mph for one period of time and then 30 mph for another, Mr. Nash traveled 280 mi. Had he gone 10 mph faster throughout, he would have covered 390 miles. How many hours did he travel at each speed?

Solution:

b) Let t = first time in hr.
T = second time in hr.

$$20t + 30T = 280$$
$$30t + 40T = 390.$$

Solving, $t = 5$ and $T = 6$.

Ans. The times were 5 hr. at one speed and 6 hr. at the other.

14. DIGIT PROBLEMS

If t = the tens digit of a two-digit number and u = the units digit of a two-digit number, then

$$10t + u = \text{the number}$$

and $\qquad 10u + t$ = the number with the digits reversed.

Thus, the number 27 has two digits 2 and 7. The value of 27 is found by adding 2 tens and 7. If the digits are reversed or interchanged, the new number, 72, is found by adding 7 tens and 2. Note that the new number is found by adding 10 times the units digit and the tens digit of the original number.

Caution: A number whose digits are t and u is not represented by tu since tu is the product of the digits. In the case of 27, $tu = 2(7)$ or 14 but not the number 27.

14.1 Translation and Solution of Problems Involving a Number and the Number Reversed

Letting t and u represent the tens and units digits respectively of a two-digit number, express each sentence as an equation; then solve and find the number.

a) The number is 7 times the sum of the digits. The number is 9 more than the number with the digits reversed.

b) The number with the digits reversed is 9 less than twice the number. The tens digit is 3 less than the units digit.

Solutions:

In (a) and (b), let t = the tens digit and u = the units digit, then

$$10t + u = \text{the number}$$

and $\qquad 10u + t$ = the number with the digits reversed

a) Solve the system $\begin{cases} 10t + u = 7(t + u) \\ 10t + u = 10u + t + 9 \end{cases}$

In the first equation, clear of parentheses, collect like terms and simplify:

$$10t + u = 7t + 7u$$
$$10t - 7t = 7u - u$$
$$3t = 6u \text{ and } t = 2u.$$

Substitute $2u$ for t in the second equation: $20u + u = 10u + 2u + 9$
$$9u = 9$$
$$u = 1, \quad t = 2$$

Hence, the digits are 2 and 1, and the number is 21. *Ans.* 21

15. STATISTICS PROBLEMS

Understanding Statistical Terminology

1. **A rank order** is an arrangement of items into ordered sets. Thus, the final marks in the table have been distributed into separate sets beginning with 100's, then 95's, etc.

2. **A frequency distribution** is a distribution which indicates the tally or frequency of each set of items. Thus, the frequency or number of 100's is 3, the number of 95's is 8, etc.

Frequency Distribution of Final Mathematics Marks

Marks	Tally	Frequency
100	III	3
95	IHH III	8
90	IHH IHH IHH	15
85	IHH I	6
80	III	3

3. **The range of a group of items** is the interval between the smallest and largest sets. Thus, the range of final marks is from 80 to 100.

4. **The mode** is the set of items having the largest frequency. Thus, 90 is the mode since it has the largest frequency, 15.

5. **The arithmetic mean** is the average mark of the group. Thus, $90\frac{2}{7}$ is the average of the 35 marks. This can be obtained by dividing the sum total of all the marks by 35, as follows:

$$\text{Average} = \frac{3(100) + 8(95) + 15(90) + 6(85) + 3(80)}{35} = 90\frac{2}{7}$$

6. **The median** is the middle item of an ordered group. Thus, 90 is the median of the 35 marks since it is the 18th or middle mark.

7. **The measures of central tendency** of a frequency distribution are the **mode**, **median** and **arithmetic mean**.

Frequency Distribution of Grouped Items

The table shown is a frequency distribution of the following 29 contest scores: 96, 87, 85, 76, 74, 71, 70, 68, 67, 67, 64, 64, 63, 60, 59, 57, 57, 57, 54, 53, 52, 52, 48, 46, 46, 42, 41, 38, 32.

These were tallied in seven groups as shown.

Thus, 52 was tallied twice in the 49.5 to 59.5 group.

Frequency Distribution of Grouped Contest Scores

Group Interval	Group Midpoint	Tally	Frequency
89.5 – 99.5	94.5	I	1
79.5 – 89.5	84.5	II	2
69.5 – 79.5	74.5	IIII	4
59.5 – 69.5	64.5	IHH II	7
49.5 – 59.5	54.5	IHH III	8
39.5 – 49.5	44.5	IHH	5
29.5 – 39.5	34.5	II	2
			Total: 29

Frequency Distribution Graphs: Histogram and Frequency Polygon

The bar graph shown is the **histogram** of the grouped contest scores above. The height of each vertical bar is the frequency of the group being represented. The group intervals are placed along the horizontal axis.

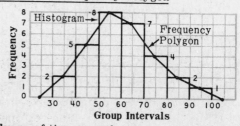

The broken-line graph of lines connecting the group midpoints is the **frequency polygon** of the grouped scores.

For a very large number of groups of scores, frequency polygons tend to be bell-shaped in the form of the **normal probability curve**, as shown in the diagram at the left.

15.1 Tallying Items

Make a frequency distribution of the following 51 readings, representing the maximum daily temperatures during a 51-day period. State its range, mode, median and arithmetic mean.

66, 69, 66, 66, 65, 68, 61, 62, 65, 63, 67, 62, 63, 63, 65, 65, 66

64, 65, 64, 68, 68, 67, 67, 64, 64, 63, 62, 64, 65, 65, 69, 66, 68

65, 64, 64, 65, 67, 66, 68, 67, 65, 66, 61, 62, 63, 60, 65, 67, 67

Solution:

Maximum Temperatures	69	68	67	66	65	64	63	62	61	60	
Tally	II	ʜʜ	ʜʜ II	ʜʜ II	ʜʜ ʜʜ I	ʜʜ II	ʜʜ	IIII	II	I	
Frequency	2	5	7	7	11	7	5	4	2	1	Total: 51

The range is from 60 to 69.

The mode (most frequent) = 65.

The median (middle score is 26th in rank) = 65.

The average or arithmetic mean

$$= \frac{69(2)+68(5)+67(7)+66(7)+65(11)+64(7)+63(5)+62(4)+61(2)+60(1)}{51} = 65.04$$

15.2 Tallying Groups of Items

Make a frequency distribution of the 51 temperatures of the previous problem by tallying them in the following five groups:

59.5 − 61.5,   61.5 − 63.5,   63.5 − 65.5,   65.5 − 67.5,   67.5 − 69.5

Solution: **Grouped Frequency Distribution**

Group Interval	Group Midpoint	Tally	Frequency
67.5 − 69.5	68.5	ʜʜ II	7
65.5 − 67.5	66.5	ʜʜ ʜʜ IIII	14
63.5 − 65.5	64.5	ʜʜ ʜʜ ʜʜ III	18
61.5 − 63.5	62.5	ʜʜ IIII	9
59.5 − 61.5	60.5	III	3

15.3 Making Histogram and Frequency Polygon

Make a histogram and frequency polygon of the 5 groups of the previous problem:

Solution:

Histogram and Frequency Polygon

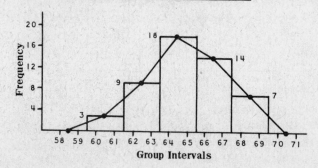

The histogram is the bar graph.

The frequency polygon is the broken line graph.

SUPPLEMENTARY PROBLEMS

Number Problems Having One Unknown

1. Express each sentence as an equation; then find the unknown: **(1.1)**

	Equation	Unknown

a) The sum of *n* and 12 is 21.   *Ans. a*) $n + 12 = 21$ $n = 9$

b) The result of adding *m* and 15 is 4*m*.   *Ans. b*) $m + 15 = 4m$ $m = 5$

c) 27 is the difference obtained when *p* is subtracted from 40.   *Ans. c*) $27 = 40 - p$ $p = 13$

d) 20 increased by twice *a* is 32.   *Ans. d*) $20 + 2a = 32$ $a = 6$

e) 7 less than three times *b* is 23.   *Ans. e*) $3b - 7 = 23$ $b = 10$

f) Four times *d* exceeds 15 by *d*.   *Ans. f*) $4d - 15 = d$ $d = 5$

g) The product of 3 and *n*+6 equals 20.   *Ans. g*) $3(n+6) = 20$ $n = \frac{2}{3}$

h) 5 more than half of *x* equals 29.   *Ans. h*) $\frac{x}{2} + 5 = 29$ $x = 48$

i) The difference between 15 and half of *y* is 6.   *Ans. i*) $15 - \frac{y}{2} = 6$ $y = 18$

2. Check each statement: **(1.2)**

a) Is 5 the correct number for "the result of adding a number and 15 is four times the number"?

Ans. a) $5 + 15 \overset{?}{=} 4(5)$

$20 = 20$ Yes.

b) Is 11 the correct number for "7 less than three times the number is 23"?

Ans. b) $3(11) - 7 \overset{?}{=} 23$

$26 \neq 23$ No.

c) Is 2 the correct number for "the product of 3 and 6 more than a number equals 20"?

Ans. c) $3(6+2) \overset{?}{=} 20$

$24 \neq 20$ No.

d) Is 48 the correct number for "5 more than half a number equals 29"?

Ans. d) $\frac{48}{2} + 5 \overset{?}{=} 29$

$29 = 29$ Yes.

3. Find the number in each: **(1.3)**

a) Four times the number, increased by 2, equals 30.   *Ans. a*) 7

b) Seven times the number, less 6, equals 29.   *Ans. b*) 5

c) The result of combining five times the number and the number is 24.   *Ans. c*) 4

d) If the number is added to 42 the sum is eight times the number.   *Ans. d*) 6

e) If twice the number is subtracted from 13, the remainder is 8.   *Ans. e*) $2\frac{1}{2}$

f) If twice the number is increased by 6, the result is the same as decreasing four   *Ans. f*) 10
times the number by 14.

g) Five times the number, minus 12, equals three times the number, increased by 10.   *Ans. g*) 11

h) The sum of one-half the number and one-third the number is 15.   *Ans. h*) 18

Number Problems Having Two Unknowns

4. If *n* represents a number, represent another number that is   **(2.1)**

   a) 4 more than three times *n*.   *e*) the sum of three times *n* and 20.

   b) 5 less than twice *n*.   *f*) 40 reduced by twice *n*.

   c) one-half of *n*, increased by 3.   *g*) the product of (*n*+4) and 7.

   d) two-thirds of *n*, decreased by 6.   *h*) the quotient of (*n*−2) and 4.

Ans. a) $3n+4$, *b*) $2n-5$, *c*) $\frac{n}{2}+3$, *d*) $\frac{2}{3}n-6$, *e*) $3n+20$, *f*) $40-2n$, *g*) $7(n+4)$, *h*) $\frac{n-2}{4}$

5. Express each sentence as an equation; then find the numbers .   **(2.2)**

    a) Two numbers are represented by n and $(n-8)$.   *Ans. a*) $n = 3(n-8)-16$,   20 and 12
        The first is 16 less than three times the second.

    b) Two numbers are represented by n and $(30-n)$.   *Ans. b*) $n = 2(30-n)+6$,   22 and 8
        The first is six more than twice the second.

    c) Two numbers are represented by n and $8n$.   *Ans. c*) $4n-3n = 15$,   15 and 120
        Half the second exceeds three times the first by 15.

6. Using s for the smaller number and l for the larger, obtain two equations for each problem; then find l and s.   **(2.3, 2.4)**

       a) The sum of two numbers is 20. Their difference is 11.
       b) The sum of two numbers is 12. Twice the larger plus the smaller equals 21.
       c) The difference of two numbers is 7. The larger is one less than twice the smaller.
       d) Separate 50 into two parts such that the larger is nine times the smaller.
       e) Separate 42 into two parts such that the smaller is 3 less than one-half the larger.

Ans. a) $l+s = 20$ b) $l+s = 12$ c) $l-s = 7$ d) $l+s = 50$ e) $l+s = 42$
       $l-s = 11$ $2l+s = 21$ $l = 2s-1$ $l = 9s$ $s = \frac{l}{2}-3$
       $l=15\frac{1}{2}$, $s=4\frac{1}{2}$ $l=9$, $s=3$ $l=15$, $s=8$ $l=45$, $s=5$ $l=30$, $s=12$

7. Can you find two integers   **(2.3, 2.4)**
       a) whose sum is 15 and whose difference is 5?
       b) whose sum is 20 and whose difference is 9?
       c) whose sum is 40 and the larger is 10 more than the smaller?

Ans. a) Yes, 10 and 5. b) No, the numbers $14\frac{1}{2}$ and $5\frac{1}{2}$ are not integers. c) Yes, 25 and 15.

Consecutive Integer Problems

8. Using n for the first integer, represent   **(3.1)**
       a) two consecutive odd integers and their sum.   *Ans.* n, $n+2$; sum $= 2n+2$
       b) four consecutive even integers and their sum.   *Ans.* n, $n+2$, $n+4$, $n+6$; sum $= 4n+12$
       c) five consecutive integers and their sum.   *Ans.* n, $n+1$, $n+2$, $n+3$, $n+4$; sum $= 5n+10$
       d) six consecutive odd integers and their sum.   *Ans.* n, $n+2$, $n+4$, $n+6$, $n+8$, $n+10$; sum $= 6n+30$

9. Using n for the middle integer, represent   **(3.2)**
       a) three consecutive odd integers and their sum.   *Ans.* $n-2$, n, $n+2$; sum $= 3n$
       b) five consecutive integers and their sum.   *Ans.* $n-2$, $n-1$, n, $n+1$, $n+2$; sum $= 5n$

10. Using n, $n+1$ and $n+2$ for three consecutive integers, express each statement as an equation; then find the integers.   **(3.3)**
       a) Their sum is 3 less than five times the first.
       b) The sum of the first and second is six more than the third.
       c) The sum of the first and third is 11 less than three times the second.
       d) Twice the sum of the first and second is 16 more than twice the third.
       e) Twice the third is 21 more than three times the sum of the first and second.
       f) The product of the second and third is 8 more than the square of the first.

Ans. a) $3n+3 = 5n-3$; 3, 4, 5 d) $2(2n+1) = 2(n+2)+16$; 9, 10, 11
       b) $2n+1 = (n+2)+6$; 7, 8, 9 e) $2(n+2) = 3(2n+1)+21$; -5, -4, -3
       c) $2n+2 = 3(n+1)-11$; 10, 11, 12 f) $(n+1)(n+2) = n^2+8$; 2, 3, 4

11. Using n, $n+2$ and $n+4$ for three consecutive odd integers, express each statement as an equation; then find the integers. **(3.4)**
    a) Their sum is 45.
    b) The sum of the first and second is 19 less than three times the third.
    c) Five times the sum of the first and third equals 18 more than eight times the second.
    d) Twenty times the sum of the second and third equals 3 more than the first.
    e) Twice the sum of the first and second equals four times the sum of the second and third.

   Ans. a) $3n+6 = 45$; 13, 15, 17   d) $20(2n+6) = n+3$; $-3, -1, 1$
        b) $2n+2 = 3(n+4)-19$; 9, 11, 13   e) $2(2n+2) = 4(2n+6)$; $-5, -3, -1$
        c) $5(2n+4) = 8(n+2)+18$; 7, 9, 11

12. Can you find **(3.5)**
    a) three consecutive integers whose sum is 36?
    b) three consecutive odd integers whose sum is 33?
    c) five consecutive even integers whose sum is 60?
    d) five consecutive odd integers whose sum is 50?

   Ans. a) Yes; 11, 12, 13   b) Yes; 9, 11, 13   c) Yes; 8, 10, 12, 14, 16
        d) No. If n is used for the middle odd integer, $5n = 50$, $n = \underline{10}$ which is not odd.

Age Problems

13. Represent the age of a person **(4.1, 4.2)**
    a) in y yr. if his present age is 50 yr.   *Ans.* a) $50+y$
    b) in 5 yr. if his present age is F yr.   *Ans.* b) $F+5$
    c) in 5 yr. if his age 10 yr. ago was S yr.   *Ans.* c) $S+10+5$ or $S+15$
    d) 10 yr. ago if his present age is J yr.   *Ans.* d) $J-10$
    e) y yr. ago if his present age is 40 yr.   *Ans.* e) $40-y$

14. Using $5S$ and S to represent the present ages of a father and son, express each sentence as an equation; then find their present ages. **(4.3)**
    a) In 7 yr., the father will be three times as old as his son will be then.
    b) 2 yr. ago, the father was seven times as old as his son was then.
    c) In 3 yr., the father will be 1 yr. less than four times as old as his son will be then.
    d) 9 yr. ago, the father was three times as old as his son will be 3 yr. hence.

   Ans. a) $5S+7 = 3(S+7)$; 35, 7   c) $5S+3 = 4(S+3)-1$; 40, 8
        b) $5S-2 = 7(S-2)$; 30, 6   d) $5S-9 = 3(S+3)$; 45, 9

15. Obtain two equations for each problem using J and C to represent the present ages of John and Charles respectively; then find their present ages: **(4.4)**
    a) The sum of their present ages is 45.
       John is 5 yr. older than Charles.
    b) John is 10 yr. older than Charles.
       12 yr. ago, John was three times as old as Charles was then.
    c) In 5 yr., John will be twice as old as Charles will be then.
       4 yr. ago, John was three times as old as Charles was then.
    d) At present John is six times as old as Charles.
       2 yr. hence, John will be ten times as old as Charles was 3 yr. ago.
    e) In 5 yr., John will be 25 yr. older than Charles will be then.
       2 yr. ago, John was seven times as old as Charles was last year.

   Ans. a) $J+C = 45$ b) $J = C+10$ c) $J+5 = 2(C+5)$ d) $J = 6C$ e) $J+5 = (C+5)+25$
        $J = C+5$ $J-12 = 3(C-12)$ $J-4 = 3(C-4)$ $J+2 = 10(C-3)$ $J-2 = 7(C-1)$
        25, 20   27, 17   31, 13   48, 8   30, 5

16. George is now 8 yr. older than Harry. Find their present ages if   **(4.5)**
    a) 14 yr. ago, George was twice as old as Harry was then.   *Ans. a*) 30, 22
    b) 2 yr. hence, George will be three times as old as Harry will be then.   *Ans. b*) 10, 2
    c) 5 yr. hence, George will be twice as old as Harry was 2 yr. ago.   *Ans. c*) 25, 17

17. The sum of the present ages of Will and Sam is 60 yr. In 8 yr., Will will be 5 yr. older than three times as old as Sam was 3 yr. ago.   **(4.5)**
    Ans. 42 and 18 $\{W + S = 60$ and $W + 8 = 3(S-3) + 5\}$

Ratio Problems

18. Express each ratio in lowest terms: **(5.1)**

a) 20¢ to 5¢	*f*) 50% to 25%	*k*) $\frac{1}{2}$ lb. to $\frac{1}{4}$ lb.
b) 5 dimes to 15 dimes	*g*) 15% to 75%	*l*) $2\frac{1}{2}$ d. to $3\frac{1}{2}$ d.
c) 30 lb. to 25 lb.	*h*) 33% to 77%	*m*) 5 ft. to $\frac{1}{4}$ ft.
d) 2 oz. to 14 oz.	*i*) $2.20 to $3.30	*n*) $\frac{1}{2}$ yd. to $1\frac{1}{2}$ yd.
e) 27 min. to 21 min.	*j*) $.84 to $.96	*o*) $16\frac{1}{2}$ ft. to $5\frac{1}{2}$ ft.

Ans. a) 4 *c*) $\frac{6}{5}$ *e*) $\frac{9}{7}$ *f*) 2 *h*) $\frac{3}{7}$ *j*) $\frac{7}{8}$ *k*) 2 *m*) 20 *o*) 3
    b) $\frac{1}{3}$ *d*) $\frac{1}{7}$ *g*) $\frac{1}{5}$ *i*) $\frac{2}{3}$ *l*) $\frac{5}{7}$ *n*) $\frac{1}{3}$

19. Express each ratio in lowest terms: **(5.2)**

a) 1 yr. to 2 mo.	*e*) 2 yd. to 2 ft.	*i*) 100 lb. to 1 ton
b) 2 wk. to 5 d.	*f*) $2\frac{1}{3}$ yd. to 2 ft.	*j*) $2 to 25¢
c) 3 d. to 3 wk.	*g*) $1\frac{1}{2}$ ft. to 9 in.	*k*) 2 quarters to 3 dimes
d) $\frac{1}{2}$ hr. to 20 min.	*h*) 2 lb. to 8 oz.	*l*) 1 sq. yd. to 2 sq. ft.

Ans. a) 6 *c*) $\frac{1}{7}$ *e*) 3 *g*) 2   *i*) $\frac{1}{20}$ *k*) $\frac{5}{3}$
    b) $\frac{14}{5}$ *d*) $\frac{3}{2}$ *f*) $\frac{7}{2}$ *h*) 4   *j*) 8 *l*) $\frac{9}{2}$

20. Express each continued ratio in lowest terms: **(5.3)**

a) 20¢ to 30¢ to $1	*d*) 1 da. to 4 da. to 1 wk.	*g*) 1 ton to 200 lb. to 40 lb.
b) $3 to $1.50 to 25¢	*e*) $\frac{1}{2}$ da. to 9 hr. to 3 hr.	*h*) 3 lb. to 1 lb. to 8 oz.
c) 1 quarter to 1 dime to 1 nickel	*f*) 2 hr. to $\frac{1}{2}$ hr. to 15 min.	*i*) 1 gal. to 1 qt. to 1 pt.

Ans. a) 2 : 3 : 10   *c*) 5 : 2 : 1   *e*) 4 : 3 : 1   *g*) 50 : 5 : 1   *i*) 8 : 2 : 1
      b) 12 : 6 : 1   *d*) 1 : 4 : 7   *f*) 8 : 2 : 1   *h*) 6 : 2 : 1

21. Express each ratio in lowest terms: **(5.4)**

a) 60 to 70 *Ans.* $\frac{6}{7}$	*g*) .7 to 2.1 *Ans.* $\frac{1}{3}$	*m*) $7\frac{1}{2}$ to $2\frac{1}{2}$ *Ans.* 3
b) 84 to 7 *Ans.* 12	*h*) .36 to .24 *Ans.* $\frac{3}{2}$	*n*) $1\frac{1}{2}$ to 12 *Ans.* $\frac{1}{8}$
c) 65 to 15 *Ans.* $\frac{13}{3}$	*i*) .002 to .007 *Ans.* $\frac{2}{7}$	*o*) 5 to $\frac{1}{3}$ *Ans.* 15
d) 125 to 500 *Ans.* $\frac{1}{4}$	*j*) .055 to .005 *Ans.* 11	*p*) $\frac{1}{3}$ to $3\frac{1}{3}$ *Ans.* $\frac{1}{10}$
e) 630 to 105 *Ans.* 6	*k*) 6.4 to 8 *Ans.* .8 or $\frac{4}{5}$	*q*) $\frac{5}{6}$ to $1\frac{2}{3}$ *Ans.* $\frac{1}{2}$
f) 1760 to 990 *Ans.* $\frac{16}{9}$	*l*) 144 to 2.4 *Ans.* 60	*r*) $\frac{7}{4}$ to $\frac{1}{8}$ *Ans.* 14

22. Express each ratio in lowest terms: **(5.5)**

a) x to $8x$	*e*) πab to πa^2	*i*) x to $4x$ to $10x$
b) $15c$ to 5	*f*) $4S$ to S^2	*j*) $15y$ to $10y$ to $5y$
c) $11d$ to 22	*g*) S^3 to $6S^2$	*k*) x^3 to x^2 to x
d) $2\pi r$ to πD	*h*) $9r^2 t$ to $6rt^2$	*l*) $12w$ to $10w$ to $8w$ to $2w$

Ans. a) $\frac{1}{8}$, *b*) $3c$, *c*) $\frac{d}{2}$, *d*) $\frac{2r}{D}$, *e*) $\frac{b}{a}$, *f*) $\frac{4}{S}$, *g*) $\frac{S}{6}$, *h*) $\frac{3r}{2t}$,
    i) 1 : 4 : 10, *j*) 3 : 2 : 1, *k*) $x^2 : x : 1$, *l*) 6 : 5 : 4 : 1.

23. Using x as their common factor, represent the numbers and their sum if   (5.6)
  a) two numbers have a ratio of 5:4.   *Ans. a*) $5x$ and $4x$; sum $= 9x$
  b) two numbers have a ratio of 9 to 1.   *Ans. b*) $9x$ and x; sum $= 10x$
  c) three numbers have a ratio of 2:5:11.   *Ans. c*) $2x$, $5x$ and $11x$; sum $= 18x$
  d) five numbers have a ratio of 1:2:2:3:7.   *Ans. d*) x, $2x$, $2x$, $3x$ and $7x$; sum $= 15x$

24. If two numbers in the ratio of 7 to 4 are represented by $7x$ and $4x$, express each sentence as an equation; then find x and the numbers.   (5.7)
  a) The sum of the numbers is 99.   *Ans. a*) $11x = 99$, $x = 9$, 63 and 36
  b) The difference of the numbers is 39.   *Ans. b*) $3x = 39$, $x = 13$, 91 and 52
  c) Twice the smaller is 2 more than the larger.   *Ans. c*) $8x = 7x + 2$, $x = 2$, 14 and 8
  d) The sum of the larger and one-half the smaller is 36.   *Ans. d*) $7x + 2x = 36$, $x = 4$, 28 and 16

25. The perimeter of a triangle is 60 in. Find each side if   (5.8)
  a) the sides are in the ratio of 5:4:3.
  b) the sides are in the ratio of 2:6:7.
  c) two sides are in the ratio of 3 to 2 and the third side is 25 in.

  Ans. a) Using $5x$, $4x$ and $3x$ for sides: $12x = 60$, $x = 5$. Sides are 25in., 20 in., 15 in.
       b) Using $2x$, $6x$ and $7x$ for sides: $15x = 60$, $x = 4$. Sides are 8 in., 24 in., 28 in.
       c) Using $3x$ and $2x$ for sides; $5x = 35$, $x = 7$. Sides are 21 in., 14 in., 25 in.

26. The ratio of Fred's money to Lee's money is 5:2. How much does each have according to the following: (5.9)
  a) They will have equal amount if Fred gives Lee 24¢.
  b) Fred will have twice as much as Lee if Fred gives Lee 30¢.

  Ans. a) Using $5x$ and $2x$; $5x - 24 = 2x + 24$, $x = 16$. Amounts are 80¢ and 32¢.
       b) Using $5x$ and $2x$; $5x - 30 = 2(2x + 30)$, $x = 90$. Amounts are \$4.50 and \$1.80.

27. An estate of \$8800 is to be divided among three heirs according to the conditions of a will. Find the amounts to be received if   (5.10)
  a) the estate is to be divided in the ratio of 5:2:1.
  b) one heir is to get \$4000 and the others are to get the rest in the ratio of 7 to 5.

  Ans. a) Using $5x$, $2x$ and x: $8x = 8800$, $x = 1100$. Amounts are \$5500, \$2200, \$1100.
       b) Using $7x$ and $5x$: $12x = 8800 - 4000$, $x = 400$. Amounts are \$2800, \$2000, \$4000.

Angle Problems

28. If two angles in the ratio of 5:4 are represented by $5x$ and $4x$, express each sentence as an equation; then find x and the angles.   (6.1)
  a) The angles are adjacent and form an angle of 45°.
  b) The angles are complementary.
  c) The angles are supplementary.
  d) The larger angle is 30° more than one-half the smaller.
  e) The smaller angle is 25° more than three-fifths the larger.
  f) The angles are the acute angles of a right triangle.
  g) The angles are two angles of a triangle whose third angle is their difference.
  h) The first angle is one of two equal angles of an isosceles triangle. The remaining angle of the triangle is half of the other angle.

  Ans. a) $5x + 4x = 45$, $x = 5$, 25° and 20°. e) $4x = 3x + 25$, $x = 25$, 125° and 100°.
       b) $5x + 4x = 90$, $x = 10$, 50° and 40°. f) $5x + 4x = 90$, $x = 10$, 50° and 40°.
       c) $5x + 4x = 180$, $x = 20$, 100° and 80°. g) $5x + 4x + x = 180$, $x = 18$, 90° and 72°.
       d) $5x = 2x + 30$, $x = 10$, 50° and 40°. h) $5x + 5x + 2x = 180$, $x = 15$, 75° and 60°.

29. If two angles are represented by a and b, obtain two equations for each problem; then find the angles. **(6.2)**

a) The angles are adjacent forming an angle of 75°. Their difference is 21°.

b) The angles are complementary. One is 10° less than three times the other.

c) The angles are supplementary. One is 20° more than four times the other.

d) The angles are two angles of a triangle whose third angle is 50°. Twice the first added to three times the second equals 300°.

Ans. a) $a + b = 75$ b) $a + b = 90$ c) $a + b = 180$ d) $a + b = 130$
      $a - b = 21$ $a = 3b - 10$ $a = 4b + 20$ $2a + 3b = 300$
      48°, 27°   65°, 25°   148°, 32°   90°, 40°

30. If three angles in the ratio of $7:6:5$ are represented by $7x$, $6x$ and $5x$, express each sentence as an equation; then find x and the angles. **(6.3)**

a) The first and second are adjacent and form an angle of 91°.

b) The first and third are supplementary.

c) The first and one-half the second are complementary.

d) The angles are the three angles of a triangle.

e) The sum of the second and third is 20° more than the first.

f) The second is 12° more than one-third the sum of the first and third.

Ans. a) $7x + 6x = 91$, $x = 7$, 49°, 42° and 35°.   d) $7x + 6x + 5x = 180$, $x = 10$, 70°, 60° and 50°.
      b) $7x + 5x = 180$, $x = 15$, 105°, 90° and 75°.   e) $6x + 5x = 7x + 20$, $x = 5$, 35°, 30° and 25°.
      c) $7x + 3x = 90$, $x = 9$, 63°, 54° and 45°.   f) $6x = 4x + 12$, $x = 6$, 42°, 36° and 30°.

31. a) One of two complementary angles is 5° less than four times the other. Find the angles. **(6.4)**
      Ans. 19°, 71°   {If x is the other angle, $x + (4x - 5) = 90$}

b) One of two supplementary angles is 10° more than two-thirds of the other. Find the angles.
      Ans. 78°, 102°   {If x is the other angle, $x + (\frac{2}{3}x + 10) = 180$}

32. In a triangle, one angle is 9° less than twice another. The third angle is 18° more than twice their sum. Find the angles. **(6.5)**
      Ans. 33°, 21°, 126°   {If x is the second angle, $x + (2x - 9) + 6x = 180$}

Perimeter Problems

33. The length and width of a rectangle are represented by l and $2l - 20$ respectively. Express each sentence as an equation; then find l and the dimensions of the rectangle. **(7.1)**

a) The perimeter is 50 yd.

b) The semi-perimeter is 22 in.

c) A fence around the rectangle but not including BC is 25 ft.

d) If each dimension is increased 10 rd., the perimeter of the rectangle will be 72 rd.

e) If the width is unchanged and the length is doubled, the perimeter will be 128 in.

f) The rectangle is a square.

g) The perimeter of a square having the width as a side exceeds the perimeter of an equilateral triangle having the length as a side by 10 ft.

Ans. a) $6l - 40 = 50$, $l = 15$, 15 yd. and 10 yd.   e) $2(2l) + 2(2l - 20) = 128$, $l = 21$, 21 in. and 22 in.
      b) $3l - 20 = 22$, $l = 14$, 14 in. and 8 in.   f) $l = 2l - 20$, $l = 20$, 20 and 20.
      c) $5l - 40 = 25$, $l = 13$, 13 ft. and 6 ft.   g) $4(2l - 20) = 3l + 10$, $l = 18$, 18 ft. and 16 ft.
      d) $2(l + 10) + 2(2l - 10) = 72$, $l = 12$, 12 rd. and 4 rd.

34. Using b for the base and a for each of the equal sides of an isosceles triangle, obtain two equations for each problem; then find AB
and AC. 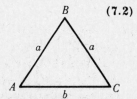   **(7.2)**

    a) The perimeter is 32. AB is 4 more than AC.
    b) The perimeter is 42. AB is 9 less than twice AC.
    c) The perimeter is 28.   The sum of twice AB and one-half of AC is 24.
    d) If each of the equal sides is doubled, the new perimeter will be 43.
      If each of the equal sides is increased by 10, the new perimeter will be 45.

Ans. *a*) $2a + b = 32$	*b*) $2a + b = 42$	*c*) $2a + b = 28$	*d*) $4a + b = 43$
$a = b + 4$	$a = 2b - 9$	$2a + \frac{b}{2} = 24$	$2(a+10) + b = 45$
$AB = 12,\ AC = 8$	$AB = 15,\ AC = 12$	$AB = 10,\ AC = 8$	$AB = 9,\ AC = 7$

35. In a trapezoid having equal sides, the bases and sides are represented as shown in the adjoining diagram. Express each sentence
as an equation; then find x, AB and AD. 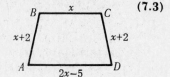   **(7.3)**

    a) The perimeter is 49 in.
    b) The combined length of the upper and lower bases is 28 ft.
    c) A fence around the trapezoid not including CD is 19 yd.

    Ans. *a*) $5x - 1 = 49$, $x = 10$, $AB = 12$ in., $AD = 15$ in.,   *b*) $3x - 5 = 28$, $x = 11$, $AB = 13$ ft., $AD = 17$ ft.
      c) $4x - 3 = 19$, $x = 5\frac{1}{2}$, $AB = 7\frac{1}{2}$ yd., $AD = 6$ yd.

36. Three sides of a quadrilateral in the ratio of $2 : 3 : 5$ are represented
by $2x$, $3x$ and $5x$, respectively. If the base is 20, express each
sentence as an equation; then find x and AB. 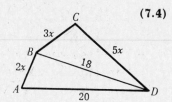   **(7.4)**

    a) The perimeter is 95.
    b) AD is 40 less than the combined length of the other three sides.
    c) BC is 12 less than the combined length of AD and AB.
    d) The perimeter of triangle BCD exceeds that of triangle ABD by 22.

    Ans. *a*) $10x + 20 = 95$, $x = 7\frac{1}{2}$, $AB = 15$ *c*) $3x = (2x + 20) - 12$, $x = 8$, $AB = 16$
      b) $20 = 10x - 40$, $x = 6$, $AB = 12$ *d*) $8x + 18 = (2x + 38) + 22$, $x = 7$, $AB = 14$

37. A piece of wire 72 inches long is to be used to make a wire model of an isosceles triangle. How
long should the sides be if   **(7.5)**
    a) the ratio of one of the equal sides to the base is $3 : 2$?
    b) the base is to be 6 inches less than one of the equal sides?

    Ans. *a*) 27, 27 and 18 in.   *b*) 26, 26 and 20 in.

Coin or Stamp Problems

38. Write the expression that represents the total value *in cents* of each; then simplify it: **(8.1, 8.2)**
    a) n nickels and $(n - 5)$ dimes.   *Ans.* *a*) $5n + 10(n - 5)$; $15n - 50$
    b) n dimes and $(3n - 10)$ quarters.   *Ans.* *b*) $10n + 25(3n - 10)$; $85n - 250$
    c) n 3-cent and $(2n + 5)$ 2-cent stamps.   *Ans.* *c*) $3n + 2(2n + 5)$; $7n + 10$

39. Express each sentence as an equation; then find n and the number of each coin or stamp.   **(8.3)**
    a) The total value of n nickels and $2n$ dimes is \$1.25.
    b) The total value of n 2-cent and $(n - 3)$ 3-cent stamps is 91¢.
    c) The value of n quarters is \$5.75 less than the value of $(n + 10)$ half-dollars.
    d) The value of n 6-cent stamps equals that of $(2n - 7)$ 10-cent stamps.

    Ans. *a*) $5n + 10(2n) = 125$, $n = 5$, 5 nickels and 10 dimes
      b) $2n + 3(n - 3) = 91$, $n = 20$, 20 2-cent and 17 3-cent stamps
      c) $25n = 50(n + 10) - 575$, $n = 3$, 3 quarters and 13 half-dollars
      d) $6n = 10(2n - 7)$, $n = 5$, 5 6-cent and 3 10-cent stamps.

40. Using x for the number of coins of the first kind and y for the number of coins of the second kind, obtain two equations for each problem; then find the number of each kind of coin.   **(8.4)**

		Equations	No. of Coins
a) John has 25 coins, nickels and half-dollars. Their value is $6.65.	*Ans.*	$x + y = 25$ $5x + 50y = 665$	13 nickels 12 half-dollars
b) The value of a number of dimes and quarters is $2.05. If the quarters were replaced by nickels, the value would be $1.05.	*Ans.*	$10x + 25y = 205$ $10x + 5y = 105$	8 dimes 5 quarters
c) The value of a number of nickels and dimes is $1.40. If the nickels were replaced by dimes and the dimes by nickels, the value would be $1.75.	*Ans.*	$5x + 10y = 140$ $10x + 5y = 175$	14 nickels 7 dimes
d) The value of a number of nickels and quarters is $3.25. If the number of nickels were increased by 3 and the number of quarters were doubled, the value would be $5.90.	*Ans.*	$5x + 25y = 325$ $5(x+3) + 25(2y) = 590$	15 nickels 10 quarters

41. Jack has a number of coins worth $4.05. The collection consisted of 5 more nickels than dimes, and the number of quarters was 3 less than twice the number of dimes. How many of each had he?   **(8.5)**

Ans. Using d for the number of dimes: $5(d+5) + 10d + 25(2d-3) = 405$, $d = 7$.

12 nickels, 7 dimes, 11 quarters.

42. Is it possible to change a $20 bill into an equal number of nickels, dimes and quarters? If so, how many of each would be needed?   **(8.6)**

Ans. Yes. Using n for the number of nickels: $5n + 10n + 25n = 2000$, $n = 50$.

50 nickels, 50 dimes, 50 quarters.

43. At a show, the price of admission for a child was 10¢ and for an adult 25¢. Find the number of each if   **(8.7)**

a) 40 were admitted and the total paid was $6.40.

b) twice as many children as adults were admitted and the total paid was $4.05.

c) 10 more children than adults were admitted and the total paid was $6.25.

d) 15 more children than adults were admitted and the totals paid for each were equal.

Ans. a) 24 children and 16 adults. $\{10c + 25(40-c) = 640, \; c = 24\}$

b) 18 children and 9 adults. $\{10(2a) + 25a = 405, \; a = 9\}$

c) 25 children and 15 adults. $\{10(a+10) + 25a = 625, \; a = 15\}$

d) 25 children and 10 adults. $\{10(a+15) = 25a, \; a = 10\}$

Cost and Mixture Problems

44. Write the expression that represents the total value *in cents*; then simplify it.   **(9.1)**

a) n lb. of tea valued at $1.25 per lb. and 5 lb. of tea valued at $1.40 per lb.

b) n stamps valued at 50¢ each and $(n-8)$ stamps valued at 75¢ each.

c) $2n$ notebooks at 10¢ each and $(3n-5)$ notebooks at 15¢ each.

d) d dozen pens at $3.25 a dozen and $(2d+4)$ dozen pens at $2.80 a dozen.

Ans. a) $125n + 5(140)$; $125n + 700$ *c*) $10(2n) + 15(3n-5)$; $65n - 75$

b) $50n + 75(n-8)$; $125n - 600$ *d*) $325d + 280(2d+4)$; $885d + 1120$

45. Write the expression that represents the total cost *in dollars*; then simplify it.   **(9.2)**
  a) n souvenirs priced at \$3 apiece and $(n-2)$ souvenirs priced at \$1.50 each.
  b) $2n$ tickets at \$3.30 each, $\frac{n}{2}$ tickets at \$4.40 each and n tickets at \$1.60 each.
  c) 12 chairs at \$7 each, n chairs at \$8.50 each and $(2n+1)$ chairs at \$10 each.
  d) n boxes of cards at \$2.50 a box and $(5n-4)$ boxes at \$3.75 a box.

  Ans. a) $3n+1.50(n-2)$; $4.5n-3$ *c*) $7(12)+8.50n+10(2n+1)$; $28.5n+94$
      b) $3.30(2n)+4.40(\frac{n}{2})+1.60n$; $10.4n$ *d*) $2.50n+3.75(5n-4)$; $21.25n-15$

46. Express each sentence as an equation; then find n and the number of each kind: **(9.3)**
  a) The cost of n lb. of tea at 85¢ a lb. and $(10-n)$ lb. of tea at 90¢ a lb. is \$8.80.
  b) The value of n tickets at 90¢ each and $(3n+2)$ tickets at \$1.20 each is \$29.40.
  c) John's earnings for n hr. at \$1.70 per hr. and for $(n-4)$ hr. at \$2.40 per hr. is \$31.40.
  d) The cost of $(n+2)$ gifts at \$8 each, $2n$ gifts at \$10 each and n gifts at \$15 each is \$231.

  Ans. a) $85n+90(10-n)=880$, $n=4$, 4 lb. at 85¢ and 6 lb. at 90¢.
     b) $90n+120(3n+2)=2940$, $n=6$, 6 tickets at 90¢ and 20 tickets at \$1.20.
     c) $170n+240(n-4)=3140$, $n=10$, 10 hr. at \$1.70 and 6 hr. at \$2.40.
     d) $8(n+2)+10(2n)+15n=231$, $n=5$, 7 gifts at \$8, 10 gifts at \$10 and 5 gifts at \$15.

47. A coffee merchant blended coffee worth 75¢ a lb. with coffee   **(9.4)**
worth 95¢ a lb. How many lb. of each grade did he use to make

	No. of Pounds 75¢ grade, 95¢ grade	
a) a mixture of 30 lb. valued at 85¢ a lb?	*Ans. a*) 15 lb.,	15 lb.
b) a mixture of 12 lb. valued at 80¢ a lb?	*Ans. b*) 9 lb.,	3 lb.
c) a mixture of 24 lb. valued at 90¢ a lb?	*Ans. c*) 6 lb.,	18 lb.

48. At a game, tickets were sold at 25¢, 50¢ and 80¢ each. The number sold at 50¢ was 10 more than the number sold at 80¢. The total receipts were \$16.50.   **(9.5)**
Find the number sold at each price
  a) if there were 20 sold at 25¢.
  b) if the number sold at 25¢ equaled the sum of the other tickets.
  c) if the number sold at 25¢ was 5 more than that at 50¢.

  Ans. a) 15 at 50¢, 5 at 80¢, 20 at 25¢ $\{20(25)+50(x+10)+80x=1650,\ x=5\}$
     b) 15 at 50¢, 5 at 80¢, 20 at 25¢ $\{25(2x+10)+50(x+10)+80x=1650,\ x=5\}$
     c) 15 at 50¢, 5 at 80¢, 20 at 25¢ $\{25(x+15)+50(x+10)+80x=1650,\ x=5\}$

Investment and Interest Problems

49. Write the expression that represents the annual interest earned by each principal;   **(10.1)**
then simplify it.
  a) \$1000 at 5%, \$2000 at 3% and \$$P$ at 4%.   *Ans. a*) $.05(1000)+.03(2000)+.04P$; $.04P+110$
  b) \$$P$ at 2%, \$$2P$ at 5% and \$7500 at 6%.   *Ans. b*) $.02P+.05(2P)+.06(7500)$; $.12P+450$
  c) \$$P$ at 3% and \$$(2P-600)$ at 7%.   *Ans. c*) $.03P+.07(2P-600)$; $.17P-42$
  d) \$$P$ at 8%, \$$3P$ at 3% and \$$(P+2500)$ at 4%.   *Ans. d*) $.08P+.03(3P)+.04(P+2500)$; $.21P+100$

50. Express each sentence as an equation; then solve and state each principal.   **(10.2)**
  a) The total annual income from \$800 at 3% and \$$P$ at 4% is \$56.
  b) The total annual interest from \$$P$ at 2% and \$$(P+2000)$ at 5% is \$380.
  c) The annual interest from \$$P$ at 6% equals that from \$$(2P-3000)$ at 5%.
  d) The annual interest from \$$2P$ at $3\frac{1}{2}$% exceeds that from \$$P$ at 5% by \$40.

  Ans. a) $.03(800)+.04P=56$, $P=800$.   \$800 at 4%
     b) $.02P+.05(P+2000)=380$, $P=4000$.   \$4000 at 2%, \$6000 at 5%
     c) $.06P=.05(2P-3000)$, $P=3750$.   \$3750 at 6%, \$4500 at 5%
     d) $.03\frac{1}{2}(2P)=.05P+40$, $P=2000$.   \$4000 at $3\frac{1}{2}$%, \$2000 at 5%

51. Mr. Baker invested two sums of money, the first at 5% and the second at 6%. State the amount invested at each rate if the ratio of the investments was **(10.3)**

a) 3:1 and the interest from the 5% investment exceeded that from the 6% investment by $180.

b) 4:3 and the total interest was $342.

Ans. a) Using $3x$ and x, $.05(3x) - .06x = 180$, $x = 2000$, $6000 at 5% and $2000 at 6%.

b) Using $4x$ and $3x$, $.05(4x) + .06(3x) = 342$, $x = 900$, $3600 at 5% and $2700 at 6%.

52. A total of $1200 is invested, partly at 3% and the rest at 5%. Find the amounts invested at each rate **(10.4)**

a) if the total interest is $54.   *Ans.* a) $300 at 3%, $900 at 5%

b) if the annual interests are both equal.   *Ans.* b) $750 at 3%, $450 at 5%

c) if the annual interest from the 3% investment exceeds   *Ans.* c) $800 at 3%, $400 at 5%
   that from the 5% investment by $4.

53. On a total investment of $5400, Mr. Adams lost 4% on one part and earned 5% on the other. How large was each investment **(10.5)**

a) if his losses equaled his earnings?   *Ans.* $3000 at (-4%) and $2400 at 5%

b) if his net income was $144?   *Ans.* $1400 at (-4%) and $4000 at 5%

54. Mr. Howard has $400 invested at 2% and $600 at 3%. State the amount he must invest at 6% so that his annual income will be a) 4% of the entire investment, b) 5% of the entire investment.

Ans. Using x for the added investment: **(10.6)**

a) $.02(400) + .03(600) + .06x = .04(1000+x)$, $700 to be added at 6%

b) $.02(400) + .03(600) + .06x = .05(1000+x)$, $2400 to be added at 6%

Motion Problems

55. Write the expression, in simplified form, that represents the distance *in miles* traveled **(11.1)**

a) in 7 hr. at 20 mph and in T hr. more at 42 mph.   *Ans.* a) $7(20) + 42T$; $42T + 140$

b) in 10 hr. at R mph and in 12 hr. more at 10 mph.   *Ans.* b) $10R + 12(10)$; $10R + 120$

c) in T hr. at 25 mph and in $(T+8)$ hr. more at 15 mph.   *Ans.* c) $25T + 15(T+8)$; $40T + 120$

d) in 5 hr. at R mph and in $3\frac{1}{2}$ hr. more at $(2R+8)$ mph.   *Ans.* d) $5R + 3\frac{1}{2}(2R+8)$; $12R + 28$

56. Write the expression, in simplified form, that represents the time *in hours* needed to travel **(11.2)**

a) 240 mi. at 40 mph and D mi. farther at 27 mph.   *Ans.* a) $\frac{240}{40} + \frac{D}{27}$; $\frac{D}{27} + 6$

b) 100 mi. at R mph and 75 mi. farther at 15 mph.   *Ans.* b) $\frac{100}{R} + \frac{75}{15}$; $\frac{100}{R} + 5$

c) D mi. at 15 mph and $3D$ mi. farther at 45 mph.   *Ans.* c) $\frac{D}{15} + \frac{3D}{45}$; $\frac{2D}{15}$

d) 40 mi. at 4 mi. per min. and 50 mi. farther at R mph.   *Ans.* d) $\frac{40}{240} + \frac{50}{R}$; $\frac{50}{R} + \frac{1}{6}$

57. Two trains leave the same terminal at the same time and travel in opposite directions. After 8 hr. they are 360 mi. apart. The speed of the faster train is 3 mph less than twice that of the slower train. Find the rate of each train. **(11.3)**

Ans. Using R for speed of slower train in mph, $8R + 8(2R-3) = 360$; rates are 16 mph and 29 mph.

58. In each situation the travelers start from the same place at the same time and travel in *opposite directions*. Using the variable indicated, express each sentence as an equation; then solve and find each quantity represented.   **(11.4)**

a) At speeds of 25 mph and 15 mph, they travel until they are 210 mi. apart. Find the time of each using T in hr.

b) After 7 hr., both are 707 mi. apart, one going 39 mph slower. Find the faster rate, using R in mph for this.

c) At speeds in the ratio of 6 : 5, both are 308 mi. apart in 14 hr. Find their respective rates, using $6x$ and $5x$ in mph. for these.

Ans. a) $25T + 15T = 210$; time is $5\frac{1}{4}$ hr.   b) $7R + 7(R-39) = 707$; faster rate is 70 mph.

c) $14(6x) + 14(5x) = 308$, $x = 2$; rates are 12 mph and 10 mph.

59. Two planes leave from points 1925 mi. apart at the same time and fly toward each other. Their average speeds are 225 mph and 325 mph. How soon will the planes meet and how far will each have traveled?   **(11.5)**

Ans. Using T for the time of travel, $225T + 325T = 1925$. Planes will meet in $3\frac{1}{2}$ hr.
The distances traveled will be $787\frac{1}{2}$ mi. and $1137\frac{1}{2}$ mi.

60. In each situation, the travelers start from distant places and travel toward each other until they meet. Using the variable indicated, express each sentence as an equation; then solve and find each quantity represented.   **(11.6)**

a) Starting 297 mi. apart, they travel at 38 mph and 28 mph. Find the time of each in hr., using T.

b) Starting 630 mi. apart, they meet in 5 hr., one traveling 46 mph faster than the other. Find the rate of the faster in mph, using R for this.

c) Starting 480 mi. apart, they meet in 6 hr., one traveling five times as fast as the other. Find the rate of the slower in mph, using R for this.

Ans. a) $38T + 28T = 297$; time is $4\frac{1}{2}$ hr.

b) $5R + 5(R-46) = 630$; rate of faster is 86 mph.

c) $6R + 6(5R) = 480$; rate of slower is $13\frac{1}{3}$ mph.

61. A plane traveled from its base to a distant point and back again along the same route in a total of 8 hr. Its average rate going was 180 mph and its average rate returning was 300 mph. How long did it take in each direction and what was the distance covered each way?   **(11.7)**

Ans. Using T for the time in hr. going, $180T = 300(8-T)$; time going was 5 hr.
The distance covered each way was 900 mi.

62. In each situation, a traveler traveled out and back to the starting place along the same road. Using the variable indicated, express each sentence as an equation, then solve and find each quantity represented.   **(11.8)**

a) A traveler traveled out for 3 hr. at an average rate of 44 mph and returned in $5\frac{1}{2}$ hr. Find the average rate returning in mph, using R.

b) A traveler took 3 hr. less to travel back than to go out. If he averaged 45 mph out and 54 mph back, find his time in hr. returning, using T for this.

c) A traveler required a total of 8 hr. for a round trip. If he averaged 24 mph out and 36 mph back, find his time in hr. returning, using T for this.

d) After taking 3 hr. going out, a traveler came back in 5 hr., averaging 28 mph slower on the way back. Find the average rate going in mph, using R for this.

Ans. a) $3(44) = 5\frac{1}{2}R$; rate returning 24 mph.   c) $24(8-T) = 36T$; time back 3.2 hr.

b) $45(T+3) = 54T$; time back 15 hr.   d) $3R = 5(R-28)$; rate going 70 mph.

63. A boat travels at 24 mph. A patrol boat starts 3 hr. later from the same place and travels at 32 mph in the same direction. How long will it need to overtake the first and what distance will it cover?

Ans. Using T for the time of the patrol boat in hr., $32T = 24(T+3)$.   **(11.9)**

The time needed to overtake is 9 hr. and the distance to cover is 288 mi.

64. In each situation, after a traveler has begun his trip, a second traveler starts from the same place along the same road and, going in the same direction, overtakes the first.   **(11.10)**

  a) The second starts $2\frac{1}{2}$ hr. later and travels for 6 hr. at 34 mph. Find the rate of the first in mph, using R for this.

  b) Their speeds are 15 mph and 24 mph. The second starts 2 hr. after the first. Find the time of the first in hr., using T for this.

  c) The first travels 18 mph slower than twice the speed of the second. If the second starts out 2 hr. later and overtakes the first in 5 hr., find the rate of the second in mph, using R for this.

  d) The ratio of their rates is $4:5$. The first was delayed 2 hr. along the way and also made a detour of 10 extra mi. The second overtook the first in 6 hr. after starting 4 hr. later. Find their rates in mph, using $4x$ and $5x$ for these.

Ans. a) $8\frac{1}{2}R = 6(34)$; rate of first is 24 mph.

  b) $15T = 24(T-2)$; time of first is $5\frac{1}{3}$ hr.

  c) $7(2R-18) = 5R$; rate of second is 14 mph.

  d) $8(4x) - 10 = 6(5x)$, $x = 5$; rates are 20 mph and 25 mph.

65. Write the expression that represents the rate of work per unit of time in each case. **(12.1)**

  a) Write the expression for the rate of production if 240 pens are manufactured in (1) 30 minutes, (2) 2 minutes, (3) $\frac{1}{2}$ minute, (4) m minutes,

  b) Write the expression for the rate of filling freight trains if (1) 9 trains are filled in 3 hours, (2) 3 trains are filled in 9 hours, (3) t trains are filled in h hours.

  c) Write the expression that represents the rate of work if 1 job requires (1) 3 days, (2) $\frac{1}{2}$ hour, (3) m minutes.

Ans. a) (1) 8 pens per minute   (3) 480 pens per minute

  (2) 120 pens per minute   (4) $\frac{240}{m}$ pens per minute

  b) (1) 3 trains per hour, (2) $\frac{1}{3}$ train per hour, (3) $\frac{t}{h}$ trains per hour
  c) (1) $\frac{1}{3}$ job per day, (2) 2 jobs per hour, (3) $\frac{1}{m}$ job per minute

66. In each case, determine the part of the job accomplished by the two workers working together or by the two pipes emptying the pool together.   **(12.2)**

  a) Henry, who can do the job in 6 hours working alone, works for 2 hours and Jim, who can do the same job alone in 8 hours, works for 4 hours.   *Ans.* $\frac{1}{3} + \frac{1}{2} = \frac{5}{6}$

  b) A and B work together to construct a brick wall for a period of 4 days. A requires 20 days to do the job alone, while B can complete the same job alone in 16 days.   *Ans.* $\frac{1}{5} + \frac{1}{4} = \frac{9}{20}$

  c) Separately, the smaller of two pipes can empty a pool in 10 hours, while separately the larger pipe requires 4 hours. Both pipes are used together for a period of $2\frac{1}{2}$ hours.   *Ans.* $\frac{1}{4} + \frac{5}{8} = \frac{7}{8}$

67. Express each sentence as an equation; then solve and find the value of each represented quantity.   **(12.3)**

  a) Machine A can do a job alone in 15 minutes while machine B can do the same job alone in 25 minutes. Working together, they complete the job in m minutes.

  b) A mason can make a concrete walk in 8 hours alone, while his helper requires h hours alone for the same job. Working together they complete the job in 6 hours.

  c) Ernest can plow a field in 3 days working alone, while Jack works one-third as fast doing the same job. Both together plow the field in d days.

Ans. a) $\frac{m}{15} + \frac{m}{25} = 1$, $m = 9\frac{3}{8}$ b) $\frac{6}{8} + \frac{6}{h} = 1$, $R = 24$ c) $\frac{d}{3} + \frac{d}{9} = 1$, $d = 2\frac{1}{4}$

Combination Problems

68. Find the price of a shirt and the price of a hat in each problem: **(13.1a)**
   a) 6 shirts and 8 hats cost $64. At the same price, 4 shirts and 1 hat cost $21.
   b) 3 shirts and 5 hats cost $65. If each price is increased by $1, 2 shirts and 6 hats would cost $78.

   Ans. Using s for the price of 1 shirt in $ and h for the price of 1 hat in $:
   a) $6s + 8h = 64$ and $4s + h = 21$. Prices are $4 per shirt and $5 per hat.
   b) $3s + 5h = 65$ and $2(s+1) + 6(h+1) = 78$. Prices are $5 per shirt and $10 per hat.

69. Find the number of lb. of each grade of tea in each problem: **(13.1b)**
   a) A mixture of tea worth $1.20 a lb. and tea worth $1.80 a lb. is valued at $18.
      If the price per lb. of each grade is increased 30¢, the new value would be $21.30.
   b) A mixture of tea worth $1 a lb. and tea worth $1.40 a lb. is valued at $17.
      Had there been twice as many lb. of the second tea, the value would have been $24.

   Ans. Using n for the no. of lb. of the cheaper tea and N for the no. of lb. of the dearer tea:
   a) $120n + 180N = 1800$ and $150n + 210N = 2130$. 3 lb. at $1.20 and 8 lb. at $1.80.
   b) $100n + 140N = 1700$ and $100n + 140(2N) = 2400$. 10 lb. at $1 and 5 lb. at $1.40.

70. Find the two rates in each problem: **(13.2a)**
   a) By traveling for 5 hr. at one speed and then for 3 hr. at another, Mr. Hart covered 250 mi. Had he traveled for two hours longer at each speed, he would have covered 370 mi.
   b) By traveling for 2 hr. at one speed and then 7 hr. at another, Mr. Hayes completed a trip of 258 mi. Had the first rate been 10 mph faster and the second rate twice as fast, he would have gone 488 mi.

   Ans. Using r for the first rate in mph and R for the second rate in mph:
   a) $5r + 3R = 250$ and $7r + 5R = 370$. Rates were 35 mph and 25 mph.
   b) $2r + 7R = 258$ and $2(r+10) + 7(2R) = 488$. Rates were 24 mph and 30 mph.

71. Find the number of hours traveled at each speed in each problem: **(13.2b)**
   a) Mr. Ford completed 282 mi. by going 22 mph for one period of time and then 27 mph for another. Had he increased each speed 5 mph, he would have covered 337 mi.
   b) Mr. Plymouth completed 420 mi. by going 15 mph for one period of time and then 36 mph for another. Had he gone twice as fast during the first time and one-half as fast during the second, he would have gone 300 mi.

   Ans. Using t for the first time in hr. and T for the second time in hr.:
   a) $22t + 27T = 282$ and $27t + 32T = 337$. Times are 3 hr. and 8 hr.
   b) $15t + 36T = 420$ and $30t + 18T = 300$. Times are 4 hr. and 10 hr.

72. If t and u represent the tens and units digits respectively of a two-digit number, evaluate the expressions in the first column of the table for each of the numbers in the first row of the table.   **(14.1)**

	12	38	69	95
$t + u$	(a)	(b)	(c)	(d)
tu	(e)	(f)	(g)	(h)
$3t + 2u$	(i)	(j)	(k)	(m)
$10t + u$	(n)	(o)	(p)	(q)
$10u + t$	(r)	(s)	(t)	(u)

Ans. (a) 3, (b) 11, (c) 15, (d) 14, (e) 2, (f) 24, (g) 54, (h) 45, (i) 7, (j) 25, (k) 36, (m) 37, (n) 12, (o) 38, (p) 69, (q) 95, (r) 21, (s) 83, (t) 96, (u) 59

73. Letting t and u represent the tens and units digits respectively of a two-digit number, express each sentence as an equation; then solve and find the number.   **(14.1)**

    a) The sum of the digits is 12. The tens digit is twice the units digit.

    b) The sum of twice the units digit and the tens digit is 16 while the sum of twice the tens digit and the units digit is 20.

    c) The ratio of the tens digit to the units digit is 2:3 while the tens digit is 10 less than the units digit increased by 7.

$Ans.\ \ a)\ \begin{cases} t + u = 12 \\ \quad\ \ t = 2u \end{cases} ; 84 \quad b)\ \begin{cases} 2u + t = 16 \\ 2t + u = 20 \end{cases} ; 84 \quad c)\ \begin{cases} \dfrac{t}{u} = \dfrac{2}{3} \\ t = (u + 7) - 10 \end{cases} ; 69$

74. Letting t and u represent the tens and units digits respectively of a two-digit number, express each sentence as an equation, then solve and find the number.   **(14.1)**

    a) The number is four times the sum of the digits. The number with the digits reversed is 27 more than the original number.

    b) The number is 9 less than 3 times the number with the digits reversed. The tens digit is 1 more than 3 times the units digit.

    c) The tens digit exceeds twice the units digit by 1. The number with the digits reversed is 80 less than 3 times the original number.

    d) The sum of twice the tens digit and the units digit is 10. The original number is 6 less than twice the number with the digits reversed.

$Ans.\ \ a)\ \begin{cases} 10t + u = 4(t + u) \\ 10u + t = 10t + u + 27 \end{cases} ; 36 \qquad c)\ \begin{cases} t = 2u + 1 \\ 10u + t = 3(10t + u) - 80 \end{cases} ; 31$

$\qquad\quad b)\ \begin{cases} 10t + u = 3(10u + t) - 9 \\ \quad\quad\ t = 3u + 1 \end{cases} ; 72 \qquad d)\ \begin{cases} 2t + u = 10 \\ 10t + u = 2(10u + t) = 6 \end{cases} ; 42$

75. Make a frequency distribution of the following 47 class registers in a school. State its range, mode, median and arithmetic mean.   **(15.1)**

                30, 32, 35, 31, 36, 28, 29, 34, 34, 32, 35, 31, 30, 29, 30, 28
                33, 33, 34, 33, 32, 34, 29, 30, 33, 33, 34, 33, 30, 34, 35, 27
                32, 31, 34, 31, 33, 32, 31, 29, 32, 33, 31, 32, 31, 32, 33

Ans.

Frequency Distribution

Registers	Frequency	Registers	Frequency
36	1	31	7
35	3	30	5
34	7	29	4
33	9	28	2
32	8	27	1

Range = 27 to 36. Mode = 33.
Average or arithmetic mean = 31.87.
Median = 32 (24th score in rank).

76. Make a frequency distribution of the 47 class registers of the previous problem by tallying them in the following five groups: 26.5−28.5, 28.5−30.5, 30.5−32.5, 32.5−34.5, 34.5−36.5.

    Make a histogram and a frequency polygon of the five groups.   **(15.2, 15.3)**

Ans.

Grouped Frequency Distribution

Group Intervals	Group Midpoints	Frequency
34.5 − 36.5	35.5	4
32.5 − 34.5	33.5	16
30.5 − 32.5	31.5	15
28.5 − 30.5	29.5	9
26.5 − 28.5	27.5	3

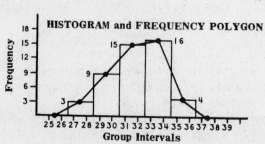

HISTOGRAM and FREQUENCY POLYGON

Chapter 10

Special Products and Factoring

1. UNDERSTANDING FACTORS AND PRODUCTS

Factors, Multiples, Divisors, and Prime Numbers

Since $4 \cdot 5 = 20$, then 20 is the product of 4 and 5; also, 4 and 5 are **factors** of 20. Furthermore, 20 is an integral multiple of 5, or simply a **multiple** of 5; and 20 is a multiple of 4. The statements, "5 is a factor of 20" and "5 is a **divisor** of 20" mean the same thing because if an integer is a factor of another integer, then it is a divisor of the other integer. The use of "divisor" for "factor" implies that the division is exact; that is, that there is no remainder.

Our discussion of factors, multiples, and divisors of numbers is simplified if we consider the numbers to be **positive integers**. Hence, although 20 is the product of $\frac{1}{2}$ and 40, $\frac{1}{2}$ and 40 are not to be considered factors or divisors of 20.

In the complete set of factors of 20, {1, 2, 4, 5, 10, and 20}, the only factors that are **prime numbers** are 2 and 5, according to the following definition:

A **prime number** is an integer greater than 1 that has no positive integral factors, other than 1 and itself.

The first 15 prime numbers are 2, 3, 5, 7, 11, 13, 17, 19, 23, 29, 31, 37, 41, 43, and 47.

A **composite number** is a positive integer, other than 1, that is not a prime number.

Thus, the first 10 composite numbers are 4, 6, 8, 9, 10, 12, 14, 15, 16, and 18.

Fundamental Theorem of Arithmetic: Prime Factorization

Every composite number is the product of a unique set of prime numbers, apart from the order of the factors.

Thus, $2 \cdot 2 \cdot 5$ is the product of the unique prime factors of 20. Reordering the prime factors does not change the product; that is, $20 = 2 \cdot 2 \cdot 5 = 2 \cdot 5 \cdot 2 = 5 \cdot 2 \cdot 2$. Note that in the factoring of a composite number, a prime factor may be repeated.

A process known as "peeling" can be used to find the unique set of prime factors. The process of "peeling" is demonstrated in the following problems:

Prime Factorization of a Composite Number by "Peeling"

Find the unique set of prime factors of   *a*) 630   *b*) 8008

Procedure:

1. Divide the number by its smallest prime divisor as many times as this may be done.

   1. $2\overline{)630}$
      $\quad 315$

   1. $2\overline{)8008}$
      $\quad 2\overline{)4004}$
      $\quad 2\overline{)2002}$

2. Divide the resulting number by the next greater prime divisor as many times as this may be done, and so on until the result is a prime number.

   2. $3\overline{)315}$
      $3\overline{)105}$
      $5\overline{)35}$
      $\quad 7$

   2. $7\overline{)1001}$
      $11\overline{)143}$
      $\quad 13$

3. Combine the prime divisors so obtained into a set of factors of the given number.

   3. $630 = 2 \cdot 3 \cdot 3 \cdot 5 \cdot 7$
      $\quad = 2 \cdot 3^2 \cdot 5 \cdot 7$ *Ans.*

   3. $8008 = 2 \cdot 2 \cdot 2 \cdot 7 \cdot 11 \cdot 13$
      $\quad = 2^3 \cdot 7 \cdot 11 \cdot 13$ *Ans.*

Some Helpful Tests of Divisibility

1. Divisibility by 2, 4, or 8:

A positive integer is **divisible by 2** if its final digit is divisible by 2.

Thus, 23457<u>8</u> is divisible by 2 since 8 is divisible by 2.

A positive integer is **divisible by 4** if the number determined by its two final digits is divisible by 4.

Thus, 3579<u>12</u> is divisible by 4 since 12 is divisible by 4.

A positive integer is **divisible by 8** if the number determined by its three final digits is divisible by 8.

Thus, 357<u>248</u> is divisible by 8 since 248 is divisible by 8.

2. Divisibility by 3 or 9:

A positive integer is **divisible by 3** if the sum of its digits is divisible by 3.

Thus, 123456 is divisible by 3 since $1 + 2 + 3 + 4 + 5 + 6$ is divisible by 3.

A positive integer is **divisible by 9** if the sum of its digits is divisible by 9.

Thus, 123453 is divisible by 9 since $1 + 2 + 3 + 4 + 5 + 3$ is divisible by 9.

3. Divisibility by 5 or 25:

A positive integer is **divisible by 5** if its final digit is 5 or 0.

Thus, 1234<u>5</u> is divisible by 5 since its last digit is 5.

A positive integer is **divisible by 25** if the number determined by its two final digits is divisible by 25.

Thus, 23489<u>75</u> is divisible by 25 since 75 is divisible by 25.

Greatest Common Factor (G.C.F.) or Greatest Common Divisor (G.C.D.)

The positive integers 36 and 54 have three common factors, 6, 9, and 18. The greatest of the common factors (G.C.F.) is 18. The greatest common factor is also called the greatest common divisor (G.C.D.)

Rule. The **greatest common factor** (G.C.F.), or the **greatest common divisor** (G.C.D.), of two or more numbers is found by multiplying all the common prime factors of the numbers.

Thus, $36 = 2 \cdot 2 \cdot 3 \cdot 3$

$54 = \quad 2 \cdot 3 \cdot 3 \cdot 3$ (Each arrow indicates a common prime factor.)

$\qquad\quad \downarrow \;\; \downarrow \;\; \downarrow$

$\qquad\quad 2 \cdot 3 \cdot 3 \quad = 18$ (G.C.F.) or (G.C.D.)

Least Common Multiple (L.C.M.) and Least Common Denominator (L.C.D.)

The positive integers 12 and 18 have an unlimited number of common multiples. These common multiples can be found by examining the separate sets of their multiples:

Multiples of 18: 18, 36, 54, 72, 90, 108, ...

Multiples of 12: 12, 24, 36, 48, 60, 72, 84, 96, 108, ...

Common Multiples of 12 and 18: 36, 72, 108, ...

The **least common multiple** (L.C.M.) of two or more numbers is the least of their common multiples.

Thus, 36 is the L.C.M. of 12 and 18.

The **least common denominator** (L.C.D.) of the denominators of a set of fractions is the least common multiple of the denominators.

Thus, 36 is the L.C.D. of the fractions $\dfrac{11}{12}$ and $\dfrac{13}{18}$.

Greatest Common Factor and Least Common Multiple of Monomials

1. Finding the G.C.F. of Two Monomials

Find the greatest common factor (G.C.F.) of $12a^2b^2$ and $18ab^3$.

Procedure: Solution:

1. Find the G.C.F. of the numerical coefficients: 1. G.C.F. of 12 and 18 is $\underline{6}$.
2. Find the G.C.F. of the literal coefficients.   2. G.C.F. of a^2b^2 and ab^3 is $\underline{ab^2}$

   (Multiply the powers of **least degree** of the
   variables in the literal coefficients.)
3. Multiply both G.C.F.'s.   3. The required G.C.F. is $6ab^2$. *Ans.*

2. Finding the L.C.M. of Two Monomials

Find the least common multiple (L.C.M.) of $12a^2b^2$ and $18ab^3$.

Procedure: Solution:

1. Find the L.C.M. of the numerical coefficients.   1. L.C.M. of 12 and 18 is $\underline{36}$.
2. Find the L.C.M. of the literal coefficients.   2. L.C.M. of a^2b^2 and ab^3 is $\underline{a^2b^3}$.

   (Multiply the powers of **greatest degree** of the
   variables in the literal coefficients.)
3. Multiply both L.C.M.'s.   3. The required L.C.M. is $36a^2b^3$. *Ans.*

Rule. With respect to the literal coefficients of two or more monomials,

(*1*) the G.C.F. of the literal coefficients is the product of the powers of **least degree**.

(*2*) the L.C.M. of the literal coefficients is the product of the powers of **greatest degree**.

Thus, with respect to a^2b^2 and ab^3:

(*1*) the G.C.F. is ab^2, and (*2*) the L.C.M. is a^2b^3.

1.1 Finding a Monomial Product

Find each monomial product:

a) $5 \cdot 7 \cdot x$ *Ans.* a) $35x$ d) $4(3a)(10b)$ *Ans.* d) $120ab$

b) $3xxx$ *Ans.* b) $3x^3$ e) $(5x^2)(11y)$ *Ans.* e) $55x^2y$

c) $8x^2 \cdot x^3 \cdot x^4$ *Ans.* c) $8x^9$ f) $(2ab)(3ac)(4ad)$ *Ans.* f) $24a^3bcd$

1.2 Finding a Polynomial Product by Applying the Distributive Law

Find each product:

a) $4(a+b)$ *Ans.* $4a+4b$ d) $-7x(x-2)$ *Ans.* $-7x^2+14x$ g) $\pi r(r+h)$ *Ans.* $\pi r^2 + \pi rh$

b) $y(w+z)$ *Ans.* $wy+yz$ e) $3a^2(3a-5)$ *Ans.* $9a^3-15a^2$ h) $a(x-y+1)$ *Ans.* $ax-ay+a$

c) $3(4y-1)$ *Ans.* $12y-3$ f) $P(1+rn)$ *Ans.* $P + Prn$ i) $-3(a+b-2)$ *Ans.* $-3a-3b+6$

1.3 Finding Products Involving Fractions and Decimals by Applying the Distributive Law

Find each product:

a) $6(5 + \frac{1}{2})$ *Ans.* a) $30 + 3 = \underline{33}$ f) $24(\frac{x}{2} + \frac{x}{3})$ *Ans.* f) $12x + 8x = \underline{20x}$

b) $12(\frac{1}{3} + \frac{3}{4})$ *Ans.* b) $4 + 9 = \underline{13}$ g) $20(\frac{x}{5} - \frac{x}{4})$ *Ans.* g) $4x - 5x = \underline{-x}$

c) $14(10 - \frac{1}{7})$ *Ans.* c) $140 - 2 = \underline{138}$ h) $9(\frac{x}{3} - \frac{2x}{9})$ *Ans.* h) $3x - 2x = \underline{x}$

d) $.02\frac{1}{2}(1000-40)$ *Ans.* d) $25 - 1 = \underline{24}$ i) $.05(2000-x)$ *Ans.* i) $100 - .05x$

e) $.03(2000+250)$ *Ans.* e) $60 + 7.50 = \underline{67.50}$ j) $.03\frac{1}{2}(4000-2x)$ *Ans.* j) $140 - .07x$

1.4 Prime Factorization of a Positive Integer: "Peeling Process"

Find the set of prime factors of each number:

a) 222,   *b*) 378,   *c*) 640,   *d*) 2,002,   *e*) 2200

Ans. *a*) 2·3·37,   *b*) 2·3·3·3·7,   *c*) 2·2·2·2·2·2·2·5,   *d*) 2·7·11·13,   *e*) 2·2·2·5·5·11
                or 2·3^3·7   or 2^7·5   or 2^3·5^2·11

1.5 Finding the Greatest Common Factor and Least Common Multiple of Positive Integers

Given: $12 = 2·2·3$, $18 = 2·3·3$, $42 = 2·3·7$, and $105 = 3·5·7$

Find the G.C.F. and L.C.M. of each set of numbers:

a) 12 and 18,   *b*) 18 and 42,   *c*) 42 and 105,   *d*) 12, 18, 42, and 105

Ans. *a*) 6, 36;   *b*) 6, 126;   *c*) 21, 210;   *d*) 3, 1260

1.6 Finding the Greatest Common Factor and Least Common Multiple of Two Monomials

Find the G.C.F. and L.C.M. of each set of monomials:

a) $12a$ and $36b$,   *b*) $2a^2$ and $8b^3$,   *c*) $3a^3$ and $27a^4$,   *d*) $18ab^2c^5$ and $27a^2bc^3d$

Ans. *a*) $12, 36ab$;   *b*) $2, 8a^2b^3$;   *c*) $3a^3, 27a^4$;   *d*) $3abc^3, 54a^2b^2c^5d$

2. FACTORING A POLYNOMIAL HAVING A COMMON MONOMIAL FACTOR

A common monomial factor of a polynomial is a monomial that is a factor of each term of the polynomial.

Thus, 7 and a^2 are common monomial factors of $7a^2x + 7a^2y - 7a^2z$.

The greatest common monomial factor of a polynomial (G.C.F.) is the product of all its common monomial factors.

Thus, $7ab$ is the highest common monomial factor of $7abc + 7abd$.

To Factor a Polynomial Having a Common Monomial Factor

Factor: $7ax^2 + 14bx^2 - 21cx^2$

Procedure:

Solution:

1. Use the greatest common monomial factor (G.C.F.) as one factor.

1. G.C.F. is $7x^2$.

2. Find the other factor by dividing each term of the polynomial by the G.C.F.

2. Divide each term by the G.C.F.:
$$\frac{7ax^2 + 14bx^2 - 21cx^2}{7x^2} = a + 2b - 3c$$

Hence, by factoring:
$$7ax^2 + 14bx^2 - 21cx^2 = 7x^2(a + 2b - 3c)$$

Note. A fraction may be used as a common factor if it is the numerical coefficient of each term of the original polynomial.

Thus, by factoring, $\frac{1}{2}x + \frac{1}{2}y = \frac{1}{2}(x+y)$.

2.1 Factoring Polynomials Having a Common Monomial Factor

Factor, removing the greatest common factor, G.C.F.:

a) $5a - 5b$ *Ans.* $5(a-b)$ *d*) $9x^2 - 9x$ *Ans.* $9x(x-1)$ *g*) $\pi R^2 - \pi r^2$ *Ans.* $\pi(R^2 - r^2)$

b) $\frac{1}{2}h + \frac{1}{2}k$ *Ans.* $\frac{1}{2}(h+k)$ *e*) $x^5 + 3x^2$ *Ans.* $x^2(x^3 + 3)$ *h*) $5bx + 10by - 15b$ *Ans.* $5b(x+2y-3)$

c) $2ay - 2by$ *Ans.* $2y(a-b)$ *f*) $S - Snd$ *Ans.* $S(1-nd)$ *i*) $4x^3 + 8x^2 - 24x$ *Ans.* $4x(x^2 + 2x - 6)$

2.2 Factoring Numerical Polynomials

Evaluate each, using factoring:

a) $7(14) - 6\frac{1}{2}(14)$

b) $6(8\frac{1}{2}) + 4(8\frac{1}{2})$

c) $17\frac{1}{4}(10) - 15\frac{1}{4}(10)$

d) $.03(800) + .03(750) - .03(550)$

e) $.02\frac{1}{2}(8500) - .02\frac{1}{2}(7500) - .02\frac{1}{2}(1000)$

f) $8.4(3^3) + 5.3(3^3) - 3.7(3^3)$

Ans. a) $14(7 - 6\frac{1}{2}) = 14(\frac{1}{2}) = 7$

Ans. b) $8\frac{1}{2}(6+4) = 8\frac{1}{2}(10) = 85$

Ans. c) $10(17\frac{1}{4} - 15\frac{1}{4}) = 10(2) = 20$

Ans. d) $.03(800 + 750 - 550) = .03(1000) = 30$

Ans. e) $.02\frac{1}{2}(8500 - 7500 - 1000) = .02\frac{1}{2}(0) = 0$

Ans. f) $3^3(8.4 + 5.3 - 3.7) = 3^3(10) = 270$

3. SQUARING A MONOMIAL

The square of a number is the product of the number multiplied by itself. The number is used twice as a factor.

Thus, the square of 7   or $7^2 = (7)(7) = 49$.

Also, the square of (-7) or $(-7)^2 = (-7)(-7) = 49$.

Opposites have the same square.

Thus, both $(+7)$ and (-7) have the same square, 49; that is, $(+7)^2 = (-7)^2$.

Rule 1. **To square a fraction**, square both its numerator and its denominator.

Thus, the square of $\frac{2}{3}$ or $(\frac{2}{3})^2 = (\frac{2}{3})(\frac{2}{3}) = \frac{2^2}{3^2} = \frac{4}{9}$.

In general, $(\frac{a}{b})^2 = \frac{a^2}{b^2}$.

Rule 2. **To square a monomial**, square its numerical coefficient, keep each base and double the exponent of each base.

Thus, $(5ab^3)^2 = (5ab^3)(5ab^3)$ or $25a^2b^6$.

3.1 Squaring Numbers: Rule 1

Find each square:

a) $(+.8)^2$ *Ans. a)* .64

b) $(-.8)^2$ *Ans. b)* .64

c) $(.3)^2$ *Ans. c)* .09

d) $(-.3)^2$ *Ans. d)* .09

e) $(-.07)^2$ *Ans. e)* .0049

f) $(\frac{1}{5})^2$ *Ans. f)* $\frac{1}{25}$

g) $(-\frac{1}{5})^2$ *Ans. g)* $\frac{1}{25}$

h) $(\frac{10}{11})^2$ *Ans. h)* $\frac{100}{121}$

i) $(\frac{5}{3})^2$ or $(1\frac{2}{3})^2$ *Ans. i)* $\frac{25}{9}$ or $2\frac{7}{9}$

j) $(-1\frac{2}{3})^2$ *Ans. j)* $\frac{25}{9}$ or $2\frac{7}{9}$

k) $(.002)^2$ *Ans. k)* .000004

l) $(-1.2)^2$ *Ans. l)* 1.44

m) $(1.25)^2$ *Ans. m)* 1.5625

n) $(-.125)^2$ *Ans. n)* .015625

o) $(-.101)^2$ *Ans. o)* .010201

3.2 Squaring Monomials: Rule 2

Find each square:

a) $(r^3)^2$ *Ans. a)* r^6

b) $(x^4)^2$ *Ans. b)* x^8

c) $(\frac{a^5}{b^3})^2$ *Ans. c)* $\frac{a^{10}}{b^6}$

d) $(\frac{x^{11}}{r})^2$ *Ans. d)* $\frac{x^{22}}{y^2}$

e) $(2ab)^2$ *Ans. e)* $4a^2b^2$

f) $(-4x^4)^2$ *Ans. f)* $16x^8$

g) $(-\frac{ab^2}{c^7})^2$ *Ans. g)* $\frac{a^2b^4}{c^{14}}$

h) $(-\frac{10}{3}w^{20})^2$ *Ans. h)* $\frac{100}{9}w^{40}$

i) $(-8a^2b^3c)^2$ *Ans. i)* $64a^4b^6c^2$

j) $(.1x^{100})^2$ *Ans. j)* $.01x^{200}$

k) $(\frac{rst}{uv})^2$ *Ans. k)* $\frac{r^2s^2t^2}{u^2v^2}$

l) $(-\frac{7}{10}x^7y^{10})^2$ *Ans. l)* $\frac{49}{100}x^{14}y^{20}$

3.3 Finding Areas of Squares: $A = s^2$

Find the area of a square whose side is

a) 3 ft.　　*Ans. a*) 9 sq. ft.

b) $\frac{3}{4}$ yd.　　*Ans. b*) $\frac{9}{16}$ sq. yd.

c) 1.3 mi.　　*Ans. c*) 1.69 sq. mi.

d) $8x$　　*Ans. d*) $64x^2$

e) $1.5y^2$　　*Ans. e*) $2.25y^4$

f) $\frac{2}{3}m^3$　　*Ans. f*) $\frac{4}{9}m^6$

Square

Area

$A = s^2$

Side, s

4. FINDING THE SQUARE ROOT OF A MONOMIAL

The square root of a number is one of its two equal factors.

Thus, the square root of 49 is either $+7$ or -7, since $49 = (+7)(+7) = (-7)(-7)$.

A positive number has two square roots which are opposites or additive inverses of each other. (Opposites have the same absolute value but differ in sign.)

Thus, $\frac{25}{36}$ has two square roots, either $+\frac{5}{6}$ or $-\frac{5}{6}$.

The principal square root of a number is its positive square root.

Thus, the principal square root of 81 is $+9$.

The symbol $"\sqrt{\ }"$ is used to indicate the principal or positive square root of a number.

Thus, $\sqrt{81} = 9$, $\sqrt{\frac{49}{64}} = \frac{7}{8}$, $\sqrt{.09} = .3$.

Rule 1. **To find the principal square root of a monomial,** find the principal square root of its numerical coefficient, keep each base and use half the exponent of each base.

Thus, $\sqrt{16y^{16}} = 4y^8$.

Rule 2. **The principal square root of a fraction** is the principal square root of its numerator divided by the principal square root of its denominator.

Thus, $\sqrt{\frac{100}{121}} = \frac{10}{11}$, $\sqrt{\frac{x^8}{y^6}} = \frac{x^4}{y^3}$.

4.1 Finding Principal Square Roots: Rules 1 and 2

Find each principal square root:

a) $\sqrt{100}$　　*Ans. a*) 10

b) $\sqrt{2500}$　　*Ans. b*) 50

c) $\sqrt{.0001}$　　*Ans. c*) .01

d) $\sqrt{\frac{81}{400}}$　　*Ans. d*) $\frac{9}{20}$

e) $\sqrt{a^6}$　　*Ans. e*) a^3

f) $\sqrt{a^8 b^{12}}$　　*Ans. f*) $a^4 b^6$

g) $\sqrt{100s^{100}}$　　*Ans. g*) $10s^{50}$

h) $\sqrt{\frac{x^{18}}{y^2}}$　　*Ans. h*) $\frac{x^9}{y}$

i) $\sqrt{900a^2b^2}$　　*Ans. i*) $30ab$

j) $\sqrt{.09c^{20}}$　　*Ans. j*) $.3c^{10}$

k) $\sqrt{36r^{36}}$　　*Ans. k*) $6r^{18}$

l) $\sqrt{\frac{169}{x^{10}}}$　　*Ans. l*) $\frac{13}{x^5}$

4.2 Finding Sides of Squares: $s = \sqrt{A}$

Find the side of a square whose area is

a) 49 sq. in.　　*Ans. a*) 7 in.

b) .0004 sq. ft.　　*Ans. b*) .02 ft.

c) $\frac{25}{81}$ sq. yd.　　*Ans. c*) $\frac{5}{9}$ yd.

d) $169a^2$　　*Ans. d*) $13a$

e) $1.21b^4$　　*Ans. e*) $1.1b^2$

f) $\frac{100}{169x^2y^2}$　　*Ans. f*) $\frac{10}{13xy}$

5. FINDING THE PRODUCT OF THE SUM AND DIFFERENCE OF TWO NUMBERS

$$(x+y)(x-y) = x^2 - y^2$$

If the sum of two numbers is multiplied by their difference, the product is the square of the first minus the square of the second.

Thus, $(x+5)(x-5) = x^2 - 25$.

Note below how the middle term drops out in each case.

(1) Multiply $(x+y)$ by $(x-y)$:	(2) Multiply (a^3+8) by (a^3-8):	(3) Multiply 103×97:
$x + y$	$a^3 + 8$	$103 = 100 + 3$
$x - y$	$a^3 - 8$	$97 = 100 - 3$
$x^2 + xy$	$a^6 + 8a^3$	$10{,}000 + 300$
$\quad -xy - y^2$	$\quad -8a^3 - 64$	$\quad -300 - 9$
$Ans.\ x^2 \qquad -y^2$	$Ans.\ a^6 \qquad -64$	$Ans.\quad 10{,}000 \qquad -9 = 9991$

Note, in (3) above, a new method for multiplying 103×97. This process of multiplying the sum of two numbers by their difference is a valuable shortcut in arithmetic in such cases as the following:

(a) $33 \times 27 = (30+3)(30-3) = 900 - 9$ or 891

(b) $2\frac{1}{2} \times 1\frac{1}{2} = (2+\frac{1}{2})(2-\frac{1}{2}) = 4 - \frac{1}{4}$ or $3\frac{3}{4}$

(c) $9.8 \times 10.2 = (10-.2)(10+.2) = 100 - .04$ or 99.96

5.1 Multiplying the Sum of Two Numbers by their Difference

Find each product:

(First + Second)(First − Second)	1. (First)^2	2. (Second)^2	3. Product (Ans.)
a) $(\ m\ +\ 7\ )(\ m\ -\ 7\ )$	m^2	49	$m^2 - 49$
b) $(\ 8\ +\ 3x\ )(\ 8\ -\ 3x\ )$	64	$9x^2$	$64 - 9x^2$
c) $(\ 11a\ +\ 5b\ )(\ 11a\ -\ 5b\ )$	$121a^2$	$25b^2$	$121a^2 - 25b^2$
d) $(\ x^2\ +\ y^3\ )(\ x^2\ -\ y^3\ )$	x^4	y^6	$x^4 - y^6$
e) $(\ 1\ +\ y^4z^5\ )(\ 1\ -\ y^4z^5\ )$	1	y^8z^{10}	$1 - y^8z^{10}$
f) $(\ ab\ +\ \frac{2}{3}\ )(\ ab\ -\ \frac{2}{3}\ )$	a^2b^2	$\frac{4}{9}$	$a^2b^2 - \frac{4}{9}$
g) $(\ .2\ +\ \frac{3}{5}p\ )(\ .2\ -\ \frac{3}{5}p\ )$	$.04$	$\frac{9}{25}p^2$	$.04 - \frac{9}{25}p^2$

5.2 Multiplying Two Numbers by the Sum and Difference Method

Multiply, using the sum and difference of two numbers:

a) 18×22 — *Ans. a)* $18 \times 22 = (20-2)(20+2) = 400 - 4 = 396$

b) 25×35 — *Ans. b)* $25 \times 35 = (30-5)(30+5) = 900 - 25 = 875$

c) $.96 \times 1.04$ — *Ans. c)* $.96 \times 1.04 = (1-.04)(1+.04) = 1 - .0016 = .9984$

d) 7.1×6.9 — *Ans. d)* $7.1 \times 6.9 = (7+.1)(7-.1) = 49 - .01 = 48.99$

e) $2\frac{1}{4} \times 1\frac{3}{4}$ — *Ans. e)* $2\frac{1}{4} \times 1\frac{3}{4} = (2+\frac{1}{4})(2-\frac{1}{4}) = 4 - \frac{1}{16} = 3\frac{15}{16}$

5.3 Multiplying a Monomial by Sum and Difference Factors

Find each product. (*First, multiply the sum and difference factors.*)

a) $2(x+5)(x-5)$	b) $x^2(1-3y)(1+3y)$	c) $t^2(t+u)(t-u)$	d) $24(m^2+\frac{1}{2})(m^2-\frac{1}{2})$
Solutions:			
$2(x^2-25)$	$x^2(1-9y^2)$	$t^2(t^2-u^2)$	$24(m^4-\frac{1}{4})$
Ans. $2x^2 - 50$	*Ans.* $x^2 - 9x^2y^2$	*Ans.* $t^4 - t^2u^2$	*Ans.* $24m^4 - 6$

6. FACTORING THE DIFFERENCE OF TWO SQUARES

$$x^2 - y^2 = (x-y)(x+y)$$

The expression $x^2 - y^2$ is the difference of two squares, x^2 and y^2.

The factor, $x+y$, is the sum of the principal square roots of x^2 and y^2, while the other factor, $x-y$, is their difference.

To Factor the Difference of Two Squares

Procedure:

1. Obtain principal square root of each square.

2. One factor is the sum of the principal square roots. The other factor is their difference.

Factor: $c^2 - 49$

Solution:

1. Principal square roots: $\sqrt{c^2} = c$, $\sqrt{49} = 7$

2. Factors:

Ans. $(c+7)(c-7)$

6.1 Procedure for Factoring the Difference of Two Squares

Factor:

First Square − Second Square	1. $\sqrt{\text{First Square}}$	2. $\sqrt{\text{Second Square}}$	3. Factors (Ans.)
a) $36 - b^2$	6	b	$(6+b)(6-b)$
b) $1 - 25y^2$	1	$5y$	$(1+5y)(1-5y)$
c) $a^2b^2 - 100$	ab	10	$(ab+10)(ab-10)$
d) $x^6y^8 - z^{10}$	x^3y^4	z^5	$(x^3y^4+z^5)(x^3y^4-z^5)$
e) $16 - x^{16}$	4	x^8	$(4+x^8)(4-x^8)$
f) $u^4 - \frac{9}{25}$	u^2	$\frac{3}{5}$	$(u^2+\frac{3}{5})(u^2-\frac{3}{5})$
g) $(a+b)^2 - c^2$	$a+b$	c	$(a+b+c)(a+b-c)$

6.2 Complete Factoring Involving the Difference of Two Squares

Factor completely: (*Hint. Remove the greatest common monomial factor first.*)

a) $10 - 40x^2$ b) $75y^3 - 27y$ c) $\pi R^2 - \pi r^2$ d) $5abc^4 - 80ab$

Solutions:

a) 10 is **G.C.F.**
  $10(1-4x^2)$
Ans. $10(1+2x)(1-2x)$

b) $3y$ is **G.C.F.**
  $3y(25y^2-9)$
Ans. $3y(5y+3)(5y-3)$

c) π is **G.C.F.**
  $\pi(R^2-r^2)$
Ans. $\pi(R+r)(R-r)$

d) $5ab$ is **G.C.F.**
  $5ab(c^4-16)$
Ans. $5ab(c^2+4)(c+2)(c-2)$

7. FINDING THE PRODUCT OF TWO BINOMIALS WITH LIKE TERMS

Two Methods of Multiplying $3x+5$ by $2x+4$

$$\begin{array}{r} 3x + 5 \\ 2x + 4 \\ \hline 6x^2 + 10x \\ + 12x + 20 \\ \hline \end{array}$$
Ans. $6x^2 + 22x + 20$

Method 1. (Usual Method)

Using **Method 1**, each separate operation is shown. The middle term of the answer, $22x$, is obtained by adding the cross-products, $12x$ and $10x$. The arrows indicate the cross-products.

$(3x+5)\ (2x+4)$

with $12x$ (outer) and $10x$ (inner)

Ans. $6x^2 + 22x + 20$

Method 2. (By Inspection)

Using **Method 2**, the answer is written **by inspection**. The middle term of the answer, $22x$, is obtained **mentally** by adding the product of the outer terms to the product of the inner terms. The arrows indicate the outer and inner products.

To Multiply Two Binomials By Inspection

Multiply: $(3x+5)(2x+4)$

Procedure: **Solution:**

1. To obtain the first term of the product, **multiply the first terms.**
Key: First

1. Multiply **first** terms:
$$(3x)(2x) = 6x^2$$

2. To obtain the middle term of the product, **add the product of the outer terms to the product of the inner terms.**
Key: Outer + Inner

2. Add **outer** and **inner** products:

$$\overset{\longleftarrow 12x \longrightarrow}{(3x+5)\ (2x+4)}$$
$$\underset{\underset{10x}{\longleftarrow\longrightarrow}}{}$$

$$12x + 10x = 22x$$

3. To obtain the last term of the product, **multiply the last terms.**
Key: Last

3. Multiply **last** terms:
$$(+5)(+4) = +20$$

4. Combine the results to obtain answer.

4. Combine: $6x^2 + 22x + 20$ **Ans.**

Since a **mixed number** is the sum of an integer and a fraction, it may be expressed as a binomial. Thus, $3\frac{1}{2}$ and $4\frac{1}{3}$ are mixed numbers.

Two mixed numbers may be multiplied in the same way as two binomials. Thus,

$$3\tfrac{1}{2} \times 4\tfrac{1}{3} = \overset{\longleftarrow 1 \longrightarrow}{(3+\tfrac{1}{2})\ (4+\tfrac{1}{3})} = 12 + 3 + \tfrac{1}{6} = 15\tfrac{1}{6} \ Ans.$$

7.1 Products of Binomials by Steps

Multiply, showing each separate product:

Binomial × Binomial	(First)	(Outer + Inner)	(Last)	Product (Ans.)
a) $(x+7)\ (x+3)$	x^2	$(+3x) + (+7x)$	$+21$	$x^2 + 10x + 21$
b) $(x-7)\ (x-3)$	x^2	$(-3x) + (-7x)$	$+21$	$x^2 - 10x + 21$
c) $(x+7)\ (x-3)$	x^2	$(-3x) + (+7x)$	-21	$x^2 + 4x - 21$
d) $(3w-5)\ (4w+7)$	$12w^2$	$(+21w) + (-20w)$	-35	$12w^2 + w - 35$
e) $(a+3b)\ (a-8b)$	a^2	$(-8ab) + (+3ab)$	$-24b^2$	$a^2 - 5ab - 24b^2$

7.2 Products of Two Binomials Mentally

Multiply mentally:

a) $(x+7)(x+7)$ *Ans.* $x^2 + 14x + 49$

b) $(x-3)(x-3)$ *Ans.* $x^2 - 6x + 9$

c) $(3y+1)(2y+1)$ *Ans.* $6y^2 + 5y + 1$

d) $(2c-b)(5c-b)$ *Ans.* $10c^2 - 7bc + b^2$

e) $(3-7d)(1-d)$ *Ans.* $3 - 10d + 7d^2$

f) $(2r+3s)(3r+2s)$ *Ans.* $6r^2 + 13rs + 6s^2$

g) $(ab+4)(ab-3)$ *Ans.* $a^2b^2 + ab - 12$

h) $(p-qr)(p-3qr)$ *Ans.* $p^2 - 4pqr + 3q^2r^2$

i) $(pqr-7)(pqr-10)$ *Ans.* $p^2q^2r^2 - 17pqr + 70$

j) $(t^2+5)(t^2+9)$ *Ans.* $t^4 + 14t^2 + 45$

k) $(10-v^2)(6-v^2)$ *Ans.* $60 - 16v^2 + v^4$

l) $(c^2d-5g)(c^2d+3g)$ *Ans.* $c^4d^2 - 2c^2dg - 15g^2$

7.3 Representing Areas of Rectangles: $A = LW$

Represent the area of a rectangle whose dimensions are:

a) $l+8$ and $l-2$ *Ans.* $A = (l+8)(l-2) = l^2 + 6l - 16$

b) $2l-1$ and $l+5$ *Ans.* $A = (2l-1)(l+5) = 2l^2 + 9l - 5$

c) $w+3$ and $w+7$ *Ans.* $A = (w+3)(w+7) = w^2 + 10w + 21$

d) $2w-1$ and $3w+1$ *Ans.* $A = (2w-1)(3w+1) = 6w^2 - w - 1$

e) $3s-5$ and $s+8$ *Ans.* $A = (3s-5)(s+8) = 3s^2 + 19s - 40$

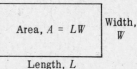

Area, $A = LW$ Width, W

Length, L

8. FACTORING TRINOMIALS IN FORM OF $x^2 + bx + c$: Coefficient of x^2 is 1.

A trinomial in the form of $x^2 + bx + c$ may or may not be factorable into binomial factors. If factoring is possible, use the following procedure.

To Factor a Trinomial in Form of $x^2 + bx + c$

Factor: a) $x^2 + 6x + 5$ b) $x^4 - 6x^2 + 8$

Procedure:

Solutions:

1. **Obtain the factors** x and x of x^2. Use each as the first term of each binomial.

2. **Select from the factors of the last term,** c, those factors whose sum $= b$, the coefficient of x. Use each as the second term of each binomial.

3. **Form binomial factors** from factors obtained in steps 1 and 2.

a) 1. Factor x^2:
   (x, x)

2. Factor $+5$:
   Select $(+5, +1)$
   since sum $= +6$
   Discard $(-5, -1)$

3. $(x+5)(x+1)$ *Ans.*

b) 1. Factor x^4:
   (x^2, x^2)

2. Factor $+8$:
   Select $(-4, -2)$
   since sum $= -6$
   Discard $(+4, +2)$,
   $(-8, -1)$ and $(+8, +1)$

3. $(x^2-4)(x^2-2)$ *Ans.*

8.1 Factoring Trinomials in Form of $x^2 + bx + c$

Factor each trinomial:

Trinomial Form: $x^2 + bx + c$	1. Factors of x^2, each $= \sqrt{x^2}$	2. Factors of c whose sum $= b$	3. Binomial Factors (Ans.) (Combine 1 and 2)
a) $x^2 + 4x + 3$	x, x	$+3, +1$	$(x+3)(x+1)$
b) $x^2 - 4x + 3$	x, x	$-3, -1$	$(x-3)(x-1)$
c) $y^2 + 4y - 12$	y, y	$+6, -2$	$(y+6)(y-2)$
d) $w^2 - w - 12$	w, w	$-4, +3$	$(w-4)(w+3)$
e) $r^2 + 6rs + 5s^2$	r, r	$+5s, +s$	$(r+5s)(r+s)$
f) $a^2b^2 - 12ab + 20$	ab, ab	$-10, -2$	$(ab-10)(ab-2)$
g) $x^4 - 5x^2 - 14$	x^2, x^2	$-7, +2$	$(x^2-7)(x^2+2)$

9. FACTORING TRINOMIALS IN FORM OF $ax^2 + bx + c$: Coefficient of x^2 is a, $a \neq 0$.

A trinomial in the form of $ax^2 + bx + c$ may or may not be factorable into binomial factors. If this is possible, use the following procedure.

To Factor a Trinomial in Form of $ax^2 + bx + c$

Factor: a) $2x^2 - 11x + 5$ b) $3a^2 + 10ab + 7b^2$

Procedure:

Solutions:

1. **Factor** ax^2, **the first term.*** Use each factor as the first term of a binomial factor.

2. **Select from the factors of** c, **the last term,** those factors to be used as the second term of each binomial such that the middle term, bx, results.

3. **Form binomial factors** from factors obtained in steps 1 and 2 and test for middle term, bx.

a) 1. Factor $2x^2$:
   $(2x, x)$

2. Factor $+5$:
   Select $(-1, -5)$ to obtain middle term, $-11x$.
   Discard $(+1, +5)$.

3. $(2x-1)(x-5)$

   $\overbrace{}^{-x}$
   $\underbrace{}_{-10x}$

   Middle term, $-11x$, results.
   Ans. $(2x-1)(x-5)$

b) 1. Factor $3a^2$:
   $(3a, a)$

2. Factor $+7b^2$:
   Select $(+7b, +b)$ to obtain middle term, $10ab$.
   Discard $(-7b, -b)$.

3. $(3a+7b)(a+b)$

   $\overbrace{}^{7ab}$
   $\underbrace{}_{3ab}$

   Middle term, $10ab$, results.
   Ans. $(3a+7b)(a+b)$

* When the first term ax^2 is positive, use positive factors.
Thus, in $2x^2 - 11x + 5$, do not use $-2x$ and $-x$ as factors of $2x^2$.

9.1 Factoring Trinomials in Form of $ax^2 + bx + c$.

Factor each trinomial:

Trinomial Form: $ax^2 + bx + c$	1. Factors of ax^2	2. Factors of c to Obtain Middle Term, bx	3. Binomial Factors (Ans.) (Test Middle Term)
a) $5x^2 + 11x + 2$	$5x, x$	$+1, +2$	$(5x+1)\ (x+2)$ [x; $10x$]
b) $4w^2 + 7w + 3$	$4w, w$ Discard $(2w, 2w)$	$+3, +1$	$(4w+3)\ (w+1)$ [$+3w$; $+4w$]
c) $4y^2 - 8w + 3$	$2y, 2y$ Discard $(4y, y)$	$-3, -1$	$(2y-3)\ (2y-1)$ [$-6y$; $-2y$]
d) $4w^2 + 13wx + 3x^2$	$4w, w$ Discard $(2w, 2w)$	$+x, +3x$	$(4w+x)\ (w+3x)$ [wx; $+12wx$]
e) $8 + 15h - 2h^2$	$8, 1$ Discard $(4, 2)$	$-h, +2h$	$(8-h)\ (1+2h)$ [$-h$; $+16h$]

10. SQUARING A BINOMIAL

$$(x+y)^2 = x^2 + 2xy + y^2$$

The square of a binomial is a perfect square trinomial.

Thus, the square of $x+y$ or $(x+y)^2$ is the perfect square trinomial, $x^2 + 2xy + y^2$.

To Square a Binomial

Square: $3x + 5$

Procedure:

Solution:

1. **Square the first term** to obtain the first term of the trinomial.

1. **Square** $3x$: $(3x)^2 = 9x^2$

2. **Double the product of both terms** to obtain the middle term of the trinomial.

2. **Double** $(3x)(+5)$:
      $2(3x)(+5) = 30x$

3. **Square the last term** to obtain the last term of the trinomial.

3. **Square** $+5$: $5^2 = 25$

4. **Combine results** into answer.

4. **Combine:** $9x^2 + 30x + 25$ **Ans.**

Squaring Numbers Expressed as a Binomial

Numbers may be squared by expressing them first as a binomial.

Thus to square 35, express 35 as $(30+5)$.

$$35^2 = (30+5)^2 = 30^2 + 2(5)(30) + 5^2$$
$$= 900 + 300 + 25 = 1225$$

10.1 Squaring a Binomial

Find each square:

(Binomial)^2	1. Square First Term	2. Double Product	3. Square Last Term	4. Combine Into Square (Ans.)
a) $(b-6)^2$	b^2	$-12b$	$+36$	$b^2 - 12b + 36$
b) $(b+6)^2$	b^2	$+12b$	$+36$	$b^2 + 12b + 36$
c) $(1-3b)^2$	1	$-6b$	$+9b^2$	$1 - 6b + 9b^2$
d) $(c^2+3d)^2$	c^4	$+6c^2d$	$+9d^2$	$c^4 + 6c^2d + 9d^2$
e) $(5x+7y)^2$	$25x^2$	$+70xy$	$+49y^2$	$25x^2 + 70xy + 49y^2$
f) $(ab-11)^2$	a^2b^2	$-22ab$	$+121$	$a^2b^2 - 22ab + 121$
g) $(x^3+y^3)^2$	x^6	$+2x^3y^3$	$+y^6$	$x^6 + 2x^3y^3 + y^6$
h) $(t+\frac{1}{2})^2$	t^2	$+t$	$+\frac{1}{4}$	$t^2 + t + \frac{1}{4}$
i) $(t^2-1.3)^2$	t^4	$-2.6t$	$+1.69$	$t^4 - 2.6t^2 + 1.69$

10.2 Squaring a Number

Find each square by expressing each number as a binomial:

(Number)^2	1. As (Binomial)^2	2. Square First Term		3. Double Product		4. Square Last Term		5. Combine Into Square (Ans.)
a) 25^2	$(20+5)^2$	400	$+$	200	$+$	25	$=$	625
b) $(2\frac{1}{2})^2$	$(2+\frac{1}{2})^2$	4	$+$	2	$+$	$\frac{1}{4}$	$=$	$6\frac{1}{4}$
c) $(12\frac{1}{4})^2$	$(12+\frac{1}{4})^2$	144	$+$	6	$+$	$\frac{1}{16}$	$=$	$150\frac{1}{16}$
d) 10.4^2	$(10+.4)^2$	100	$+$	8	$+$	$.16$	$=$	108.16
e) 9.5^2	$(10-.5)^2$	100	$-$	10	$+$	$.25$	$=$	90.25
f) $(29\frac{2}{3})^2$	$(30-\frac{1}{3})^2$	900	$-$	20	$+$	$\frac{1}{9}$	$=$	$880\frac{1}{9}$

10.3 Representing the Area of a Square: $A = s^2$

Represent the area of a square whose side is

a) $(l+10)$ in.   b) $(w-8)$ ft.   c) $(2s+5)$ yd.   d) $9-5s$

Solutions:

a) $A = (l+10)^2$	b) $A = (w-8)^2$	c) $A = (2s+5)^2$	d) $A = (9-5s)^2$
$A = l^2 + 20l + 100$	$A = w^2 - 16w + 64$	$A = 4s^2 + 20s + 25$	$A = 81 - 90s + 25s^2$
Ans. $(l^2+20l+100)$ sq. in.	Ans. $(w^2-16w+64)$ sq. ft.	Ans. $(4s^2+20s+25)$ sq. yd.	Ans. $81-90s+25s^2$

11. FACTORING A PERFECT SQUARE TRINOMIAL

$$x^2 + 2xy + y^2 = (x+y)(x+y) = (x+y)^2$$
$$x^2 - 2xy + y^2 = (x-y)(x-y) = (x-y)^2$$

The factors of a perfect square trinomial are two equal binomials.

Thus, the factors of the perfect square trinomial $x^2+2xy+y^2$ are $(x+y)$ and $(x+y)$.

A perfect square trinomial has

   (1) two terms which are positive perfect squares,

   (2) a remaining term which is double the product of the square roots of the other two terms. This term may be positive or negative.

Thus, $x^2+14x+49$ and $x^2-14x+49$ are perfect square trinomials.

The last term of each binomial factor has the same sign as the middle term of the perfect square trinomial.

Thus, $x^2-14x+49 = (x-7)^2$ and $x^2+14x+49 = (x+7)^2$.

To Factor a Perfect Square Trinomial

Factor: $4x^2 - 20x + 25$

Procedure:

Solution:

1. **Find the principal square root of the first term.** This becomes the first term of each binomial.

1. Find $\sqrt{4x^2}$:
$$\sqrt{4x^2} = 2x$$

2. **Find the principal square root of the last term and prefix the sign of the middle term.** This becomes the last term of each binomial.

2. Find $\sqrt{25}$:
$\sqrt{25} = 5$. Prefix $-$ before 5 since middle term is negative.

3. **Form binomial** from results in steps 1 and 2. The answer is the binomial squared.

3. Form $2x - 5$.
Ans. $4x^2 - 20x + 25 = (2x-5)^2$.

11.1 Factoring a Perfect Square Trinomial

Factor each perfect square trinomial:

Perfect Square Trinomial	1. $\sqrt{\text{First Term}}$	2. Sign of Middle Term	3. $\sqrt{\text{Last Term}}$	(Binomial)^2 Ans.
a) $25y^2 - 10y + 1$	$5y$	$-$	1	$(5y-1)^2$
b) $25y^2 + 10y + 1$	$5y$	$+$	1	$(5y+1)^2$
c) $9a^2 + 42a + 49$	$3a$	$+$	7	$(3a+7)^2$
d) $9a^2 - 42a + 49$	$3a$	$-$	7	$(3a-7)^2$
e) $49 + 14ab + a^2b^2$	7	$+$	ab	$(7+ab)^2$
f) $16x^6 - 24x^3 + 9$	$4x^3$	$-$	3	$(4x^3-3)^2$
g) $16t^2 + 4t + \frac{1}{4}$	$4t$	$+$	$\frac{1}{2}$	$(4t+\frac{1}{2})^2$
h) $a^4b^8 - 2a^2b^4c^5 + c^{10}$	a^2b^4	$-$	c^5	$(a^2b^4-c^5)^2$

11.2 Representing the Side of a Square: $s = \sqrt{A}$

Represent the side of a square whose area is

a) $(l^2 - 14w + 49)$ sq. in.　　b) $(w^2 + 20w + 100)$ sq. ft.　　c) $4s^2 + 4s + 1$　　d) $9s^2 - 30s + 25$

Ans. a) $(l-7)$ in.　　b) $(w+10)$ ft.　　c) $2s+1$　　d) $3s-5$

12. COMPLETELY FACTORING POLYNOMIALS

To factor an expression completely, continue factoring until the polynomial factors cannot be factored further. Thus, to factor $5x^2 - 5$ completely, first factor it into $5(x^2-1)$. Then factor further into $5(x-1)(x+1)$.

If an expression has a common monomial factor:

1. Remove the greatest common factor (G.C.F.).
2. Continue factoring its polynomial factors until no further factors remain.

Procedure to Completely Factor Expressions Having Common Monomial Factor

Factor completely:　　a) $8a^2 - 50$　　b) $3y^3 - 60y^2 + 300y$　　c) $10y^2 - 15xy^2 + 5x^2y^2$

Procedure:

Solutions:

1. **Remove the greatest common factor (G.C.F.).**

1. G.C.F. $= 2$
$2(4a^2 - 25)$

1. G.C.F. $= 3y$
$3y(y^2 - 20y + 100)$

1. G.C.F. $= 5y^2$
$5y^2(2 - 3x + x^2)$

2. **Continue factoring polynomial factors.**

2. Factor $4a^2 - 25$:
$2(2a+5)(2a-5)$

2. Factor $y^2 - 20y + 100$:
$3y(y-10)(y-10)$

2. Factor $2 - 3x + x^2$:
$5y^2(2-x)(1-x)$

Ans. $2(2a+5)(2a-5)$　　Ans. $3y(y-10)^2$　　Ans. $5y^2(2-x)(1-x)$

Procedure to Completely Factor Expressions Having No Common Monomial Factor

	Factor completely: *a*) $x^4 - 1$	*b*) $16a^4 - 81$
Procedure:	**Solutions:**	
1. Factor into polynomials.	1. $(x^2+1)(x^2-1)$	1. $(4a^2+9)(4a^2-9)$
2. Continue factoring.	2. $(x^2+1)(x+1)(x-1)$ **Ans.**	2. $(4a^2+9)(2a+3)(2a-3)$ **Ans.**

12.1 Factoring Completely Expressions Having Common Monomial Factor

Factor completely:

Polynomial	1. Remove G.C.F.	2. Continue Factoring
a) $3b^2 - 27$	$3(b^2-9)$	$3(b+3)(b-3)$ *Ans.*
b) $a^5 - 16a^3$	$a^3(a^2-16)$	$a^3(a+4)(a-4)$ *Ans.*
c) $a^5 - 16a$	$a(a^4-16)$	$a(a^2+4)(a^2-4)$ $a(a^2+4)(a+2)(a-2)$ *Ans.*
d) $5x^2+10x+5$	$5(x^2+2x+1)$	$5(x+1)^2$ *Ans.*
e) $x^5 - 6x^4y + 9x^3y^2$	$x^3(x^2-6xy+9y^2)$	$x^3(x-3y)^2$ *Ans.*
f) $y^5 - 4y^3 + 3y$	$y(y^4-4y^2+3)$	$y(y^2-3)(y^2-1) = y(y^2-3)(y+1)(y-1)$ *Ans.*

12.2 Factoring Completely Expressions Having No Common Monomial Factor

Factor completely:

Polynomial	1. Factor Into Polynomials	2. Continue Factoring
a) $1 - a^4$	$(1+a^2)(1-a^2)$	$(1+a^2)(1+a)(1-a)$ *Ans.*
b) $x^4 - 16y^4$	$(x^2+4y^2)(x^2-4y^2)$	$(x^2+4y^2)(x+2y)(x-2y)$ *Ans.*
c) $p^8 - q^{12}$	$(p^4+q^6)(p^4-q^6)$	$(p^4+q^6)(p^2+q^3)(p^2-q^3)$ *Ans.*

SUPPLEMENTARY PROBLEMS

1. Find each monomial product: **(1.1)**

    a) $3 \cdot x \cdot 4 \cdot x$ *c*) $(-2)5\,x\,y^3\,x^4$ *e*) $(-5ab^2)(2a^2b)$ *g*) $-3 \cdot \dfrac{1}{x} \cdot \dfrac{1}{y}$

    b) $(-3)4\,x\,y\,y$ *d*) $(-3x)(-7x^2)y$ *f*) $(3a^4b)(10ac^4)$ *h*) $5 \cdot \dfrac{1}{a^2} \cdot \dfrac{1}{b^2} \cdot c$

Ans. *a*) $12x^2$ *c*) $-10x^5y^3$ *e*) $-10a^3b^3$ *g*) $-\dfrac{3}{xy}$

    b) $-12xy^2$ *d*) $21x^3y$ *f*) $30a^5bc^4$ *h*) $\dfrac{5c}{a^2b^2}$

2. Find each product: **(1.2)**

    a) $3(x-3)$ *d*) $a(b+c)$ *g*) $x^2(x-3)$ *j*) $a(b-c+d)$

    b) $-5(a+4)$ *e*) $-3c(d-g)$ *h*) $-3x(x^2-5x)$ *k*) $-3x(x^2-2x+5)$

    c) $-8(r-7)$ *f*) $2gh(3k-5)$ *i*) $7a^3(5a^2-8a)$ *l*) $2b^2c(b-3c-10c^2)$

Ans. *a*) $3x-9$ *d*) $ab+ac$ *g*) x^3-3x^2 *j*) $ab-ac+ad$

    b) $-5a-20$ *e*) $-3cd+3cg$ *h*) $-3x^3+15x^2$ *k*) $-3x^3+6x^2-15x$

    c) $-8r+56$ *f*) $6ghk-10gh$ *i*) $35a^5-56a^4$ *l*) $2b^3c-6b^2c^2-20b^2c^3$

3. Find each product: **(1.3)**

a) $4(8-\frac{1}{2})$

b) $20(5-.7)$

c) $36(1\frac{1}{4}+\frac{2}{9})$

d) $50(\frac{2x}{5}-\frac{3x}{10})$

e) $12(\frac{x}{4}+\frac{x}{3}-\frac{x}{2})$

f) $70(2-\frac{5r}{14})$

g) $.06(2000+500+25)$

h) $.03(7000-x)$

i) $.05\frac{1}{2}(3000+2x)$

Ans. a) $32-2 = 30$ d) $20x-15x = 5x$ g) $120+30+1.50 = 151.50$

b) $100-14 = 86$ e) $3x+4x-6x = x$ h) $210-.03x$

c) $45+8 = 53$ f) $140-25r$ i) $165+.11x$

4. Find the set of prime factors of each number: **(1.4)**

a) 36,   b) 96,   c) 333,   d) 3003,   e) 3300,   f) 420,   g) 1728,   h) 5280

Ans. a) $2^2 \cdot 3^2$, b) $2^5 \cdot 3$, c) $3^2 \cdot 37$, d) $3 \cdot 7 \cdot 11 \cdot 13$, e) $2^2 \cdot 3 \cdot 5^2 \cdot 11$, f) $2^2 \cdot 3 \cdot 5 \cdot 7$, g) $2^6 \cdot 3^3$, h) $2^5 \cdot 3 \cdot 5 \cdot 11$

5. Find the greatest common factor (G.C.F.) and the least common multiple (L.C.M.)   **(1.5)**
of each set of numbers:

a) 4, 6, 8;   b) 15, 18;   c) 24, 36;   d) 18, 24, 36;   e) 15, 21, 105

Ans. a) 2, 24;   b) 3, 90;   c) 12, 72;   d) 6, 72;   e) 3, 105

6. Find the greatest common factor (G.C.F.) and the least common multiple (L.C.M.)   **(1.6)**
of each set of monomials:

a) $4x, 8y$;   b) $3x^2, 9x^3$;   c) $15xy, 25yz, 75xz$;   d) $12a^2b^3, 18ab, 36a^3b^2c$

Ans. a) $4, 8xy$;   b) $3x^2, 9x^3$;   c) $5, 75xyz$;   d) $6ab, 36a^3b^3c$

7. Factor, removing highest common factor: **(2.1)**

a) $3a-21b$

b) $-5c-15d$

c) $xy+2xz$

d) $5RS-10RT$

e) $p+prt$

f) $7hm-7h$

g) $6V^2+3V$

h) y^5+y^4

i) $\pi rh+\pi r^2$

j) $\pi R^2+\pi r^2$

k) $\frac{1}{2}bh+\frac{1}{2}b'h$

l) $\frac{1}{4}mnr-\frac{1}{4}mn$

m) $8x^2-16x+32$

n) $10x^3+20x^2-55x$

o) $a^2bc+ab^2c-abc^2$

p) $x^2y^3-x^2y^2+x^2y$

Ans. a) $3(a-7b)$

b) $-5(c+3d)$

c) $x(y+2z)$

d) $5R(S-2T)$

e) $p(1+rt)$

f) $7h(m-1)$

g) $3V(2V+1)$

h) $y^4(y+1)$

i) $\pi r(h+r)$

j) $\pi(R^2+r^2)$

k) $\frac{1}{2}h(b+b')$

l) $\frac{1}{4}mn(r-1)$

m) $8(x^2-2x+4)$

n) $5x(2x^2+4x-11)$

o) $abc(a+b-c)$

p) $x^2y(y^2-y+1)$

8. Evaluate each, using factoring: **(2.2)**

a) $6(11)+4(11)$

b) $8(11\frac{1}{2})+12(11\frac{1}{2})$

c) $21(2\frac{1}{3})-12(2\frac{1}{3})$

d) $2.7(.3)-.7(.3)$

e) $18(7^2)+2(7^2)$

f) $\frac{3}{4}(11)-\frac{3}{4}(3)$

g) $10(8^2)-7(8^2)$

h) $\frac{1}{2}(13)(6)+\frac{1}{2}(7)(6)$

i) $5^3(28)-5^3(25)$

Ans. a) $11(6+4) = 11(10) = 110$ d) $.3(2.7-.7) = .3(2) = .6$ g) $8^2(10-7) = 8^2(3) = 192$

b) $11\frac{1}{2}(8+12) = 11\frac{1}{2}(20) = 230$ e) $7^2(18+2) = 7^2(20) = 980$ h) $\frac{1}{2}(6)(13+7) = \frac{1}{2}(6)(20) = 60$

c) $2\frac{1}{3}(21-12) = 2\frac{1}{3}(9) = 21$ f) $\frac{3}{4}(11-3) = \frac{3}{4}(8) = 6$ i) $5^3(28-25) = 5^3(3) = 375$

9. Find each square: **(3.1)**

a) 6^2

b) $(-6)^2$

c) $(.6)^2$

d) 600^2

e) $(\frac{1}{6})^2$

f) $(\frac{2}{5})^2$

g) $(-\frac{3}{7})^2$

h) $(-\frac{9}{2})^2$

i) $(1\frac{1}{3})^2$

j) 35^2

k) 3.5^2

l) $(-.35)^2$

Ans. a) 36

b) 36

c) .36

d) 360,000

e) $\frac{1}{36}$

f) $\frac{4}{25}$

g) $\frac{9}{49}$

h) $\frac{81}{4}$

i) $\frac{16}{9}$ or $1\frac{7}{9}$

j) 1225

k) 12.25

l) .1225

10. Find each square: **(3.2)**

   a) $(b^2)^2$ d) $(5a^5)^2$ g) $(rs^2t^3)^2$

   b) $(w^5)^2$ e) $(-10b^{10})^2$ h) $(-.1r^4s^9)^2$

   c) $(\frac{1}{V^7})^2$ f) $(\frac{3}{C^3})^2$ i) $(-\frac{5r^5}{3t^3})^2$

   Ans. a) b^4 d) $25a^{10}$ g) $r^2s^4t^6$

   b) w^{10} e) $100b^{20}$ h) $.01r^8s^{18}$

   c) $\frac{1}{V^{14}}$ f) $\frac{.09}{C^6}$ i) $\frac{25r^{10}}{9t^6}$

11. Find the area of a square whose side is   **(3.3)**

   a) 5 yd. c) 2.5 mi. e) $.7y^2$

   b) $\frac{7}{8}$ rd. d) $\frac{x}{7}$ in. f) $\frac{5m^2}{3p^3}$

   Ans. a) 25 sq. yd. c) 6.25 sq. mi. e) $.49y^4$

   b) $\frac{49}{64}$ sq. rd. d) $\frac{x^2}{49}$ sq. in. f) $\frac{25m^4}{9p^6}$

12. Find each principal square root: **(4.1)**

   a) $\sqrt{144}$ d) $\sqrt{c^6}$ g) $\sqrt{36x^{36}}$ j) $\sqrt{.0001h^{50}}$

   b) $\sqrt{1.44}$ e) $\sqrt{p^8q^{10}}$ h) $\sqrt{16a^4b^{16}}$ k) $\sqrt{.0144m^{14}}$

   c) $\sqrt{\frac{900}{49}}$ f) $\sqrt{\frac{r^{14}}{s^{20}}}$ i) $\sqrt{\frac{.01}{d^{100}}}$ l) $\sqrt{\frac{25h^{10}}{64k^{16}}}$

   Ans. a) 12 d) c^3 g) $6x^{18}$ j) $.01h^{25}$

   b) 1.2 e) p^4q^5 h) $4a^2b^8$ k) $.12m^7$

   c) $\frac{30}{7}$ f) $\frac{r^7}{s^{10}}$ i) $\frac{.1}{d^{50}}$ l) $\frac{5h^5}{8k^8}$

13. Find the side of a square whose area is   **(4.2)**

   a) 100 sq. ft.   *Ans.* 10 ft. d) $9x^2$ sq. in.   *Ans.* $3x$ in. g) $100x^{20}$ *Ans.* $10x^{10}$

   b) .25 sq. mi.   *Ans.* .5 mi. e) $2.25b^8$ sq. yd. *Ans.* $1.5b^4$ yd. h) $169(a+b)^2$ *Ans.* $13(a+b)$

   c) $\frac{16}{81}$ sq. rd. *Ans.* $\frac{4}{9}$ rd. f) $2500c^{10}$ sq. cm. *Ans.* $50c^5$ cm. i) $\frac{4x^2y^2}{9}$ *Ans.* $\frac{2xy}{3}$

14. Find each product: **(5.1)**

   a) $(s+4)(s-4)$ *Ans.* s^2-16 g) $(a^2+b^2)(a^2-b^2)$ *Ans.* a^4-b^4

   b) $(10-t)(10+t)$ *Ans.* $100-t^2$ h) $(ab+c^2)(ab-c^2)$ *Ans.* $a^2b^2-c^4$

   c) $(2x+1)(2x-1)$ *Ans.* $4x^2-1$ i) $(v+\frac{1}{5})(v-\frac{1}{5})$ *Ans.* $v^2-\frac{1}{25}$

   d) $(3y-7z)(3y+7z)$ *Ans.* $9y^2-49z^2$ j) $(d-1.2)(d+1.2)$ *Ans.* $d^2-1.44$

   e) $(rs+1)(rs-1)$ *Ans.* r^2s^2-1 k) $(3x^2-\frac{2}{y})(3x^2+\frac{2}{y})$ *Ans.* $9x^4-\frac{4}{y^2}$

   f) $(1-8x^2)(1+8x^2)$ *Ans.* $1-64x^4$ l) $(3c^3+.1)(3c^3-.1)$ *Ans.* $9c^6-.01$

15. Multiply, using the sum and difference of two numbers: **(5.2)**

   a) 21×19 c) $10\frac{1}{3} \times 9\frac{2}{3}$ e) 89×91 g) $3\frac{1}{2} \times 2\frac{1}{2}$

   b) 3.4×2.6 d) 17×23 f) 10.3×9.7 h) 7.5×8.5

   Ans. a) $20^2-1^2 = 399$ c) $10^2-(\frac{1}{3})^2 = 99\frac{8}{9}$ e) $90^2-1^2 = 8099$ g) $3^2-(\frac{1}{2})^2 = 8\frac{3}{4} = 8.75$

   b) $3^2-.4^2 = 8.84$ d) $20^2-3^2 = 391$ f) $10^2-.3^2 = 99.91$ h) $8^2-(\frac{1}{2})^2 = 63\frac{3}{4} = 63.75$

16. Find each product: **(5.3)**

   a) $3(x+2)(x-2)$ c) $5(1-d)(1+d)$ e) $q^2(10-q)(10+q)$ g) $36(w^2-\frac{1}{3})(w^2+\frac{1}{3})$

   b) $a^2(b+c)(b-c)$ d) $x(x-3)(x+3)$ f) $160(1-\frac{q}{4})(10+\frac{q}{4})$ h) $ab(c^3+1)(c^3-1)$

   Ans. a) $3x^2-12$ c) $5-5d^2$ e) $100q^2-q^4$ g) $36w^4-4$

   b) $a^2b^2-a^2c^2$ d) x^3-9x f) $160-10q^2$ h) abc^6-ab

17. Factor: **(6.1)**

a) $r^2 - 25$ e) $t^2 - \frac{4}{9}$ i) $d^2 - .01e^2$ m) $\frac{9}{v^2} - .25$

b) $64 - u^2$ f) $100t^2 - 225s^2$ j) $.09A^2 - 49$ n) $\frac{x^4}{81} - \frac{25}{49}$

c) $81 - c^2d^2$ g) $x^4 - 9$ k) $B^2 - .0001$ o) $\frac{p^2}{q^2} - \frac{r^2}{16}$

d) $9x^2 - 1600$ h) $25 - 16y^{16}$ l) $R^2S^2 - 1.21$ p) $k^6 - 25m^{10}$

Ans. a) $(r+5)(r-5)$ e) $(t+\frac{2}{3})(t-\frac{2}{3})$ i) $(d+.1e)(d-.1e)$ m) $(\frac{3}{v}+.5)(\frac{3}{v}-.5)$

b) $(8+u)(8-u)$ f) $(10t+15s)(10t-15s)$ j) $(.3A+7)(.3A-7)$ n) $(\frac{x^2}{9}+\frac{5}{7})(\frac{x^2}{9}-\frac{5}{7})$

c) $(9+cd)(9-cd)$ g) $(x^2+3)(x^2-3)$ k) $(B+.01)(B-.01)$ o) $(\frac{p}{q}+\frac{r}{4})(\frac{p}{q}-\frac{r}{4})$

d) $(3x+40)(3x-40)$ h) $(5-4y^8)(5+4y^8)$ l) $(RS+1.1)(RS-1.1)$ p) $(k^3+5m^5)(k^3-5m^5)$

18. Factor completely: **(6.2)**

a) $3x^2 - 3$ d) $y^5 - y^3$ g) $12x^4 - 12$

b) $5x^3 - 45x$ e) $\pi R^3 - 25\pi R$ h) $15x^4 - 240$

c) $175 - 7y^2$ f) $\frac{1}{3}\pi R^2h - \frac{1}{3}\pi r^2h$ i) $x^7 - 81x^3$

Ans. a) $3(x+1)(x-1)$ d) $y^3(y+1)(y-1)$ g) $12(x^2+1)(x+1)(x-1)$

b) $5x(x+3)(x-3)$ e) $\pi R(R+5)(R-5)$ h) $15(x^2+4)(x+2)(x-2)$

c) $7(5+y)(5-y)$ f) $\frac{\pi h}{3}(R+r)(R-r)$ i) $x^3(x^2+9)(x+3)(x-3)$

19. Multiply, showing each separate product: **(7.1)**

	First	Outer $+$ Inner	Last	Combine (Ans.)
a) $(x+5)(x+1)$	x^2	(x) $+$ $(5x)$	$+5$	x^2+6x+5
b) $(x+8)(x-2)$	x^2	$(-2x)$ $+$ $(+8x)$	-16	$x^2+6x-16$
c) $(x-7)(x-6)$	x^2	$(-6x)$ $+$ $(-7x)$	$+42$	$x^2-13x+42$
d) $(x-10)(x+9)$	x^2	$(+9x)$ $+$ $(-10x)$	-90	x^2-x-90
e) $(3a-1)(4a+1)$	$12a^2$	$(+3a)$ $+$ $(-4a)$	-1	$12a^2-a-1$
f) $(5b+2)(5b-2)$	$25b^2$	$(-10b)$ $+$ $(+10b)$	-4	$25b^2-4$
g) $(c-3)(2c+8)$	$2c^2$	$(+8c)$ $+$ $(-6c)$	-24	$2c^2+2c-24$
h) $(r-4s)(r-11s)$	r^2	$(-11rs)$ $+$ $(-4rs)$	$+44s^2$	$r^2-15rs+44s^2$
i) $(3s+2t)(3s-2t)$	$9s^2$	$(-6st)$ $+$ $(+6st)$	$-4t^2$	$9s^2-4t^2$
j) $(x^2+5)(x^2+8)$	x^4	$(+8x^2)$ $+$ $(+5x^2)$	$+40$	x^4+13x^2+40
k) $(3w^2+2x)(w^2-x)$	$3w^4$	$(-3w^2x)$ $+$ $(+2w^2x)$	$-2x^2$	$3w^4-w^2x-2x^2$
l) $(2w^3-3)(6w^3+9)$	$12w^6$	$(+18w^3)$ $+$ $(-18w^3)$	-27	$12w^6-27$

20. Multiply mentally: **(7.2)**

a) $(3c+1)(4c+5)$ d) $(pq-8)(pq+11)$ g) $(d^2+6)(d^2+1)$

b) $(2+7c)(1-c)$ e) $(2AB+7)(2AB-7)$ h) $(8-g^2)(3-2g^2)$

c) $(c+3d)(c+12d)$ f) $(3x-2y)(4x-9y)$ i) $(4c^3+1)(c^3-2)$

Ans. a) $12c^2 + 19c + 5$ d) $p^2q^2 + 3pq - 88$ g) $d^4 + 7d^2 + 6$

b) $2 + 5c - 7c^2$ e) $4A^2B^2 - 49$ h) $24 - 19g^2 + 2g^4$

c) $c^2 + 15cd + 36d^2$ f) $12x^2 - 35xy + 18y^2$ i) $4c^6 - 7c^3 - 2$

21. Represent the area of a rectangle whose dimensions are   **(7.3)**

a) $l-3$ and $l-8$ c) $w+10$ and $w-12$ e) $13-2s$ and $2-s$

b) $2l+5$ and $3l-1$ d) $6-w$ and $8-w$ f) $7s+1$ and $9s+2$

Ans. a) $l^2 - 11l + 24$ c) $w^2 - 2w - 120$ e) $26 - 17s + 2s^2$

b) $6l^2 + 13l - 5$ d) $48 - 14w + w^2$ f) $63s^2 + 23s + 2$

22. Factor each trinomial: **(8.1)**

a) $a^2 + 7a + 10$ g) $x^2 - x - 2$ m) $a^2b^2 + 8ab + 15$

b) $b^2 + 8b + 15$ h) $y^2 - 3y - 4$ n) $d^2e^2 - 15def + 36f^2$

c) $r^2 - 12r + 27$ i) $w^2 + 2w - 8$ o) $x^4 + 5x^2 + 4$

d) $s^2 - 14s + 33$ j) $w^2 + 7w - 18$ p) $y^4 - 6y^2 - 7$

e) $h^2 - 27h + 50$ k) $x^2 + 14xy + 24y^2$ q) $x^4 + 8x^2y^2 + 16y^4$

f) $m^2 + 19m + 48$ l) $c^2 - 17cd + 30d^2$ r) $x^4y^4 - 10x^2y^2 + 25$

Ans. a) $(a+5)(a+2)$ g) $(x-2)(x+1)$ m) $(ab+5)(ab+3)$

b) $(b+5)(b+3)$ h) $(y-4)(y+1)$ n) $(de-12f)(de-3f)$

c) $(r-9)(r-3)$ i) $(w+4)(w-2)$ o) $(x^2+4)(x^2+1)$

d) $(s-11)(s-3)$ j) $(w+9)(w-2)$ p) $(y^2-7)(y^2+1)$

e) $(h-25)(h-2)$ k) $(x+12y)(x+2y)$ q) $(x^2+4y^2)(x^2+4y^2)$

f) $(m+16)(m+3)$ l) $(c-15d)(c-2d)$ r) $(x^2y^2-5)(x^2y^2-5)$

---

23. Factor each trinomial: **(9.1)**

a) $5x^2 + 6x + 1$ Ans. $(5x+1)(x+1)$ g) $7h^2 + 10h + 3$ Ans. $(7h+3)(h+1)$

b) $5x^2 - 6x + 1$ Ans. $(5x-1)(x-1)$ h) $7h^2 - 10h + 3$ Ans. $(7h-3)(h-1)$

c) $5x^2 + 4x - 1$ Ans. $(5x-1)(x+1)$ i) $7h^2 - 20h - 3$ Ans. $(7h+1)(h-3)$

d) $5x^2 - 4x - 1$ Ans. $(5x+1)(x-1)$ j) $7h^2 - 22h + 3$ Ans. $(7h-1)(h-3)$

e) $5 + 8x + 3x^2$ Ans. $(5+3x)(1+x)$ k) $7h^4 - 15h^2 + 2$ Ans. $(7h^2-1)(h^2-2)$

f) $5 + 14x - 3x^2$ Ans. $(5-x)(1+3x)$ l) $3 + 4h^2 - 7h^4$ Ans. $(3+7h^2)(1-h^2)$

---

24. Factor each trinomial: **(9.1)**

a) $4a^2 + 5a + 1$ f) $7x^2 - 15x + 2$ k) $5c^2 + 11cd + 2d^2$

b) $2a^2 + 3a + 1$ g) $7x^2 + 13x - 2$ l) $5c^2d^2 + 7cd + 2$

c) $3a^2 + 4a + 1$ h) $3 - 10y + 7y^2$ m) $2x^4 - 9x^2 + 7$

d) $5 + 7b + 2b^2$ i) $3 + 4y - 7y^2$ n) $35 - 17r^2 + 2r^4$

e) $4 + 16b + 15b^2$ j) $3x^2 + 10xy + 7y^2$ o) $3t^6 + 8t^3 - 3$

Ans. a) $(4a+1)(a+1)$ f) $(7x-1)(x-2)$ k) $(5c+d)(c+2d)$

b) $(2a+1)(a+1)$ g) $(7x-1)(x+2)$ l) $(5cd+2)(cd+1)$

c) $(3a+1)(a+1)$ h) $(3-7y)(1-y)$ m) $(2x^2-7)(x^2-1)$

d) $(5+2b)(1+b)$ i) $(3+7y)(1-y)$ n) $(5-r^2)(7-2r^2)$

e) $(2+3b)(2+5b)$ j) $(3x+7y)(x+y)$ o) $(t^3+3)(3t^3-1)$

---

25. Find each square: **(10.1)**

a) $(b+4)^2$ f) $(2d-3)^2$ k) $(6ab-c)^2$

b) $(b-4)^2$ g) $(x-4y)^2$ l) $(8-3abc)^2$

c) $(5-c)^2$ h) $(5x+4y)^2$ m) $(x^2+2y^2)^2$

d) $(5-2c)^2$ i) $(7xy+2)^2$ n) $(x^3-8)^2$

e) $(3d+2)^2$ j) $(2xy-7)^2$ o) $(1-5x^5)^2$

Ans. a) $b^2 + 8b + 16$ f) $4d^2 - 12d + 9$ k) $36a^2b^2 - 12abc + c^2$

b) $b^2 - 8b + 16$ g) $x^2 - 8xy + 16y^2$ l) $64 - 48abc + 9a^2b^2c^2$

c) $25 - 10c + c^2$ h) $25x^2 + 40xy + 16y^2$ m) $x^4 + 4x^2y^2 + 4y^4$

d) $25 - 20c + 4c^2$ i) $49x^2y^2 + 28xy + 4$ n) $x^6 - 16x^3 + 64$

e) $9d^2 + 12d + 4$ j) $4x^2y^2 - 28xy + 49$ o) $1 - 10x^5 + 25x^{10}$

---

26. Find each square by expressing each number as a binomial: **(10.2)**

a) 31^2 Ans. $(30+1)^2 = 961$ | d) 55^2 Ans. $(50+5)^2 = 3025$ | g) $(8\frac{1}{4})^2$ Ans. $(8+\frac{1}{4})^2 = 68\frac{1}{16}$

b) 42^2 Ans. $(40+2)^2 = 1764$ | e) 5.5^2 Ans. $(5+.5)^2 = 30.25$ | h) $(19\frac{3}{4})^2$ Ans. $(20-\frac{1}{4})^2 = 390\frac{1}{16}$

c) 29^2 Ans. $(30-1)^2 = 841$ | f) $(6.5)^2$ Ans. $(6+.5)^2 = 42.25$ | i) 9.8^2 Ans. $(10-.2)^2 = 96.04$

27. Represent the area of a square whose side is   **(10.3)**

   a) $(l+7)$ ft.   d) $(2w-3)$ cm.   g) $a + b$
   b) $(l-2)$ in.   e) $(10-w)$ mi.   h) $c - 2d$
   c) $(2l+9)$ rd.   f) $7 - 5w$ i) $15 - S^2$

Ans. a) $(l^2+14l+49)$ sq. ft.   d) $(4w^2-12w+9)$ sq. cm.   g) $a^2 + 2ab + b^2$
       b) (l^2-4l+4) sq. in.   e) $(100-20w+w^2)$ sq. mi.   h) $c^2-4cd+4d^2$
       c) $(4l^2+36l+81)$ sq. rd.   f) $49 - 70w + 25w^2$ i) $225 - 30S^2 + S^4$

28. Factor (*in* (g) *to* (i), *rearrange before factoring*):   **(11.1)**

   a) $d^2 + 10d + 25$ d) $a^2b^2 - 40ab + 400$ g) $x^2 + 100y^2 + 20xy$
   b) $9 - 6h + h^2$ e) $25x^2 - 30x + 9$ h) $16ab + a^2b^2 + 64$
   c) $144 - 24r + r^2$ f) $49x^2 + 28xy + 4y^2$ i) $x^4 + 4y^4 - 4x^2y^2$

Ans. a) $(d+5)^2$ d) $(ab-20)^2$ g) $x^2 + 20xy + 100y^2 = (x+10y)^2$
       b) $(3-h)^2$ e) $(5x-3)^2$ h) $a^2b^2 + 16ab + 64 = (ab+8)^2$
       c) $(12-r)^2$ f) $(7x+2y)^2$ i) $x^4 - 4x^2y^2 + 4y^4 = (x^2-2y^2)^2$

29. Represent the side of a square whose area is   **(11.2)**

   a) $(81l^2 + 18l + 1)$ sq. in.   c) $(4w^2 - 36w + 81)$ sq. mi.   e) $s^2-12s + 36$
   b) $(9 - 30l + 25l^2)$ sq. ft.   d) $(9 + 42s + 49s^2)$ sq. cm.   f) $s^4 - 24s^2 + 144$

Ans. a) $(9l+1)$ in.   c) $(2w-9)$ mi.   e) $s - 6$
       b) $(3-5l)$ ft.   d) $(3+7s)$ cm.   f) $s^2 - 12$

30. Factor completely: **(12.1)**

   a) $b^3 - 16b$ d) $2x^3 + 8x^2 + 8x$ g) $r^3 - 2r^2 - 15r$
   b) $3b^2 - 75$ e) $x^4 - 12x^3 + 36x^2$ h) $24 - 2r - 2r^2$
   c) $3abc^2 - 3abd^2$ f) $100 - 40x + 4x^2$ i) $x^2y^2z - 16xyz + 64z$

Ans. a) $b(b+4)(b-4)$ d) $2x(x+2)^2$ g) $r(r-5)(r+3)$
       b) $3(b+5)(b-5)$ e) $x^2(x-6)^2$ h) $2(3-r)(4+r)$
       c) $3ab(c+d)(c-d)$ f) $4(5-x)^2$ i) $z(xy-8)^2$

31. Factor completely: **(12.2)**

   a) $a^4 - b^4$ c) $81 - a^4$ e) $a^8 - 1$
   b) $1 - c^{12}$ d) $16 - 81b^4$ f) $1 - a^{16}$

Ans. a) $(a^2+b^2)(a+b)(a-b)$ c) $(9+a^2)(3+a)(3-a)$ e) $(a^4+1)(a^2+1)(a+1)(a-1)$
       b) $(1+c^8)(1+c^3)(1-c^3)$ d) $(4+9b^2)(2+3b)(2-3b)$ f) $(1+a^8)(1+a^4)(1+a^2)(1+a)(1-a)$

Chapter 11

Fractions and Rational Expressions

1. UNDERSTANDING FRACTIONS AND RATIONAL EXPRESSIONS

Understanding Fractions

In an earlier chapter, we used fractions of a simple kind, those whose numerator and denominator are natural numbers. The ancient peoples worked with such simple fractions. The word "fraction" comes from the Latin word "fractus," which means broken. The Romans thought of a fraction as a "broken" whole such as a part of a stick or a part of a loaf of bread. The Romans, like the Babylonians, divided a whole into sixtieths, calling these parts "partes **minutiae** primae," meaning "first little parts." When a second division divided each sixtieth into sixty parts, the Romans called these parts "partes minutiae **secundae**," meaning "second little parts." Eventually, a minute became a sixtieth part of an hour or a degree, while a second became a sixtieth part of a minute, which is $\frac{1}{3600}$ of an hour or $\frac{1}{3600}$ of a degree. The Romans also divided a whole into 12 parts, calling each part an "uncial." From "uncial" we derived "ounce" and "inch." In Troy measure, a pound is 12 ounces.

When we write a fraction, we used a fraction bar to separate the numerals used for the numerator and denominator. The Hindus wrote fractions in the same way. The Hindus thought of the fraction $\frac{2}{3}$ as a way of indicating that the whole is divided into 3 equal parts, 2 of which are to be taken or used. Printers use a slanted bar because of its convenience in setting type.

The terms of a fraction are its numerator and its denominator.

The Meanings of a Fraction

Meaning 1. A fraction may mean **division.**

Thus, $\frac{3}{4}$ may mean 3 divided by 4 or 3 ÷ 4.

When a fraction means division, its numerator is the **dividend** and its denominator is the **divisor.**

Thus, if $\frac{14}{5}$ means 14 ÷ 5, then 14 is the dividend and 5 is the divisor.

Meaning 2. A fraction may mean **ratio.**

Thus, $\frac{3}{4}$ may mean the ratio of 3 to 4 or 3:4.

When a fraction means the ratio of two quantities, the quantities must have a common unit.

Thus, the ratio of 3 days to 2 weeks equals 3:14 or $\frac{3}{14}$. This is found by changing 2 weeks to 14 days and eliminating the common unit.

Meaning 3. A fraction may mean **a part of a whole thing** or **a part of a group of things.**

Thus, $\frac{3}{4}$ may mean three-fourths of a dollar, or 3 out of 4 dollars.

Zero Numerators or Zero Denominators

(1) **When the numerator of a fraction is zero,** the value of the fraction is zero provided the denominator is not zero also.

Thus, $\frac{0}{3} = 0$. Also, $\frac{x}{3} = 0$ if $x = 0$.

In $\frac{x-5}{3}$, if $x = 5$, then the fraction equals zero. However, $\frac{0}{0}$ is meaningless.

(2) **Since division by zero is impossible**, a fraction with a zero denominator has no meaning.

Thus, $3 \div 0$ is impossible. Hence, $\frac{3}{0}$ is meaningless.

Also, if $x = 0$, $5 \div x$ is impossible and $\frac{5}{x}$ is meaningless.

Today, a fraction may involve integers, or numbers such as $\sqrt{2}$, $\sqrt{-1}$, and π. A fraction may be a complex fraction which contains a fraction or fractions within it. A fraction may have terms which are polynomials. We must extend our knowledge to cover more advanced fractions. We begin by considering fractions which are rational expressions.

Understanding Rational Expressions

Expressions such as $\frac{5}{y}$ and $\frac{x}{x-5}$ are not polynomials since a variable appears in the denominator. Expressions such as these are **rational expressions** according to the following definition:

A **rational expression** is an expression that may be stated in the form of a fraction whose numerator is a polynomial and whose denominator is a nonzero polynomial.

Thus, $\frac{5}{y}$ when $y \neq 0$ is a rational expression. Also, $\frac{x}{x-5}$ when $x \neq 5$ is a rational expression. The restrictions in both of these cases are necessary so that the denominator of each rational expression is not zero.

Note. In all future problems, **unless otherwise stated, assume that the values of the variable or variables in the denominator are those values which do not make the denominator zero.**

When a rational expression is stated in the form of a fraction, the **terms of the rational expression** are the polynomials that are its numerator and its denominator.

Thus, when the polynomial $x^2 + 5$ is in the form $\frac{x^2 + 5}{1}$, it is a rational expression whose numerator is $x^2 + 5$ and whose denominator is the polynomial 1. (Recall that a constant is a polynomial of degree 1 with the exception of 0.)

Rational expressions stated in the form of a fraction may be called "fractions". Keep in mind, however, that **a fraction need not be a rational expression.**

Thus, $\frac{\sqrt{x}}{2}$ is a fraction that is not a rational expression since $\sqrt{x}$ is not a polynomial.

Note. In this chapter, inasmuch as we are not going to consider any fractions other than those that are rational expressions, the terms "fraction" and "rational expression" are to be used interchangeably.

1.1 Meaning 1: Fractions Meaning Division

Express each in fractional form:

a) 10 divided by 17   *Ans.* $\frac{10}{17}$

c) $(x+5) \div 3$ *Ans.* $\frac{x+5}{3}$

b) 5 divided by a *Ans.* $\frac{5}{a}$

d) the quotient of x and $(x-2)$.   *Ans.* $\frac{x}{x-2}$

1.2 Meaning 2: Fractions Meaning Ratio

Express each in fractional form:

[*In (d) to (f), a common unit must be used.*]

a) the ratio of 5 to 8   *Ans.* $\frac{5}{8}$

d) the ratio of a ft. to 5 yd.   *Ans.* $\frac{a}{15}$

b) the ratio of 15 to t *Ans.* $\frac{15}{t}$

e) the ratio of 7 min. to 1 hr.   *Ans.* $\frac{7}{60}$

c) the ratio of a ft. to b ft.   *Ans.* $\frac{a}{b}$

f) the ratio of 3¢ to one quarter.   *Ans.* $\frac{3}{25}$

1.3 Meaning 3: Fractions Meaning Parts of a Whole or of a Group

Express each in fractional form:

a) 3 of 32 equal parts of an inch $Ans. \frac{3}{32}$
d) 5 members out of a team of 21 $Ans. \frac{5}{21}$

b) 3 of n equal parts of a circle $Ans. \frac{3}{n}$
e) n students out of a group of 30 $Ans. \frac{n}{30}$

c) a out of b dollars $Ans. \frac{a}{b}$
f) s squads out of t squads. $Ans. \frac{s}{t}$

1.4 Fractions Having Zero Numerators and Nonzero Denominators

State the value of

a) $\frac{0}{10}$ $Ans.$ 0
d) x when $\frac{x}{5}=0$ $Ans.$ 0

b) $\frac{x}{10}$ when $x=0$ $Ans.$ 0
e) x when $\frac{x-7}{10}=0$ $Ans.$ 7

c) $\frac{x-2}{10}$ when $x=2$ $Ans.$ 0
f) x when $\frac{3x+6}{12}=0$. $Ans. -2$

1.5 Fractions Having Zero Denominators and Nonzero Numerators

For what value of x is the fraction meaningless?

a) $\frac{3}{x}$ $Ans.$ when $x=0$
d) $\frac{x+4}{4x-16}$ $Ans.$ when $4x-16=0$ or $x=4$

b) $\frac{10}{3x}$ $Ans.$ when $3x=0$ or $x=0$
e) $\frac{8x}{5x+5}$ $Ans.$ when $5x+5=0$ or $x=-1$

c) $\frac{10}{x-3}$ $Ans.$ when $x-3=0$ or $x=3$
f) $\frac{2x-12}{2x+12}$ $Ans.$ when $2x+12=0$ or $x=-6$

1.6 Determining If a Rational Expression is a Polynomial

Which rational expressions are polynomials?

a) $\frac{x}{10}$, b) $\frac{10}{x}$, c) $\frac{x-2}{x}$, d) $\frac{x^2+4}{3}$, e) $\frac{x^2+4}{3x}$, f) $\frac{3x^2-5x+12}{7}$

$Ans.$ The only polynomials are (a), (d), and (f). The remaining expressions are not polynomials since a variable appears in the denominator.

1.7 Division by Zero in Rational Expressions

In each, what restriction must be made on the replacement set of the variables?

a) $\frac{y}{2}$, b) $\frac{2}{y}$, c) $\frac{x+2}{x}$, d) $\frac{x}{x+2}$, e) $\frac{2x-4}{x(x+2)}$, f) $\frac{xy}{5}$, g) $\frac{5}{xy}$, h) $\frac{x(y-5)}{y(x-5)}$

$Ans.$ a) none c) $x \neq 0$ e) $x \neq 0$ and $x \neq -2$ g) $x \neq 0$ and $y \neq 0$
b) $y \neq 0$ d) $x \neq -2$ f) none h) $y \neq 0$ or $x \neq 5$

2. EQUIVALENT FRACTIONS

Equivalent fractions are fractions having the same value although they have different terms.

Thus, since $\frac{2}{3}=\frac{20}{30}$, then $\frac{2}{3}$ and $\frac{20}{30}$ are equivalent fractions.

Equivalence Sets

Equivalent fractions are elements of an **equivalence set**.

Thus, the set $\left\{ \frac{2}{3}, \frac{4}{6}, \frac{6}{9}, \ldots, \frac{20}{30}, \ldots, \frac{200}{300}, \ldots \right\}$ is an equivalence set.

Using a Number Line to Understand Equivalence Sets

Note on the number line how a point may represent the numbers of an equivalence set:

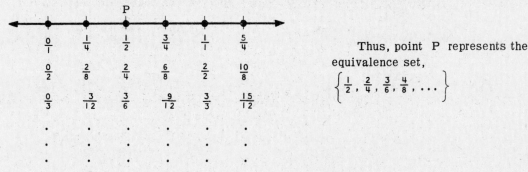

Thus, point P represents the equivalence set,

$$\left\{ \frac{1}{2}, \frac{2}{4}, \frac{3}{6}, \frac{4}{8}, \dots \right\}$$

In each of the equivalence sets, the fraction just below the number line is the fraction whose terms are the least. The fractions just below the number line have terms that are either prime numbers, 0, 1, or do not have a common factor, except 1.

Thus, $\frac{3}{4}$ is a fraction whose terms 3 and 4 do not have a common factor, except 1.

Using Multiplication or Division to Obtain Equivalent Fractions

To obtain equivalent rational expressions or fractions, use one of the following rules:

Rule 1. The value of a rational expression or fraction is not changed if its numerator and denominator are both **multiplied by the same number, excluding zero.**

Thus, $\frac{3}{4} = \frac{30}{40}$. Here both 3 and 4 are multiplied by 10.

Note. Rule 1 makes use of the multiplicative identity property of 1, as follows:

$$\frac{3}{4} = \frac{3}{4} \cdot \frac{10}{10} = \frac{30}{40}. \text{ (The fraction } \frac{10}{10} \text{ equals 1.)}$$

Rule 2. The value of a rational expression or fraction is not changed if its numerator and denominator are both **divided by the same number, excluding zero.**

Thus, $\frac{30}{40} = \frac{3}{4}$. Here both 30 and 40 are divided by 10.

Also, $\frac{7a^2}{9a^2} = \frac{7}{9}$ when $a \neq 0$. Here both $7a^2$ and $9a^2$ are divided by a^2.

2.1 Rule 1: Using Multiplication to Obtain Equivalent Fractions

Change each of the following to equivalent fractions by multiplying its numerator and denominator by 2, 5, x, $4x$, x^2, and $x^2 + x - 3$ when $x \neq 0$:

			Multiply Both Numerator and Denominator by					
			2	5	x	$4x$	$x-3$	x^2	$x^2 + x - 3$
a) $\frac{2}{3}$	Ans. $\frac{2}{3}$ =	$\frac{4}{6}$ =	$\frac{10}{15}$ =	$\frac{2x}{3x}$ =	$\frac{8x}{12x}$ =	$\frac{2x-6}{3x-9}$ =	$\frac{2x^2}{3x^2}$ =	$\frac{2x^2+2x-6}{3x^2+3x-9}$
b) $\frac{a}{7}$	Ans. $\frac{a}{7}$ =	$\frac{2a}{14}$ =	$\frac{5a}{35}$ =	$\frac{ax}{7x}$ =	$\frac{4ax}{28x}$ =	$\frac{ax-3a}{7x-21}$ =	$\frac{ax^2}{7x^2}$ =	$\frac{ax^2+ax-3a}{7x^2+7x-21}$
c) $\frac{3}{x}$	Ans. $\frac{3}{x}$ =	$\frac{6}{2x}$ =	$\frac{15}{5x}$ =	$\frac{3x}{x^2}$ =	$\frac{12x}{4x^2}$ =	$\frac{3x-9}{x^2-3x}$ =	$\frac{3x^2}{x^3}$ =	$\frac{3x^2+3x-9}{x^3+x^2-3x}$

2.2 Rule 2: Using Division to Obtain Equivalent Fractions

Change each of the following to equivalent fractions by dividing its numerator and denominator by 2, 5, x, $4x$, x^2, and $20x^2$ when $x \neq 0$:

	Divide Both Numerator and Denominator by					
	2	5	x	$4x$	x^2	$20x^2$

a) $\dfrac{20x^2}{80x^2}$ *Ans.* $\dfrac{20x^2}{80x^2} = \dfrac{10x^2}{40x^2} = \dfrac{4x^2}{16x^2} = \dfrac{20x}{80x} = \dfrac{5x}{20x} = \dfrac{20}{80} = \dfrac{1}{4}$

b) $\dfrac{40x^3}{60x^2}$ *Ans.* $\dfrac{40x^3}{60x^2} = \dfrac{20x^3}{30x^2} = \dfrac{8x^3}{12x^2} = \dfrac{40x^2}{60x} = \dfrac{10x^2}{15x} = \dfrac{40x}{60} = \dfrac{2x}{3}$

2.3 Obtaining Missing Terms

Show how to obtain each missing term:

a) $\dfrac{3}{7} = \dfrac{30}{(?)}$ a) To get 30, multiply 3 by 10. Hence, multiply 7 by 10 to get 70.   a) $\dfrac{3}{7} = \dfrac{30}{(70)}$ *Ans.* 70

b) $\dfrac{27}{33} = \dfrac{9}{(?)}$ b) To get 9, divide 27 by 3. Hence, divide 33 by 3 to get 11.   b) $\dfrac{27}{33} = \dfrac{9}{(11)}$ *Ans.* 11

c) $\dfrac{3a}{b} = \dfrac{3ab}{(?)}$ c) To get $3ab$, multiply $3a$ by b. Hence, multiply b by b to get b^2.   c) $\dfrac{3a}{b} = \dfrac{3ab}{(b^2)}$ *Ans.* b^2

d) $\dfrac{6ac}{3c^2} = \dfrac{(?)}{c}$ d) To get c, divide $3c^2$ by $3c$. Hence, divide $6ac$ by $3c$ to get $2a$.   d) $\dfrac{6ac}{3c^2} = \dfrac{(2a)}{c}$ *Ans.* $2a$

e) $\dfrac{5}{x-5} = \dfrac{25}{(?)}$ e) To get 25, multiply 5 by 5. Hence, multiply $x-5$ by 5 to get $5x-25$.   e) $\dfrac{5}{x-5} = \dfrac{25}{(5x-25)}$ *Ans.* $5x-25$

3. RECIPROCALS AND MULTIPLICATIVE INVERSES

Reciprocal of a Number

The **reciprocal of a number** is 1 divided by the number except when the number is 0.

Thus, the reciprocal of 5 is $\dfrac{1}{5}$ and the reciprocal of $\dfrac{2}{3}$ is $\dfrac{3}{2}$ since $1 \div \dfrac{2}{3} = 1 \cdot \dfrac{3}{2}$.

Note. The reciprocal of a fraction is obtained by interchanging the terms of the fraction or "inverting the fraction."

$$\text{The reciprocal of } n \text{ is } \dfrac{1}{n} \text{ when } n \neq 0.$$

The reciprocal of a number is also its multiplicative inverse, because of rule 1 and the following definition:

Multiplicative inverses are two numbers whose product is 1.

Rules of Reciprocals

Rule 1. The product of a number and its reciprocal is 1.

Thus, the product of $\dfrac{2}{3}$ and its reciprocal, $\dfrac{3}{2}$, is 1; that is, $\dfrac{2}{3}\left(\dfrac{3}{2}\right) = 1$. Hence, $\dfrac{2}{3}$ and $\dfrac{3}{2}$ are also multiplicative inverses.

Rule 2. A number is the reciprocal of its reciprocal; that is, a number and its reciprocal are reciprocals of each other.

Thus, $\dfrac{3}{4}$ is the reciprocal of $\dfrac{4}{3}$, and $\dfrac{4}{3}$ is the reciprocal of $\dfrac{3}{4}$. In other words, $\dfrac{3}{4}$ and $\dfrac{4}{3}$ are reciprocals of each other.

Rule 3. A number and its reciprocal have the same sign; that is, numbers that are reciprocals of each other are either both positive or both are negative.

Thus, the reciprocal of $-\frac{4}{5}$ is $-\frac{5}{4}$.

Rule 4. The rational expressions $\frac{a}{b}$ and $\frac{b}{a}$ are reciprocals of each other when $a \neq 0$ and $b \neq 0$.

Thus, $\frac{x}{2x-8}$ and $\frac{2x-8}{x}$ are reciprocals of each other when $x \neq 0$ and $x \neq 4$.

Rule 5. To divide by a number, multiply by its reciprocal.

Thus, $10 \div \frac{5}{7} = 10\left(\frac{7}{5}\right) = 14$. Also, $2y \div \frac{2}{3} = 2y\left(\frac{3}{2}\right) = 3y$.

Rule 6. To solve an equation of the first degree in one variable when the variable has a fractional coefficient, multiply both members by the reciprocal of the coefficient.

Thus, to solve $\frac{3}{4}x = 27$, multiply both sides by $\frac{4}{3}$ to obtain $\frac{4}{3}\left(\frac{3}{4}x\right) = \frac{4}{3}(27)$. Hence, $x = 36$

3.1 Rule 1: The product of a number and its reciprocal is 1.

Supply the missing entry:

a) $\left(\frac{2}{7}\right)\left(\frac{7}{2}\right) = (?)$ *Ans.* 1

b) $\frac{3}{8}(?) = 1$ *Ans.* $\frac{8}{3}$

c) $10\left(\frac{5}{9}\right)\left(\frac{9}{5}\right) = ?$ *Ans.* 10

d) $\left(\frac{x}{17}\right)\left(\frac{17}{x}\right)\left(\frac{2}{5}\right) = (?)$ *Ans.* $\frac{2}{5}$

e) $\left(\frac{8}{7}\right)\left(\frac{7}{8}\right) + ? = 5$ *Ans.* 4

f) $3\left(\frac{3}{5}\right)\left(\frac{5}{3}\right) + \left(\frac{8}{15}\right)(?) = 4$ *Ans.* $\frac{15}{8}$

3.2 Rule 2: A number and its reciprocal are reciprocals of each other.

State the reciprocal of each:

a) 5   *Ans.* $\frac{1}{5}$ or .2

b) .2   *Ans.* 5

c) 25   *Ans.* $\frac{1}{25}$ or .04

d) .04   *Ans.* 25

e) .001   *Ans.* 1000 since .001 $= \frac{1}{1000}$

f) $\frac{2}{5}$ *Ans.* $\frac{5}{2}$ or $2\frac{1}{2}$

g) $2\frac{1}{2}$ *Ans.* $\frac{2}{5}$

h) 2.4   *Ans.* $\frac{10}{24}$ or $\frac{5}{12}$

i) 1.001   *Ans.* $\frac{1000}{1001}$ since 1.001 $= \frac{1001}{1000}$

3.3 Rule 3: A number and its reciprocal have the same sign.

Supply the missing entry:

a) $\left(-\frac{2}{7}\right)(?) = 1$ *Ans.* $-\frac{7}{2}$

b) $(-10)(-.1) = (?)$ *Ans.* 1

c) $\left(\frac{3}{4}\right)\left(-\frac{4}{3}\right)(-3) = (?)$ *Ans.* 3

d) $\left(-\frac{x}{3}\right)(?) = 1$ *Ans.* $-\frac{3}{x}$

e) $\left(-\frac{8}{y}\right)\left(-\frac{y}{8}\right)(-2) = (?)$ *Ans.* -2

f) $2(3)\left(\frac{1}{3}\right) - 9\left(-\frac{1}{4}\right)(-4) = (?)$ *Ans.* -7

3.4 Rule 4: Rational expressions $\frac{a}{b}$ and $\frac{b}{a}$ are reciprocals of each other when $a \neq 0$ and $b \neq 0$

State the reciprocal of each:

a) x, $x \neq 0$ *Ans.* $\frac{1}{x}$

b) $\frac{1}{y}$, $y \neq 0$ *Ans.* y

c) $\frac{3x}{4y}$, $x \neq 0$ and $y \neq 0$ *Ans.* $\frac{4y}{3x}$

d) $\frac{x-3}{y+3}$, $x \neq 3$ and $y \neq -3$ *Ans.* $\frac{y+3}{x-3}$

3.5 Rule 5: To divide by a number, multiply by its reciprocal.

Show how to change each division to multiplication by using the reciprocal of a number:

a) $8 \div \frac{4}{5}$

b) $\frac{2}{x} \div y$

c) $\frac{1}{r} \div \frac{t}{s}$

d) $\frac{3}{x} \div \frac{y}{7}$

Ans. a) $8 \cdot \frac{5}{4} = 10$

b) $\frac{2}{x} \cdot \frac{1}{y} = \frac{2}{xy}$

c) $\frac{1}{r} \cdot \frac{s}{t} = \frac{s}{rt}$

d) $\frac{3}{x} \cdot \frac{7}{y} = \frac{21}{xy}$

3.6 Using a Reciprocal to Solve an Equation (Rule 6)

Solve:

a) $\frac{3}{4}x = 21$ b) $2\frac{1}{3}y = 70$ c) 30% of $P = 24$ d) $\frac{ax}{3} = 5a$

Solutions:

$$\frac{3}{4}x = 21 \qquad\qquad 2\frac{1}{3}y = 70 \qquad\qquad 30\% \text{ of } P = 24 \qquad\qquad \frac{ax}{3} = 5a$$

$$\mathbf{M}_{\frac{4}{3}} \ \ \frac{4}{3}\cdot\frac{3}{4}x = \frac{4}{3}\cdot 21 \qquad \mathbf{M}_{\frac{3}{7}} \ \ \frac{3}{7}\cdot\frac{7}{3}y = \frac{3}{7}\cdot 70 \qquad \mathbf{M}_{\frac{10}{3}} \ \ \frac{10}{3}\cdot\frac{3}{10}P = \frac{10}{3}\cdot 24 \qquad \mathbf{M}_{\frac{3}{a}} \ \ \frac{3}{a}\cdot\frac{ax}{3} = \frac{3}{a}\cdot 5a$$

Ans. $x = 28$ | *Ans.* $y = 30$ | *Ans.* $P = 80$ | *Ans.* $x = 15$

4. REDUCING FRACTIONS TO LOWEST TERMS

A fraction is reduced to lowest terms when its numerator and denominator have no common factor except 1.

Thus, $\frac{3x}{7x}$ is not in lowest terms because x is a common factor of the numerator and denominator. After x has been eliminated by division, the resulting fraction, $\frac{3}{7}$, will be in lowest terms.

To reduce a fraction to lowest terms, use the following rule:

The value of a fraction is not changed if its numerator and denominator are both divided by the same number, excluding zero.

To Reduce a Fraction to Lowest Terms

Reduce: a) $\frac{3ab^2c}{3ab^2d}$ b) $\frac{8a+8b}{12a+12b}$ c) $\frac{2a^2-2b^2}{5a+5b}$

Procedure: **Solutions:**

1. Factor its terms:
(Numerator and Denominator)

$$\frac{3ab^2c}{3ab^2d} \qquad\qquad \frac{8(a+b)}{12(a+b)} \qquad\qquad \frac{2(a+b)(a-b)}{5(a+b)}$$

2. Divide both terms by every common factor:
Note. This process may be referred to as "*canceling common factors.*"

$$\frac{\overset{1}{\cancel{3ab^2c}}}{\underset{1}{\cancel{3ab^2d}}} \qquad\qquad \frac{\overset{2}{\cancel{8}}\overset{(1)}{\cancel{(a+b)}}}{\underset{3}{\cancel{12}}\underset{(1)}{\cancel{(a+b)}}} \qquad\qquad \frac{\overset{1}{\cancel{2}}\overset{}{\cancel{(a+b)}}(a-b)}{\underset{1}{\cancel{5}}\underset{}{\cancel{(a+b)}}}$$

Ans. $\frac{c}{d}$ | *Ans.* $\frac{2}{3}$ | *Ans.** $\frac{2(a-b)}{5}$

*Note. In answers, algebraic factors which remain need not be multiplied out.

Rule 1. If two expressions are exactly alike or have the same value, their quotient is 1.

Thus, $\frac{5abc}{5abc} = 1$, $\frac{a+b}{b+a} = 1$, $\frac{\overset{4}{\cancel{8}}\overset{(1)}{\cancel{(x^2+x-5)}}}{\underset{2}{\cancel{2}}\underset{}{\cancel{(x^2+x-5)}}} = 4$.

Binomials Which are Negatives of Each Other.

Binomials such as $x-y$ and $y-x$ are negatives of each other if x and y have different values.

Thus, if $x=5$ and $y=2$, $x-y = +3$ and $y-x = -3$.

Hence, either $(x-y) = -(y-x)$ or $(y-x) = -(x-y)$.

Rule 2. If two binomials are negatives of each other, their quotient is -1.

Thus, $\frac{x-y}{y-x} = -1$, $\frac{\overset{1}{\cancel{(5+x)}}\overset{(-1)}{\cancel{(5-x)}}}{\underset{}{\cancel{(x+5)}}\underset{}{\cancel{(x-5)}}} = -1$, $\frac{\overset{(-1)}{\cancel{(a-b)}}\overset{(-1)}{\cancel{(7-c)}}}{\underset{}{\cancel{(b-a)}}\underset{}{\cancel{(c-7)}}} = 1$.

Warning! How NOT to Reduce a Fraction to Lowest Terms:

1. **Do NOT Subtract** the same number from the numerator and denominator.

Thus, $\frac{5}{6}$ does **NOT** equal $\frac{5-4}{6-4}$ or $\frac{1}{2}$. Also, $\frac{n+1}{n+2}$ does **NOT** equal $\frac{\not n+1}{\not n+2}$ or $\frac{1}{2}$.

2. **Do NOT Add** the same number to both numerator and denominator.

Thus, $\frac{1}{2}$ does **NOT** equal $\frac{1+3}{2+3}$ or $\frac{4}{5}$. Also, $\frac{x-3}{y-3}$ does **NOT** equal $\frac{x-\not 3}{y-\not 3}$ or $\frac{x}{y}$.

4.1 Reducing Fractions Whose Terms Have Common Monomial Factors

Reduce to lowest terms:

a) $\dfrac{39rs}{52rs}$ b) $\dfrac{32a^3b^3}{64a^2b}$ c) $\dfrac{5x-35}{15x}$ d) $\dfrac{21a^2}{14a^2-7ab}$

Solutions:

$$\frac{\overset{3\ (1)}{\cancel{39}\,\cancel{rs}}}{\underset{4\ (1)}{\cancel{52}\,\cancel{rs}}}$$

$$\frac{\overset{1\quad ab^2}{\cancel{32}a^3b^3}}{\underset{2\ (1)}{\cancel{64}a^2b}}$$

$$\frac{\overset{1}{\cancel{5}(x-7)}}{\underset{3}{15x}}$$

$$\frac{\overset{3a}{\cancel{21}a^2}}{\underset{1}{\cancel{7}a(2a-b)}}$$

Ans. $\dfrac{3}{4}$ Ans. $\dfrac{ab^2}{2}$ Ans. $\dfrac{x-7}{3x}$ Ans. $\dfrac{3a}{2a-b}$

4.2 Rule 1. Reducing Fractions Whose Terms Have a Common Binomial Factor

Reduce to lowest terms:

a) $\dfrac{2x+6}{3ax+9a}$ b) $\dfrac{x^2+x}{2+2x}$ c) $\dfrac{3x+3y}{3y^2-3x^2}$ d) $\dfrac{(b+c)^2}{-acx-abx}$

Solutions:

$$\frac{2(x+3)}{3a(x+3)}$$

$$\frac{x(x+1)}{2(1+x)}$$

$$\frac{3(x+y)}{3(y+x)(y-x)}$$

$$\frac{(b+c)(b+c)}{-ax(c+b)}$$

$$\frac{\overset{1}{2\cancel{(x+3)}}}{3a\cancel{(x+3)}}$$

$$\frac{\overset{1}{x\cancel{(x+1)}}}{2\cancel{(1+x)}}$$

$$\frac{\overset{1\ \ (1)}{\cancel{3}\cancel{(x+y)}}}{\cancel{3}\cancel{(y+x)}(y-x)}$$

$$\frac{\overset{1}{(b+c)\cancel{(b+c)}}}{-ax\cancel{(c+b)}}$$

Ans. $\dfrac{2}{3a}$ Ans. $\dfrac{x}{2}$ Ans. $\dfrac{1}{y-x}$ Ans. $-\dfrac{b+c}{ax}$

4.3 Rule 2. Reducing Fractions Having Binomial Factors Which Are Negatives of Each Other

Reduce to lowest terms:

a) $\dfrac{4-y}{3y-12}$ b) $\dfrac{d^2-49}{14-2d}$ c) $\dfrac{5-5r}{10rt-10t}$ d) $\dfrac{(w-x)^2}{x^2-w^2}$

Solutions:

$$\frac{\overset{-1}{\cancel{(4-y)}}}{3\cancel{(y-4)}}$$

$$\frac{\overset{(-1)}{\cancel{(d-7)}(d+7)}}{2\cancel{(7-d)}}$$

$$\frac{\overset{1\quad(-1)}{\cancel{5}\cancel{(1-r)}}}{\underset{2}{\cancel{10}t\cancel{(r-1)}}}$$

$$\frac{\overset{-1}{\cancel{(w-x)}(w-x)}}{\cancel{(x-w)}(x+w)}$$

Ans. $-\dfrac{1}{3}$ Ans. $-\dfrac{d+7}{2}$ Ans. $-\dfrac{1}{2t}$ Ans. $-\dfrac{w-x}{x+w}$ or $\dfrac{x-w}{x+w}$

4.4 Fractions Having at Least One Trinomial Term

Reduce to lowest terms:

a) $\dfrac{b^2 + 3b}{b^2 + 10b + 21}$ b) $\dfrac{x^2 - 9x + 20}{4x - x^2}$ c) $\dfrac{y^2 + 2y - 15}{2y^2 - 12y + 18}$

Solutions:

$$\dfrac{\overset{1}{b\,\cancel{(b+3)}}}{\cancel{(b+3)}(b+7)}$$ $$\dfrac{(x-5)\overset{-1}{\cancel{(x-4)}}}{x\cancel{(4-x)}}$$ $$\dfrac{(y+5)\overset{1}{\cancel{(y-3)}}}{2(y-3)\cancel{(y-3)}}$$

Ans. $\dfrac{b}{b+7}$ Ans. $-\dfrac{x-5}{x}$ or $\dfrac{5-x}{x}$ Ans. $\dfrac{y+5}{2(y-3)}$

5. MULTIPLYING FRACTIONS

To Multiply Fractions Having No Cancelable Common Factor

Multiply: a) $\dfrac{3}{5} \cdot \dfrac{7}{11}$ b) $\dfrac{x}{3} \cdot \dfrac{5}{r}$ c) $\dfrac{a}{4} \cdot \dfrac{9}{2} \cdot \dfrac{c}{d} \cdot \dfrac{7}{a+c}$

Procedure: Solutions:

1. **Multiply numerators** to obtain numerator of answer.

1. $\dfrac{3(7)}{}$ 1. $\dfrac{x(5)}{}$ 1. $\dfrac{a(9)(c)(7)}{}$

2. **Multiply denominators** to obtain denominator of answer.

2. $5(11)$ 2. $3(r)$ 2. $4(2)(d)(a+c)$

Ans. $\dfrac{21}{55}$ Ans. $\dfrac{5x}{3r}$ Ans. $\dfrac{63ac}{8d(a+c)}$

To Multiply Fractions Having a Cancelable Common Factor

Multiply: a) $\dfrac{3}{5} \cdot \dfrac{10}{7} \cdot \dfrac{77}{6}$ b) $\dfrac{7x}{a} \cdot \dfrac{2a}{7+7x}$ c) $\dfrac{5x}{a^2 - b^2} \cdot \dfrac{3a+3b}{x}$

Procedure: Solutions:

1. **Factor those numerators and denominators which are polynomials.**

$\dfrac{3}{5} \cdot \dfrac{10}{7} \cdot \dfrac{77}{6}$ $\dfrac{7x}{a} \cdot \dfrac{2a}{7(1+x)}$ $\dfrac{5x}{(a+b)(a-b)} \cdot \dfrac{3(a+b)}{x}$

2. **Divide out factors common to any numerator and any denominator.**

$\dfrac{\overset{(1)}{\cancel{3}} \cdot \overset{(2)}{\cancel{10}} \cdot \overset{(11)}{\cancel{77}}}{\underset{(1)}{\cancel{5}} \cdot \underset{(1)}{\cancel{7}} \cdot \underset{(2)}{\cancel{6}}}$ $\dfrac{\overset{1}{\cancel{7x}} \cdot \overset{(1)}{\cancel{2a}}}{\underset{(1)}{\cancel{a}} \cdot \underset{(1)}{7(1+x)}}$ $\dfrac{\overset{1}{5\cancel{x}}}{\underset{(1)}{\cancel{(a+b)}(a-b)}} \cdot \dfrac{\overset{1}{3\cancel{(a+b)}}}{\underset{(1)}{\cancel{x}}}$

3. **Multiply remaining factors.**

Ans. 11   Ans. $\dfrac{2x}{1+x}$ Ans. $\dfrac{15}{a-b}$

5.1 Multiplying Fractions Having No Cancelable Common Factor

Multiply:

a) $\dfrac{1}{5} \cdot \dfrac{2}{5} \cdot \dfrac{4}{7}$ b) $\dfrac{2}{d} \cdot \dfrac{c}{5} \cdot \dfrac{x}{y}$ c) $5xy \cdot \dfrac{3c}{ab}$ d) $\dfrac{a}{4} \cdot \dfrac{3}{r} \cdot \dfrac{r+5}{a-2}$

Solutions:

$\dfrac{1(2)(4)}{5(5)(7)}$ $\dfrac{2(c)(x)}{d(5)(y)}$ $\dfrac{5xy \cdot 3c}{ab}$ $\dfrac{a(3)(r+5)}{4(r)(a-2)}$

Ans. $\dfrac{8}{175}$ Ans. $\dfrac{2cx}{5dy}$ Ans. $\dfrac{15cxy}{ab}$ Ans. $\dfrac{3a(r+5)}{4r(a-2)}$

5.2 Multiplying Fractions Having a Cancelable Common Factor

Multiply:

a) $\dfrac{9}{5} \cdot \dfrac{7}{3} \cdot \dfrac{15}{14}$

b) $\dfrac{12c}{d} \cdot \dfrac{h}{3} \cdot \dfrac{d^2}{h^2}$

c) $\dfrac{c}{a+b} \cdot \dfrac{5a+5b}{2c^2+2c}$

d) $\dfrac{9x}{3x-15} \cdot \dfrac{(x-5)^2}{2(5-x)}$

Solutions:

$\overset{3}{\underset{(1)}{\cancel{9}}} \cdot \overset{(1)}{\underset{(1)}{\cancel{7}}} \cdot \overset{3}{\underset{(2)}{\cancel{15}}}$

$\overset{4}{\underset{(1)}{\cancel{12c}}} \cdot \overset{(1)}{\underset{(1)}{\cancel{h}}} \cdot \overset{d}{\underset{h}{\cancel{d^2}}}$

$\overset{(1)}{\cancel{c}} \cdot \dfrac{5\cancel{(a+b)}}{2\cancel{c}(c+1)}$

$\overset{3}{\underset{}{\cancel{9x}}} \cdot \dfrac{(x-5)\cancel{(x-5)}}{2\cancel{(5-x)}}$

Ans. $\dfrac{9}{2}$

Ans. $\dfrac{4cd}{h}$

Ans. $\dfrac{5}{2(c+1)}$

Ans. $-\dfrac{3x}{2}$

5.3 More Difficult Multiplication of Fractions

Multiply:

a) $\dfrac{y^2+6y+5}{7y^2-63} \cdot \dfrac{7y+21}{(5+y)^2}$

b) $\dfrac{a+4}{4a} \cdot \dfrac{2a-8}{4+a} \cdot \dfrac{a^2-4}{24-12a} \cdot \dfrac{4a^2}{4-a}$

Solutions:

$\dfrac{\cancel{(y+5)}(y+1)}{7(y-3)\cancel{(y+3)}} \cdot \dfrac{\cancel{7}\cancel{(y+3)}}{\cancel{(5+y)}(5+y)}$

$\dfrac{\cancel{a+4}}{4a} \cdot \dfrac{2\cancel{(a-4)}}{\cancel{(4+a)}} \cdot \dfrac{(a+2)\cancel{(a-2)}}{\underset{6}{12}\cancel{(2-a)}} \cdot \dfrac{a}{\cancel{4-a}}$

Ans. $\dfrac{y+1}{(y-3)(5+y)}$ or $\dfrac{y+1}{(y-3)(y+5)}$

Ans. $\dfrac{a(a+2)}{6}$

6. DIVIDING BY A FRACTION

Rule. **To divide by a number, multiply by its reciprocal.**

Thus, to divide 4 by $\dfrac{2}{3}$, multiply 4 by $\dfrac{3}{2}$.

Since the reciprocal of a fraction is found by interchanging its terms or "inverting the fractions," the rule may be stated as follows:

> **To divide by a fraction, invert the fraction and multiply.**

To Divide by a Fraction

Divide: a) $\dfrac{2}{3} \div 5$ | b) $\dfrac{9}{4} \div \dfrac{a}{3}$ | c) $\dfrac{14}{x} \div 2\dfrac{1}{3}$ | d) $\dfrac{a^2}{b^2} \div \dfrac{a}{b}$

Procedure: Solutions:

1. **Invert fraction which is divisor:**   Invert $\dfrac{5}{1}$ | Invert $\dfrac{a}{3}$ | $2\dfrac{1}{3} = \dfrac{7}{3}$. Invert $\dfrac{7}{3}$ | Invert $\dfrac{a}{b}$

2. **Multiply resulting fractions:** $\dfrac{2}{3} \cdot \dfrac{1}{5}$ | $\dfrac{9}{4} \cdot \dfrac{3}{a}$ | $\dfrac{14}{x} \cdot \dfrac{3}{7}$ | $\dfrac{a^2}{b^2} \cdot \dfrac{b}{a}$

Ans. $\dfrac{2}{15}$ | Ans. $\dfrac{27}{4a}$ | Ans. $\dfrac{6}{x}$ | Ans. $\dfrac{a}{b}$

6.1 Division Involving Fractions Having Monomial Terms

Divide:

a) $2\dfrac{3}{4} \div 22$

b) $\dfrac{8}{x^3} \div \dfrac{12}{x^2}$

c) $b^2 \div \dfrac{7}{b^3}$

d) $\dfrac{5y}{7} \cdot \dfrac{2x}{y} \div \dfrac{x^5}{42}$

Solutions:

a) $\overset{1}{\underset{2}{\cancel{\dfrac{11}{4}}}} \cdot \dfrac{1}{22}$

b) $\dfrac{\overset{2}{\cancel{8}}}{\underset{x}{\cancel{x^3}}} \cdot \dfrac{\overset{(1)}{\cancel{x^2}}}{\underset{3}{\cancel{12}}}$

c) $\dfrac{b^2}{1} \cdot \dfrac{b^3}{7}$

d) $\dfrac{\overset{1}{\cancel{5y}}}{\underset{1}{\cancel{7}}} \cdot \dfrac{\overset{(1)}{\cancel{2x}}}{\underset{1}{\cancel{y}}} \cdot \dfrac{\overset{6}{\cancel{42}}}{\underset{x^4}{\cancel{x^5}}}$

Ans. $\dfrac{1}{8}$

Ans. $\dfrac{2}{3x}$

Ans. $\dfrac{b^5}{7}$

Ans. $\dfrac{60}{x^4}$

6.2 Division Involving Fractions Having Polynomial Terms

Divide:

a) $\dfrac{a^2-100}{8} \div \dfrac{2a+20}{20}$ b) $\dfrac{5a^2}{b^2-36} \div \dfrac{25ab-25a}{b^2-7b+6}$ c) $\dfrac{4x^2-1}{9x-3x^2} \div \dfrac{2x^2-7x-4}{x^2-7x+12}$

Solutions:

a) $\dfrac{a^2-100}{8} \cdot \dfrac{20}{2a+20}$

$\dfrac{\overset{1}{\cancel{(a+10)}}(a-10)}{\underset{(2)}{\cancel{8}}} \cdot \dfrac{\overset{5}{\cancel{20}}}{2(a+10)}$

Ans. $\dfrac{5(a-10)}{4}$

b) $\dfrac{5a^2}{b^2-36} \cdot \dfrac{b^2-7b+6}{25ab-25a}$

$\dfrac{\overset{(1)\,a}{\cancel{5a^2}}}{(b+6)\cancel{(b-6)}} \cdot \dfrac{\overset{1}{\cancel{(b-6)}}\overset{1}{\cancel{(b-1)}}}{\underset{5(1)}{\cancel{25a}\cancel{(b-1)}}}$

Ans. $\dfrac{a}{5(b+6)}$

c) $\dfrac{4x^2-1}{9x-3x^2} \cdot \dfrac{x^2-7x+12}{2x^2-7x-4}$

$\dfrac{\overset{1}{\cancel{(2x+1)}}(2x-1)}{3x(3-x)} \cdot \dfrac{\overset{(-1)}{\cancel{(x-3)}}\overset{1}{\cancel{(x-4)}}}{\cancel{(2x+1)}\cancel{(x-4)}}$

Ans. $-\dfrac{2x-1}{3x}$ or $\dfrac{1-2x}{3x}$

7. ADDING OR SUBTRACTING FRACTIONS HAVING THE SAME DENOMINATOR

To Combine (Add or Subtract) Fractions Having the Same Denominator

Combine: a) $\dfrac{2a}{15} + \dfrac{7a}{15} - \dfrac{4a}{15}$ b) $\dfrac{5a}{3} - \dfrac{2a-9}{3}$ c) $\dfrac{7}{x-2} - \dfrac{5+x}{x-2}$

Procedure: Solutions:

1. Keep denominator and combine numerators.* $\dfrac{2a+7a-4a}{15}$ $\dfrac{5a-(2a-9)}{3}$ $\dfrac{7-(5+x)}{x-2}$

2. Reduce resulting fraction. $\dfrac{\overset{(1)}{\cancel{5a}}}{\underset{3}{\cancel{15}}}$ $\dfrac{3a+9}{3} = \dfrac{\overset{(1)}{\cancel{3}(a+3)}}{\underset{(1)}{\cancel{3}}}$ $\dfrac{\overset{-1}{\cancel{2-x}}}{\cancel{x-2}}$

Ans. $\dfrac{a}{3}$ Ans. $a+3$ Ans. -1

*Note. In combining numerators, enclose each polynomial numerator in parentheses preceded by the sign of its fraction.

7.1 Combining Fractions Having Same Monomial Denominator

Combine:

a) $2\dfrac{4}{5} + \dfrac{4}{5} - 1\dfrac{3}{5}$ b) $\dfrac{8}{3c} - \dfrac{1}{3c} + \dfrac{11}{3c}$ c) $\dfrac{5x}{8} - \dfrac{x-4}{8}$ d) $\dfrac{x+5}{3x} - \dfrac{1-x}{3x} - \dfrac{7x+4}{3x}$

Solutions:

a) $\dfrac{14+4-8}{5}$

$\dfrac{\overset{2}{\cancel{10}}}{\underset{1}{\cancel{5}}}$

Ans. 2

b) $\dfrac{8-1+11}{3c}$

$\dfrac{\overset{6}{\cancel{18}}}{\underset{(1)}{\cancel{3c}}}$

Ans. $\dfrac{6}{c}$

c) $\dfrac{5x-(x-4)}{8}$

$\dfrac{4x+4}{8} = \dfrac{\overset{1}{\cancel{4}(x+1)}}{\underset{2}{\cancel{8}}}$

Ans. $\dfrac{x+1}{2}$

d) $\dfrac{(x+5)-(1-x)-(7x+4)}{3x}$

$\dfrac{x+5-1+x-7x-4}{3x} = \dfrac{\overset{(1)}{-5\cancel{x}}}{3\cancel{x}}$

Ans. $-\dfrac{5}{3}$

7.2 Combining Fractions Having Same Polynomial Denominator

Combine:

a) $\dfrac{10x}{2x-6} - \dfrac{9x+3}{2x-6}$ b) $\dfrac{2b}{a-b} - \dfrac{2a}{a-b}$ c) $\dfrac{5}{x^2+3x-4} + \dfrac{7x-8}{x^2+3x-4} - \dfrac{3x+1}{x^2+3x-4}$

Solutions:

a) $\dfrac{10x-(9x+3)}{2x-6}$

$\dfrac{\overset{1}{\cancel{x-3}}}{2\cancel{(x-3)}}$

Ans. $\dfrac{1}{2}$

b) $\dfrac{2b-2a}{a-b}$

$\dfrac{\overset{(-1)}{2\cancel{(b-a)}}}{\cancel{a-b}}$

Ans. -2

c) $\dfrac{5+(7x-8)-(3x+1)}{x^2+3x-4}$

$\dfrac{4x-4}{x^2+3x-4}$ or $\dfrac{\overset{1}{4\cancel{(x-1)}}}{\cancel{(x-1)}(x+4)}$

Ans. $\dfrac{4}{x+4}$

8. ADDING OR SUBTRACTING FRACTIONS HAVING DIFFERENT DENOMINATORS

Least Common Denominator (L.C.D.)

The least common denominator of two or more fractions is the smallest number divisible without remainder by their denominators.

Thus, 12 is the **L.C.D.** of $\frac{1}{3}$ and $\frac{1}{4}$. Of the common denominators, 12, 24, 36, etc., the least or smallest is 12.

(Recall that the least common denominator of a set of fractions is the least common multiple of the denominators. Think of the common denominators as common multiples of the denominators and the L.C.D. as the least of the common denominators.)

To Find the L.C.D.

Rule 1. If no two denominators have a common factor, find the **L.C.D.** by multiplying all the denominators.

Thus, $3ax$ is the **L.C.D.** of $\frac{1}{3}$, $\frac{1}{a}$ and $\frac{1}{x}$.

Rule 2. If two of the denominators have a common factor, find the **L.C.D.** by multiplying the common factor by the remaining factors.

Thus, for $\frac{1}{3xy}$ and $\frac{1}{5xy}$, the **L.C.D.**, $15xy$, is obtained by multiplying the common factor, xy, by the remaining factors 3 and 5.

Rule 3. If there is a common literal factor with more than one exponent, use its greatest exponent in the **L.C.D.**

Thus, $3y^5$ is the **L.C.D.** of $\frac{1}{3y}$, $\frac{1}{y^2}$ and $\frac{1}{y^5}$.

To Combine (Add or Subtract) Fractions Having Different Denominators

Combine: a) $\frac{1}{3} + \frac{3}{4} - \frac{1}{12}$ b) $\frac{5}{x} + \frac{3}{y}$

Procedure:

Solutions:

1. Find the L.C.D.

2. Change each fraction to an equivalent fraction whose denominator is L.C.D.
   (*Note how each fraction is multiplied by 1.*)

3. Combine fractions having the same denominator and reduce, if necessary.

a)	b)
1. L.C.D. = 12	1. L.C.D. = xy
2. $\frac{1}{3}\cdot\frac{4}{4} + \frac{3}{4}\cdot\frac{3}{3} - \frac{1}{12}$	2. $\frac{5}{x}\cdot\frac{y}{y} + \frac{3}{y}\cdot\frac{x}{x}$
$\frac{4}{12} + \frac{9}{12} - \frac{1}{12}$	$\frac{5y}{xy} + \frac{3x}{xy}$
$\frac{12}{12}$	
3. 1 *Ans.*	3. $\frac{5y+3x}{xy}$ *Ans.*

8.1 Rule 1. Combining Fractions Whose Denominators Have No Common Factor

Combine: a) $\frac{2}{5} + \frac{3}{4}$ b) $\frac{3}{x} - \frac{3}{x+1}$ c) $r + 2 - \frac{4r-1}{2r}$

Procedure:

Solutions:

1. Find L.C.D. (Rule 1):

2. Change to equivalent fractions having same L.C.D.:

3. Combine fractions:

a)	b)	c)
L.C.D. = $(5)(4) = 20$	L.C.D. = $x(x+1)$	L.C.D. = $2r$
$\frac{2}{5}\cdot\frac{4}{4} + \frac{3}{4}\cdot\frac{5}{5}$	$\frac{3}{x}\cdot\frac{(x+1)}{(x+1)} - \frac{3}{(x+1)}\cdot\frac{x}{x}$	$\frac{(r+2)}{1}\cdot\frac{2r}{2r} - \frac{4r-1}{2r}$
$\frac{8}{20} + \frac{15}{20}$	$\frac{3x+3}{x(x+1)} - \frac{3x}{x(x+1)}$	$\frac{2r^2+4r}{2r} - \frac{4r-1}{2r}$
$\frac{23}{20}$ or $1\frac{3}{20}$ *Ans.*	$\frac{3}{x(x+1)}$ *Ans.*	$\frac{2r^2+1}{2r}$ *Ans.*

8.2 Rule 2. Combining Fractions Whose Denominators Have a Common Factor

Combine: $a)$ $\dfrac{5}{6} - \dfrac{1}{12} + \dfrac{3}{2}$ $b)$ $\dfrac{2}{5a} + \dfrac{7}{5a+5}$ $c)$ $\dfrac{a+4}{3a} - \dfrac{2-4a}{6a}$

Procedure:

1. Find L.C.D. (Rule 2).
2. Change to equivalent fractions having same L.C.D.
3. Combine fractions.

Solutions:

L.C.D. = 12	L.C.D. = $5a(a+1)$	L.C.D. = $6a$
$\dfrac{5}{6}\cdot\dfrac{2}{2} - \dfrac{1}{12} + \dfrac{3}{2}\cdot\dfrac{6}{6}$	$\dfrac{2}{5a}\cdot\dfrac{(a+1)}{(a+1)} + \dfrac{7}{5(a+1)}\cdot\dfrac{a}{a}$	$\dfrac{(a+4)}{3a}\cdot\dfrac{2}{2} - \dfrac{2-4a}{6a}$
$\dfrac{10}{12} - \dfrac{1}{12} + \dfrac{18}{12}$	$\dfrac{2a+2}{5a(a+1)} + \dfrac{7a}{5a(a+1)}$	$\dfrac{2a+8}{6a} - \dfrac{2-4a}{6a}$
$\dfrac{27}{12} = \dfrac{9}{4}$ *Ans.*	$\dfrac{9a+2}{5a(a+1)}$ *Ans.*	$\dfrac{6a+6}{6a} = \dfrac{a+1}{a}$ *Ans.*

8.3 Rule 3. Combining Fractions Whose L.C.D. Includes Base with the Greatest Exponent

Combine:

$a)$ $\dfrac{5}{x} + \dfrac{7}{x^2}$ $b)$ $\dfrac{3}{x^3} - \dfrac{2}{x^7} + \dfrac{1}{x^5}$ $c)$ $\dfrac{s^2}{9r^2} - \dfrac{s^3}{12r^3}$ $d)$ $\dfrac{2}{a^2b} + \dfrac{3}{ab^2}$

Solutions:

L.C.D. = x^2	L.C.D. = x^7	L.C.D. = $36r^3$	L.C.D. = a^2b^2
$\dfrac{5}{x}\cdot\dfrac{x}{x} + \dfrac{7}{x^2}$	$\dfrac{3}{x^3}\cdot\dfrac{x^4}{x^4} - \dfrac{2}{x^7} + \dfrac{1}{x^5}\cdot\dfrac{x^2}{x^2}$	$\dfrac{s^2}{9r^2}\cdot\dfrac{4r}{4r} - \dfrac{s^3}{12r^3}\cdot\dfrac{3}{3}$	$\dfrac{2}{a^2b}\cdot\dfrac{b}{b} + \dfrac{3}{ab^2}\cdot\dfrac{a}{a}$
$\dfrac{5x}{x^2} + \dfrac{7}{x^2}$	$\dfrac{3x^4}{x^7} - \dfrac{2}{x^7} + \dfrac{x^2}{x^7}$	$\dfrac{4rs^2}{36r^3} - \dfrac{3s^3}{36r^3}$	$\dfrac{2b}{a^2b^2} + \dfrac{3a}{a^2b^2}$
$\dfrac{5x+7}{x^2}$ *Ans.*	$\dfrac{3x^4+x^2-2}{x^7}$ *Ans.*	$\dfrac{4rs^2-3s^3}{36r^3}$ *Ans.*	$\dfrac{2b+3a}{a^2b^2}$ *Ans.*

8.4 Combining Fractions Having Binomial Denominators

Combine:

$a)$ $\dfrac{3x}{x-2} + \dfrac{5x}{x+2}$ $b)$ $\dfrac{3}{2y+4} - \dfrac{5}{3y+6}$ $c)$ $\dfrac{2a-3}{a^2-25} - \dfrac{7}{5a-25}$

Solutions (*factor denominators first*):

$a)$	$b)$ $\dfrac{3}{2(y+2)} - \dfrac{5}{3(y+2)}$	$c)$ $\dfrac{2a-3}{(a+5)(a-5)} - \dfrac{7}{5(a-5)}$
L.C.D. = $(x-2)(x+2)$	L.C.D. = $6(y+2)$	L.C.D. = $5(a+5)(a-5)$
$\dfrac{3x}{(x-2)}\cdot\dfrac{(x+2)}{(x+2)} + \dfrac{5x}{(x+2)}\cdot\dfrac{(x-2)}{(x-2)}$	$\dfrac{3}{2(y+2)}\cdot\dfrac{3}{3} - \dfrac{5}{3(y+2)}\cdot\dfrac{2}{2}$	$\dfrac{(2a-3)}{(a+5)(a-5)}\cdot\dfrac{5}{5} - \dfrac{7}{5(a-5)}\cdot\dfrac{(a+5)}{(a+5)}$
$\dfrac{3x^2+6x}{(x-2)(x+2)} + \dfrac{5x^2-10x}{(x+2)(x-2)}$	$\dfrac{9}{6(y+2)} - \dfrac{10}{6(y+2)}$	$\dfrac{10a-15}{5(a+5)(a-5)} - \dfrac{(7a+35)}{5(a+5)(a-5)}$
Ans. $\dfrac{8x^2-4x}{(x-2)(x+2)}$	*Ans.* $-\dfrac{1}{6(y+2)}$	*Ans.* $\dfrac{3a-50}{5(a+5)(a-5)}$

9. SIMPLIFYING COMPLEX FRACTIONS

A complex fraction is a fraction containing at least one other fraction within it.

Thus, $\dfrac{\frac{3}{4}}{2}$, $\dfrac{5}{\frac{2}{3}}$ and $\dfrac{x+\frac{1}{2}}{x-\frac{1}{4}}$ are complex fractions.

To Simplify a Complex Fraction: L.C.D.-Multiplication Method

Simplify: a) $\dfrac{\frac{2}{3}}{\frac{3}{4}}$ b) $\dfrac{\frac{1}{2}-\frac{1}{3}}{5}$ c) $\dfrac{x-\frac{1}{3}}{\frac{3}{5}+\frac{7}{10}}$

Procedure:

1. Find L.C.D. of fractions in complex fraction:

2. Multiply both numerator and denominator by L.C.D. and reduce, if necessary:

Solutions:

L.C.D. = 12   L.C.D. = 6   L.C.D. = 30

$\dfrac{\frac{2}{3}}{\frac{3}{4}}\cdot\dfrac{12}{12}$ $\dfrac{(\frac{1}{2}-\frac{1}{3})}{5}\cdot\dfrac{6}{6}$ $\dfrac{(x-\frac{1}{3})}{(\frac{3}{5}+\frac{7}{10})}\cdot\dfrac{30}{30}$

$\dfrac{8}{9}$ _Ans._ $\dfrac{3-2}{30}=\dfrac{1}{30}$ _Ans._ $\dfrac{30x-10}{18+21}=\dfrac{30x-10}{39}$ _Ans._

To Simplify a Complex Fraction: Combining-Division Method

Simplify: a) $\dfrac{\frac{1}{2}-\frac{1}{3}}{\frac{1}{2}+\frac{1}{3}}$ b) $\dfrac{x-\frac{1}{3}}{x+\frac{1}{3}}$ c) $\dfrac{\frac{x}{2}+\frac{x}{5}}{2x-\frac{3x}{10}}$ d) $\dfrac{1+\frac{2}{y}}{1-\frac{4}{y^2}}$

Procedure:

1. Combine terms of numerator.

2. Combine terms of denominator.

3. Divide new numerator by new denominator.

Solutions:

$\frac{1}{2}-\frac{1}{3}=\frac{1}{6}$ $x-\frac{1}{3}=\frac{3x-1}{3}$ $\frac{x}{2}+\frac{x}{5}=\frac{7x}{10}$ $1+\frac{2}{y}=\frac{y+2}{y}$

$\frac{1}{2}+\frac{1}{3}=\frac{5}{6}$ $x+\frac{1}{3}=\frac{3x+1}{3}$ $2x-\frac{3x}{10}=\frac{17x}{10}$ $1-\frac{4}{y^2}=\frac{y^2-4}{y^2}$

$\frac{1}{6}\div\frac{5}{6}$ $\frac{3x-1}{3}\div\frac{3x+1}{3}$ $\frac{7x}{10}\div\frac{17x}{10}$ $\frac{y+2}{y}\div\frac{y^2-4}{y^2}$

$\frac{1}{6}\cdot\frac{6}{5}$ $\frac{3x-1}{3}\cdot\frac{3}{3x+1}$ $\frac{7x}{10}\cdot\frac{10}{17x}$ $\frac{y+2}{y}\cdot\frac{y^2}{y^2-4}$

$\frac{1}{5}$ _Ans._ $\frac{3x-1}{3x+1}$ _Ans._ $\frac{7}{17}$ _Ans._ $\frac{y}{y-2}$ _Ans._

9.1 Simplifying Numerical Complex Fractions

Simplify:

a) $\dfrac{4-\frac{1}{3}}{5}$ b) $\dfrac{5+\frac{2}{5}}{7-\frac{1}{10}}$ c) $\dfrac{\frac{1}{2}-\frac{1}{4}}{\frac{3}{8}+\frac{1}{16}}$ d) $\dfrac{1-\frac{1}{6}+\frac{2}{3}}{\frac{2}{9}+3-\frac{1}{2}}$

L.C.D. = 3   **Division Method**   L.C.D. = 16   L.C.D. = 18

$\dfrac{(4-\frac{1}{3})}{5}\cdot\dfrac{3}{3}$ $\dfrac{27}{5}\div\dfrac{69}{10}$ $\dfrac{(\frac{1}{2}-\frac{1}{4})}{(\frac{3}{8}+\frac{1}{16})}\cdot\dfrac{16}{16}$ $\dfrac{(1-\frac{1}{6}+\frac{2}{3})}{(\frac{2}{9}+3-\frac{1}{2})}\cdot\dfrac{18}{18}$

$\dfrac{12-1}{15}$ $\dfrac{27}{5}\cdot\dfrac{10}{69}$ $\dfrac{8-4}{6+1}$ $\dfrac{18-3+12}{4+54-9}$

$\dfrac{11}{15}$ _Ans._ $\dfrac{18}{23}$ _Ans._ $\dfrac{4}{7}$ _Ans._ $\dfrac{27}{49}$ _Ans._

9.2 Simplifying Complex Fractions

Simplify:

a) $\dfrac{x-\frac{1}{2}}{4}$ b) $\dfrac{\frac{x}{3}-\frac{x}{5}}{\frac{1}{2}}$ c) $\dfrac{\frac{1}{x}+\frac{1}{x^2}}{\frac{4}{x^3}}$ d) $\dfrac{\frac{1}{2x}-\frac{4}{y}}{\frac{1}{x}+\frac{2}{3y}}$

L.C.D. = 2   **Division Method**   L.C.D. = x^3 L.C.D. = $6xy$

$\dfrac{(x-\frac{1}{2})}{4}\cdot\dfrac{2}{2}$ $\dfrac{2x}{15}\div\dfrac{1}{2}$ $\dfrac{(\frac{1}{x}+\frac{1}{x^2})}{(\frac{4}{x^3})}\cdot\dfrac{x^3}{x^3}$ $\dfrac{(\frac{1}{2x}-\frac{4}{y})}{(\frac{1}{x}+\frac{2}{3y})}\cdot\dfrac{6xy}{6xy}$

$\dfrac{2x-1}{8}$ _Ans._ $\dfrac{2x}{15}\cdot\dfrac{2}{1}=\dfrac{4x}{15}$ _Ans._ $\dfrac{x^2+x}{4}$ _Ans._ $\dfrac{3y-24x}{6y+4x}$ _Ans._

SUPPLEMENTARY PROBLEMS

1. Express each in fractional form: **(1.1 to 1.3)**

    a) $10 \div 19$ *d*) the ratio of 25 to 11   *g*) 3 of 8 equal portions of a pie

    b) $n \div (p+3)$ *e*) the ratio of 7¢ to a dime   *h*) 3 out of 8 equal pies

    c) 34 divided by x *f*) the quotient of $(r-7)$ and 30   *i*) the ratio of 1 sec. to 1 hr.

   Ans. a) $\frac{10}{19}$,   *b*) $\frac{n}{p+3}$,   *c*) $\frac{34}{x}$,   *d*) $\frac{25}{11}$,   *e*) $\frac{7}{10}$,   *f*) $\frac{r-7}{30}$,   *g*) $\frac{3}{8}$,   *h*) $\frac{3}{8}$,   *i*) $\frac{1}{3600}$

2. State the value of x when   **(1.4, 1.5)**

    a) $\frac{x}{10} = 0$ *Ans.* 0   *d*) $\frac{3x-12}{3x+12} = 0$ *Ans.* 4   *g*) $\frac{5}{x-10}$ is meaningless *Ans.* 10

    b) $\frac{x-3}{5} = 0$ *Ans.* 3   *e*) $\frac{3x+12}{3x-12} = 0$ *Ans.* -4 *h*) $\frac{x}{5x+20}$ is meaningless *Ans.* -4

    c) $\frac{2x+5}{7x} = 0$ *Ans.* $-2\frac{1}{2}$ *f*) $\frac{1}{3x}$ is meaningless *Ans.* 0   *i*) $\frac{2x+1}{2x-1}$ is meaningless *Ans.* $\frac{1}{2}$

3. Which rational expressions are polynomials?   **(1.6)**

    a) $\frac{y}{5}$,   *b*) $\frac{5}{y}$,   *c*) $\frac{y+5}{y}$,   *d*) $\frac{5}{y+5}$,   *e*) $\frac{y^2+5y}{5}$,   *f*) $\frac{y^2+5y}{y-5}$,   *g*) $\frac{y^2+5y+5}{5}$

   Ans. The only polynomials are (*a*), (*e*), and (*g*). Since a variable appears in the denominator of
       each, (*b*), (*c*), (*d*), and (*f*) are not polynomials.

4. In each, what restriction must be made on the replacement set of the variables?   **(1.7)**

    a) $\frac{x}{3}$ *c*) $\frac{x-3}{3}$ *e*) $\frac{x-3}{x+3}$ *g*) $\frac{y(y+3)}{x(x-3)}$ *i*) $\frac{(x-1)(y+3)}{(x+1)(y-3)}$

    b) $\frac{3}{x}$ *d*) $\frac{x+3}{x-3}$ *f*) $\frac{3}{xy}$ *h*) $\frac{x(y-3)}{y(x+3)}$

   Ans. a) none   *d*) $x \neq 3$ *g*) $x \neq 0$ and $x \neq 3$

         b) $x \neq 0$ *e*) $x \neq -3$ *h*) $y \neq 0$ and $x \neq -3$

         c) none   *f*) $x \neq 0$ and $y \neq 0$ *i*) $x \neq -1$ and $y \neq 3$

5. Change each to equivalent fractions by performing the operations indicated on its numerator and
   denominator (terms):   **(2.1, 2.2)**

    a) Multiply terms of $\frac{1}{2}$ by 5.   *d*) Divide terms of $\frac{10}{15}$ by 5.

    b) Multiply terms of $\frac{2}{3}$ by $5x$.   *e*) Divide terms of $\frac{3x}{6x^2}$ by $3x$.

    c) Multiply terms of $\frac{a}{7}$ by $(a+2)$.   *f*) Divide terms of $\frac{5(a-2)^2}{7(a-2)}$ by $(a-2)$.

   Ans. a) $\frac{5}{10}$,   *b*) $\frac{10x}{15x}$,   *c*) $\frac{a(a+2)}{7(a+2)} = \frac{a^2+2a}{7a+14}$,   *d*) $\frac{2}{3}$,   *e*) $\frac{1}{2x}$,   *f*) $\frac{5(a-2)}{7}$

6. Change $\frac{x}{5}$ to equivalent fractions by multiplying its terms by

    a) 6, *b*) y, *c*) x^2, *d*) $3x-2$, *e*) $a+b$.   **(2.1)**

   Ans. a) $\frac{6x}{30}$,   *b*) $\frac{xy}{5y}$,   *c*) $\frac{x^3}{5x^2}$,   *d*) $\frac{3x^2-2x}{15x-10}$,   *e*) $\frac{ax+bx}{5a+5b}$

7. Change $\frac{12a^2}{36a^3}$ to equivalent fractions by dividing its terms by

    a) 2, *b*) 12, *c*) $4a$, *d*) a^2, *e*) $12a^2$ **(2.2)**

   Ans. a) $\frac{6a^2}{18a^3}$,   *b*) $\frac{a^2}{3a^3}$,   *c*) $\frac{3a}{9a^2}$,   *d*) $\frac{12}{36a}$,   *e*) $\frac{1}{3a}$

8. Obtain each missing term: (2.3)

a) $\frac{3}{7} = \frac{(?)}{28}$ *Ans.* 12

b) $\frac{5}{9} = \frac{20}{(?)}$ *Ans.* 36

c) $\frac{7a}{8} = \frac{(?)}{8a}$ *Ans.* $7a^2$

d) $\frac{10}{x} = \frac{10ab}{(?)}$ *Ans.* abx

e) $\frac{2a}{3} = \frac{(?)}{30bc}$ *Ans.* $20abc$

f) $\frac{x+2}{3} = \frac{(?)}{3(x-2)}$ *Ans.* $x^2 - 4$

g) $\frac{7ac}{14cd} = \frac{a}{(?)}$ *Ans.* $2d$

h) $\frac{a^2 - b^2}{2a+2b} = \frac{(?)}{2}$ *Ans.* $a - b$

i) $\frac{24(a+2)}{36(a+2)^2} = \frac{(?)}{3(a+2)}$ *Ans.* 2

9. Supply the missing entry: (3.1)

a) $(\frac{3}{4})(\frac{4}{3}) = (?)$

b) $(\frac{8}{5})(?) = 1$

c) $(\frac{3}{7})(\frac{7}{3})(?)(\frac{2}{5}) = 1$

d) $(\frac{2}{x})(?) = 1$

e) $(\frac{7}{4})(\frac{4}{7}y) = (?)$

f) $(?)(\frac{6}{5}x) = x$

Ans. a) 1   b) $\frac{5}{8}$ c) $\frac{5}{2}$ d) $\frac{x}{2}$ e) y f) $\frac{5}{6}$

10. State the reciprocal of each: (3.2)

a) 10   *Ans.* $\frac{1}{10}$ or .1

b) .1   *Ans.* 10

c) 100   *Ans.* $\frac{1}{100}$ or .01

d) .01   *Ans.* 100

e) $\frac{2}{3}$ *Ans.* $\frac{3}{2}$ or $1\frac{1}{2}$ or 1.5

f) 1.5   *Ans.* $\frac{10}{15}$ or $\frac{2}{3}$

g) $\frac{10}{17}$ *Ans.* $\frac{17}{10}$ or 1.7

h) 2.7   *Ans.* $\frac{10}{27}$

i) $3\frac{1}{2}$ *Ans.* $\frac{2}{7}$

j) $\frac{3}{5}$ *Ans.* $\frac{5}{3}$ or $1\frac{2}{3}$

k) $2\frac{3}{5}$ *Ans.* $\frac{5}{13}$

l) 1.07   *Ans.* $\frac{100}{107}$

m) 2.007   *Ans.* $\frac{1000}{2007}$

11. Supply the missing entry: (3.3)

a) $(-\frac{3}{5})(?) = 1$ *Ans.* $-\frac{5}{3}$ or $-1\frac{2}{3}$

b) $(-100)(-.01) = (?)$ *Ans.* 1

c) $(-\frac{7}{5})(-\frac{5}{7})(-4) = (?)$ *Ans.* -4

d) $(-\frac{2}{x})(?) = 1$ *Ans.* $-\frac{x}{2}$

e) $(-\frac{9}{y})(-\frac{y}{9})(\frac{z}{2})(-\frac{2}{z}) = (?)$ *Ans.* -1

f) $\frac{1}{2}(-5)(-\frac{1}{5}) + 2(-\frac{3}{4})(-1\frac{1}{3}) = (?)$ *Ans.* $2\frac{1}{2}$

Note. In (d), assume $x \neq 0$; in (e), assume $y \neq 0$ and $z \neq 0$.

12. State the reciprocal of each: (3.4)

a) y, $y \neq 0$

b) $\frac{2}{z}$, $z \neq 0$

c) $\frac{5y}{x}$, $x \neq 0$ and $y \neq 0$

d) $\frac{1}{2}x$, $x \neq 0$

e) $.1y$, $y \neq 0$

f) $20\% y$, $y \neq 0$

g) $\frac{x+3}{x-3}$, $x \neq 3$ and -3

h) $\frac{y-3}{3x}$, $y \neq 3$ and $x \neq 0$

Ans. a) $\frac{1}{y}$ d) $\frac{2}{x}$ g) $\frac{x-3}{x+3}$

b) $\frac{z}{2}$ e) $\frac{10}{y}$ h) $\frac{3x}{y-3}$

c) $\frac{x}{5y}$ f) $\frac{5}{y}$

13. Show how to change each division to multiplication by using the reciprocal of a number: **(3.5)**

     a) $12 \div \frac{6}{7}$ c) $20y \div \frac{y}{x}$ e) $(3a - 6b) \div \frac{3}{2}$

     b) $\frac{6}{7} \div 12$ d) $3x^2 \div \frac{x}{y}$ f) $(x^3 + 8x^2 - 14x) \div \frac{x}{10}$

Ans. a) $12 \cdot \frac{7}{6} = 14$,   b) $\frac{6}{7} \cdot \frac{1}{12} = \frac{1}{14}$,   c) $20y\left(\frac{x}{y}\right) = 20x$,   d) $3x^2\left(\frac{y}{x}\right) = 3xy$,

     e) $\frac{2}{3}(3a - 6b) = 2a - 4b$,   f) $\frac{10}{x}(x^3 + 8x^2 - 14x) = 10x^2 + 80x - 140$

14. Solve for x, indicating each multiplier of both sides: **(3.6)**

     a) $\frac{5}{9}x = 35$ c) $1\frac{1}{3}x = 20$ e) $\frac{bx}{2} = 7b$

     b) $\frac{8}{3}x = 20$ d) $.3x = \frac{9}{5}$ f) $\frac{3x}{c} = 6c$

Ans. a) $M_{\frac{9}{5}}$, $x = 63$ c) $M_{\frac{3}{4}}$, $x = 15$ e) $M_{\frac{2}{b}}$, $x = 14$

     b) $M_{\frac{3}{8}}$, $x = 7\frac{1}{2}$ d) $M_{\frac{10}{3}}$, $x = 6$ f) $M_{\frac{c}{3}}$, $x = 2c^2$

15. Reduce to lowest terms:

                                                                    (4.1)

     a) $\frac{21}{35}$ b) $\frac{42}{24}$ c) $\frac{3ab}{9ac}$ d) $\frac{15d^2}{5d^3}$ e) $\frac{8g - 4h}{12g}$ f) $\frac{10rs}{5s^2 + 20s}$

Ans. a) $\frac{3}{5}$ b) $\frac{7}{4}$ c) $\frac{b}{3c}$ d) $\frac{3}{d}$ e) $\frac{2g - h}{3g}$ f) $\frac{2r}{s + 4}$

16. Reduce to lowest terms:

                                                                    (4.2)

     a) $\frac{5(x + 5)}{11(x + 5)}$ c) $\frac{3a - 3b}{6a - 6b}$ e) $\frac{(l - 5)^2}{8l - 40}$ g) $\frac{km + kn}{n^2 + nm}$

     b) $\frac{8ab(2c - 3)}{4ac(2c - 3)}$ d) $\frac{a^2 - 9}{7a + 21}$ f) $\frac{c^2 - d^2}{(c - d)^2}$ h) $\frac{cd + 5d}{5x + cx}$

Ans. a) $\frac{5}{11}$,   b) $\frac{2b}{c}$,   c) $\frac{1}{2}$,   d) $\frac{a - 3}{7}$,   e) $\frac{l - 5}{8}$,   f) $\frac{c + d}{c - d}$,   g) $\frac{k}{n}$,   h) $\frac{d}{x}$

17. Reduce to lowest terms:

                                                                    (4.3)

     a) $\frac{6 - x}{5x - 30}$ c) $\frac{y^2 - 4}{2a - ay}$ e) $\frac{1 - 2p}{2p^2 - p}$ g) $\frac{ac^2 - ad^2}{d^2 - cd}$

     b) $\frac{x^2 - 3x}{21 - 7x}$ d) $\frac{2b - 3ab}{9a^2 - 4}$ f) $\frac{3w - 3x}{2x^2 - 2w^2}$ h) $\frac{(r - s)^2}{s^2 - r^2}$

Ans. a) $-\frac{1}{5}$ c) $-\frac{y + 2}{a}$ e) $-\frac{1}{p}$ g) $-\frac{a(c + d)}{d}$

     b) $-\frac{x}{7}$ d) $-\frac{b}{3a + 2}$ f) $-\frac{3}{2(x + w)}$ h) $-\frac{r - s}{r + s}$ or $\frac{s - r}{s + r}$

18. Reduce to lowest terms:

                                                                    (4.4)

     a) $\frac{c^2 + 5c}{c^2 + 12c + 35}$ c) $\frac{4a^2 - b^2}{4a^2 - 4ab + b^2}$ e) $\frac{2x^2 - 2}{x^2 - 4x - 5}$ g) $\frac{2w^2 - 14w + 24}{12w^2 - 32w - 12}$

     b) $\frac{b^2 + 6b - 7}{b^2 - 49}$ d) $\frac{9 - 3s}{s^2 - 5s + 6}$ f) $\frac{y^2 + 8y + 12}{y^2 - 3y - 10}$ h) $\frac{2a^2 - 9a - 5}{6a^2 + 7a + 2}$

Ans. a) $\frac{c}{c + 7}$ c) $\frac{2a + b}{2a - b}$ e) $\frac{2(x - 1)}{x - 5}$ g) $\frac{w - 4}{2(3w + 1)}$

     b) $\frac{b - 1}{b - 7}$ d) $-\frac{3}{s - 2}$ f) $\frac{y + 6}{y - 5}$ h) $\frac{a - 5}{3a + 2}$

19. Multiply: (5.1, 5.2)

a) $\frac{3}{4} \times 5$ c) $\frac{3}{4} \times \frac{28}{5}$ e) $\frac{3}{5} \times \frac{5}{8} \times \frac{8}{3}$

b) $\frac{2}{5} \times \frac{3}{7} \times 11$ d) $\frac{20}{6} \times \frac{9}{4} \times \frac{12}{13}$ f) $\frac{2}{9} \times \frac{3}{4} \times \frac{3}{8} \times \frac{16}{17}$

Ans. a) $\frac{15}{4}$,   b) $\frac{66}{35}$,   c) $\frac{21}{5}$,   d) $\frac{90}{13}$,   e) 1,   f) $\frac{1}{17}$

20. Multiply: (5.1, 5.2)

a) $\frac{3b}{c} \cdot \frac{b^2}{5}$ e) $\frac{a+b}{7} \cdot \frac{a-b}{2}$ i) $\frac{15b+15c}{16x^2-9} \cdot \frac{8x+6}{5b+5c}$

b) $7ab \cdot \frac{a}{2} \cdot \frac{3}{c}$ f) $\frac{a+b}{5} \cdot \frac{15}{11a+11b}$ j) $\frac{(v+w)^2}{bv+bw} \cdot \frac{b^2}{3v+3w}$

c) $\frac{x^2}{y} \cdot \frac{3}{y^2} \cdot x^3$ g) $\frac{x^2}{y} \cdot \frac{y^2}{3} \cdot \frac{1}{x^3}$ k) $\frac{r^4-s^4}{5r+5s} \cdot \frac{25}{2r^2+2s^2}$

d) $\frac{m+n}{3} \cdot \frac{m+n}{mn}$ h) $\frac{6r+12s}{2rs-4r} \cdot \frac{7s-14}{3r+6s}$ l) $\frac{5ax+10a}{ab-10b} \cdot \frac{200-2a^2}{ax+2a}$

Ans. a) $\frac{3b^3}{5c}$ c) $\frac{3x^5}{y^3}$ e) $\frac{a^2-b^2}{14} \cdot$ g) $\frac{y}{3x}$ i) $\frac{6}{4x-3}$ k) $\frac{5(r-s)}{2}$

b) $\frac{21a^2b}{2c}$ d) $\frac{(m+n)^2}{3mn}$ f) $\frac{3}{11}$ h) $\frac{7}{r}$ j) $\frac{b}{3}$ l) $-\frac{10(10+a)}{b}$

21. Multiply: (5.3)

a) $\frac{a^2-4}{(a-2)^2} \cdot \frac{a^2-9a+14}{a^3+2a^2}$ c) $\frac{2c+b}{b^2} \cdot \frac{3b^2-3bc}{bc+2c^2} \cdot \frac{5bc-10c^2}{b^2-3bc+2c^2}$

b) $\frac{(x+3)^2}{x^2-7x-30} \cdot \frac{7x^2-700}{x^3+3x^2}$ d) $\frac{r^2-s^2}{3-r} \cdot \frac{r^2+3rs}{4s-4r} \cdot \frac{rs-3s}{r^2+4rs+3s^2}$

Ans. a) $\frac{a-7}{a^2}$ b) $\frac{7(x+10)}{x^2}$ c) $\frac{15}{b}$ d) $\frac{rs}{4}$

22. Divide: (6.1)

a) $10 \div \frac{2}{3}$ c) $3x \div \frac{12x}{7}$ e) $\frac{ab}{4} \div \frac{b^2}{6}$ g) $\frac{r^2s}{16t} \div \frac{rs^2}{8t^2}$

b) $\frac{3}{4} \div 36$ d) $\frac{5}{y} \div \frac{7}{y}$ f) $\frac{x}{2} \div \frac{ax}{6}$ h) $\frac{2x}{y} \div \frac{10y}{3x}$

Ans. a) 15   b) $\frac{1}{48}$ c) $\frac{7}{4}$ d) $\frac{5}{7}$ e) $\frac{3a}{2b}$ f) $\frac{3}{a}$ g) $\frac{rt}{2s}$ h) $\frac{3x^2}{5y^2}$

23. Divide: (6.2)

a) $\frac{3x}{x+2} \div \frac{5x}{x+2}$ e) $\frac{d^2-1}{3d+9} \div \frac{d^2h-h}{dh+3h}$ i) $\frac{a^3-64a}{2a^2+16a} \div \frac{a^2-9a+8}{a^2+4a-5}$

b) $\frac{2(y+3)}{7} \div \frac{8(y+3)}{63}$ f) $\frac{c^2-cd}{3c^2+3cd} \div \frac{7c-7d}{c^2-d^2}$ j) $\frac{a^3-ab^2}{6a+6b} \div \frac{a^2-4ab+3b^2}{12a-36b}$

c) $\frac{2a-10}{3b-21} \div \frac{a-5}{4b-28}$ g) $\frac{2x^2+2y^2}{x^2-4y^2} \div \frac{x^2+y^2}{x+2y}$ k) $\frac{3p+p^2}{12+3p} \div \frac{9p-p^3}{12-p-p^2}$

d) $\frac{3(a^2+5)}{b(a^2-3)} \div \frac{18(a^2+5)}{7(a^2-3)}$ h) $\frac{s^2+st}{rs-st} \div \frac{s^2-t^2}{r^2-t^2}$ l) $\frac{c^2+16c+64}{2c^2-128} \div \frac{3c^2+30c+48}{c^2-6c-16}$

Ans. a) $\frac{3}{5}$ c) $\frac{8}{3}$ e) $\frac{1}{3}$ g) $\frac{2}{x-2y}$ i) $\frac{a+5}{2}$ k) $\frac{1}{3}$

b) $\frac{9}{4}$ d) $\frac{7}{6b}$ f) $\frac{c-d}{21}$ h) $\frac{r+t}{s-t}$ j) $2a$ l) $\frac{1}{6}$

24. Combine: **(7.1)**

$a)\ \dfrac{4}{9} + \dfrac{2}{9}$ 　　　　　 $d)\ \dfrac{3}{5} + \dfrac{4}{5} - \dfrac{1}{5}$ 　　　　　 $g)\ 3\dfrac{5}{12} + 2\dfrac{3}{12}$

$b)\ \dfrac{10}{13} - \dfrac{7}{13}$ 　　　　 $e)\ \dfrac{6}{15} - \dfrac{2}{15} - \dfrac{2}{15}$ 　　　 $h)\ 10\dfrac{2}{7} - 8\dfrac{1}{7}$

$c)\ \dfrac{3}{11} - \dfrac{8}{11}$ 　　　　 $f)\ \dfrac{3}{8} - \dfrac{1}{8} + \dfrac{7}{8}$ 　　　　 $i)\ \dfrac{5}{16} + \dfrac{15}{16} - \dfrac{7}{16} + \dfrac{3}{16}$

$Ans.\ a)\ \dfrac{6}{9} = \dfrac{2}{3}$ 　 $b)\ \dfrac{3}{13}$ 　 $c)\ -\dfrac{5}{11}$ 　 $d)\ \dfrac{6}{5}$ 　 $e)\ \dfrac{2}{15}$ 　 $f)\ \dfrac{9}{8}$ 　 $g)\ 5\dfrac{2}{3}$ 　 $h)\ 2\dfrac{1}{7}$ 　 $i)\ 1$

25. Combine: **(7.1)**

$a)\ \dfrac{x}{3} + \dfrac{5x}{3}$ 　　　　 $c)\ \dfrac{x^2}{6} + \dfrac{x^2}{6}$ 　　　　 $e)\ \dfrac{17}{3s} - \dfrac{14}{3s}$ 　　　 $g)\ \dfrac{5x}{y} + \dfrac{x}{y} - \dfrac{3}{y}$

$b)\ \dfrac{7y}{5} - \dfrac{3y}{5}$ 　　　　 $d)\ \dfrac{10}{r} + \dfrac{3}{r}$ 　　　　 $f)\ \dfrac{5a}{b^2} - \dfrac{3a}{b^2}$ 　　　 $h)\ \dfrac{4p}{3q} - \dfrac{p}{3q} + \dfrac{8}{3q} - \dfrac{2}{3q}$

$Ans.\ a)\ \dfrac{6x}{3} = 2x$ 　 $b)\ \dfrac{4y}{5}$ 　 $c)\ \dfrac{x^2}{3}$ 　 $d)\ \dfrac{13}{r}$ 　 $e)\ \dfrac{1}{s}$ 　 $f)\ \dfrac{2a}{b^2}$ 　 $g)\ \dfrac{6x-3}{y}$ 　 $h)\ \dfrac{p+2}{q}$

26. Combine: **(7.1)**

$a)\ \dfrac{a+2}{8} + \dfrac{7a-2}{8}$ 　　　 $c)\ \dfrac{2y-7}{5} - \dfrac{2y-10}{5}$ 　　　 $e)\ \dfrac{b+8}{5a} + \dfrac{4b+7}{5a}$

$b)\ \dfrac{5x}{7} - \dfrac{5x-35}{7}$ 　　　 $d)\ \dfrac{8}{x} + \dfrac{2}{x} - \dfrac{3x+10}{x}$ 　　 $f)\ \dfrac{x+3}{2x^2} + \dfrac{3x-3}{2x^2}$

$Ans.\ a)\ \dfrac{8a}{8} = a$ 　 $b)\ \dfrac{35}{7} = 5$ 　 $c)\ \dfrac{3}{5}$ 　 $d)\ -\dfrac{3x}{x} = -3$ 　 $e)\ \dfrac{5b+15}{5a} = \dfrac{b+3}{a}$ 　 $f)\ \dfrac{4x}{2x^2} = \dfrac{2}{x}$

27. Combine: **(7.2)**

$a)\ \dfrac{5}{x+3} + \dfrac{x-2}{x+3}$ 　　　 $d)\ \dfrac{2}{c+3} - \dfrac{c+5}{c+3}$ 　　　 $g)\ \dfrac{3a}{2(a+b)} + \dfrac{a+4b}{2(a+b)}$

$b)\ \dfrac{2x}{x+y} + \dfrac{2y}{x+y}$ 　　　 $e)\ \dfrac{7}{d^2+7} + \dfrac{d^2}{d^2+7}$ 　　 $h)\ \dfrac{7a-2}{a(b+c)} - \dfrac{a-2}{a(b+c)}$

$c)\ \dfrac{5p}{p-q} - \dfrac{5q}{p-q}$ 　　　 $f)\ \dfrac{6}{2x-3} - \dfrac{4x}{2x-3}$ 　　　 $i)\ \dfrac{3x}{x^2-4} - \dfrac{x+4}{x^2-4}$

$Ans.\ a)\ \dfrac{x+3}{x+3} = 1$ 　 $c)\ \dfrac{5p-5q}{p-q} = 5$ 　 $e)\ 1$ 　 $g)\ \dfrac{4a+4b}{2(a+b)} = 2$

$\qquad\qquad\qquad\qquad\qquad\qquad\qquad\qquad\qquad\qquad\qquad\qquad i)\ \dfrac{2x-4}{x^2-4} = \dfrac{2}{x+2}$

$b)\ \dfrac{2x+2y}{x+y} = 2$ 　 $d)\ \dfrac{-c-3}{c+3} = -1$ 　 $f)\ \dfrac{6-4x}{2x-3} = -2$ 　 $h)\ \dfrac{6a}{a(b+c)} = \dfrac{6}{b+c}$

28. Combine: **(8.1)**

$a)\ \dfrac{2}{3} + \dfrac{1}{2}$ 　　 $b)\ \dfrac{3}{4} - \dfrac{1}{5}$ 　　 $c)\ \dfrac{a}{7} - \dfrac{b}{2}$ 　　 $d)\ \dfrac{4}{3x} + \dfrac{5}{2y}$ 　　 $e)\ \dfrac{a}{b} + \dfrac{b}{a}$

$Ans.\ a)\ \dfrac{7}{6}$ 　　 $b)\ \dfrac{11}{20}$ 　　 $c)\ \dfrac{2a-7b}{14}$ 　　 $d)\ \dfrac{8y+15x}{6xy}$ 　　 $e)\ \dfrac{a^2+b^2}{ab}$

29. Combine: **(8.1)**

$a)\ \dfrac{4}{5} + \dfrac{2}{x+3}$ 　　　 $c)\ \dfrac{8c}{3c+1} - \dfrac{1}{2}$ 　　　 $e)\ \dfrac{x}{2-x} - \dfrac{x}{2+x}$

$b)\ \dfrac{3}{a} + \dfrac{2}{5-a}$ 　　　 $d)\ \dfrac{2}{y+1} + \dfrac{3}{y-1}$ 　　　 $f)\ \dfrac{4}{a+5} + \dfrac{2}{a+1}$

$Ans.\ a)\ \dfrac{4x+22}{5(x+3)}$ 　 $b)\ \dfrac{15-a}{a(5-a)}$ 　 $c)\ \dfrac{13c-1}{2(3c+1)}$ 　 $d)\ \dfrac{5y+1}{y^2-1}$ 　 $e)\ \dfrac{2x^2}{4-x^2}$ 　 $f)\ \dfrac{6a+14}{(a+5)(a+1)}$

30. Combine: (8.2)

a) $\dfrac{1}{3} + \dfrac{3}{4} + \dfrac{1}{6}$ 　　c) $\dfrac{11}{10} - \dfrac{2}{5} + \dfrac{1}{2}$ 　　e) $\dfrac{5x}{8} - \dfrac{x}{12}$ 　　g) $\dfrac{p}{8} + \dfrac{q}{3} - \dfrac{r}{6}$

b) $\dfrac{7}{8} - \dfrac{1}{2} - \dfrac{1}{4}$ 　　d) $\dfrac{a}{3} - \dfrac{a}{12}$ 　　f) $\dfrac{c}{6} + \dfrac{2c}{9}$ 　　h) $\dfrac{4}{3x} + \dfrac{3}{2x} + \dfrac{1}{6x}$

Ans. a) $\dfrac{5}{4}$ 　b) $\dfrac{1}{8}$ 　c) $\dfrac{6}{5}$ 　d) $\dfrac{a}{4}$ 　e) $\dfrac{13x}{24}$ 　f) $\dfrac{7c}{18}$ 　g) $\dfrac{3p+8q-4r}{24}$ 　h) $\dfrac{3}{x}$

31. Combine: (8.3)

a) $\dfrac{3}{a} + \dfrac{4}{a^2}$ 　　d) $\dfrac{1}{3} + \dfrac{2}{x} + \dfrac{1}{x^2}$ 　　g) $\dfrac{8}{r^2s} + \dfrac{4}{rs^2}$

b) $\dfrac{5}{b^2} - \dfrac{2}{b}$ 　　e) $\dfrac{2}{x} - \dfrac{5}{x^2} + \dfrac{3}{x^3}$ 　　h) $\dfrac{10}{a^2b^2} - \dfrac{4}{ab^2} + \dfrac{5}{a^2b}$

c) $\dfrac{7}{2b} + \dfrac{2}{3b^2}$ 　　f) $\dfrac{1}{2x^3} + \dfrac{3}{x^2} - \dfrac{7}{5x}$ 　　i) $\dfrac{1}{a^2b^2} + \dfrac{3}{a^2} + \dfrac{2}{b^2}$

Ans. a) $\dfrac{3a+4}{a^2}$ 　b) $\dfrac{5-2b}{b^2}$ 　c) $\dfrac{21b+4}{6b^2}$ 　d) $\dfrac{x^2+6x+3}{3x^2}$ 　e) $\dfrac{2x^2-5x+3}{x^3}$ 　f) $\dfrac{5+30x-14x^2}{10x^3}$

g) $\dfrac{8s+4r}{r^2s^2}$ 　h) $\dfrac{10-4a+5b}{a^2b^2}$ 　i) $\dfrac{1+3b^2+2a^2}{a^2b^2}$

32. Combine: (8.4)

a) $\dfrac{7}{2} - \dfrac{8}{h+3}$ 　　d) $\dfrac{2}{p+2} - \dfrac{2}{p+3}$ 　　g) $\dfrac{4x}{x^2-36} - \dfrac{4}{x+6}$

b) $\dfrac{4a}{3b+6} - \dfrac{a}{b+2}$ 　　e) $\dfrac{3a}{a+2} + \dfrac{a}{a-2}$ 　　h) $\dfrac{8}{7-y} - \dfrac{8y}{49-y^2}$

c) $\dfrac{10}{x^2+x} + \dfrac{2}{3x^2+3x}$ 　　f) $\dfrac{2}{3x+3y} - \dfrac{3}{5x+5y}$ 　　i) $\dfrac{3t^2}{9t^2-16s^2} - \dfrac{t}{3t+4s}$

Ans. a) $\dfrac{7h+5}{2(h+3)}$ 　b) $\dfrac{a}{3b+6}$ 　c) $\dfrac{32}{3(x^2+x)}$ 　d) $\dfrac{2}{(p+2)(p+3)}$ 　e) $\dfrac{4a^2-4a}{a^2-4}$ 　f) $\dfrac{1}{15(x+y)}$

g) $\dfrac{24}{x^2-36}$ 　h) $\dfrac{56}{49-y^2}$ 　i) $\dfrac{4st}{9t^2-16s^2}$

33. Simplify: (9.1)

a) $\dfrac{5+\frac{2}{3}}{2}$ 　　c) $\dfrac{\frac{1}{4}+\frac{1}{3}}{2}$ 　　e) $\dfrac{\frac{3}{14}-\frac{2}{7}}{5}$ 　　g) $\dfrac{2+\frac{1}{5}+\frac{3}{4}}{10}$

b) $\dfrac{4+\frac{1}{3}}{4-\frac{1}{3}}$ 　　d) $\dfrac{5}{\frac{1}{2}-\frac{1}{4}}$ 　　f) $\dfrac{\frac{1}{8}+\frac{5}{16}}{\frac{7}{12}}$ 　　h) $\dfrac{\frac{4}{5}-\frac{1}{6}}{\frac{4}{5}+\frac{1}{3}}$

Ans. a) $\dfrac{17}{6}$ 　b) $\dfrac{13}{11}$ 　c) $\dfrac{7}{24}$ 　d) 20 　e) $-\dfrac{1}{70}$ 　f) $\dfrac{3}{4}$ 　g) $\dfrac{59}{200}$ 　h) $\dfrac{19}{34}$

34. Simplify: (9.2)

a) $\dfrac{y+\frac{1}{3}}{2}$ 　　c) $\dfrac{5p+2}{\frac{2}{3}}$ 　　e) $\dfrac{5h}{\frac{1}{2}-\frac{1}{5}}$ 　　g) $\dfrac{\frac{3}{x}+\frac{1}{6x}}{\frac{7}{3x}}$

b) $\dfrac{2a-1}{\frac{1}{2}}$ 　　d) $\dfrac{\frac{x}{4}-\frac{2x}{9}}{3}$ 　　f) $\dfrac{\frac{r}{4}}{\frac{7}{8}-\frac{r}{2}}$ 　　h) $\dfrac{\frac{a}{x}+\frac{x}{a}}{\frac{a}{x}-\frac{x}{a}}$

Ans. a) $\dfrac{3y+1}{6}$ 　b) $4a-2$ 　c) $\dfrac{15p+6}{2}$ 　d) $\dfrac{x}{108}$ 　e) $\dfrac{50h}{3}$ 　f) $\dfrac{2r}{7-4r}$ 　g) $\dfrac{19}{14}$ 　h) $\dfrac{a^2+x^2}{a^2-x^2}$

Chapter 12

Roots and Radicals

1. UNDERSTANDING ROOTS AND RADICALS

If the length of a side of a square is 4, then its area is $4 \cdot 4$, which is 4^2 or 16. Since $4 \cdot 4 = 16$, then 4 is **one of two equal factors** of 16. Since $16 = 4^2$, we call 16, "the square of 4," or "4-squared." Furthermore, 4 is called, "a square root of 16," written "$4 = \sqrt{16}$."

However, 16 is also the square of (-4); that is, $(-4)^2 = 16$. Hence, a positive number such as 16 has two different square roots, one positive and the other negative.

Definition of Square Root

The square root of a positive number is one of its two equal factors.

Thus, +5 is a square root of 25 since $(+5)(+5) = 25$.

Also, −5 is another square root of 25 since $(-5)(-5) = 25$.

Rule 1. A positive number has two square roots which are **opposites** of each other (same absolute value but unlike signs). One square root is positive, the other negative.

Thus, +10 and −10 are the two square roots of 100.

To indicate both square roots, the symbol ±, which combines + and −, may be used.

Thus, the square roots of 49, +7 and −7, may be written together as ±7.

Read "±7" as "plus or minus 7."

The principal square root of a positive number is its positive square root.

Thus, the principal square root of 36 is +6.

The principal square root of a positive number a is indicated by the symbol $\sqrt{a}$. (The radical sign, $\sqrt{}$, is a modified form of the letter r, the initial of the Latin word **radix**, meaning root.)

Thus, 4 = the principal square root of $16 = \sqrt{16}$.

The negative square root of a positive number a is indicated by the symbol, $-\sqrt{a}$.

Thus, −4 = the negative square root of $16 = -\sqrt{16}$.

The number 0 has just one square root, 0. We write $\sqrt{0} = 0$.

Radical, Radical Sign, Radicand, Index

(1) **A radical** is an indicated root of a number or expression.

Thus, $\sqrt{5}$, $\sqrt[3]{8x}$ and $\sqrt[4]{7x^3}$ are radicals.

(2) The symbols $\sqrt{}$, $\sqrt[3]{}$ and $\sqrt[4]{}$ are **radical signs**.

(3) **The radicand** is the number or expression under the radical sign.

Thus, 80 is the radicand of $\sqrt[3]{80}$ or $\sqrt[4]{80}$.

(4) **The index of a root** is the small number written above and to the left of the radical sign, $\sqrt{}$. The index indicates which root is to be taken. In square roots, the index, 2, is not indicated but understood.

Thus, $\sqrt[3]{8}$ indicates the 3rd root or cube root of 8.

Rule 2. Squaring a Square Root

If a is positive or 0, then $(\sqrt{a})^2 = a$

Thus, $(\sqrt{75})^2 = 75$ and $(\sqrt{0})^2 = 0$.

By definition, the square root of a positive number is one of its two equal factors. Hence, $\sqrt{75}\ \sqrt{75} = 75$; that is $(\sqrt{75})^2 = 75$

Rule 3. Finding the Square Root of a Square

If a is a real number, $\sqrt{a^2} =$ the absolute value of a, or $|a|$.

Thus, $\sqrt{(-5)^2} = \sqrt{25} = 5$, and indeed $5 = |-5|$.

Square Root of a Negative Number

Rule 4. The square root of a negative number is **not** a real number.

Thus, $\sqrt{-4}$ and $\sqrt{-25}$ are not real numbers. There is no real number, positive or negative, which when squared, is -4 or -25.

Numbers such as $\sqrt{-1}$, $\sqrt{-4}$ and $\sqrt{-25}$ are called imaginary numbers and belong to a set of numbers called complex numbers. The name "imaginary number" was given to such numbers before it was realized that these numbers are of the greatest importance in science, engineering, and mathematics.

Cube Root of a Positive or a Negative Number

Definition of a Cube Root

The cube root of a real number is one of its three equal factors.

Thus, since $3\cdot 3\cdot 3 = 27$, then 3 is a cube root of 27, written $3 = \sqrt[3]{27}$. Also, since $(-3)(-3)(-3) = -27$, then (-3) is a cube root of -27, writen $-3 = \sqrt[3]{-27}$.

In general, **a negative number is a cube root of a negative number.**

It can be shown that a nonzero real number has three cube roots, only one of which is a real number. The other two cube roots are not real numbers.

1.1 Rule 1: A positive number has two square roots which are opposites of each other.

State the square roots of each, if each variable is a real number.

a) $25x^2$ b) $\dfrac{x^2}{25}$ c) x^4 d) $81a^2b^2$ e) $\dfrac{49}{64}c^6$ f) $\dfrac{9a^2}{16b^2}$

Ans. a) $\pm 5x$ b) $\pm\dfrac{x}{5}$ c) $\pm x^2$ d) $\pm 9ab$ e) $\pm\dfrac{7}{8}c^3$ f) $\pm\dfrac{3a}{4b}$

1.2 Rule 2: If a is positive or 0, then $(\sqrt{a})^2 = a$. (Squaring a Square Root)

State the equivalent of each without the radical sign, if each radicand is nonnegative:

a) $(\sqrt{3})^2$ b) $(\sqrt{3333})^2$ c) $(\sqrt{y})^2$ d) $(\sqrt{3x})^2$ e) $(\sqrt{5x+3})^2$ f) $(5\sqrt{2x})^2$

Ans. a) 3   b) 3333   c) y d) $3x$ e) $5x + 3$ f) $25(2x) = 50x$

1.3 Principal Square Root of a Positive Number

Find each principal (positive) square root:

a) $\sqrt{36}$ b) $\sqrt{3600}$ c) $\sqrt{.36}$ d) $\sqrt{.0036}$ e) $\sqrt{\dfrac{36}{49}}$ f) $\sqrt{2\dfrac{1}{4}}$

Ans. a) 6   b) 60   c) .6   d) .06   e) $\dfrac{6}{7}$ f) $\sqrt{\dfrac{9}{4}} = \dfrac{3}{2}$

1.4 Evaluating an Expression Containing Square Roots

Find the value of

a) $3\sqrt{4} + \sqrt{25} - 2\sqrt{9}$ b) $\sqrt{\dfrac{25}{9}} + \sqrt{\dfrac{64}{9}}$ c) $4\sqrt{\dfrac{81}{4}}$ d) $\dfrac{1}{3}\sqrt{36} + \dfrac{2}{5}\sqrt{100}$

Solutions:

a) $3(2) + 5 - 2(3)$ b) $\dfrac{5}{3} + \dfrac{8}{3}$ c) $4\left(\dfrac{9}{2}\right)$ d) $\dfrac{1}{3}(6) + \dfrac{2}{5}(10)$

Ans. 5   *Ans.* $\dfrac{13}{3}$ *Ans.* 18   *Ans.* 6

1.5 Rule 3: If a is a real number, $\sqrt{a^2} = |a|$. (Finding the Square Root of a Square)

State the equivalent of each without the radical sign if each variable is a real number.

a) $\sqrt{x^2}$ c) $\sqrt{y^2z^2}$ e) $\sqrt{(t-1)^2}$

b) $\sqrt{x^4}$ d) $\sqrt{a^4b^2}$ f) $\sqrt{1.44x^2}$ g) $\sqrt{\dfrac{x^2}{100}}$ h) $-\sqrt{\dfrac{81}{r^2}}$ i) $-\sqrt{\dfrac{p^8}{q^4}}$

Ans. a) $|x|$ d) $|a^2b| = a^2|b|$ g) $\dfrac{|x|}{10}$ i) $-\dfrac{p^4}{q^2}$

     b) x^2 (See Note.)   e) $|t-1|$

     c) $|yz|$ f) $1.2|x|$ h) $-\dfrac{9}{|r|}$

Note. In (b), $\sqrt{x^4} = \sqrt{(x^2)^2}$. Using rule 3, $\sqrt{(x^2)^2} = |x^2|$. However, if x is a real number, then x^2 must be 0 or positive. Hence, the absolute value sign is unnecessary. *Ans.* x^2

1.6 Real and Nonreal Roots

State the value of each real root:

a) $-\sqrt{400}$ b) $\sqrt{-400}$ c) $\sqrt[3]{8}$ d) $\sqrt[3]{-8}$ e) $-\sqrt[3]{-8}$ f) $-\sqrt{-64}$ g) $-\sqrt[3]{-64}$ h) $-\sqrt[3]{64}$

Ans. a) -20 b) not real   c) 2   d) -2 e) $-(-2) = 2$ f) not real   g) $-(-4) = 4$ h) -4

2. UNDERSTANDING RATIONAL AND IRRATIONAL NUMBERS

Understanding Rational Numbers

Definition:

A **rational number** is a number expressible as a fraction whose numerator is an integer and whose denominator is a nonzero integer.

Hence, if Q represents the set of rational numbers, then

$Q = \{$Numbers expressible as $\dfrac{a}{b}$ when a and b are integers and $b \neq 0\}$.

Thus, $\dfrac{3}{7}$, $-\dfrac{3}{7}$, 3 or $\dfrac{3}{1}$, $1\dfrac{2}{3}$ or $\dfrac{5}{3}$, and .1 or $\dfrac{1}{10}$ are all rational numbers.

(Think of a rational number as a **ratio**nal number.)

Zero and Rational Numbers

Zero can be the numerator of a fraction whose denominator is not zero. Such rational numbers have a value of 0.

Thus, $\dfrac{0}{1}$ and $\dfrac{0}{5}$ are rational numbers having a value of 0.

Zero cannot be used as the denominator of a fraction under any circumstances.

Why a Rational Number Cannot Have a Zero Denominator

If there is an answer when an integer such as 8 is divided by 0, the product of this answer and 0 must be 8; that is, if $\dfrac{8}{0} = n$, then $n \cdot 0 = 8$. There can be no answer since any number multiplied by 0 is 0.

If there is an answer when 0 is divided by 0, the product of this answer and 0 must be 0; that is, if $\frac{0}{0} = n$, then $n \cdot 0 = 0$. Here, the answer can be any number since any number multiplied by 0 is 0.

Hence, dividing by 0 either leads to no answer or to any answer. The only conclusion is that division has no meaning and is never permissible. Therefore, a rational number may never have a zero denominator.

Using a Number Line to Find the Graphs of Rational Numbers

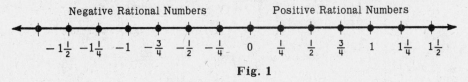

Fig. 1

The markings on the number line, Fig. 1, are like those on a ruler whose inches are divided into fourths. Each of the numbers shown are rational numbers having denominators of 1, 2, or 4. The positive rational numbers are the coordinates of points to the right of the origin and the negative rational numbers are the coordinates of points to the left of the origin.

To find the graphs of rational numbers having an integral denominator, the unit length of the number line must be divided into equal parts, the number of such parts being the denominator. To illustrate, the graphs of rational numbers having a denominator of 10 are found by dividing each unit length of the number line into 10 equal parts.

Thus, the graph of 2.3 is found by dividing the unit between 2 and 3 into 10 equal parts, and the graph of −1.7 if found by dividing the unit between −1 and −2 into 10ths.

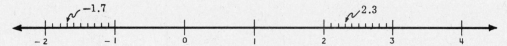

Perfect Squares and Perfect Cubes

A **perfect square** is the square of a rational number.

Thus, 25, 81, $\frac{9}{100}$ or .09, 2.25 or $\frac{9}{4}$ are perfect squares.

The first 10 positive integral perfect squares are 1, 4, 9, 16, 25, 36, 49, 64, 81, 100. While 0 is a perfect square, there cannot be negative perfect squares.

If an integer is not a perfect square, the square root of the integer cannot be a rational number. Thus, $\sqrt{2}$, $\sqrt{3}$, and $\sqrt{15}$ are not rational numbers.

A **perfect cube** is the cube of a rational number.

Thus, the first 5 positive integral cubes are 1, 8, 27, 64, and 125. 0 is also a perfect cube as are the negative integers −1, −8, −27, −64, and −125.

Kinds of Rational Numbers.

1. All integers

Thus, 5 is rational since 5 can be expressed as $\frac{5}{1}$.

2. Fractions whose numerator and denominator are integers, after simplification, and denominator $\neq 0$.

Thus, $\frac{1.5}{2}$ is rational because it equals $\frac{3}{4}$ when simplified. However, $\frac{\sqrt{2}}{3}$ is not rational.

3. Decimals which have a limited number of decimal places, called **terminating decimals**.

Thus, 3.14 is rational since it can be expressed as $\frac{314}{100}$.

4. Decimals which have an unlimited number of decimal places and the digits continue to repeat themselves. Such decimals are called **repeating decimals**.

Thus, .272727... is a rational number since it can be expressed as $\frac{3}{11}$.

5. Square root expressions whose radicand is a perfect square, such as $\sqrt{25}$; **cube root expressions** whose radicand is a perfect cube, such as $\sqrt[3]{27}$; etc.

The following table will help you determine whether a number is a rational number, expressible as the quotient of two integers, or an irrational number:

	-3	0	$\sqrt{100}$	20%	$.333\ldots$	$.333$	$\sqrt{.09}$	$\dfrac{\sqrt{25}}{12}$	$\sqrt{7}$	$\dfrac{2}{3+\sqrt{4}}$	$-\sqrt{\dfrac{32}{2}}$	$-\dfrac{\sqrt{32}}{2}$	$\sqrt[3]{25}$
					NUMBER								
Positive Integer			√										
Negative Integer	√										√		
Rational Number	√	√	√	√	√	√	√	√			√	√	
Expressed as Ratio of Two Integers	$\dfrac{-3}{1}$	$\dfrac{0}{1}$	$\dfrac{10}{1}$	$\dfrac{1}{5}$	$\dfrac{1}{3}$	$\dfrac{333}{1000}$	$\dfrac{3}{10}$	$\dfrac{5}{12}$		$\dfrac{2}{5}$	$\dfrac{-4}{1}$		
Irrational Number									√			√	√

Expressing a Rational Number as a Terminating or a Repeating Decimal

A rational number can be expressed as a decimal by performing the indicated division, as in the following cases:

(a)
```
       .85
  20)17.00
     16 0
      1 00
      1 00
         0
```

(b)
```
        .34375
  32)11.00000
      9 6
      1 40
      1 28
        120
         96
        240
        224
        160
        160
          0
```

(c)
```
       .2727...
  11)3.0000...
     2 2
       80
       77
       30
       22
       80
       77
        3
```

(d)
```
       .285714...
  7)2.000000...
    1 4
      60
      56
      40
      35
      50
      49
      10
       7
      30
      28
       2
```

Note: In (a) and in (b), when expressing $\dfrac{17}{20}$ and $\dfrac{11}{32}$ as decimals, the decimal terminates as soon as the remainder is 0. The results, .85 and .34375, are terminating decimals. A terminating decimal results whenever the rational number being expressed as a decimal has a denominator which is the product of powers of 2 and 5. In (c) and in (d), when expressing $\dfrac{3}{11}$ and $\dfrac{2}{7}$ as decimals, the decimal does **not** terminate but continues on without end. The results, .2727... and .285714 285714... are repeating decimals. Note in the case of $\dfrac{3}{11}$ that the remainders 3 and 8 continuously repeat. As soon as the remainders start to repeat, the digits in the decimal must start to repeat. In the case of $\dfrac{2}{7}$, the remainders 2, 6, 4, 5, 1, and 3 continuously repeat in that order. Hence, the digits of the decimal, 2, 8, 5, 7, 1, 4 repeat in that order. Think of each repeating section of digits as a block of digits. Keep in mind also that when dividing by 7, the only remainders are positive integers that are less than 7.

In the case of a repeating or periodic decimal, the decimal may be written by using a bar over the block of digits that repeats.

Thus, $\frac{1}{3} = .3333\ldots = .\overline{3}$, $\frac{3}{11} = .272727\ldots = .\overline{27}$, and $\frac{2}{7} = .285714\ 285714\ldots = .\overline{285714}$

Expressing a Repeating Decimal as a Rational Number

A repeating or periodic decimal can be expressed as a rational number, as in the following cases:

(a) Let $N = 0.2727\ldots$
M_{100}
$$100N = 27.2727\ldots$$
Subtract
$$\underline{N = 0.2727\ldots}$$
$$99N = 27$$
$$N = \frac{27}{99} = \frac{3}{11}$$

(b) Let $N = 0.123123\ldots$
M_{1000}
$$1000N = 123.123123\ldots$$
Subtract
$$\underline{N = 0.123123\ldots}$$
$$999N = 123$$
$$N = \frac{123}{999} = \frac{41}{333}$$

Note. In (a), in order to express $0.272727\ldots$ as a rational number, each side of the equation $N = 0.2727\ldots$ is multiplied by 10^2 since the block of digits contains 2 digits. In (b), in order to express $0.123123\ldots$ as a rational number, each side of the equation $N = 0.123123\ldots$ is multiplied by 10^3 since the block of digits contains 3 digits. In general, if the block of digits of a repeating decimal contains n digits, each side of an equation in which N represents the number is multiplied by 10^n.

Expressing a Terminating Decimal as a Rational Number

A terminating decimal can be expressed as a rational number whose denominator is a power of 10.

Thus, $.07 = \frac{7}{100}$ and $2.301 = \frac{2301}{1000}$.

Irrational Numbers

An **irrational number** is a real number that is not a rational number. Hence, an irrational number **cannot** be expressed as the ratio of two integers or as a terminating decimal or as a repeating decimal. It can be shown that $\sqrt{2}$ cannot be expressed as the quotient of two integers. Hence, $\sqrt{2}$ is an irrational number. Other examples of irrational numbers are $3 + \sqrt{2}$, $-\frac{1}{2}\sqrt{5}$ and π.

An irrational number may be approximated as closely as desired by a rational number. Thus, to the nearest thousandth, $\sqrt{2} = 1.414$, a rational number.

Using a Number Line to Graph Irrational Numbers

Fig. 1

Note in Fig. 1, the points in the number line that are the graphs of the irrational numbers, $-\frac{1}{2}\sqrt{5}$, $\sqrt{2}$, π, and $3 + \sqrt{2}$. These points can be found accurately. For example, using a right triangle, Fig. 2, the precise graph of $\sqrt{2}$ can be located.

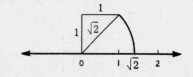

The Structure of the Real Number System

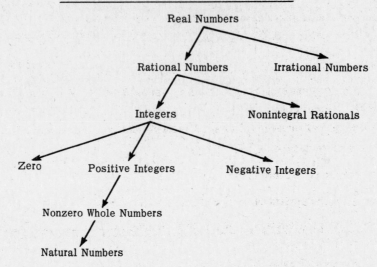

The relationship among the sets of numbers that constitute the system of real numbers is shown in the chart above. Each of these sets has been discussed in previous units of this book.

In the chart, note the following relationships among the sets of numbers:

1. A **real number** is either a rational number or an irrational number.

Thus, the real number 2 is a rational number while the real number $\sqrt{2}$ is irrational.

2. A **rational number** is either an integer or a noninteger.

Thus, the rational number $\frac{2}{1}$ is an integer while the rational number $\frac{2}{3}$ is a noninteger.

3. An **integer** is either positive, negative, or zero.

Thus, the integer 2 is positive, the integer -2 is negative, and the integer 0 is neither positive nor negative.

4. A **whole number** is either a natural number or zero.

Thus, the whole number 2 is a natural number while the whole number 0 is not.

5. A **natural number** is a nonzero whole number.

Thus, the natural number 2 is a nonzero whole number.

2.1 Expressing a Rational Number as the Ratio of Two Integers

Express each of the following rational numbers as the ratio of two integers:

a) 10   *Ans.* $\frac{10}{1}$ *e)* $\frac{\sqrt{100}}{7}$ *Ans.* $\frac{10}{7}$ *i)* $\frac{\sqrt{16}}{\sqrt{121}}$ *Ans.* $\frac{4}{11}$

b) -7 *Ans.* $\frac{-7}{1}$ *f)* $\frac{8}{\sqrt{49}}$ *Ans.* $\frac{8}{7}$ *j)* $\sqrt{\frac{18}{8}}$ *Ans.* $\frac{3}{2}$

c) 6.3   *Ans.* $\frac{63}{10}$ *g)* $3\sqrt{25}$ *Ans.* $\frac{15}{1}$ *k)* $\sqrt{6\frac{1}{4}}$ *Ans.* $\frac{5}{2}$

d) $-5\frac{1}{2}$ *Ans.* $\frac{-11}{2}$ *h)* $\frac{1}{3}\sqrt{.81}$ *Ans.* $\frac{3}{10}$ *l)* $\sqrt{.0001}$ *Ans.* $\frac{1}{100}$

2.2 Division by Zero

For what integral values of x and y will the fractions **not** be rational numbers?

a) $\frac{15}{xy}$,   *b)* $\frac{15}{2x-8}$,   *c)* $\frac{x}{y(2-x)}$,   *d)* $\frac{3y}{x(y+1)}$,   *e)* $\frac{15}{(x-4)(x+7)}$

Ans. a) $x=0$ or $y=0$,   *b)* $x=4$,   *c)* $y=0$ or $x=2$,   *d)* $x=0$ or $y=-1$,   *e)* $x=4$ or $x=-7$

2.3 Perfect Squares and Perfect Cubes

Which of the following are perfect squares or perfect cubes?

a) 1   c) 64   e) $\frac{25}{64}$ g) .1   i) .001

b) −8   d) $\frac{64}{27}$ f) $2\frac{1}{4}$ h) .01   j) −.01

Ans. a) 1 is a perfect square of 1, and also a perfect cube of 1.

b) −8 is the perfect cube of −2.

c) 64 is the perfect square of 8 and the perfect cube of 4.

d) $\frac{64}{27}$ is the perfect cube of $\frac{4}{3}$ or $1\frac{1}{3}$.

e) $\frac{25}{64}$ is the perfect square of $\frac{5}{8}$.

f) $2\frac{1}{4}$ or $\frac{9}{4}$ is the perfect square of $\frac{3}{2}$ or $1\frac{1}{2}$.

g) .1 is neither a perfect square nor a perfect cube.

h) .01 is the perfect square of .1.

i) .001 is the perfect cube of .1.

j) −.01 is neither a perfect square nor a perfect cube.

2.4 Using a Bar to Express a Block of Repeating Decimals

State the repeating decimal symbolized by each:

a) $0.\overline{7}$,   b) $0.23\overline{9}$,   c) $0.2\overline{39}$,   d) $0.\overline{239}$,   e) $3.12\overline{345}$,   f) $3.\overline{12345}$

Write each using the bar for the block of repeating digits:

g) 4.555...,   h) 5.247247...,   i) 0.428571428571...,   j) 0.3057057...,

Ans. a) .777...   c) 0.2393939...   e) 3.12345345345...   g) $4.\overline{5}$ i) $0.\overline{428571}$

b) 0.23999...   d) 0.239239239...   f) 3.123451234512345...   h) $5.\overline{247}$ j) $0.3\overline{057}$

2.5 Expressing a Rational Number as a Terminating or a Repeating Decimal

Express each rational number as a terminating or repeating decimal:

a) $\frac{7}{9}$,   b) $\frac{3}{5}$,   c) $\frac{5}{3}$,   d) $\frac{7}{8}$,   e) $-\frac{8}{7}$,   f) $\frac{10}{33}$,   g) $\frac{3}{32}$,   h) $\frac{345}{111}$

Ans. a) .777... or $.\overline{7}$ c) 1.666... or $1.\overline{6}$ e) $-1.\overline{142857}$ g) .09375

b) .6   d) .875   f) .303030... or $.\overline{30}$ h) 3.108108... or $3.\overline{108}$

2.6 Expressing a Repeating Decimal as a Rational Number

Express each repeating decimal as a rational number:

a) .111... or $.\overline{1}$,   b) .373737... or $.\overline{37}$,   c) .127127... or $.\overline{127}$,   d) 2.1515... or $2.\overline{15}$

Ans. a) $\frac{1}{9}$,   b) $\frac{37}{99}$,   c) $\frac{127}{999}$,   d) $2\frac{15}{99}$ or $2\frac{5}{33}$.

3. FINDING THE SQUARE ROOT OF A NUMBER BY USING A TABLE

Approximate square roots of numbers can be obtained using the table on page 370. The table saves time for the scientist, engineer, machinist, or mathematician.

To find the principal square root of a number, look for the number under N. Read the square root of the number under $\sqrt{N}$, immediately to the right of the number.

Thus, $\sqrt{5} = 2.236$, $\sqrt{87} = 9.327$, $\sqrt{200} = 14.14$.

Multiplying or Dividing the Radicand in a Square Root by 100

Rule 1. If the radicand of a square root is multiplied by 100, the square root is multiplied by 10.

Rule 2. If the radicand of a square root is divided by 100, the square root is divided by 10.

Thus, applying **Rule 1**:

$$\sqrt{9} = 3$$
$$\sqrt{9\ \underline{00}} = 30$$
$$\sqrt{9\ \underline{00}\ \underline{00}} = 300$$
$$\sqrt{9\ \underline{00}\ \underline{00}\ \underline{00}} = 3000$$

Thus, applying **Rule 2**:

$$\sqrt{9} = 3$$
$$\sqrt{.\underline{09}} = .3$$
$$\sqrt{.\underline{00}\ \underline{09}} = .03$$
$$\sqrt{.\underline{00}\ \underline{00}\ \underline{09}} = .003$$

Note. Each underlining above indicates a multiplication or division of the radicand by 100. This process of underlining pairs of digits is used later in the process of computing square roots.

3.1 Finding Square Roots, Using a Table

Find the approximate value of each square root, using the table of square roots:

a) $\sqrt{5}$ *Ans.* 2.236   c) $\sqrt{500}$ *Ans.* 22.36   e) $\sqrt{562}$ *Ans.* 23.71

b) $\sqrt{50}$ *Ans.* 7.071   d) $\sqrt{262}$ *Ans.* 16.19   f) $\sqrt{862}$ *Ans.* 29.36

3.2 Evaluating, Using a Square Root Table

Find the value of each to the nearest hundredth, using the table of square roots:

a) $3\sqrt{2}$

b) $2\sqrt{300} - 25$

c) $\dfrac{\sqrt{45}}{3} + \dfrac{1}{\sqrt{2}}$

Solutions:

Since $\sqrt{2} = 1.414$,

$$3\sqrt{2} = 3(1.414)$$
$$= 4.242$$

Ans. 4.24

Since $\sqrt{300} = 17.32$,

$$2\sqrt{300} - 25 = 2(17.32) - 25$$
$$= 9.64$$

Ans. 9.64

Since $\sqrt{45} = 6.708$ and $\sqrt{2} = 1.414$,

$$\frac{\sqrt{45}}{3} + \frac{1}{\sqrt{2}} = \frac{6.708}{3} + \frac{1}{1.414}$$
$$= 2.236 + .707$$
$$= 2.943 \quad Ans. \ 2.94$$

3.3 Rule 1. Multiplying the Radicand of a Square Root by a Multiple of 100

Using the table of square roots and applying **Rule 1**, find the approximate value of each square root:

a) $\sqrt{50000}$ and $\sqrt{5000000}$

b) $\sqrt{4000}$ and $\sqrt{400000}$

c) $\sqrt{53400}$ and $\sqrt{5340000}$

Solutions:

Since $\sqrt{5} = 2.236$,

$$\sqrt{5\ 00\ 00} = 223.6 \ Ans.$$
$$\sqrt{5\ 00\ 00\ 00} = 2236. \ Ans.$$

Since $\sqrt{40} = 6.325$,

$$\sqrt{40\ 00} = 63.25 \ Ans.$$
$$\sqrt{40\ 00\ 00} = 632.5 \ Ans.$$

Since $\sqrt{534} = 23.11$,

$$\sqrt{534\ 00} = 231.1 \ Ans.$$
$$\sqrt{534\ 00\ 00} = 2311. \ Ans.$$

3.4 Rule 2. Dividing the Radicand of a Square Root by a Multiple of 100

Using the table of square roots and applying **Rule 2**, find the approximate value of each square root:

a) $\sqrt{2.55}$ and $\sqrt{.0255}$

b) $\sqrt{.37}$ and $\sqrt{.0037}$

c) $\sqrt{.05}$ and $\sqrt{.0005}$

Solutions:

Since $\sqrt{255} = 15.97$,

$$\sqrt{2\ .55} = 1.597 \ Ans.$$
$$\sqrt{.02\ 55} = .1597 \ Ans.$$

Since $\sqrt{37} = 6.083$,

$$\sqrt{.37} = .6083 \ Ans.$$
$$\sqrt{.00\ 37} = .06083 \ Ans.$$

Since $\sqrt{5} = 2.236$,

$$\sqrt{.05} = .2236 \ Ans.$$
$$\sqrt{.00\ 05} = .02236 \ Ans.$$

4. COMPUTING THE SQUARE ROOT OF A NUMBER

Method 1: By Doubling and Duplicating a Number

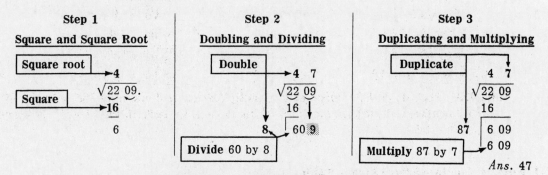

To Compute the Square Root of a Number

To compute the square root of a number, such as $\sqrt{2209}$, the following major steps and their substeps are needed.

Step 1 (Square and Square Root Step)
(1) Pair the digits of the radicand 2209, counting from the decimal point.
(2) Under the first pair 22, place 16 which is the largest perfect **square** less than 22.
(3) On top, place 4, the **square root** of 16.
(4) Subtract to obtain the remainder 6.

Step 2 (Doubling and Dividing Step)
(1) Bring down 09, the next pair of digits.
(2) **Double** 4, the number on top, and place its double, 8, on the outside as shown.
(3) Cover up 9, the last digit of 609.
(4) **Divide** 8 into 60 to obtain 7. Disregard the remainder.
(5) Make 7 the next digit on top.

Step 3 (Duplicating and Multiplying Step)
(1) **Duplicate** the next digit 7 and place it after 8 as shown.
(2) **Multiply** 87 by 7 (as in long division) to obtain 609.
(3) Subtract to obtain a remainder of zero, showing that 47 is an exact square root.
$\sqrt{2209} = 47$ *Ans.*

Step 4 (Repeating Operation Step)

If there is a positive remainder, **repeat Steps 2** and **3** until the desired number of decimal places are found.

If there is a **negative** remainder, the last digit on top is too large and should be reduced 1. Perform Step 3 over again, using the reduced digit.

Note. Decimal point of answer should be written directly above decimal point of radicand.

Method 2: By Approximation (Using Division and Averaging)

Find $\sqrt{69}$, to the nearest tenth.

Procedure:

1. Find the square root of the number that is the nearest perfect square smaller than 69.

Solution:

1. 64 is the nearest perfect square smaller than 69.
$$\sqrt{64} = 8$$

2. Divide 69 by 8, found in step 1. Carry the quotient to two digits, twice the number of digits of 8.

2. $\dfrac{69.000}{8} = 8.625 \approx 8.6$ (Note)

3. Find the average of 8, found in step 1, and 8.6, found in step 2.

3. Average $= \dfrac{8 + 8.6}{2}$

   $= 8.3$

4. Divide 69 by the average, 8.3, found in step 3. Carry the quotient to four digits, twice the number of digits of 8.3.

4. $\dfrac{69.000}{8.3} \approx 8.313$

5. Find the average of 8.3, found in step 3 and 8.313, found in step 4. Approximate to the nearest tenth.

5. Average $= \dfrac{8.3 + 8.313}{2}$

   $= 8.3$, to the nearest tenth.

Note. The symbol $\approx$ means "is approximately equal to."

4.1 Computing Exact Square Roots Showing Separate Steps: Method 1.

Find $\sqrt{3806.89}$.

Step 1	Step 2	Step 3	Step 4
Square and Square Root	**Double and Divide**	**Duplicate and Multiply**	**Repeat Steps 2 and 3**

Step 1:
```
    6
√38 06. 89
 36
  2
```

Step 2:
```
        6  1.
    √38 06. 89
     36
12 | 20 6
(12 into 20 yields 1)
```

Step 3:
```
         6  1.
     √38 06. 89
      36
121 | 2 06
    | 1 21 ←(121×1)
         85
```

Step 4:
```
          6  1. 7
      √38 06. 89
       36
121  | 2 06
     | 1 21
1227 | 85 89
     | 85 89

Ans. 61.7
```

4.2 Approximating Square Roots, Showing Separate Steps: Method 1.

Find $\sqrt{12.1}$, to nearest tenth.

Step 1	Step 2	Step 3	Step 4
Square and Square Root	**Double and Divide**	**Duplicate and Multiply**	**Repeat Steps 2 and 3**

Step 1:
```
    3.
√12. 10 00
  9
  3
```
Note. Extra zeros are needed to obtain nearest tenth.

Step 2:
```
       3.  4
   √12. 10 00
     9
6 | 31 0
```
Note. 6 into 31 yields 5 but the remainder obtainable in step 3 will be negative, showing that 5 is too large. Hence, use 4 instead of 5, as shown.

Step 3:
```
        3.  4
    √12. 10 00
      9
64 | 3 10
   | 2 56 ←(64×4)
        54
```

Step 4:
```
         3.  4  7
     √12. 10 00
       9
64  | 3 10
    | 2 56
687 | 54 00
    | 48 09
       5 91

Ans. 3.5
(to nearest tenth)
```

4.3 Computing Exact Square Roots, Showing Entire Process: Method 1.

Find each square root:

a) $\sqrt{961}$ b) $\sqrt{.4225}$ c) $\sqrt{219.04}$

Solutions:

```
        3  1
    √9 61
     9
 61  | 61
     | 61
```

```
         .  6  5
    √.42 25
     36
125  | 6 25
     | 6 25
```

```
          1  4.  8
    √2 19. 04
     1
 24  | 1 19
     |    96
288  | 23 04
     | 23 04
```

Ans. 31   *Ans.* .65   *Ans.* 14.8

4.4 Approximating Square Roots, Showing Entire Process: Method 1.

a) Find $\sqrt{17}$, to nearest tenth.

b) Find $\sqrt{.083}$, to nearest hundredth.

c) Find $\sqrt{\frac{1}{2}}$, to nearest hundredth.

Solutions:

```
        4.  1  2
    √17. 00 00
     16
 81  | 1 00
     |   81
822  | 19 00
     | 16 44
     |  2 56
```

```
         .  2  8  8 .
    √.08 30 00
     4
 48  | 4 30
     | 3 84
568  | 46 00
     | 45 44
     |    56
```

$\sqrt{\frac{1}{2}} = \sqrt{.5}$

```
          .  7  0  7
    √.50 00 00
     49
1407 | 1 00 00
     |   98 49
     |    1 51
```

Ans. 4.1   *Ans.* .29   *Ans.* .71

4.5 Using the Method of Approximation: Method 2 (Using Division and Averaging)

Find to the nearest tenth:

	a) $\sqrt{12.1}$	b) $\sqrt{86}$	c) $\sqrt{92.5}$
1. Square root of nearest smaller perfect square:	$\sqrt{9} = 3$	$\sqrt{81} = 9$	$\sqrt{81} = 9$
2. Divide and carry to 2 digits:	$\frac{12.1}{3} \approx 4.0$	$\frac{86}{9} \approx 9.6$	$\frac{92.5}{9} \approx 10$
3. Average:	$\frac{3 + 4.0}{2} = 3.5$	$\frac{9 + 9.6}{2} = 9.3$	$\frac{9 + 10}{2} = 9.5$
4. Divide and carry to 4 digits:	$\frac{12.1}{3.5} \approx 3.457$	$\frac{86}{9.3} \approx 9.247$	$\frac{92.5}{9.5} \approx 9.737$
5. Average to find answer:	$\frac{3.5 + 3.457}{2} = 3.5$	$\frac{9.3 + 9.247}{2} = 9.3$	$\frac{9.5 + 9.737}{2} = 9.6$
	to nearest tenth	to nearest tenth	to nearest tenth
	Ans. 3.5	*Ans.* 9.3	*Ans.* 9.6

5. SIMPLIFYING THE SQUARE ROOT OF A PRODUCT

Rule 1. If two or more factors of a product are nonnegative numbers, the square root of a product equals the product of the separate square roots of the factors.

$$\text{If } a, b, \text{ and } c \text{ are nonnegative, } \sqrt{ab} = \sqrt{a}\,\sqrt{b}, \quad \sqrt{abc} = \sqrt{a}\,\sqrt{b}\,\sqrt{c}$$

Thus, $\sqrt{3600} = \sqrt{(36)(100)} = \sqrt{36}\,\sqrt{100} = (6)(10) = 60$

To Simplify the Square Root of a Product

Simplify $\sqrt{72}$.

Procedure: **Solution:**

1. Factor the radicand, choosing perfect square factors: 1. $\sqrt{(4)(9)(2)}$
2. Form a separate square root for each factor: 2. $\sqrt{4}\,\sqrt{9}\,\sqrt{2}$
3. Extract the square roots of each perfect square: 3. $(2)(3)\sqrt{2}$
4. Multiply the factors outside the radical: 4. $6\sqrt{2}$

Simplifying Square Roots of Powers Having Nonnegative Bases

Rule 2. To find the square root of a power, keep the base and take one-half of the exponent.
Thus, $\sqrt{x^6} = x^3$ since $x^3 \cdot x^3 = x^6$.

Rule 3. To find the square root of the product of powers, keep each base and take one-half of the exponent.
Thus, $\sqrt{x^2 y^4} = xy^2$ since $\sqrt{x^2 y^4} = \sqrt{x^2}\,\sqrt{y^4} = xy^2$.

5.1 Rule 1. Finding Exact Square Root Through Simplification

Find each square root through simplification:

a) $\sqrt{1600}$	b) $\sqrt{256}$	c) $\sqrt{225}$	d) $\sqrt{324}$	e) $\frac{1}{2}\sqrt{576}$
Solutions:				
$\sqrt{(16)(100)}$	$\sqrt{(4)(64)}$	$\sqrt{(25)(9)}$	$\sqrt{(9)(36)}$	$\frac{1}{2}\sqrt{(4)(144)}$
$\sqrt{16}\,\sqrt{100}$	$\sqrt{4}\,\sqrt{64}$	$\sqrt{25}\,\sqrt{9}$	$\sqrt{9}\,\sqrt{36}$	$\frac{1}{2}\sqrt{4}\,\sqrt{144}$
$(4)(10)$	$(2)(8)$	$(5)(3)$	$(3)(6)$	$\frac{1}{2}(2)(12)$
Ans. 40	*Ans.* 16	*Ans.* 15	*Ans.* 18	*Ans.* 12

5.2 Rule 1. Simplifying Square Roots of Numbers

Simplify:

a) $\sqrt{75}$	b) $\sqrt{90}$	c) $\sqrt{112}$	d) $5\sqrt{288}$	e) $\frac{1}{3}\sqrt{486}$	f) $\frac{1}{2}\sqrt{1200}$
Solutions:					
$\sqrt{(25)(3)}$	$\sqrt{(9)(10)}$	$\sqrt{(16)(7)}$	$5\sqrt{(144)(2)}$	$\frac{1}{3}\sqrt{(81)(6)}$	$\frac{1}{2}\sqrt{(400)(3)}$
$\sqrt{25}\,\sqrt{3}$	$\sqrt{9}\,\sqrt{10}$	$\sqrt{16}\,\sqrt{7}$	$5\sqrt{144}\,\sqrt{2}$	$\frac{1}{3}\sqrt{81}\,\sqrt{6}$	$\frac{1}{2}\sqrt{400}\,\sqrt{3}$
Ans. $5\sqrt{3}$	*Ans.* $3\sqrt{10}$	*Ans.* $4\sqrt{7}$	*Ans.* $60\sqrt{2}$	*Ans.* $3\sqrt{6}$	*Ans.* $10\sqrt{3}$

5.3 Evaluating Simplified Square Roots

Using $\sqrt{2} = 1.414$ or $\sqrt{3} = 1.732$, evaluate to the nearest tenth:

a) $\sqrt{72}$	b) $\frac{1}{3}\sqrt{243}$	c) $3\sqrt{450}$	d) $\frac{3}{4}\sqrt{4800}$	e) $1.2\sqrt{363}$
Solutions:				
$\sqrt{36 \cdot 2}$	$\frac{1}{3}\sqrt{81 \cdot 3}$	$3\sqrt{9 \cdot 25 \cdot 2}$	$\frac{3}{4}\sqrt{16 \cdot 100 \cdot 3}$	$1.2\sqrt{121 \cdot 3}$
$\sqrt{36}\,\sqrt{2}$	$\frac{1}{3}\sqrt{81}\,\sqrt{3}$	$3\sqrt{9}\,\sqrt{25}\,\sqrt{2}$	$\frac{3}{4}\sqrt{16}\,\sqrt{100}\,\sqrt{3}$	$1.2\sqrt{121}\,\sqrt{3}$
$6\sqrt{2}$	$\frac{1}{3}(9)\sqrt{3}$	$3(3)(5)\sqrt{2}$	$\frac{3}{4}(4)(10)\sqrt{3}$	$1.2(11)\sqrt{3}$
$6(1.414)$	$3(1.732)$	$45(1.414)$	$30(1.732)$	$(13.2)(1.732)$
Ans. 8.5	*Ans.* 5.2	*Ans.* 63.6	*Ans.* 52.0	*Ans.* 22.9

5.4 Rules 2 and 3. Simplifying Square Roots of Powers

Simplify, if each variable is nonnegative:

a) $\sqrt{49b^8}$

b) $\sqrt{900c^{10}d^{16}}$

c) $\sqrt{98b^6}$

d) $2\sqrt{25t^3}$

Solutions:

$\sqrt{49}\,\sqrt{b^8}$

Ans. $7b^4$

$\sqrt{900}\,\sqrt{c^{10}}\,\sqrt{d^{16}}$

Ans. $30c^5d^8$

$\sqrt{49}\,\sqrt{2}\,\sqrt{b^6}$

Ans. $7b^3\sqrt{2}$

$2\sqrt{25}\,\sqrt{t^2}\,\sqrt{t}$

Ans. $10t\sqrt{t}$

6. SIMPLIFYING THE SQUARE ROOT OF A QUOTIENT OR A FRACTION

Rule. If the numerator is nonnegative and the denominator is positive, the square root of a fraction equals the square root of the numerator divided by the square root of the denominator.

$$\boxed{\text{If } a \text{ is nonnegative and } b \text{ is positive,}\quad \sqrt{\frac{a}{b}} = \frac{\sqrt{a}}{\sqrt{b}}}$$

Thus, $\sqrt{\dfrac{25}{64}} = \dfrac{\sqrt{25}}{\sqrt{64}} = \dfrac{5}{8}$

To simplify the square root of a fraction whose denominator is not a perfect square, **change the fraction to an equivalent fraction** which has a denominator that is a perfect square. The smallest such denominator should be chosen. Thus,

$$\sqrt{\frac{1}{8}} = \sqrt{\frac{2}{16}} = \frac{\sqrt{2}}{\sqrt{16}} = \frac{\sqrt{2}}{4} \quad \text{or} \quad \tfrac{1}{4}\sqrt{2}$$

6.1 Finding Exact Square Roots Involving Fractions

Simplify:

a) $\sqrt{2\tfrac{1}{4}}$

b) $6\sqrt{\dfrac{1600}{9}}$

c) $5\sqrt{\dfrac{144}{625}}$

d) $\dfrac{8}{5}\sqrt{\dfrac{225}{256}}$

e) $\sqrt{\dfrac{9}{49}}\,\sqrt{\dfrac{49}{400}}$

Solutions:

$\sqrt{\dfrac{9}{4}}$

$\dfrac{\sqrt{9}}{\sqrt{4}}$

Ans. $\dfrac{3}{2}$

$\dfrac{6\sqrt{1600}}{\sqrt{9}}$

$\dfrac{6(40)}{3}$

Ans. 80

$\dfrac{5\sqrt{144}}{\sqrt{625}}$

$\dfrac{5(12)}{25}$

Ans. $\dfrac{12}{5}$

$\dfrac{8}{5}\cdot\dfrac{\sqrt{225}}{\sqrt{256}}$

$\dfrac{8}{5}\cdot\dfrac{(15)}{(16)}$

Ans. $\dfrac{3}{2}$

$\dfrac{\sqrt{9}}{\sqrt{49}}\cdot\dfrac{\sqrt{49}}{\sqrt{400}}$

$\dfrac{3}{7}\cdot\dfrac{7}{20}$

Ans. $\dfrac{3}{20}$

6.2 Simplifying Square Roots of Fractions Whose Denominators are Perfect Squares

Simplify, if each variable is positive:

a) $6\sqrt{\dfrac{7}{9}}$

b) $\dfrac{2}{3}\sqrt{\dfrac{11}{100}}$

c) $\dfrac{1}{5}\sqrt{\dfrac{75}{16}}$

d) $x\sqrt{\dfrac{200}{x^2}}$

e) $10\sqrt{\dfrac{y}{25}}$

Solutions:

$\dfrac{6\sqrt{7}}{\sqrt{9}}$

$\dfrac{6\sqrt{7}}{3}$

Ans. $2\sqrt{7}$

$\dfrac{2\sqrt{11}}{3\sqrt{100}}$

$\dfrac{2\sqrt{11}}{3(10)}$

Ans. $\dfrac{\sqrt{11}}{15}$

$\dfrac{\sqrt{25}\,\sqrt{3}}{5\sqrt{16}}$

$\dfrac{5\sqrt{3}}{5(4)}$

Ans. $\dfrac{\sqrt{3}}{4}$

$\dfrac{x\sqrt{100}\,\sqrt{2}}{\sqrt{x^2}}$

$\dfrac{10x\sqrt{2}}{x}$

Ans. $10\sqrt{2}$

$\dfrac{10\sqrt{y}}{\sqrt{25}}$

$\dfrac{10\sqrt{y}}{5}$

Ans. $2\sqrt{y}$

6.3 Simplifying Square Roots of Fractions Whose Denominators Are Not Perfect Squares

Simplify, if each variable is positive:

a) $\sqrt{\dfrac{1}{5}}$ b) $\sqrt{\dfrac{3}{8}}$ c) $\sqrt{\dfrac{a}{3}}$ d) $\sqrt{\dfrac{x^2}{27}}$ e) $\sqrt{\dfrac{3}{y}}$

Solutions:

$\sqrt{\dfrac{1}{5}\cdot\dfrac{5}{5}}$ $\sqrt{\dfrac{3}{8}\cdot\dfrac{2}{2}}$ $\sqrt{\dfrac{a}{3}\cdot\dfrac{3}{3}}$ $\sqrt{\dfrac{x^2}{27}\cdot\dfrac{3}{3}}$ $\sqrt{\dfrac{3}{y}\cdot\dfrac{y}{y}}$

$\sqrt{\dfrac{5}{25}}$ $\sqrt{\dfrac{6}{16}}$ $\sqrt{\dfrac{3a}{9}}$ $\sqrt{\dfrac{3x^2}{81}}$ $\sqrt{\dfrac{3y}{y^2}}$

$\dfrac{\sqrt{5}}{\sqrt{25}}$ $\dfrac{\sqrt{6}}{\sqrt{16}}$ $\dfrac{\sqrt{3a}}{\sqrt{9}}$ $\dfrac{\sqrt{3x^2}}{\sqrt{81}}$ $\dfrac{\sqrt{3y}}{\sqrt{y^2}}$

Ans. $\dfrac{\sqrt{5}}{5}$ *Ans.* $\dfrac{\sqrt{6}}{4}$ *Ans.* $\dfrac{\sqrt{3a}}{3}$ *Ans.* $\dfrac{x\sqrt{3}}{9}$ *Ans.* $\dfrac{\sqrt{3y}}{y}$

6.4 Evaluating Square Roots after Simplification

Using $\sqrt{3}=1.732$ or $\sqrt{5}=2.236$, evaluate each to the nearest hundredth:

a) $\sqrt{\dfrac{3}{4}}$ b) $\sqrt{\dfrac{4}{3}}$ c) $30\sqrt{\dfrac{20}{9}}$ d) $10\sqrt{\dfrac{4}{5}}$ e) $\sqrt{\dfrac{49}{20}}$

Solutions:

$\dfrac{\sqrt{3}}{\sqrt{4}}$ $\sqrt{\dfrac{4}{3}\cdot\dfrac{3}{3}}$ $\dfrac{30\sqrt{20}}{\sqrt{9}}$ $10\sqrt{\dfrac{4}{5}\cdot\dfrac{5}{5}}$ $\sqrt{\dfrac{49}{20}\cdot\dfrac{5}{5}}$

$\dfrac{\sqrt{3}}{2}$ $\dfrac{\sqrt{4}\,\sqrt{3}}{\sqrt{9}}$ $10\sqrt{4}\,\sqrt{5}$ $\dfrac{10\sqrt{4}\,\sqrt{5}}{5}$ $\dfrac{\sqrt{49}\,\sqrt{5}}{\sqrt{100}}$

$\dfrac{1.732}{2}$ $\dfrac{2}{3}(1.732)$ $20(2.236)$ $4(2.236)$ $\dfrac{7}{10}(2.236)$

Ans. .87   *Ans.* 1.15   *Ans.* 44.7   *Ans.* 8.94   *Ans.* 1.6

7. ADDING AND SUBTRACTING SQUARE ROOTS OF NUMBERS

Like radicals are radicals having the same index and the same radicand.

Thus:

Like Radicals	Unlike Radicals
$5\sqrt{3}$ and $2\sqrt{3}$	$5\sqrt{3}$ and $2\sqrt{5}$
$8\sqrt{x}$ and $-3\sqrt{x}$	$8\sqrt{x}$ and $-3\sqrt{y}$
$7\sqrt[3]{6}$ and $3\sqrt[3]{6}$	$7\sqrt[3]{6}$ and $3\sqrt{6}$

Like radicals are combined by applying the law of distribution:

$$5\sqrt{3}+2\sqrt{3}-\sqrt{3}=(5+2-1)\sqrt{3}$$
$$=6\sqrt{3}$$

Rule. To combine (add or subtract) like radicals, keep the common radical and combine their coefficients.

Thus, $5\sqrt{3}+2\sqrt{3}-4\sqrt{3}=(5+2-4)\sqrt{3}=3\sqrt{3}$.

Unlike radicals may be combined into one radical if like radicals can be obtained by simplifying. Thus, $\sqrt{50}+\sqrt{32}=5\sqrt{2}+4\sqrt{2}=9\sqrt{2}$.

7.1 Combining Like Radicals

Combine (*keep radical and combine coefficients*):

a) $3\sqrt{2} + 2\sqrt{2}$

b) $5\sqrt{3} - 10\sqrt{3}$

c) $\sqrt{6} + 9\sqrt{6}$

d) $\frac{1}{2}\sqrt{5} + 1\frac{1}{2}\sqrt{5}$

e) $7\frac{3}{4}\sqrt{10} - 5\frac{3}{4}\sqrt{10}$

f) $\sqrt{2x} + 3\sqrt{2x}$

g) $2x\sqrt{7} + 3x\sqrt{7}$

h) $20\sqrt{a} - 13\sqrt{a}$

i) $5a\sqrt{y} - 2a\sqrt{y}$

Solutions:

a) $(3+2)\sqrt{2} = 5\sqrt{2}$ *Ans.*

b) $(5-10)\sqrt{3} = -5\sqrt{3}$ *Ans.*

c) $(1+9)\sqrt{6} = 10\sqrt{6}$ *Ans.*

d) $(\frac{1}{2}+1\frac{1}{2})\sqrt{5} = 2\sqrt{5}$ *Ans.*

e) $(7\frac{3}{4}-5\frac{3}{4})\sqrt{10} = 2\sqrt{10}$ *Ans.*

f) $(1+3)\sqrt{2x} = 4\sqrt{2x}$ *Ans.*

g) $(2x+3x)\sqrt{7} = 5x\sqrt{7}$ *Ans.*

h) $(20-13)\sqrt{a} = 7\sqrt{a}$ *Ans.*

i) $(5a-2a)\sqrt{y} = 3a\sqrt{y}$ *Ans.*

7.2 Combining Unlike Numerical Radicals After Simplification

Combine after simplifying:

a) $\sqrt{5} + \sqrt{20} + \sqrt{45}$

b) $\sqrt{27} + 3\sqrt{12}$

c) $\sqrt{8} - 6\sqrt{\frac{1}{2}}$

d) $\sqrt{4a} + \sqrt{25a} - \sqrt{\frac{a}{4}}$

Solutions:

$\sqrt{5} + 2\sqrt{5} + 3\sqrt{5}$

Ans. $6\sqrt{5}$

$3\sqrt{3} + 3(2\sqrt{3})$

$3\sqrt{3} + 6\sqrt{3}$

Ans. $9\sqrt{3}$

$2\sqrt{2} - 6(\frac{1}{2}\sqrt{2})$

$2\sqrt{2} - 3\sqrt{2}$

Ans. $-\sqrt{2}$

$2\sqrt{a} + 5\sqrt{a} + \frac{1}{2}\sqrt{a}$

Ans. $7\frac{1}{2}\sqrt{a}$

8. MULTIPLYING SQUARE ROOTS OF NUMBERS

Rule 1. If two or more numbers are nonnegative, the product of their separate square roots equals the square root of their product.

$$\boxed{\begin{array}{c} \text{If } a, b, \text{ and } c \text{ are nonnegative,} \\ \sqrt{a}\,\sqrt{b} = \sqrt{ab},\ \sqrt{a}\,\sqrt{b}\,\sqrt{c} = \sqrt{abc} \end{array}}$$

Thus, $\sqrt{2}\,\sqrt{3}\,\sqrt{6} = \sqrt{36} = 6$.

Note. Rule 1 does not apply to the case where numbers are negative. For example, $\sqrt{-5}\,\sqrt{-5} \neq \sqrt{(-5)(-5)}$, which equals $\sqrt{25}$ or 5. The product of $\sqrt{-5}$ and $\sqrt{-5}$ is -5.

The general equation used here and the general equation used in Section 5 of this chapter are transformable into each other by applying the symmetric property of an equality.

$$\sqrt{ab} = \sqrt{a}\,\sqrt{b} \longleftrightarrow \sqrt{a}\,\sqrt{b} = \sqrt{ab}$$

Rule 2. If a number is nonnegative, the square of the square root of the number is equal to the number. (This rule was previously used in Section 1 of this chapter.)

If a is nonnegative, $(\sqrt{a})^2 = a$.

Thus, $(\sqrt{123.45})^2 = 123.45$

Hence, to square the square root of a nonnegative number, merely eliminate the radical sign.

To Multiply Square Root Monomials

Multiply: a) $3\sqrt{2} \cdot 2\sqrt{6}$

b) $\frac{2}{3}\sqrt{2x} \cdot 6\sqrt{2y}$, $x \geq 0, y \geq 0$

Procedure:

Solutions:

1. Multiply coefficients and radicals separately:

1. $3 \cdot 2\sqrt{2}\,\sqrt{6}$

1. $\frac{2}{3} \cdot 6\sqrt{2x}\,\sqrt{2y}$

2. Multiply the resulting products:

2. $6\sqrt{12}$

2. $4\sqrt{4xy}$

3. Simplify, if possible:

3. $6(2\sqrt{3})$

3. $4 \cdot 2\sqrt{xy}$

Ans. $12\sqrt{3}$

Ans. $8\sqrt{xy}$

8.1 Multiplying Square Root Monomials

Multiply, if each variable is nonnegative:

a) $\sqrt{2}\sqrt{5}\sqrt{6}\sqrt{15}$ | b) $(2\sqrt{3})(3\sqrt{5})(5\sqrt{10})$ | c) $\sqrt{\dfrac{x}{7}}\sqrt{14x}$ | d) $(4\sqrt{m})(2\sqrt{25m})$

Solutions:

$\sqrt{2\cdot5\cdot6\cdot15}$ | $2\cdot3\cdot5\sqrt{3\cdot5\cdot10}$ | $\sqrt{(\frac{x}{7})(14x)}$ | $4\cdot2\sqrt{(m)(25m)}$

$\sqrt{900}$ | $30\sqrt{150}=30(5\sqrt{6})$ | $\sqrt{2x^2}$ | $8\sqrt{25m^2}=8(5m)$

Ans. 30 | *Ans.* $150\sqrt{6}$ | *Ans.* $x\sqrt{2}$ | *Ans.* $40m$

8.2 Rule 2. Squaring Like Radicals

Multiply, if each variable is positive:

a) $(2\sqrt{17})(3\sqrt{17})$ | b) $(3\sqrt{\frac{2}{3}})^2$ | c) $(\frac{5}{2}\sqrt{8})^2$ | d) $(2a\sqrt{2a})^2$ | e) $\left(\dfrac{x}{3}\sqrt{\dfrac{3}{x}}\right)^2$

Solutions:

$2\cdot3(\sqrt{17})^2$ | $3^2(\sqrt{\frac{2}{3}})^2$ | $(\frac{5}{2})^2(\sqrt{8})^2$ | $(2a)^2(\sqrt{2a})^2$ | $(\frac{x}{3})^2(\sqrt{\frac{3}{x}})^2$

$6(17)$ | $9(\frac{2}{3})$ | $\frac{25}{4}(8)$ | $4a^2(2a)$ | $\dfrac{x^2}{9}(\dfrac{3}{x})$

Ans. 102 | *Ans.* 6 | *Ans.* 50 | *Ans.* $8a^3$ | *Ans.* $\dfrac{x}{3}$

8.3 Multiplying a Monomial by a Polynomial

Multiply:

a) $\sqrt{3}(\sqrt{3}+\sqrt{27})$ | b) $3\sqrt{2}(\sqrt{2}+\sqrt{5})$ | c) $\dfrac{\sqrt{5}}{2}(4\sqrt{3}-6\sqrt{20})$

Solutions:

$\sqrt{3}\sqrt{3}+\sqrt{3}\sqrt{27}$ | $3\sqrt{2}\sqrt{2}+3\sqrt{2}\sqrt{5}$ | $(\frac{\sqrt{5}}{2})(4\sqrt{3})-(\frac{\sqrt{5}}{2})(6\sqrt{20})$

$3+\sqrt{81}$ | $3(2)+3\sqrt{10}$ | $2\sqrt{15}-3\sqrt{100}$

Ans. 12 | *Ans.* $6+3\sqrt{10}$ | *Ans.* $2\sqrt{15}-30$

8.4 Multiplying Binomials Containing Radicals

Multiply:

a) $(5+\sqrt{2})(5-\sqrt{2})$ | b) $(\sqrt{10}+\sqrt{3})(\sqrt{10}-\sqrt{3})$ | c) $(\sqrt{7}+\sqrt{2})(\sqrt{7}+\sqrt{2})$

Procedure: | **Solutions:**

1. Multiply first terms: | $5\cdot5=25$ | $\sqrt{10}\sqrt{10}=10$ | $\sqrt{7}\sqrt{7}=7$
2. Add products of outer and inner terms: | $5\sqrt{2}-5\sqrt{2}=0$ | $\sqrt{30}-\sqrt{30}=0$ | $\sqrt{14}+\sqrt{14}=2\sqrt{14}$
3. Multiply last terms: | $(\sqrt{2})(-\sqrt{2})=-2$ | $(\sqrt{3})(-\sqrt{3})=-3$ | $\sqrt{2}\sqrt{2}=2$
4. Combine results: | *Ans.* 23 | *Ans.* 7 | *Ans.* $9+2\sqrt{14}$

9. DIVIDING BY THE SQUARE ROOT OF A NUMBER

Rule. The square root of a nonnegative number divided by the square root of a positive number equals the square root of their quotient.

$$\boxed{\begin{array}{c}\text{If } a \text{ is nonnegative and } b \text{ is positive,}\\[4pt] \dfrac{\sqrt{a}}{\sqrt{b}}=\sqrt{\dfrac{a}{b}}\end{array}}$$

Thus, $\dfrac{\sqrt{6}}{\sqrt{2}}=\sqrt{\dfrac{6}{2}}=\sqrt{3}$

Note. The general equation used here and the general equation used in Section 6 of this chapter are transformable into each other by applying the symmetric property of an equality:

$$\sqrt{\frac{a}{b}} = \frac{\sqrt{a}}{\sqrt{b}} \longleftrightarrow \frac{\sqrt{a}}{\sqrt{b}} = \sqrt{\frac{a}{b}}$$

To Divide Square Root Monomials

Divide: $a)\ \dfrac{14\sqrt{40}}{2\sqrt{5}}$ $b)\ \dfrac{6\sqrt{x^4}}{3\sqrt{x}}\ ,\ x>0$

Procedure: **Solutions:**

1. **Divide** coefficients and radicals separately:

    1. $\dfrac{14}{2}\sqrt{\dfrac{40}{5}}$ 1. $\dfrac{6}{3}\sqrt{\dfrac{x^4}{x}}$

2. **Multiply** the resulting quotients:

    2. $7\sqrt{8}$ 2. $2\sqrt{x^3}$

3. **Simplify**, if possible:

    3. $7(2\sqrt{2})$ 3. $2(\sqrt{x^2}\sqrt{x})$

    Ans. $14\sqrt{2}$ **Ans.** $2x\sqrt{x}$

9.1 Dividing Square Root Monomials

Divide, if each variable is positive:

$a)\ \dfrac{8\sqrt{8}}{2\sqrt{2}}$ $b)\ \dfrac{6\sqrt{2}}{12\sqrt{8}}$ $c)\ \dfrac{10\sqrt{56}}{4\sqrt{7}}$ $d)\ \dfrac{9\sqrt{x^3}}{3\sqrt{x}}$ $e)\ \dfrac{5a\sqrt{5a}}{10a\sqrt{10a}}$

Solutions:

$\dfrac{8}{2}\sqrt{\dfrac{8}{2}}$ $\dfrac{6}{12}\sqrt{\dfrac{2}{8}}$ $\dfrac{10}{4}\sqrt{\dfrac{56}{7}}$ $\dfrac{9}{3}\sqrt{\dfrac{x^3}{x}}$ $\dfrac{5a}{10a}\sqrt{\dfrac{5a}{10a}}$

$4\sqrt{4}=4(2)$ $\tfrac{1}{2}\sqrt{\tfrac{1}{4}}=\tfrac{1}{2}(\tfrac{1}{2})$ $\tfrac{5}{2}\sqrt{8}=\tfrac{5}{2}(2\sqrt{2})$ $3\sqrt{x^2}$ $\tfrac{1}{2}\sqrt{\tfrac{1}{2}}=\tfrac{1}{2}(\tfrac{1}{2}\sqrt{2})$

Ans. 8   *Ans.* $\tfrac{1}{4}$ *Ans.* $5\sqrt{2}$ *Ans.* $3x$ *Ans.* $\tfrac{1}{4}\sqrt{2}$

9.2 Dividing a Polynomial by a Monomial

Divide, if each variable is positive:

$a)\ \dfrac{\sqrt{50}+\sqrt{98}}{\sqrt{2}}$ $b)\ \dfrac{2\sqrt{24}+\sqrt{96}}{\sqrt{3}}$ $c)\ \dfrac{18\sqrt{40}-10\sqrt{80}}{2\sqrt{10}}$ $d)\ \dfrac{15\sqrt{y^5}-6\sqrt{y^3}}{3\sqrt{y}}$

Solutions:

$\dfrac{\sqrt{50}}{\sqrt{2}}+\dfrac{\sqrt{98}}{\sqrt{2}}$ $\dfrac{2\sqrt{24}}{\sqrt{3}}+\dfrac{\sqrt{96}}{\sqrt{3}}$ $\dfrac{18\sqrt{40}}{2\sqrt{10}}-\dfrac{10\sqrt{80}}{2\sqrt{10}}$ $\dfrac{15\sqrt{y^5}}{3\sqrt{y}}-\dfrac{6\sqrt{y^3}}{3\sqrt{y}}$

$\sqrt{25}+\sqrt{49}$ $2\sqrt{8}+\sqrt{32}$ $9\sqrt{4}-5\sqrt{8}$ $5\sqrt{\dfrac{y^5}{y}}-2\sqrt{\dfrac{y^3}{y}}$

$5+7$ $2(2\sqrt{2})+4\sqrt{2}$ $18-5(2\sqrt{2})$ $5\sqrt{y^4}-2\sqrt{y^2}$

Ans. 12   *Ans.* $8\sqrt{2}$ *Ans.* $18-10\sqrt{2}$ *Ans.* $5y^2-2y$

10. RATIONALIZING THE DENOMINATOR

To rationalize the denominator of a fraction is to change the denominator into a rational number.

Note. In this section, the rationalizing of the denominator of a fraction is restricted to the case where the denominator is a single term involving an irrational square root.

Rule. To rationalize the denominator of a fraction when the denominator is a single term involving an irrational square root, multiply both terms of the fraction by the least square root which will make the denominator rational.

Thus, to rationalize the denominator of $\dfrac{4}{\sqrt{8}}$, multiply by $\dfrac{\sqrt{2}}{\sqrt{2}}$:

$$\frac{4}{\sqrt{8}} \cdot \frac{\sqrt{2}}{\sqrt{2}} = \frac{4\sqrt{2}}{\sqrt{16}} = \frac{4\sqrt{2}}{4} = \sqrt{2}$$

Rationalizing the denominator simplifies evaluation.

Thus, $\dfrac{4}{\sqrt{8}} = \sqrt{2} = 1.414$. Otherwise, $\dfrac{4}{\sqrt{8}} = \dfrac{4}{2.828}$, thus leading to a lengthy division.

10.1 Rationalizing the Denominator

Rationalize each denominator, if each variable is positive:

a) $\dfrac{12}{\sqrt{6}}$

Solutions:

$\dfrac{12}{\sqrt{6}} \cdot \dfrac{\sqrt{6}}{\sqrt{6}}$

$\dfrac{12\sqrt{6}}{6}$

Ans. $2\sqrt{6}$

b) $\dfrac{\sqrt{3}}{\sqrt{10}}$

$\dfrac{\sqrt{3}}{\sqrt{10}} \cdot \dfrac{\sqrt{10}}{\sqrt{10}}$

Ans. $\dfrac{\sqrt{30}}{10}$

c) $\dfrac{24}{\sqrt{8}}$

$\dfrac{24}{\sqrt{8}} \cdot \dfrac{\sqrt{2}}{\sqrt{2}}$

$\dfrac{24\sqrt{2}}{\sqrt{16}}$

Ans. $6\sqrt{2}$

d) $\dfrac{3}{\sqrt{x}}$

$\dfrac{3}{\sqrt{x}} \cdot \dfrac{\sqrt{x}}{\sqrt{x}}$

Ans. $\dfrac{3\sqrt{x}}{x}$

e) $\dfrac{1}{\sqrt{c^3}}$

$\dfrac{1}{\sqrt{c^3}} \cdot \dfrac{\sqrt{c}}{\sqrt{c}}$

$\dfrac{\sqrt{c}}{\sqrt{c^4}}$

Ans. $\dfrac{\sqrt{c}}{c^2}$

f) $\dfrac{3+\sqrt{2}}{\sqrt{2}}$

$\dfrac{\sqrt{2}}{\sqrt{2}} \cdot \dfrac{3+\sqrt{2}}{\sqrt{2}}$

$\dfrac{\sqrt{2}\,(3+\sqrt{2})}{2}$

Ans. $\dfrac{3\sqrt{2}+2}{2}$

10.2 Evaluating Fractions With Irrational Denominators

Evaluate to the nearest tenth, after rationalizing the denominator:

a) $\dfrac{7}{\sqrt{7}}$

Solutions:

$\dfrac{7}{\sqrt{7}} \cdot \dfrac{\sqrt{7}}{\sqrt{7}}$

$\dfrac{7\sqrt{7}}{7}$

$\sqrt{7}$

2.646

Ans. 2.6

b) $\dfrac{20}{\sqrt{50}}$

$\dfrac{20}{\sqrt{50}} \cdot \dfrac{\sqrt{2}}{\sqrt{2}}$

$\dfrac{20\sqrt{2}}{10}$

$2\sqrt{2}$

$2(1.414)$

Ans. 2.8

c) $\dfrac{3}{\sqrt{6}}$

$\dfrac{3}{\sqrt{6}} \cdot \dfrac{\sqrt{6}}{\sqrt{6}}$

$\dfrac{3\sqrt{6}}{6}$

$\dfrac{\sqrt{6}}{2}$

$\dfrac{2.449}{2}$

Ans. 1.2

d) $\dfrac{1}{\sqrt{12}}$

$\dfrac{1}{\sqrt{12}} \cdot \dfrac{\sqrt{3}}{\sqrt{3}}$

$\dfrac{\sqrt{3}}{\sqrt{36}}$

$\dfrac{\sqrt{3}}{6}$

$\dfrac{1.732}{6}$

Ans. $.3$

e) $\dfrac{3+\sqrt{5}}{\sqrt{5}}$

$\dfrac{(3+\sqrt{5})}{\sqrt{5}} \cdot \dfrac{\sqrt{5}}{\sqrt{5}}$

$\dfrac{\sqrt{5}\,(3+\sqrt{5})}{5}$

$\dfrac{3\sqrt{5}+5}{5}$

$\dfrac{3(2.236)+5}{5}$

Ans. 2.3

11. SOLVING RADICAL EQUATIONS

Radical equations are equations in which the variable is included in the radicand.

Thus, $2\sqrt{x} + 5 = 9$ is a radical equation.
but $2x + \sqrt{5} = 9$ is not a radical equation,

To Solve a Radical Equation

Solve: $\sqrt{2x} + 5 = 9$

Procedure:

1. **Isolate** the term containing the radical:

2. **Square** both sides:

3. **Solve** for the variable:

4. **Check** the roots obtained in the original equation:

Solution:

1.
$$\sqrt{2x} + 5 = 9$$
$$\sqrt{2x} = 4$$

2. By squaring, $2x = 16$

3. $x = 8$

4. Check for $x = 8$:
$$\sqrt{2x} + 5 \overset{?}{=} 9$$
$$\sqrt{16} + 5 \overset{?}{=} 9$$
$$9 = 9 \quad Ans.\ x = 8$$

Note. In the solution of equations, the symbol "**Sq**" means "square both sides".

An extraneous root of an equation is a value that may satisfy, **not the original equation,** but a later equation obtained from the original equation. It must be rejected.

Thus, if $\sqrt{2x} = -4$, when both sides are squared, $2x = 16$ or $x = 8$.

However, $x = 8$ does not satisfy $\sqrt{2x} = -4$, the original equation.

Hence, 8 is an *extraneous root* of $\sqrt{2x} = -4$ and must be rejected.

11.1 Solving Simple Radical Equations

Solve and check:

a) $\sqrt{5x} = 10$ | *b)* $\sqrt{\frac{x}{3}} = 2$ | *c)* $\sqrt{7x+5} = 3$ | *d)* $2\sqrt{x-8} = -3$

Solutions:

By squaring,
$5x = 100$
$x = 20$

By squaring,
$\frac{x}{3} = 4$
$x = 12$

By squaring,
$7x + 5 = 9$
$x = \frac{4}{7}$

By squaring,
$4(x-8) = 9$
$x = \frac{41}{4}$

Check: $\sqrt{5x} = 10$
$\sqrt{100} \overset{?}{=} 10$
$10 = 10$
Ans. $x = 20$

Check: $\sqrt{\frac{x}{3}} = 2$
$\sqrt{4} \overset{?}{=} 2$
$2 = 2$
Ans. $x = 12$

Check: $\sqrt{7x+5} = 3$
$\sqrt{4+5} \overset{?}{=} 3$
$3 = 3$
Ans. $x = \frac{4}{7}$

Check: $2\sqrt{x-8} = -3$
$2\sqrt{\frac{9}{4}} \overset{?}{=} -3$
$3 \neq -3$
Reject $x = \frac{41}{4}$. *(No root.)*

11.2 Isolating the Radical in Solving Radical Equations

Find each solution set and check:

a) $3\sqrt{x} - 6 = 9$ b) $5\sqrt{x} = \sqrt{x} - 12$ c) $\sqrt{3y+4} - 2 = 3$

Solutions: (*Isolate the radical term first.*)

A_6 $3\sqrt{x} - 6 = 9$
D_3 $3\sqrt{x} = 15$
Sq $\sqrt{x} = 5$
  $x = 25$

Check: $3\sqrt{x} - 6 = 9$
  $3\sqrt{25} - 6 \overset{?}{=} 9$
  $9 = 9$

Ans. {25}

$S_{\sqrt{x}}$ $5\sqrt{x} = \sqrt{x} - 12$
D_4 $4\sqrt{x} = -12$
Sq $\sqrt{x} = -3$
  $x = 9$

Check: $5\sqrt{x} = \sqrt{x} - 12$
  $5\sqrt{9} \overset{?}{=} \sqrt{9} - 12$
  $15 \neq -9$

Reject $x = 9$. (*No root.*)
Ans. $\emptyset$, empty set

A_2 $\sqrt{3y+4} - 2 = 3$
Sq $\sqrt{3y+4} = 5$
  $3y + 4 = 25$
  $y = 7$

Check: $\sqrt{3y+4} - 2 = 3$
  $\sqrt{25} - 2 \overset{?}{=} 3$
  $3 = 3$

Ans. {7}

11.3 Transforming Radical Equations

Solve for the indicated variable:

a) Solve for x:

$$\sqrt{\frac{x}{2}} = y$$

Solutions:
By squaring,

$$\frac{x}{2} = y^2$$

Ans. $x = 2y^2$

b) Solve for y:

$$\sqrt{2y-5} = x$$

By squaring,

$$2y - 5 = x^2$$

Ans. $y = \dfrac{x^2 + 5}{2}$

c) Solve for A:

$$r = \sqrt{\frac{A}{\pi}}$$

By squaring,

$$r^2 = \frac{A}{\pi}$$

Ans. $A = \pi r^2$

d) Solve for x:

$$\sqrt{x+4} = y + 2$$

By squaring,

$$x + 4 = y^2 + 4y + 4$$

Ans. $x = y^2 + 4y$

SUPPLEMENTARY PROBLEMS

1. If each variable is a real number, state the square roots of each: (1.1)

a) $100x^2$ b) $\dfrac{100}{x^2}$ c) $4c^2d^2$ d) $\dfrac{4}{81}z^2$ e) $\dfrac{25r^2}{36s^2}$ f) $\dfrac{x^4 z^{16}}{y^6}$

Ans. a) $\pm 10x$ b) $\pm\dfrac{10}{x}$ c) $\pm 2cd$ d) $\pm\dfrac{2}{9}z$ e) $\pm\dfrac{5r}{6s}$ f) $\pm\dfrac{x^2 z^8}{y^3}$

2. If each radicand is nonnegative, state the equivalent of each without the radical sign: (1.2)

a) $(\sqrt{17})^2$ c) $(\sqrt{1.776})^2$ e) $(\sqrt{10-2x})^2$ g) $\left(\dfrac{\sqrt{y}}{3}\right)^2$ i) $\left(\sqrt{\dfrac{x-5}{3y}}\right)^2$

b) $(\sqrt{1776})^2$ d) $(\sqrt{x+2})^2$ f) $(2\sqrt{x})^2$ h) $\left(\sqrt{\dfrac{y}{3}}\right)^2$

Ans. a) 17,   b) 1776,   c) 1.776,   d) $x+2$,   e) $10-2x$,   f) $4x$,   g) $\dfrac{y}{9}$,   h) $\dfrac{y}{3}$,   i) $\dfrac{x-5}{3y}$

3. Find each principal (positive) square root: (1.3)

a) $\sqrt{400}$ c) $\sqrt{144}$ e) $\sqrt{\dfrac{9}{10000}}$ g) $\sqrt{\dfrac{49}{144}}$

b) $\sqrt{.04}$ d) $\sqrt{1.44}$ f) $\sqrt{.0016}$ h) $\sqrt{2\dfrac{7}{9}}$

Ans. a) 20   c) 12   e) $\dfrac{3}{100}$ or 0.3   g) $\dfrac{7}{12}$

b) .2   d) 1.2   f) .04   h) $\dfrac{5}{3}$ or $1\dfrac{2}{3}$

4. Find the value of **(1.4)**

a) $\sqrt{81} - \sqrt{25}$ *Ans.* 4   d) $\sqrt{\frac{4}{9}} + \sqrt{\frac{1}{9}}$ *Ans.* 1   g) $\sqrt{16} + \sqrt{.16} + \sqrt{.0016}$ *Ans.* 4.44

b) $2\sqrt{9} + 3\sqrt{4}$ *Ans.* 12   e) $8\sqrt{\frac{1}{16}} + 4\sqrt{\frac{9}{16}}$ *Ans.* 5   h) $\sqrt{16} + \sqrt{1600} + \sqrt{160000}$ *Ans.* 444

c) $\frac{1}{2}\sqrt{36} - \frac{1}{3}\sqrt{81}$ *Ans.* 0   f) $\left(-\sqrt{\frac{4}{9}}\right)\left(-\sqrt{\frac{81}{100}}\right)$ *Ans.* $\frac{3}{5}$ i) $\sqrt{900} + \sqrt{.09} + \sqrt{.000009}$ *Ans.* 30.303

5. State the equivalent of each without the radical sign if each variable is a real number: **(1.5)**

a) $\sqrt{y^2}$,   b) $\sqrt{y^4}$,   c) $\sqrt{y^4z^2}$,   d) $\sqrt{9x^4} + 9\sqrt{x^4}$,   e) $16\sqrt{x^2} - \sqrt{16x^2}$,   f) $\sqrt{(2x-5)^2}$

Ans. a) $|y|$,   b) y^2,   c) $y^2|z|$,   d) $12x^2$,   e) $12|x|$,   f) $|2x-5|$

6. State the value of each real root: **(1.6)**

a) $-\sqrt{9}$ c) $-\sqrt{-9}$ e) $-\sqrt[3]{-27}$ g) $-\sqrt{-1}$ i) $-\sqrt[3]{-1}$

b) $\sqrt{-9}$ d) $\sqrt[3]{-27}$ f) $\sqrt{-1}$ h) $\sqrt[3]{-1}$

Ans. a) -3 c) not real   e) $-(-3)$ or $+3$ g) not real   i) $-(-1)$ or $+1$

b) not real   d) -3 f) not real   h) -1

7. Express each of the following rational numbers as the ratio of two integers: **(2.1)**

a) 5   b) -13 c) .07   d) $-11\frac{2}{3}$ e) $\frac{\sqrt{25}}{3}$ f) $\frac{17}{\sqrt{144}}$ g) $\frac{16-\sqrt{16}}{\sqrt{25}}$ h) $\sqrt{\frac{50}{32}}$

Ans. a) $\frac{5}{1}$ b) $\frac{-13}{1}$ c) $\frac{7}{100}$ d) $\frac{-35}{3}$ e) $\frac{5}{3}$ f) $\frac{17}{12}$ g) $\frac{12}{5}$ h) $\frac{5}{4}$

8. For what integral values of x and y will the fractions not be rational numbers? **(2.2)**

a) $\frac{50}{xy}$,   b) $\frac{30}{x(y-2)}$,   c) $\frac{40}{(x-3)(x+3)}$,   d) $\frac{60}{(2x-5)(y+4)}$

Ans. a) $x = 0$ or $y = 0$,   b) $x = 0$ or $y = 2$,   c) $x = 3$ or -3,   d) $x = 2\frac{1}{2}$ or $y = -4$

9. Which of the following are perfect squares or perfect cubes? **(2.3)**

a) 27   c) .027   e) .04   g) 8000   i) 1000

b) $\frac{1}{27}$ d) .27   f) .4   h) 100   j) 10,000

Ans. a) perfect cube of 3

b) perfect cube of $\frac{1}{3}$

c) perfect cube of .3 or $\frac{3}{10}$

d) neither

e) perfect square of .2 or $\frac{2}{10}$ or $\frac{1}{5}$

f) neither

g) perfect cube of 20

h) perfect square of 10

i) perfect cube of 10

j) perfect square of 100

10. State the repeating decimal symbolized by each: **(2.4)**

a) $0.\overline{675}$,   b) $0.6\overline{75}$ c) $0.67\overline{5}$,   d) $1.\overline{3579}$,   e) $0.\overline{13579}$

Write each using the bar for the block of repeating digits:

f) 0.222...   g) 0.235235235...   h) 0.2353535...   i) 0.27535353...

Ans. a) 0.675675675...   d) 1.357935793579...   g) $0.\overline{235}$

b) 0.6757575...   e) 0.135791357913579...   h) $0.2\overline{35}$

c) 0.67555...   f) $0.\overline{2}$ i) $0.27\overline{53}$

11. Express each rational number as a terminating or repeating decimal: **(2.5)**

a) $\frac{5}{9}$,   b) $\frac{3}{11}$,   c) $\frac{5}{16}$,   d) $\frac{7}{320}$,   e) $\frac{53}{99}$,   f) $\frac{203}{999}$,   g) $-\frac{2}{3}$,   h) $1\frac{13}{33}$,   i) $10\frac{1}{7}$

Ans. a) $.555\ldots$ or $.\overline{5}$ d) $.021875$ g) $-.666\ldots$ or $-.\overline{6}$

      b) $.272727\ldots$ or $.\overline{27}$ e) $.535353\ldots$ or $.\overline{53}$ h) $1.393939\ldots$ or $1.\overline{39}$

      c) $.3125$ f) $.203203203\ldots$ or $.\overline{203}$ i) $10.\overline{142857}$

12. Express each repeating decimal as a rational number: **(2.6)**

     a) $.888\ldots$ or $.\overline{8}$ c) $.123123123$ or $.\overline{123}$ e) $1.234234234\ldots$ or $1.\overline{234}$

     b) $.515151\ldots$ or $.\overline{51}$ d) $2.444\ldots$ or $2.\overline{4}$ f) $1.2343434\ldots$ or $1.2\overline{34}$

Ans. a) $\frac{8}{9}$

                c) $\frac{123}{999}$ or $\frac{41}{333}$ e) $1\frac{26}{111}$ or $\frac{137}{111}$

     b) $\frac{51}{99}$ or $\frac{17}{33}$ d) $2\frac{4}{9}$ or $\frac{22}{9}$ f) $1\frac{116}{495}$ or $\frac{611}{495}$

13. Find the approximate value of each square root, using the table of square roots: **(3.1)**

     a) $\sqrt{7}$ d) $\sqrt{46}$ g) $\sqrt{275}$ j) $\sqrt{528}$ m) $\sqrt{780}$

     b) $\sqrt{70}$ e) $\sqrt{94}$ h) $\sqrt{329}$ k) $\sqrt{576}$ n) $\sqrt{892}$

     c) $\sqrt{700}$ f) $\sqrt{138}$ i) $\sqrt{486}$ l) $\sqrt{747}$ o) $\sqrt{917}$

Ans. a) 2.646 d) 6.782 g) 16.58 j) 22.98 m) 27.93

      b) 8.367 e) 9.695 h) 18.14 k) 24.00 n) 29.87

      c) 26.46 f) 11.75 i) 22.05 l) 27.33 o) 30.28

14. Find the value of each to the nearest tenth, using the table of square roots: **(3.2)**

     a) $2\sqrt{3}$ c) $\frac{1}{2}\sqrt{140}$ e) $100 - 10\sqrt{83}$ g) $\frac{\sqrt{3}+\sqrt{2}}{5}$

     b) $10\sqrt{50}$ d) $\frac{2}{5}\sqrt{280}$ f) $\frac{3+\sqrt{2}}{5}$ h) $\frac{10-\sqrt{2}}{3}$

Ans. a) 3.5 b) 70.7 c) 5.9 d) 6.7 e) 8.9 f) $.9$ g) $.6$ h) 2.9

15. Find the approximate value of each, using the table and **Rule 1**:   **(3.3)**

     a) $\sqrt{3000}$ c) $\sqrt{19000}$ e) $\sqrt{5000} + \sqrt{500}$, to nearest tenth.

     b) $\sqrt{30000}$ d) $\sqrt{190000}$ f) $\sqrt{8300} - \sqrt{830}$, to nearest tenth.

Ans. a) 54.77 c) 137.8 e) $70.71 + 22.36 = 93.07$ or 93.1

      b) 173.2 d) 435.9 f) $91.10 - 28.81 = 62.29$ or 62.3

16. Find the approximate value of each, using the table and **Rule 2**:   **(3.4)**

     a) $\sqrt{.03}$ d) $\sqrt{3.85}$ g) $\sqrt{55} + \sqrt{.55}$,   to nearest hundredth.

     b) $\sqrt{.0003}$ e) $\sqrt{.0385}$ h) $\sqrt{427} - \sqrt{4.27}$, to nearest hundredth.

     c) $\sqrt{.30}$ f) $\sqrt{.3}$ i) $\sqrt{.02} + \sqrt{.0002}$, to nearest hundredth.

Ans. a) $.1732$,   b) $.01732$,   c) $.5477$,   d) 1.962,   e) $.1962$,   f) $.5477 (= \sqrt{.30})$,

     g) 8.16,   h) 18.59,   i) $.16$

17. Find each square root, using Method 1.   **(4.1 to 4.3)**

     a) $\sqrt{2304}$ d) $\sqrt{29.16}$ g) $\sqrt{67.24}$ j) $\sqrt{.012544}$

     b) $\sqrt{3025}$ e) $\sqrt{12.96}$ h) $\sqrt{4.1209}$ k) $\sqrt{.014641}$

     c) $\sqrt{7396}$ f) $\sqrt{466.56}$ i) $\sqrt{5.0625}$ l) $\sqrt{.050625}$

Ans. a) 48,   b) 55,   c) 86,   d) 5.4,   e) 3.6,   f) 21.6,   g) 8.2,   h) 2.03,   i) 2.25

     j) $.112$,   k) $.121$,   l) $.225$

18. Find each square root, to the nearest tenth. Use Method 1. **(4.4)**

a) $\sqrt{96.24}$ *Ans.* 9.8   c) $\sqrt{463.45}$ *Ans.* 21.5   e) $\sqrt{.1750}$ *Ans.* .4

b) $\sqrt{135.06}$ *Ans.* 11.6   d) $\sqrt{207.86}$ *Ans.* 14.4   f) $\sqrt{.4545}$ *Ans.* .7

19. Verify each value to the nearest hundredth, using Method 1. **(4.4)**

a) $\sqrt{5}$ = 2.24   c) $\sqrt{28}$ = 5.29   e) $\sqrt{48}$ = 6.93   g) $\sqrt{692}$ = 26.31

b) $\sqrt{10}$ = 3.16   d) $\sqrt{34}$ = 5.83   f) $\sqrt{57}$ = 7.55   h) $\sqrt{765}$ = 27.66

20. Find each square root, to the nearest tenth. Use Method 1. **(4.4)**

a) $\sqrt{7\frac{1}{2}}$ or $\sqrt{7.5}$ *Ans.* 2.7   b) $\sqrt{4\frac{1}{4}}$ or $\sqrt{4.25}$ *Ans.* 2.1   c) $\sqrt{52\frac{3}{8}}$ or $\sqrt{52.375}$ *Ans.* 7.2

21. Using Method 2, find each to the nearest tenth: **(4.5)**

a) $\sqrt{27}$,   b) $\sqrt{35}$,   c) $\sqrt{62}$,   d) $\sqrt{125}$,   e) $\sqrt{12.5}$,   f) $\sqrt{1.29}$,   g) $\sqrt{1215}$

Ans. a) 5.2,   b) 5.9,   c) 7.9   d) 11.2   e) 3.5   f) 1.1   g) 34.9

22. Find each square root through simplification: **(5.1)**

a) $\sqrt{2500}$ *Ans.* 50   c) $\sqrt{2025}$ *Ans.* 45   e) $\sqrt{729}$ *Ans.* 27   g) $\sqrt{48400}$ *Ans.* 220

b) $\sqrt{19600}$ *Ans.* 140   d) $\sqrt{441}$ *Ans.* 21   f) $\sqrt{784}$ *Ans.* 28   h) $\sqrt{562500}$ *Ans.* 750

23. Simplify: **(5.2)**

a) $\sqrt{63}$ d) $\frac{1}{2}\sqrt{32}$ g) $\sqrt{17500}$ j) $\frac{3}{7}\sqrt{392}$

b) $\sqrt{96}$ e) $\frac{1}{5}\sqrt{300}$ h) $\sqrt{4500}$ k) $\frac{2}{5}\sqrt{250}$

c) $\sqrt{448}$ f) $\frac{7}{8}\sqrt{320}$ i) $\sqrt{21600}$ l) $\frac{5}{3}\sqrt{999}$

Ans. a) $3\sqrt{7}$,   b) $4\sqrt{6}$,   c) $8\sqrt{7}$,   d) $2\sqrt{2}$,   e) $2\sqrt{3}$,   f) $7\sqrt{5}$,   g) $50\sqrt{7}$,   h) $30\sqrt{5}$

i) $60\sqrt{6}$,   j) $6\sqrt{2}$,   k) $2\sqrt{10}$,   l) $5\sqrt{111}$

24. Using $\sqrt{2}$ =1.414 or $\sqrt{5}$ = 2.236, evaluate to the nearest tenth: **(5.3)**

a) $\frac{2}{3}\sqrt{18}$ *Ans.* $2\sqrt{2}$ = 2.8   c) $10\sqrt{20}$ *Ans.* $20\sqrt{5}$ = 44.7   e) $\frac{1}{4}\sqrt{8000}$ *Ans.* $10\sqrt{5}$ = 22.4

b) $\frac{1}{3}\sqrt{45}$ *Ans.* $\sqrt{5}$ = 2.2   d) $5\sqrt{98}$ *Ans.* $35\sqrt{2}$ = 49.5   f) $\frac{1}{2}\sqrt{16200}$ *Ans.* $45\sqrt{2}$ = 63.6

25. Simplify, if each variable is nonnegative. **(5.4)**

a) $\sqrt{49m^2}$ *Ans.* $7m$ e) $\sqrt{7r^2s^2}$ *Ans.* $rs\sqrt{7}$ i) $\sqrt{400a^8b^{10}}$ *Ans.* $20a^4b^5$

b) $\sqrt{100a^2b^2}$ *Ans.* $10ab$ f) $\sqrt{4s^2t^2u}$ *Ans.* $2st\sqrt{u}$ j) $\sqrt{25x^3}$ *Ans.* $5x\sqrt{x}$

c) $\sqrt{64r^2p^2q^2}$ *Ans.* $8rpq$ g) $\sqrt{81x^4}$ *Ans.* $9x^2$ k) $\sqrt{9u^5w^{12}}$ *Ans.* $3u^2w^6\sqrt{u}$

d) $\sqrt{4p^2q}$ *Ans.* $2p\sqrt{q}$ h) $\sqrt{144y^6}$ *Ans.* $12y^3$ l) $\sqrt{27t^3x^5}$ *Ans.* $3tx^2\sqrt{3tx}$

26. Simplify: **(6.1)**

a) $\sqrt{6\frac{1}{4}}$ *Ans.* $\frac{5}{2}$ | c) $\sqrt{\frac{2500}{81}}$ *Ans.* $\frac{50}{9}$ | e) $\sqrt{\frac{441}{169}}$ *Ans.* $\frac{21}{13}$ | g) $\sqrt{\frac{4}{9}}\sqrt{\frac{25}{16}}$ *Ans.* $\frac{5}{6}$

b) $\sqrt{7\frac{1}{9}}$ *Ans.* $\frac{8}{3}$ | d) $\sqrt{\frac{9}{6400}}$ *Ans.* $\frac{3}{80}$ | f) $\sqrt{\frac{289}{10000}}$ *Ans.* $\frac{17}{100}$ | h) $\sqrt{\frac{36}{225}}\sqrt{\frac{1}{4}}\sqrt{\frac{25}{16}}$ *Ans.* $\frac{1}{4}$

27. Simplify, if each variable is positive: **(6.2)**

a) $\sqrt{\frac{5}{16}}$ *Ans.* $\frac{\sqrt{5}}{4}$ | c) $\sqrt{\frac{8}{25}}$ *Ans.* $\frac{2}{5}\sqrt{2}$ | e) $10\sqrt{\frac{x}{25}}$ *Ans.* $2\sqrt{x}$ | g) $\frac{1}{y}\sqrt{\frac{y^3}{900}}$ *Ans.* $\frac{\sqrt{y}}{30}$

b) $9\sqrt{\frac{13}{9}}$ *Ans.* $3\sqrt{13}$ | d) $21\sqrt{\frac{32}{49}}$ *Ans.* $12\sqrt{2}$ | f) $\sqrt{\frac{150}{x^4}}$ *Ans.* $\frac{5}{x^2}\sqrt{6}$ | h) $y^4\sqrt{\frac{45}{y^6}}$ *Ans.* $3y\sqrt{5}$

28. Simplify, if each variable is positive: **(6.3)**

a) $\sqrt{\dfrac{1}{7}}$ Ans. $\dfrac{\sqrt{7}}{7}$ | c) $\sqrt{\dfrac{5}{18}}$ Ans. $\dfrac{\sqrt{10}}{6}$ | e) $\sqrt{\dfrac{1}{b}}$ Ans. $\dfrac{1}{b}\sqrt{b}$ | g) $\sqrt{\dfrac{2s}{g}}$ Ans. $\dfrac{1}{g}\sqrt{2sg}$

b) $\sqrt{\dfrac{3}{11}}$ Ans. $\dfrac{\sqrt{33}}{11}$ | d) $5\sqrt{\dfrac{7}{20}}$ Ans. $\dfrac{\sqrt{35}}{2}$ | f) $\sqrt{\dfrac{1}{c^3}}$ Ans. $\dfrac{1}{c^2}\sqrt{c}$ | h) $\sqrt{\dfrac{x^3}{50}}$ Ans. $\dfrac{x}{10}\sqrt{2x}$

29. Using $\sqrt{2}=1.414$ or $\sqrt{3}=1.732$, evaluate each to the nearest hundredth: **(6.4)**

a) $\sqrt{\dfrac{1}{2}}$ b) $\sqrt{\dfrac{1}{3}}$ c) $\sqrt{\dfrac{9}{50}}$ d) $6\sqrt{\dfrac{1}{12}}$ e) $16\sqrt{\dfrac{9}{32}}$ f) $45\sqrt{\dfrac{4}{27}}$ g) $\sqrt{2\dfrac{1}{12}}$ h) $\sqrt{2\dfrac{13}{18}}$

Ans. a) $\dfrac{1}{2}\sqrt{2}=.71$ c) $\dfrac{3}{10}\sqrt{2}=.42$ e) $6\sqrt{2}=8.48$ g) $\dfrac{5}{6}\sqrt{3}=1.44$

     b) $\dfrac{1}{3}\sqrt{3}=.58$ d) $\sqrt{3}=1.73$ f) $10\sqrt{3}=17.32$ h) $\dfrac{7}{6}\sqrt{2}=1.65$

30. Combine: **(7.1)**

a) $5\sqrt{3}+\sqrt{3}$ c) $3\sqrt{2}+4\sqrt{3}-2\sqrt{2}$ e) $x\sqrt{15}+2x\sqrt{15}$ g) $12\sqrt{b}-2\sqrt{a}+6\sqrt{b}$

b) $7\sqrt{11}-10\sqrt{11}$ d) $5\sqrt{5}-2\sqrt{5}+\sqrt{10}$ f) $11\sqrt{a}+\sqrt{a}-3\sqrt{a}$ h) $5b\sqrt{c}+3b\sqrt{c}+c\sqrt{b}$

Ans. a) $6\sqrt{3}$ c) $\sqrt{2}+4\sqrt{3}$ e) $3x\sqrt{15}$ g) $18\sqrt{b}-2\sqrt{a}$

    b) $-3\sqrt{11}$ d) $3\sqrt{5}+\sqrt{10}$ f) $9\sqrt{a}$ h) $8b\sqrt{c}+c\sqrt{b}$

31. Simplify and combine: **(7.2)**

a) $\sqrt{2}+\sqrt{32}$ e) $2\sqrt{27}-4\sqrt{12}$ i) $8\sqrt{3}-6\sqrt{\dfrac{1}{3}}$

b) $2\sqrt{5}+3\sqrt{20}$ f) $\sqrt{700}-2\sqrt{63}$ j) $10\sqrt{18}+20\sqrt{\dfrac{1}{2}}$

c) $2\sqrt{28}-3\sqrt{7}$ g) $-3\sqrt{90}-5\sqrt{40}$ k) $6\sqrt{\dfrac{5}{12}}-\sqrt{60}$

d) $x\sqrt{3}+x\sqrt{27}$ h) $\sqrt{9y}+2\sqrt{25y}$ l) $\sqrt{\dfrac{a^2}{2}}-\sqrt{\dfrac{a^2}{8}}$

Ans. a) $\sqrt{2}+4\sqrt{2}=5\sqrt{2}$ e) $6\sqrt{3}-8\sqrt{3}=-2\sqrt{3}$ i) $8\sqrt{3}-2\sqrt{3}=6\sqrt{3}$

    b) $2\sqrt{5}+6\sqrt{5}=8\sqrt{5}$ f) $10\sqrt{7}-6\sqrt{7}=4\sqrt{7}$ j) $30\sqrt{2}+10\sqrt{2}=40\sqrt{2}$

    c) $4\sqrt{7}-3\sqrt{7}=\sqrt{7}$ g) $-9\sqrt{10}-10\sqrt{10}=-19\sqrt{10}$ k) $\sqrt{15}-2\sqrt{15}=-\sqrt{15}$

    d) $x\sqrt{3}+3x\sqrt{3}=4x\sqrt{3}$ h) $3\sqrt{y}+10\sqrt{y}=13\sqrt{y}$ l) $\dfrac{a}{2}\sqrt{2}-\dfrac{a}{4}\sqrt{2}=\dfrac{a}{4}\sqrt{2}$

32. Multiply: **(8.1)**

a) $4\sqrt{2}\cdot5\sqrt{3}$ d) $\sqrt{2}\ \sqrt{3}\ \sqrt{12}$ g) $\sqrt{21}\ \sqrt{3}$ j) $\dfrac{1}{2}\sqrt{3}\cdot6\sqrt{18}$

b) $7\sqrt{7}\cdot10\sqrt{10}$ e) $3\sqrt{6}\cdot5\sqrt{24}$ h) $\sqrt{10}\ \sqrt{20}$ k) $\dfrac{2}{3}\sqrt{7}\cdot15\sqrt{14}$

c) $4\sqrt{3}\cdot3\sqrt{2}\cdot6\sqrt{5}$ f) $10\sqrt{\dfrac{1}{3}}\cdot7\sqrt{75}$ i) $\sqrt{8}\ \sqrt{12}\ \sqrt{10}$ l) $\dfrac{3}{2}\sqrt{24}\cdot4\sqrt{3}$

Ans. a) $20\sqrt{6}$ d) $6\sqrt{2}$ g) $\sqrt{63}=3\sqrt{7}$ j) $3\sqrt{54}=9\sqrt{6}$

    b) $70\sqrt{70}$ e) $15\sqrt{144}=180$ h) $\sqrt{200}=10\sqrt{2}$ k) $10\sqrt{98}=70\sqrt{2}$

    c) $72\sqrt{30}$ f) $70\sqrt{25}=350$ i) $\sqrt{960}=8\sqrt{15}$ l) $6\sqrt{72}=36\sqrt{2}$

33. Multiply, if each variable is positive: **(8.1)**

a) $2\sqrt{a}\cdot4\sqrt{b}$ d) $\sqrt{pq}\ \sqrt{p}\ \sqrt{q}$ g) $\sqrt{5a}\ \sqrt{3a}$ j) $\sqrt{\dfrac{y}{x}}\ \sqrt{\dfrac{x}{y}}$

b) $c\sqrt{5}\cdot d\sqrt{7}$ e) $\sqrt{4m}\ \sqrt{25m}$ h) $\sqrt{\dfrac{1}{2}b}\ \sqrt{40b}$ k) $3x\sqrt{x}\cdot5x\sqrt{x}$

c) $r\sqrt{x}\cdot s\sqrt{y}$ f) $\sqrt{3n}\ \sqrt{27n^3}$ i) $\sqrt{8h^3}\ \sqrt{2k^2}$ l) $y^2\sqrt{y}\cdot y\sqrt{y^2}$

Ans. a) $8\sqrt{ab}$ d) $\sqrt{p^2q^2}=pq$ g) $\sqrt{15a^2}=a\sqrt{15}$ j) 1

    b) $cd\sqrt{35}$ e) $\sqrt{100m^2}=10m$ h) $\sqrt{20b^2}=2b\sqrt{5}$ k) $15x^2\sqrt{x^2}=15x^3$

    c) $rs\sqrt{xy}$ f) $\sqrt{81n^4}=9n^2$ i) $\sqrt{16h^3k^2}=4hk\sqrt{h}$ l) $y^3\sqrt{y^3}=y^4\sqrt{y}$

34. Multiply, if each variable is positive: (8.2)

    a) $5\sqrt{10} \cdot \sqrt{10}$ d) $(\sqrt{14})^2$ g) $\sqrt{7x} \cdot \sqrt{7x}$ j) $5\sqrt{2b} \cdot 4\sqrt{2b}$

    b) $\sqrt{12} \cdot \frac{1}{2}\sqrt{12}$ e) $(3\sqrt{6})^2$ h) $x\sqrt{5} \cdot y\sqrt{5}$ k) $(2x\sqrt{2x})^2$

    c) $2\sqrt{\frac{2}{3}} \cdot 3\sqrt{\frac{3}{2}}$ f) $(\frac{1}{2}\sqrt{8})^2$ i) $(7\sqrt{2a})^2$ l) $(c\sqrt{\frac{5}{c}})^2$

Ans. a) $5 \cdot 10 = 50$ d) 14 g) $7x$ j) $20(2b) = 40b$

    b) $\frac{1}{2} \cdot 12 = 6$ e) $9 \cdot 6 = 54$ h) $5xy$ k) $4x^2(2x) = 8x^3$

    c) 6 f) $\frac{1}{4} \cdot 8 = 2$ i) $49(2a) = 98a$ l) $c^2(\frac{5}{c}) = 5c$

35. Multiply, if each variable is positive: (8.3)

    a) $\sqrt{2}(5 + \sqrt{2})$ c) $3\sqrt{3}(\sqrt{27} + 7\sqrt{3})$ e) $\sqrt{6}(\sqrt{6x} + \sqrt{24x})$

    b) $\sqrt{5}(2\sqrt{5} - 3\sqrt{20})$ d) $\sqrt{x}(\sqrt{16x} - \sqrt{9x})$ f) $\sqrt{8}(\sqrt{2x} + \sqrt{18y})$

Ans. a) $5\sqrt{2} + 2$ c) $27 + 63 = 90$ e) $6\sqrt{x} + 12\sqrt{x} = 18\sqrt{x}$

    b) $10 - 30 = -20$ d) $4x - 3x = x$ f) $4\sqrt{x} + 12\sqrt{y}$

36. Multiply: (8.4)

    a) $(6 + \sqrt{3})(6 - \sqrt{3})$ d) $(3 + \sqrt{2})^2$ g) $(2 - \sqrt{6})(3 - \sqrt{6})$

    b) $(\sqrt{5} - 2)(\sqrt{5} + 2)$ e) $(\sqrt{11} - 3)^2$ h) $(\sqrt{7} + 3)(\sqrt{7} + 2)$

    c) $(\sqrt{7} + \sqrt{2})(\sqrt{7} - \sqrt{2})$ f) $(\sqrt{3} + \sqrt{5})^2$ i) $(4\sqrt{2} - \sqrt{5})(3\sqrt{2} + 2\sqrt{5})$

Ans. a) $36 - 3 = 33$ d) $9 + 6\sqrt{2} + 2 = 11 + 6\sqrt{2}$ g) $6 - 5\sqrt{6} + 6 = 12 - 5\sqrt{6}$

    b) $5 - 4 = 1$ e) $11 - 6\sqrt{11} + 9 = 20 - 6\sqrt{11}$ h) $7 + 5\sqrt{7} + 6 = 13 + 5\sqrt{7}$

    c) $7 - 2 = 5$ f) $3 + 2\sqrt{15} + 5 = 8 + 2\sqrt{15}$ i) $24 + 5\sqrt{10} - 10 = 14 - 5\sqrt{10}$

37. Divide, if each variable is positive: (9.1)

    a) $\frac{15\sqrt{60}}{5\sqrt{15}}$ *Ans.* $3\sqrt{4} = 6$ d) $\frac{\sqrt{120}}{2\sqrt{5}}$ *Ans.* $\frac{\sqrt{24}}{2} = \sqrt{6}$ g) $\frac{5c\sqrt{5c}}{c\sqrt{c}}$ *Ans.* $5\sqrt{5}$

    b) $\frac{24\sqrt{2}}{3\sqrt{32}}$ *Ans.* $8\sqrt{\frac{1}{16}} = 2$ e) $\frac{3\sqrt{24}}{\sqrt{2}}$ *Ans.* $3\sqrt{12} = 6\sqrt{3}$ h) $\frac{3x\sqrt{x^5}}{9x\sqrt{x}}$ *Ans.* $\frac{1}{3}\sqrt{x^4} = \frac{x^2}{3}$

    c) $\frac{6\sqrt{3}}{3\sqrt{27}}$ *Ans.* $2\sqrt{\frac{1}{9}} = \frac{2}{3}$ f) $\frac{14\sqrt{a^3}}{2\sqrt{a}}$ *Ans.* $7\sqrt{a^2} = 7a$ i) $\frac{a\sqrt{ab}}{ab\sqrt{b}}$ *Ans.* $\frac{1}{b}\sqrt{a}$

38. Divide, if each variable is positive: (9.2)

    a) $\frac{\sqrt{200} + \sqrt{50}}{\sqrt{5}}$ *Ans.* $\sqrt{40} + \sqrt{10} = 3\sqrt{10}$ | d) $\frac{\sqrt{20} + \sqrt{80}}{2\sqrt{5}}$ *Ans.* $\frac{\sqrt{4}}{2} + \frac{\sqrt{16}}{2} = 3$

    b) $\frac{9\sqrt{200} - 12\sqrt{32}}{3\sqrt{2}}$ *Ans.* $3\sqrt{100} - 4\sqrt{16} = 14$ | e) $\frac{\sqrt{27a} - 2\sqrt{3a}}{\sqrt{a}}$ *Ans.* $\sqrt{27} - 2\sqrt{3} = \sqrt{3}$

    c) $\frac{8\sqrt{2} - 4\sqrt{8}}{\sqrt{32}}$ *Ans.* $8\sqrt{\frac{1}{16}} - 4\sqrt{\frac{1}{4}} = 0$ | f) $\frac{\sqrt{y^7} - \sqrt{y^5}}{\sqrt{y^3}}$ *Ans.* $\sqrt{y^4} - \sqrt{y^2} = y^2 - y$

39. Rationalize each denominator, if each denominator is positive: (10.1)

    a) $\frac{2}{\sqrt{5}}$ *Ans.* $\frac{2\sqrt{5}}{5}$ | d) $\frac{\sqrt{5}}{\sqrt{15}}$ *Ans.* $\frac{\sqrt{3}}{3}$ | g) $\frac{4 + \sqrt{2}}{\sqrt{2}}$ *Ans.* $2\sqrt{2} + 1$ | j) $\frac{5}{\sqrt{y}}$ *Ans.* $\frac{5\sqrt{y}}{y}$

    b) $\frac{12}{\sqrt{2}}$ *Ans.* $6\sqrt{2}$ | e) $\frac{12}{\sqrt{6}}$ *Ans.* $2\sqrt{6}$ | h) $\frac{3\sqrt{3} - 6}{\sqrt{3}}$ *Ans.* $3 - 2\sqrt{3}$ | k) $\frac{2a}{\sqrt{10}}$ *Ans.* $\frac{a\sqrt{10}}{5}$

    c) $\frac{10}{\sqrt{50}}$ *Ans.* $\sqrt{2}$ | f) $\frac{\sqrt{2}}{\sqrt{3}}$ *Ans.* $\frac{\sqrt{6}}{3}$ | i) $\frac{16 - 2\sqrt{2}}{\sqrt{8}}$ *Ans.* $4\sqrt{2} - 1$ | l) $\frac{3x}{\sqrt{x}}$ *Ans.* $3\sqrt{x}$

40. Evaluate to the nearest tenth, after rationalizing the denominator: **(10.2)**

$a)$ $\dfrac{2}{\sqrt{2}}$ *Ans.* $\sqrt{2} = 1.4$ $d)$ $\dfrac{40}{\sqrt{8}}$ *Ans.* $10\sqrt{2} = 14.1$ $g)$ $\dfrac{12 - \sqrt{3}}{\sqrt{3}}$ *Ans.* $4\sqrt{3} - 1 = 5.9$

$b)$ $\dfrac{12}{\sqrt{6}}$ *Ans.* $2\sqrt{6} = 4.9$ $e)$ $\dfrac{30}{\sqrt{45}}$ *Ans.* $2\sqrt{5} = 4.5$ $h)$ $\dfrac{1 + \sqrt{5}}{\sqrt{5}}$ *Ans.* $\dfrac{\sqrt{5} + 5}{5} = 1.4$

$c)$ $\dfrac{10\sqrt{2}}{\sqrt{5}}$ *Ans.* $2\sqrt{10} = 6.3$ $f)$ $\dfrac{9\sqrt{5}}{\sqrt{15}}$ *Ans.* $3\sqrt{3} = 5.2$ $i)$ $\dfrac{\sqrt{20} + \sqrt{5}}{\sqrt{10}}$ *Ans.* $\dfrac{3}{2}\sqrt{2} = 2.1$

41. Solve: **(11.1)**

$a)$ $\sqrt{3x} = 6$ *Ans.* $x = 12$ $e)$ $\frac{1}{2}\sqrt{b} = 5$ *Ans.* $b = 100$ $i)$ $\sqrt{3h} = 5$ *Ans.* $h = \frac{25}{3}$

$b)$ $3\sqrt{x} = 15$ *Ans.* $x = 25$ $f)$ $\frac{2}{3}\sqrt{c} = 8$ *Ans.* $c = 144$ $j)$ $\sqrt{10 - x} = 2$ *Ans.* $x = 6$

$c)$ $8 = 2\sqrt{y}$ *Ans.* $y = 16$ $g)$ $\sqrt{c + 3} = 4$ *Ans.* $c = 13$ $k)$ $\sqrt{2r - 5} = 3$ *Ans.* $r = 7$

$d)$ $5\sqrt{a} = 2$ *Ans.* $a = \frac{4}{25}$ $h)$ $\sqrt{d - 5} = 3$ *Ans.* $d = 14$ $l)$ $\sqrt{54 - 3s} = 6$ *Ans.* $s = 6$

42. Find each solution set and check: **(11.2)**

$a)$ $2\sqrt{a} - 3 = 7$ $d)$ $8\sqrt{r} - 5 = \sqrt{r} + 9$ $g)$ $\sqrt{2x - 7} + 8 = 11$

$b)$ $8 + 3\sqrt{b} = 20$ $e)$ $20 - 3\sqrt{t} = \sqrt{t} - 4$ $h)$ $22 = 17 + \sqrt{40 - 3y}$

$c)$ $7 - \sqrt{2b} = 3$ $f)$ $2\sqrt{5x} - 3 = 7$ $i)$ $30 - \sqrt{20 - 2y} = 26$

Ans. $a)$ $\{25\}$, $b)$ $\{16\}$, $c)$ $\{8\}$, $d)$ $\{4\}$, $e)$ $\{36\}$, $f)$ $\{5\}$, $g)$ $\{8\}$, $h)$ $\{5\}$, $i)$ $\{2\}$

43. Solve and show, by checking, that each value for the unknown is extraneous: **(11.2)**

$a)$ $\sqrt{a} = -2$ $c)$ $5 + \sqrt{c} = 4$ $e)$ $2\sqrt{t} + 5 = \sqrt{t}$ $g)$ $\sqrt{y + 5} = -4$

$b)$ $-\sqrt{b} = 3$ $d)$ $6 - \sqrt{r} = 10$ $f)$ $10 - \sqrt{3v} = 12$ $h)$ $3 - \sqrt{12 - x} = 8$

44. Solve for the indicated variable: **(11.3)**

$a)$ $a = \sqrt{2b}$ for b $c)$ $g = \sqrt{3h}$ for h $e)$ $2u = \sqrt{\dfrac{v}{2}}$ for v $g)$ $R = \frac{1}{2}\sqrt{\dfrac{A}{\pi}}$ for A

$b)$ $g = 3\sqrt{h}$ for h $d)$ $s = \dfrac{\sqrt{t}}{3}$ for t $f)$ $h = \sqrt{3g - 4}$ for g $h)$ $R = \sqrt{\dfrac{3V}{\pi H}}$ for V

Ans. $a)$ $b = \dfrac{a^2}{2}$ $c)$ $h = \dfrac{g^2}{3}$ $e)$ $v = 8u^2$ $g)$ $A = 4\pi R^2$

     $b)$ $h = \dfrac{g^2}{9}$ $d)$ $t = 9s^2$ $f)$ $g = \dfrac{h^2 + 4}{3}$ $h)$ $V = \frac{1}{3}\pi R^2 H$

Chapter 13

Quadratic Equations in One Variable

1. UNDERSTANDING QUADRATIC EQUATIONS IN ONE VARIABLE

A quadratic equation in one variable is an equation in which the highest power of the variable is the second.

Thus, $2x^2 + 3x - 5 = 0$ is a quadratic equation in x.

Standard Quadratic Equation Form: $ax^2 + bx + c = 0$, $a \neq 0$

The **standard form of a quadratic equation** in one variable is $ax^2 + bx + c = 0$ where a, b and c are real numbers, $a \neq 0$.

Thus, $3x^2 - 5x + 6 = 0$ is in standard form. Here, $a = 3$, $b = -5$ and $c = 6$.

To Transform a Quadratic Equation into Standard Form, $ax^2 + bx + c = 0$

(1) **Remove parentheses:** Thus, $x(x+1) - 5 = 0$ becomes $x^2 + x - 5 = 0$.

(2) **Clear of fractions:** Thus, $x - 4 + \frac{3}{x} = 0$ becomes $x^2 - 4x + 3 = 0$.

(3) **Remove radical signs:** Thus, $\sqrt{x^2 - 3x} = 2$ becomes $x^2 - 3x - 4 = 0$.

(4) **Collect like terms:** Thus, $x^2 + 7x = 2x + 6$ becomes $x^2 + 5x - 6 = 0$.

1.1. Expressing Quadratic Equations in Standard Form

Express each quadratic equation in the standard form, $ax^2 + bx + c = 0$, so that a has a positive value:

a) $x(x+1) = 6$ | b) $\frac{3}{x} + x = 4$ | c) $x^2 = 25 - 5x - 15$ | d) $2x = \sqrt{x+3}$

Solutions:

Remove ( ):	Clear fractions:	Collect like terms:	Remove radical signs:
$x^2 + x = 6$	$3 + x^2 = 4x$	$x^2 = 10 - 5x$	Squaring: $4x^2 = x + 3$
Ans. $x^2 + x - 6 = 0$	*Ans.* $x^2 - 4x + 3 = 0$	*Ans.* $x^2 + 5x - 10 = 0$	*Ans.* $4x^2 - x - 3 = 0$

1.2. Values of a, b and c in Standard Quadratic Equation Form

Express each quadratic equation in standard form, so that a has a positive value. Then state the values of a, b and c.

	Standard Form	a	b	c
a) $x^2 - 9x = 10$	*Ans.* $x^2 - 9x - 10 = 0$	1	-9	-10
b) $5x^2 = 125$	*Ans.* $5x^2 - 125 = 0$	5	0	-125
c) $2x^2 = 8x$	*Ans.* $2x^2 - 8x = 0$	2	-8	0
d) $2x^2 + 9x = 2x - 3$	*Ans.* $2x^2 + 7x + 3 = 0$	2	$+7$	$+3$
e) $x(x+3) = 10$	*Ans.* $x^2 + 3x - 10 = 0$	1	$+3$	-10
f) $5(x^2 + 2) = 7(x + 3)$	*Ans.* $5x^2 - 7x - 11 = 0$	5	-7	-11
g) $x - 5 = \frac{7}{x}$	*Ans.* $x^2 - 5x - 7 = 0$	1	-5	-7
h) $\sqrt{2x^2 - 1} = x + 2$	*Ans.* $x^2 - 4x - 5 = 0$	1	-4	-5

2. SOLVING QUADRATIC EQUATIONS BY FACTORING

Rule 1. Every quadratic equation has two roots.

Thus, $x^2 = 9$ has two roots, 3 and -3; that is, $x = \pm 3$.

In the case of the quadratic equation $x^2 = 0$, the equation is considered to have two equal roots, each equal to 0, while the quadratic equation $(x - 3)^2 = 0$ is considered to have two equal roots, each equal to 3.

Rule 2. If the product of two factors is zero, then one or the other of the factors equals zero.

Thus, if $x(2x - 1) = 0$, then $x = 0$ or $2x - 1 = 0$. Also, if $(x - 5)(3x + 4) = 0$ then $x - 5 = 0$ or $3x + 4 = 0$.

Note. "$x - 5 = 0$ **or** $3x + 4 = 0$" is a **disjunction of linear equations.**

Hence, the quadratic equation $(x - 5)(3x + 4) = 0$ is true if either $(x - 5) = 0$ is true or $3x + 4 = 0$ is true; that is, if $x = 5$ or if $x = -\frac{4}{3}$.

To Solve a Quadratic Equation by Factoring

Find the solution set of $x(x - 4) = 5$

Procedure:

1. **Express in form** $ax^2 + bx + c = 0$:

2. **Factor** $ax^2 + bx + c$:

3. **Let each factor** $= 0$:

4. **Solve** each resulting equation:

5. **Check** each root in original equation:

Solution:

1. S_5 $x^2 - 4x = 5$
   $x^2 - 4x - 5 = 0$

2. $(x - 5)(x + 1) = 0$

3. $x - 5 = 0$ | $x + 1 = 0$

4. $x = 5$ | $x = -1$

5. Check in $x(x - 4) = 5$:
   If $x = 5$, $5(1) \overset{?}{=} 5$ | If $x \overset{?}{=} -1$, $(-1)(-5) = 5$
   $5 = 5$ | $5 = 5$

Ans. $\{5, -1\}$

2.1. Solving Quadratic Equations by Factoring

Solve: a) $x^2 - x = 6$ | b) $x + \frac{16}{x} = 8$

Procedure:

1. **Express as** $ax^2 + bx + c = 0$:

2. **Factor** $ax^2 + bx + c$:

3. **Let each factor** $= 0$:

4. **Solve:**

5. **Check** (*in original equation*):

Solutions:

1. $x^2 - x - 6 = 0$ | 1. $x^2 + 16 = 8x$
    | $x^2 - 8x + 16 = 0$

2. $(x - 3)(x + 2) = 0$ | 2. $(x - 4)(x - 4) = 0$

3. $x - 3 = 0$ | $x + 2 = 0$ | 3. $x - 4 = 0$ | $x - 4 = 0$

4. $x = 3$ | $x = -2$ | 4. $x = 4$ | $x = 4$

5. (*Check to be done by the student.*)

Ans. $x = 3$ or -2 | Ans. $x = 4$ (equal roots)

2.2. Solving Quadratic Equations in Standard Form

Find the solution set:

a) $x^2 + 9x + 20 = 0$

Solutions:

$(x + 4)(x + 5) = 0$
$x + 4 = 0$ | $x + 5 = 0$
$x = -4$ | $x = -5$

Ans. $x = -4$ or -5; solution set is $\{-4, -5\}$.

b) $a^2 - 49 = 0$

$(a + 7)(a - 7) = 0$
$a + 7 = 0$ | $a - 7 = 0$
$a = -7$ | $a = +7$

Ans. $a = -7$ or $+7$; solution set is $\{-7, 7\}$.

c) $3r^2 - 21r = 0$

$3r(r - 7) = 0$
$3r = 0$ | $r - 7 = 0$
$r = 0$ | $r = +7$

Ans. $r = 0$ or $+7$; solution set is $\{0, 7\}$.

2.3. More Difficult Solutions by Factoring

Solve by factoring:

a) $2 + \dfrac{5}{x} = \dfrac{12}{x^2}$

b) $(y-8)(2y-3) = 34$

c) $x - 6 = \sqrt{x}$

Solutions:

Clear of fractions:

$$2x^2 + 5x = 12$$
$$2x^2 + 5x - 12 = 0$$
$$(2x-3)(x+4) = 0$$

$2x - 3 = 0 \mid x + 4 = 0$
$x = \frac{3}{2} \mid \quad x = -4$

Ans. $x = \frac{3}{2}$ or -4

Remove ( ):

$$2y^2 - 19y + 24 = 34$$
$$2y^2 - 19y - 10 = 0$$
$$(2y+1)(y-10) = 0$$

$2y + 1 = 0 \mid y - 10 = 0$
$y = -\frac{1}{2} \mid \quad y = 10$

Ans. $y = -\frac{1}{2}$ or 10

Remove radical sign:

Sq $\quad x^2 - 12x + 36 = x$
$$x^2 - 13x + 36 = 0$$
$$(x-9)(x-4) = 0$$

$x - 9 = 0 \mid x - 4 = 0$
$x = 9 \mid \quad x = 4$

Ans. $x = 9$
(Show that 4 is extraneous.)

2.4. Number Problems Involving Quadratic Equations

a) Find a number whose square is 2 less than three times the number.

b) Find two consecutive integers such that the sum of their squares is 25.

Solutions:

Let n = the number.
$$n^2 = 3n - 2$$
$$n^2 - 3n + 2 = 0$$
$$(n-2)(n-1) = 0$$
$$n = 2 \text{ or } 1$$

Ans. 2 or 1

Let n and $n+1$ = the consecutive integers.
$$n^2 + (n+1)^2 = 25$$
$$n^2 + n^2 + 2n + 1 = 25$$
$$2n^2 + 2n - 24 = 0$$
$$n^2 + n - 12 = 0$$
$$(n+4)(n-3) = 0$$

$n = -4 \mid \quad n = 3$
$n + 1 = -3 \mid n + 1 = 4$

Ans. Either -4 and -3 or 3 and 4.

2.5. Area Problems Involving Quadratic Equations

The length of a rectangular lot is 3 yd. more than its width. Find its dimensions if the area

a) equals 40 sq. yd.

b) increases 70 sq. yd. when the width is doubled.

Solutions:

In (a) and (b), let w = width in yd. and $(w+3)$ = length in yd.

Area of lot = 40 sq. yd.
$$w(w+3) = 40$$
$$w^2 + 3w - 40 = 0$$
$$(w-5)(w+8) = 0$$

$w = 5 \mid w = -8$ Reject since width
$l = 8 \mid$ cannot be negative.

Ans. 8 yd. and 5 yd.

New area = old area + 70 sq. yd.
$$2w(w+3) = w(w+3) + 70$$
$$2w^2 + 6w = w^2 + 3w + 70$$
$$w^2 + 3w - 70 = 0$$
$$(w-7)(w+10) = 0$$

$w = 7 \mid w = -10$ Reject.
$l = 10 \mid$ *Ans.* 10 yd. and 7 yd.

3. SOLVING INCOMPLETE QUADRATIC EQUATIONS

An **incomplete quadratic equation** in one variable lacks either

(1) the term containing the first power of the variable, as in the case of $x^2 - 4 = 0$, or

(2) the constant term, as in the case of $x^2 - 4x = 0$.

Rule. If an incomplete quadratic equation lacks the constant term, then one of the roots is zero.

Thus, if $x^2 - 4x = 0$, $x = 0$ or 4.

To Solve an Incomplete Quadratic Equation Lacking the First Power of the Variable

Solve: $2(x^2-8) = 11 - x^2$

Procedure:

Solution:

1. **Express** in form, $ax^2 = k$ where k is a constant.

1. Tr $2x^2 - 16 = 11 - x^2$
$$3x^2 = 27$$

2. **Divide** both sides by a, obtaining $x^2 = \frac{k}{a}$.

2. Dividing by 3,
$$x^2 = 9 \ \ (See\ note.)$$

3. **Take the square root** of both sides, obtaining $x = \pm\sqrt{\frac{k}{a}}$.

3. Taking the sq. rt. of both sides,
$$x = \pm 3$$

4. **Check** each root in the original equation.

4. (*Check is left to the student.*)

Alternate Method: $x^2 = 9$ may be solved by factoring, as follows: $x^2 - 9 = 0$,
$$(x + 3)(x - 3) = 0, \ \ x = \pm 3.$$

To Solve an Incomplete Quadratic Equation Lacking Constant Term

Find the solution set of $3x^2 = 18x$

Procedure:

Solution:

1. **Express** in form $ax^2 + bx = 0$:

1. $3x^2 - 18x = 0$

2. **Factor** $ax^2 + bx$:

2. $3x(x-6) = 0$

3. **Let each factor** $= 0$:

3. $3x = 0 \mid x - 6 = 0$

4. **Solve** each resulting equation:

4. $x = 0 \mid \ \ \ \ x = 6$

5. **Check** each root in the original equation:

5. Check in $3x^2 = 18x$:

     If $x = 0$,   If $x = 6$,
     $3(0^2) \stackrel{?}{=} 18(0)$ $3(6^2) \stackrel{?}{=} 18(6)$
        $0 = 0$ $108 = 108$

Ans. Solution set is $\{0, 6\}$.

3.1. Solving Incomplete Quadratic Equations Lacking First Power of the Variable

Solve (*leave irrational answers in radical form*):

a) $4x^2 - 49 = 0$

Solutions:

D_4 $4x^2 = 49$

Sq Rt $x^2 = \frac{49}{4}$

Ans. $x = \pm\frac{7}{2}$

b) $2y^2 = 125 - 3y^2$

D_5 $5y^2 = 125$

Sq Rt $y^2 = 25$

Ans. $y = \pm 5$

c) $9x^2 - 2 = 5$

D_9 $9x^2 = 7$

Sq Rt $x^2 = \frac{7}{9}$

Ans. $x = \pm\frac{\sqrt{7}}{3}$

d) $\frac{8x}{25} = \frac{16}{x}$

D_8 $8x^2 = 400$

Sq Rt $x^2 = 50$

Ans. $x = \pm 5\sqrt{2}$

3.2. Solving Incomplete Quadratic Equations Lacking Constant Term

Find the solution set:

a) $3x^2 = 21x$

Solutions:

$3x^2 - 21x = 0$
$3x(x - 7) = 0$
$3x = 0 \mid x - 7 = 0$
$x = 0 \mid \ \ \ \ x = 7$

Ans. $x = 0$ or 7;
solution set is $\{0, 7\}$.

b) $5y(y-6) - 8y = 2y$

$5y^2 - 30y - 8y = 2y$
$5y^2 - 40y = 0$
$5y(y-8) = 0$
$5y = 0 \mid y - 8 = 0$
$y = 0 \mid \ \ \ \ y = 8$

Ans. $y = 0$ or 8;
solution set is $\{0, 8\}$.

c) $\frac{x^2}{5} = \frac{x}{15}$

$15x^2 = 5x$
$15x^2 - 5x = 0$
$5x(3x - 1) = 0$
$5x = 0 \mid 3x - 1 = 0$
$x = 0 \mid \ \ \ \ x = \frac{1}{3}$

Ans. $x = 0$ or $\frac{1}{3}$;
solution set is $\{0, \frac{1}{3}\}$.

d) $3(y^2 + 8) = 24 - 15y$

$3y^2 + 24 = 24 - 15y$
$3y^2 + 15y = 0$
$3y(y + 5) = 0$
$3y = 0 \mid y + 5 = 0$
$y = 0 \mid \ \ \ \ y = -5$

Ans. $y = 0$ or -5;
solution set is $\{0, -5\}$.

3.3. Solving Incomplete Quadratics for an Indicated Variable

Solve for the variable indicated:

a) Solve for x:	b) Solve for y:	c) Solve for a:	d) Solve for a:
$9x^2 - 64y^2 = 0$	$4y^2 - 95x^2 = 5x^2$	$3a^2 = b^2 - a^2$	$a(a-4) = b^2 - 4a$

Solutions:

$\mathbf{D_9}$ $\quad 9x^2 = 64y^2$	$\mathbf{D_4}$ $\quad 4y^2 = 100x^2$	$\mathbf{D_4}$ $\quad 4a^2 = b^2$	$\quad a^2 - 4a = b^2 - 4a$
Sq Rt $\quad x^2 = \dfrac{64y^2}{9}$	**Sq Rt** $\quad y^2 = 25x^2$	**Sq Rt** $\quad a^2 = \dfrac{b^2}{4}$	**Sq Rt** $\quad a^2 = b^2$
Ans. $\quad x = \pm\dfrac{8y}{3}$	*Ans.* $\quad y = \pm 5x$	*Ans.* $\quad a = \pm\dfrac{b}{2}$	*Ans.* $\quad a = \pm b$

3.4. Solving Formulas for an Indicated Variable

Solve for *positive* value of the variable indicated, when the other variables are positive:

a) Solve for r:	b) Solve for r:	c) Solve for a:	d) Solve for s:
$\pi r^2 = A$	$\pi r^2 h = V$	$a^2 + b^2 = c^2$	$\dfrac{s^2}{4} = A$

Solutions:

$\mathbf{D_\pi}$ $\quad \dfrac{\pi r^2}{\pi} = \dfrac{A}{\pi}$	$\mathbf{D_{\pi h}}$ $\quad \dfrac{\pi r^2 h}{\pi h} = \dfrac{V}{\pi h}$	$\mathbf{S_{b^2}}$ $\quad a^2 + b^2 = c^2$	$\mathbf{M_4}$ $\quad 4\left(\dfrac{s^2}{4}\right) = 4A$
Sq Rt $\quad r^2 = \dfrac{A}{\pi}$	**Sq Rt** $\quad r^2 = \dfrac{V}{\pi h}$	**Sq Rt** $\quad a^2 = c^2 - b^2$	**Sq Rt** $\quad s^2 = 4A$
Ans. $\quad r = \sqrt{\dfrac{A}{\pi}}$	*Ans.* $\quad r = \sqrt{\dfrac{V}{\pi h}}$	*Ans.* $\quad a = \sqrt{c^2 - b^2}$	*Ans.* $\quad s = 2\sqrt{A}$

4. SOLVING A QUADRATIC EQUATION BY COMPLETING THE SQUARE

The square of a binomial is a perfect trinomial square.

Thus, $x^2 + 6x + 9$ is the perfect trinomial square of $x + 3$.

Rule. If x^2 is the first term of a perfect trinomial square and the term in x is also given, the last term may be found by squaring one-half the coefficient of x.

Thus, if $x^2 + 6x$ is given, 9 is needed to complete the perfect trinomial square, $x^2 + 6x + 9$. This last term, 9, is found by squaring $\frac{1}{2}$ of 6 or 3.

To Solve a Quadratic Equation by Completing the Square

Solve $x^2 + 6x - 7 = 0$ by completing the square.

Procedure:

Solution:

1. Express the equation in the form $x^2 + px = q$.

1. Change $x^2 + 6x - 7 = 0$
$$x^2 + 6x = 7$$

2. Square one-half the coefficient of x and add this to both sides.

2. The square of $\frac{1}{2}(6) = 3^2 = 9$. Add 9 to get
$$x^2 + 6x \underline{+ 9} = 7 \underline{+ 9}$$

3. Replace the perfect trinomial square by its binomial squared.

3. $$(x + 3)^2 = 16$$

4. Take a square root of both sides. Set the binomial equal to $\pm$ the square root of the number on the other side.

4. **Sq Rt:**
$$x + 3 = \pm 4$$

5. Solve the two resulting equations.

5. $\quad x + 3 = 4 \mid x + 3 = -4$
$\qquad\quad x = 1 \mid \qquad x = -7$

6. Check both roots in the original equation.

6. (*Check is left to the student.*)
Ans. $x = 1$ or -7

4.1. Completing the Perfect Trinomial Square

Complete each perfect trinomial square and state its binomial squared:

a) $x^2 + 14x + ?$

Ans. a) The square of $\frac{1}{2}(14) = 7^2 = 49$.   Add 49 to get
$$x^2 + 14x + 49 = (x+7)^2$$

b) $x^2 - 20x + ?$

Ans. b) The square of $\frac{1}{2}(-20) = (-10)^2 = 100$.   Add 100 to get
$$x^2 - 20x + 100 = (x-10)^2$$

c) $x^2 + 5x + ?$

Ans. c) The square of $\frac{1}{2}(5) = (\frac{5}{2})^2 = \frac{25}{4}$.   Add $\frac{25}{4}$ to get
$$x^2 + 5x + \frac{25}{4} = (x+\frac{5}{2})^2$$

d) $y^2 + \frac{4}{3}y + ?$

Ans. d) The square of $\frac{1}{2}(\frac{4}{3}) = (\frac{2}{3})^2 = \frac{4}{9}$.   Add $\frac{4}{9}$ to get
$$y^2 + \frac{4}{3}y + \frac{4}{9} = (y+\frac{2}{3})^2$$

4.2. Solving Quadratic Equations by Completing the Square

Solve by completing the square: a) $x^2 + 14x - 32 = 0$ | b) $x(x+18) = 19$

Procedure:

1. Express as $x^2 + px = q$.

2. Add the square of half the coefficient of x to both sides.

3. Replace the perfect trinomial square by its binomial squared.

4. Take a square root of both sides.

5. Solve each resulting equation.

6. Check both roots.

Solutions:

1. $x^2 + 14x - 32 = 0$
   $x^2 + 14x = 32$

2. Square of $\frac{1}{2}(14) = 7^2 = 49$
   $\mathbf{A}_{49}$ $x^2 + 14x + 49 = 32 + 49$

3. $x^2 + 14x + 49 = 81$
   $(x+7)^2 = 81$

4. **Sq Rt** $x + 7 = \pm 9$

5. $x+7 = 9$ | $x+7 = -9$
   $x = 2$ | $x = -16$

6. (*Check is left to the student.*)
Ans. $x = 2$ or -16

---

1. $x(x+18) = 19$
   $x^2 + 18x = 19$

2. Square of $\frac{1}{2}(18) = 9^2 = 81$
   $\mathbf{A}_{81}$ $x^2 + 18x + 81 = 19 + 81$

3. $x^2 + 18x + 81 = 100$
   $(x+9)^2 = 100$

4. **Sq Rt** $x + 9 = \pm 10$

5. $x+9 = 10$ | $x+9 = -10$
   $x = 1$ | $x = -19$

Ans. $x = 1$ or -19

4.3. Equations Requiring Fractions to Complete the Square

Find the solution set by completing the square:

a) $x(x-5) = -4$

Solutions:
$$x^2 - 5x = -4$$

Square of $\frac{1}{2}(-5) = (-\frac{5}{2})^2 = \frac{25}{4}$

$\mathbf{A}_{\frac{25}{4}}$ $x^2 - 5x + \frac{25}{4} = \frac{25}{4} - 4$

$$(x - \frac{5}{2})^2 = \frac{9}{4}$$

Sq Rt $x - \frac{5}{2} = \pm \frac{3}{2}$

$x - \frac{5}{2} = \frac{3}{2}$ | $x - \frac{5}{2} = -\frac{3}{2}$

$x = 4$ | $x = 1$

Ans. $x = 4$ or 1; solution set is $\{4, 1\}$.

b) $5t^2 - 4t = 33$

$$t^2 - \frac{4t}{5} = \frac{33}{5}$$

Square of $\frac{1}{2}(-\frac{4}{5}) = (-\frac{2}{5})^2 = \frac{4}{25}$

$\mathbf{A}_{\frac{4}{25}}$ $t^2 - \frac{4t}{5} + \frac{4}{25} = \frac{33}{5} + \frac{4}{25}$

$$(t - \frac{2}{5})^2 = \frac{169}{25}$$

Sq Rt $t - \frac{2}{5} = \pm \frac{13}{5}$

$t - \frac{2}{5} = \frac{13}{5}$ | $t - \frac{2}{5} = -\frac{13}{5}$

$t = 3$ | $t = -\frac{11}{5}$

Ans. $t = 3$ or $-\frac{11}{5}$; solution set is
$$\{3, -\frac{11}{5}\}.$$

4.4. Solving the Quadratic Equation in Standard Form

If $ax^2 + bx + c = 0$, then $x = \dfrac{-b \pm \sqrt{b^2 - 4ac}}{2a}$. Prove this by completing the square.

Solution:

$$ax^2 + bx + c = 0$$

Tr $\quad ax^2 + bx = -c$

D$_a$ $\quad x^2 + \dfrac{bx}{a} = -\dfrac{c}{a}$

Square of $\dfrac{1}{2}(\dfrac{b}{a}) = (\dfrac{b}{2a})^2 = \dfrac{b^2}{4a^2}$

A$_{\frac{b^2}{4a^2}}$ $\quad x^2 + \dfrac{bx}{a} + \dfrac{b^2}{4a^2} = \dfrac{b^2}{4a^2} - \dfrac{c}{a}$

$$(x + \tfrac{b}{2a})^2 = \dfrac{b^2 - 4ac}{4a^2}$$

Sq Rt $\quad x + \dfrac{b}{2a} = \pm \dfrac{\sqrt{b^2 - 4ac}}{2a}$

$$x = -\dfrac{b}{2a} \pm \dfrac{\sqrt{b^2 - 4ac}}{2a}$$

By combining fractions,

$$x = \dfrac{-b \pm \sqrt{b^2 - 4ac}}{2a} \quad Ans.$$

5. SOLVING A QUADRATIC EQUATION BY QUADRATIC FORMULA

Quadratic Formula: If $ax^2 + bx + c = 0$, then $x = \dfrac{-b \pm \sqrt{b^2 - 4ac}}{2a}$ when $a \neq 0$.

(See proof of this in Example 4.4 of the previous unit.)

To Solve a Quadratic Equation by the Quadratic Formula

Solve $x^2 - 4x = -3$ by quadratic formula.

Procedure:

1. Express in form of $ax^2 + bx + c = 0$:

2. State the values of a, b and c:

3. Substitute the values of a, b and c in the formula:

4. Solve for x:

5. Check each root in the original equation:

Solution:

1. $\quad x^2 - 4x = -3$
$\quad x^2 - 4x + 3 = 0$

2. $\quad a = 1, \quad b = -4, \quad c = 3$

3. $\quad x = \dfrac{-b \pm \sqrt{b^2 - 4ac}}{2a}$

$\quad x = \dfrac{-(-4) \pm \sqrt{(-4)^2 - 4(1)(3)}}{2(1)}$

4. $\quad x = \dfrac{+4 \pm \sqrt{16 - 12}}{2}$

$\quad x = \dfrac{+4 \pm \sqrt{4}}{2}$

$\quad x = \dfrac{4 \pm 2}{2}$

$\quad x = \dfrac{4 + 2}{2} \quad | \quad x = \dfrac{4 - 2}{2}$

$\quad x = 3 \quad | \quad x = 1$

5. *(Check left to student.)*

Ans. $x = 3$ or 1

5.1. Finding $b^2 - 4ac$ in the Quadratic Formula

For each equation, state the values of a, b and c. Then find the value of $b^2 - 4ac$.

a) $3x^2 + 4x - 5 = 0$

b) $x^2 - 2x - 10 = 0$

c) $3x^2 - 5x = 10$

Solutions:

$a = 3$
$b = 4$
$c = -5$
$\quad \left.\begin{array}{c} \\ \\ \end{array}\right\}$
$b^2 - 4ac$
$4^2 - 4(3)(-5)$
$16 + 60$

Ans. 76

$a = 1$
$b = -2$
$c = -10$
$\quad \left.\begin{array}{c} \\ \\ \end{array}\right\}$
$b^2 - 4ac$
$(-2)^2 - 4(1)(-10)$
$4 + 40$

Ans. 44

Tr $\quad 3x^2 - 5x - 10 = 0$

$a = 3$
$b = -5$
$c = -10$
$\quad \left.\begin{array}{c} \\ \\ \end{array}\right\}$
$b^2 - 4ac$
$(-5)^2 - 4(3)(-10)$
$25 + 120$

Ans. 145

5.2. Expressing Roots in Simplified Radical Form

Express the roots of each equation in simplified radical form, using the value of $b^2 - 4ac$ obtained in Example **5.1**:

a) $3x^2 + 4x - 5 = 0$

Solutions:

$$x = \frac{-b \pm \sqrt{b^2 - 4ac}}{2a}$$

$\left. \begin{array}{l} a = 3 \\ b = 4 \\ c = -5 \end{array} \right\}$ $x = \dfrac{-4 \pm \sqrt{76}}{6}$

b) $x^2 - 2x - 10 = 0$

$$x = \frac{-b \pm \sqrt{b^2 - 4ac}}{2a}$$

$\left. \begin{array}{l} a = 1 \\ b = -2 \\ c = -10 \end{array} \right\}$ $x = \dfrac{2 \pm \sqrt{44}}{2}$

c) $3x^2 - 5x = 10$

$$x = \frac{-b \pm \sqrt{b^2 - 4ac}}{2a}$$

$\left. \begin{array}{l} a = 3 \\ b = -5 \\ c = -10 \end{array} \right\}$ $x = \dfrac{5 \pm \sqrt{145}}{6}$

5.3. Evaluating Roots in Radical Form

Solve for x, to the nearest tenth, using the simplified radical form obtained in Example **5.2**:
(Find square root to two decimal places.)

a) $3x^2 + 4x - 5 = 0$

Solutions:

$$x = \frac{-4 \pm \sqrt{76}}{6}$$

```
            8.  7  1
       √ 76. 00 00
         64
 167   | 12 00
       | 11 69
 1741  |    31 00
       |    17 41
       |    13 59
```

$x = \dfrac{-4 + 8.71}{6}$ | $x = \dfrac{-4 - 8.71}{6}$

$x = \dfrac{4.71}{6}$ | $x = \dfrac{-12.71}{6}$

Ans. $x = .8$ or $x = -2.1$

b) $x^2 - 2x - 10 = 0$

$$x = \frac{2 \pm \sqrt{44}}{2}$$

```
            6.  6  3
       √ 44. 00 00
         36
 126   | 8 00
       | 7 56
 1323  |    44 00
       |    39 69
       |     4 31
```

$x = \dfrac{2 + 6.63}{2}$ | $x = \dfrac{2 - 6.63}{2}$

$x = \dfrac{8.63}{2}$ | $x = \dfrac{-4.63}{2}$

Ans. $x = 4.3$ or $x = -2.3$

c) $3x^2 - 5x = 10$

$$x = \frac{5 \pm \sqrt{145}}{6}$$

```
            1  2. 0  4
       √ 1 45. 00 00
         1
 22    | 45
       | 44
 2404  |  1 00 00
       |    96 16
       |     3 84
```

$x = \dfrac{5 + 12.04}{6}$ | $x = \dfrac{5 - 12.04}{6}$

$x = \dfrac{17.04}{6}$ | $x = \dfrac{-7.04}{6}$

Ans. $x = 2.8$ or $x = -1.2$

6. SOLVING QUADRATIC EQUATIONS GRAPHICALLY

To Solve a Quadratic Equation Graphically

Procedure:

1. Express in form of $ax^2 + bx + c = 0$.

2. Graph the curve, $y = ax^2 + bx + c$. *(The curve is called a parabola.)*

3. Find where $y = 0$ intersects $y = ax^2 + bx + c$.

   The values of x at the points of intersection are the roots of $ax^2 + bx + c = 0$.

   (**Note.** Think of $ax^2 + bx + c = 0$ as the result of combining $y = ax^2 + bx + c$ with $y = 0$.)

Solve graphically, $x^2 - 5x + 4 = 0$.

Solution:

1. $x^2 - 5x + 4 = 0$

2.

GRAPH of
$y = x^2 - 5x + 4$
(parabola)

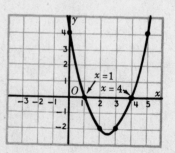

3. $x = 1$ and $x = 4$ *Ans.*

Line Symmetry: Axis of Symmetry of Parabola

1. A line is the **axis of symmetry of two points** if it is the perpendicular bisector of the line joining the two points.

Thus, $\overleftrightarrow{BC}$ is the axis of symmetry of points A and A'.

2. A line is an **axis of symmetry of a figure** if any line perpendicular to it is bisected by the figure.

Thus, $\overleftrightarrow{FE}$ is the axis of symmetry of the curve (parabola) shown. $\overleftrightarrow{FE}$ is perpendicular to and bisects $\overleftrightarrow{AA'}$, $\overleftrightarrow{BB'}$, etc. $\overleftrightarrow{FE}$ is the "folding line" of the parabola.

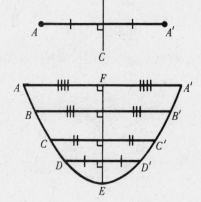

The following graphical solution of a quadratic equation makes use of the axis of symmetry of a parabola to prepare a table of values.

To Solve a Quadratic Equation Graphically

Solve graphically: $x^2 - 2x = 3$

Procedure:

Solution:

1. Express in form of $ax^2 + bx + c = 0$.

1. Tr $x^2 - 2x - 3 = 0$

2. Graph parabola, $y = ax^2 + bx + c$.

2. Graph $x^2 - 2x - 3 = y$

x	x^2	$-$	$2x$	$-$	3	$=$	y
4	16	$-$	8	$-$	3	$=$	5
3	9	$-$	6	$-$	3	$=$	0
2	4	$-$	4	$-$	3	$=$	-3
$-\frac{b}{2a} = \frac{2}{2} = 1$	1	$-$	2	$-$	3	$=$	-4
0	0		0	$-$	3	$=$	-3
-1	1	$+$	2	$-$	3	$=$	0
-2	4	$+$	4	$-$	3	$=$	5

a) Obtain a **table of values**, using a suitable sequence of values for x:

(This may be done by finding the value of $-\frac{b}{2a}$ and choosing values of x greater or smaller than $-\frac{b}{2a}$.)

b) Join plotted points:

(Note that $x = -\frac{b}{2a}$ is the folding line or axis of symmetry of the parabola.)

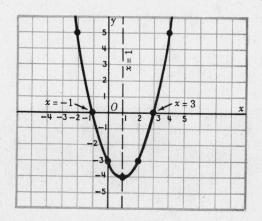

3. Find roots where parabola crosses x-axis.

3. $x = -1$ or 3   *Ans.*

6.1. Obtaining Tables of Values for a Parabola

Obtain a table of values for each, using the indicated sequence of values for x:

a) $y = x^2 - 4$
for $x = -3$ to $+3$

b) $y = x^2 - 3x$
for $x = -1$ to 4

c) $y = x^2 - 3x - 4$
for $x = -1$ to 5

Solutions:

$x^2 - 4 = y$

x	$x^2 - 4 = y$
3	$9 - 4 = 5$
2	$4 - 4 = 0$
1	$1 - 4 = -3$
→ 0	$0 - 4 = -4$
-1	$1 - 4 = -3$
-2	$4 - 4 = 0$
-3	$9 - 4 = 5$

$x^2 - 3x = y$

x	$x^2 - 3x = y$
4	$16 - 12 = 4$
3	$9 - 9 = 0$
$x = 1\frac{1}{2}$ → 2	$4 - 6 = -2$
1	$1 - 3 = -2$
0	$0 + 0 = 0$
-1	$1 + 3 = 4$

$x^2 - 3x - 4 = y$

x	$x^2 - 3x - 4 = y$
5	$25 - 15 - 4 = 6$
4	$16 - 12 - 4 = 0$
3	$9 - 9 - 4 = -4$
$x = 1\frac{1}{2}$ → 2	$4 - 6 - 4 = -6$
1	$1 - 3 - 4 = -6$
0	$0 + 0 - 4 = -4$
-1	$1 + 3 - 4 = 0$

(The arrow in each table indicates $x = -\dfrac{b}{2a}$, the axis of symmetry of the parabola.)

6.2. Graphing Parabolas $y = ax^2 + bx + c$

Graph each, using the table of values obtained in Example **6.1**:

a) $y = x^2 - 4$

b) $y = x^2 - 3x$

c) $y = x^2 - 3x - 4$

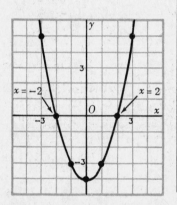
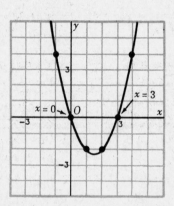
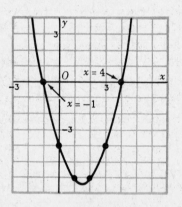

6.3. Finding Roots Graphically

Find the roots of each, using the parabolas obtained in Example **6.2**:

a) $0 = x^2 - 4$

b) $0 = x^2 - 3x$

c) $0 = x^2 - 3x - 4$

Solutions:

(In each case, find the values of x at the points where the parabola crosses the x-axis.)

Ans. $x = -2$ or 2

Ans. $x = 0$ or 3

Ans. $x = -1$ or 4

SUPPLEMENTARY PROBLEMS

1. Express in standard quadratic equation form, $ax^2 + bx + c = 0$, so that a has a positive value: **(1.1)**

   a) $3(x^2 - 5) = 4x$ c) $\frac{7}{x} - 5 = 2x$ e) $3x - 9 = x^2 - 7x$ g) $\sqrt{2x^2 + 3x} = x$

   b) $2x(x + 4) = 42$ d) $\frac{6}{x} + x = \frac{11}{2}$ f) $x(2x - 7) = 3x^2 - 8$ h) $x + 1 = \sqrt{3x + 7}$

   Ans. a) $3x^2 - 4x - 15 = 0$ c) $0 = 2x^2 + 5x - 7$ e) $0 = x^2 - 10x + 9$ g) $x^2 + 3x = 0$

   b) $2x^2 + 8x - 42 = 0$ d) $2x^2 - 11x + 12 = 0$ f) $0 = x^2 + 7x - 8$ h) $x^2 - x - 6 = 0$

2. Express in standard quadratic equation form, so that a has a positive value. Then state the values of a, b and c. **(1.2)**

	Standard Form	a	b	c
a) $x^2 = 5x - 4$	*Ans.* a) $x^2 - 5x + 4 = 0$	1	-5	$+4$
b) $20 + 6x = 2x^2$	*Ans.* b) $0 = 2x^2 - 6x - 20$	2	-6	-20
c) $3x^2 = -5x$	*Ans.* c) $3x^2 + 5x = 0$	3	$+5$	0
d) $18 = 2x^2$	*Ans.* d) $0 = 2x^2 - 18$	2	0	-18
e) $x(8 - 2x) = 6$	*Ans.* e) $0 = 2x^2 - 8x + 6$	2	-8	$+6$
f) $7(x^2 - 9) = x(x - 5)$	*Ans.* f) $6x^2 + 5x - 63 = 0$	6	$+5$	-63
g) $\frac{10}{x} + 1 = 4x$	*Ans.* g) $0 = 4x^2 - x - 10$	4	-1	-10
h) $\sqrt{x^2 - 5x} = 3x$	*Ans.* h) $0 = 8x^2 + 5x$	8	$+5$	0

3. Solve by factoring: **(2.1, 2.2)**

   a) $x^2 - 5x + 6 = 0$ d) $4a^2 = 28a$ g) $c^2 + 6c = -8$ j) $5 = r(2r + 3)$

   b) $y^2 + y - 20 = 0$ e) $4x^2 = 1$ h) $d^2 = 5d + 24$ k) $t + 8 = \frac{20}{t}$

   c) $w^2 - 64 = 0$ f) $9b^2 = 3b$ i) $p(3p + 20) = 7$ l) $\frac{7}{x} = 9 - 2x$

   Each answer is underlined:

   a) $(x - 2)(x - 3) = 0$ d) $4a(a - 7) = 0$ g) $(c + 4)(c + 2) = 0$ j) $0 = (r - 1)(2r + 5)$
   $\underline{x = 2 \text{ or } 3}$ $\underline{a = 0 \text{ or } 7}$ $\underline{c = -4 \text{ or } -2}$ $\underline{r = 1 \text{ or } -\frac{5}{2}}$

   b) $(y + 5)(y - 4) = 0$ e) $(2x + 1)(2x - 1) = 0$ h) $(d - 8)(d + 3) = 0$ k) $(t - 2)(t + 10) = 0$
   $\underline{y = -5 \text{ or } 4}$ $\underline{x = -\frac{1}{2} \text{ or } \frac{1}{2}}$ $\underline{d = 8 \text{ or } -3}$ $\underline{t = 2 \text{ or } -10}$

   c) $(w - 8)(w + 8) = 0$ f) $3b(3b - 1) = 0$ i) $(3p - 1)(p + 7) = 0$ l) $(2x - 7)(x - 1) = 0$
   $\underline{w = 8 \text{ or } -8}$ $\underline{b = 0 \text{ or } \frac{1}{3}}$ $\underline{p = \frac{1}{3} \text{ or } -7}$ $\underline{x = \frac{7}{2} \text{ or } 1}$

4. Solve by factoring: **(2.3)**

   a) $\frac{3x - 2}{5} = \frac{8}{x}$ c) $(y - 2)(3y - 1) = 100$ e) $x + 1 = \sqrt{5x + 1}$

   b) $\frac{21}{x - 3} = x - 7$ d) $(y + 3)(y - 3) = 2y - 1$ f) $\sqrt{x} - 2 = x - 8$

   Each answer is underlined:

   a) $(x - 4)(3x + 10) = 0$ c) $(y - 7)(3y + 14) = 0$ e) $x(x - 3) = 0$
   $\underline{x = 4 \text{ or } -\frac{10}{3}; \{4, -\frac{10}{3}\}}$ $\underline{y = 7 \text{ or } -\frac{14}{3}; \{7, -\frac{14}{3}\}}$ $\underline{x = 0 \text{ or } 3; \{0, 3\}}$

   b) $0 = x(x - 10)$ d) $(y - 4)(y + 2) = 0$ f) $0 = (x - 9)(x - 4)$
   $x = 0 \text{ or } 10; \{0, 10\}$ $\underline{y = 4 \text{ or } -2; \{4, -2\}}$ $\underline{x = 9(4 \text{ is an extraneous root}); \{9\}}$

5. Find a number such that **(2.4)**

   a) its square is 12 more than the number.

   b) its square decreased by three times the number is 18.

   c) the product of the number and 4 less than the number is 32.

   d) the square of one more than the number is 4 more than four times the number.

   Each answer is underlined:

   a) $n^2 = n + 12$ b) $n^2 - 3n = 18$ c) $n(n - 4) = 32$ d) $(n + 1)^2 = 4n + 4$
   $\underline{4 \text{ or } -3}$ $\underline{6 \text{ or } -3}$ $\underline{8 \text{ or } -4}$ $\underline{3 \text{ or } -1}$

6. Find two consecutive integers such that   (2.4)
   a) the sum of their squares is 13.
   b) their product is 30.
   c) the square of the first added to twice the second is 5.
   d) the product of the first and twice the second is 40.
   Each answer is underlined:

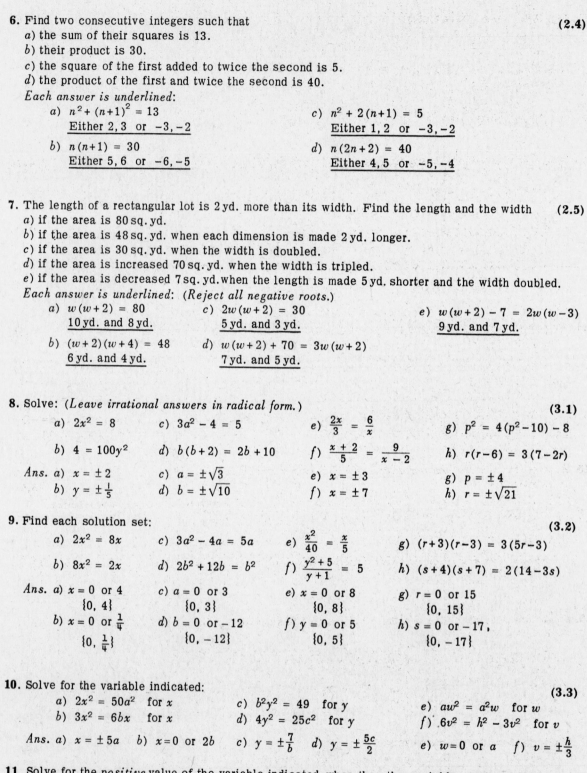

   a) $n^2 + (n+1)^2 = 13$
   Either 2, 3 or −3, −2

   c) $n^2 + 2(n+1) = 5$
   Either 1, 2 or −3, −2

   b) $n(n+1) = 30$
   Either 5, 6 or −6, −5

   d) $n(2n+2) = 40$
   Either 4, 5 or −5, −4

7. The length of a rectangular lot is 2 yd. more than its width. Find the length and the width   (2.5)
   a) if the area is 80 sq. yd.
   b) if the area is 48 sq. yd. when each dimension is made 2 yd. longer.
   c) if the area is 30 sq. yd. when the width is doubled.
   d) if the area is increased 70 sq. yd. when the width is tripled.
   e) if the area is decreased 7 sq. yd. when the length is made 5 yd. shorter and the width doubled.
   Each answer is underlined: (*Reject all negative roots.*)

   a) $w(w+2) = 80$
   10 yd. and 8 yd.

   c) $2w(w+2) = 30$
   5 yd. and 3 yd.

   e) $w(w+2) - 7 = 2w(w-3)$
   9 yd. and 7 yd.

   b) $(w+2)(w+4) = 48$
   6 yd. and 4 yd.

   d) $w(w+2) + 70 = 3w(w+2)$
   7 yd. and 5 yd.

8. Solve: (*Leave irrational answers in radical form.*)   (3.1)

   a) $2x^2 = 8$
   c) $3a^2 - 4 = 5$
   e) $\frac{2x}{3} = \frac{6}{x}$
   g) $p^2 = 4(p^2 - 10) - 8$

   b) $4 = 100y^2$
   d) $b(b+2) = 2b + 10$
   f) $\frac{x+2}{5} = \frac{9}{x-2}$
   h) $r(r-6) = 3(7-2r)$

   Ans. *a*) $x = \pm 2$
   c) $a = \pm\sqrt{3}$
   e) $x = \pm 3$
   g) $p = \pm 4$

   b) $y = \pm\frac{1}{5}$
   d) $b = \pm\sqrt{10}$
   f) $x = \pm 7$
   h) $r = \pm\sqrt{21}$

9. Find each solution set: (3.2)

   a) $2x^2 = 8x$
   c) $3a^2 - 4a = 5a$
   e) $\frac{x^2}{40} = \frac{x}{5}$
   g) $(r+3)(r-3) = 3(5r-3)$

   b) $8x^2 = 2x$
   d) $2b^2 + 12b = b^2$
   f) $\frac{y^2+5}{y+1} = 5$
   h) $(s+4)(s+7) = 2(14-3s)$

   Ans. *a*) $x = 0$ or 4
   {0, 4}

   c) $a = 0$ or 3
   {0, 3}

   e) $x = 0$ or 8
   {0, 8}

   g) $r = 0$ or 15
   {0, 15}

   b) $x = 0$ or $\frac{1}{4}$
   {0, $\frac{1}{4}$}

   d) $b = 0$ or −12
   {0, −12}

   f) $y = 0$ or 5
   {0, 5}

   h) $s = 0$ or −17,
   {0, −17}

10. Solve for the variable indicated: (3.3)
   a) $2x^2 = 50a^2$ for *x*
   c) $b^2y^2 = 49$ for *y*
   e) $aw^2 = a^2w$ for *w*
   b) $3x^2 = 6bx$ for *x*
   d) $4y^2 = 25c^2$ for *y*
   f) $6v^2 = h^2 - 3v^2$ for *v*

   Ans. *a*) $x = \pm 5a$ *b*) $x = 0$ or $2b$ *c*) $y = \pm\frac{7}{b}$ *d*) $y = \pm\frac{5c}{2}$ *e*) $w = 0$ or *a*   *f*) $v = \pm\frac{h}{3}$

11. Solve for the *positive* value of the variable indicated, when the other variables are positive: (3.4)
   a) $S = 16t^2$ for *t*
   c) $S = 4\pi r^2$ for *r*
   e) $a^2 + b^2 = c^2$ for *b*

   b) $K = \frac{1}{2}mv^2$ for *v*
   d) $F = \frac{mv^2}{r}$ for *v*
   f) $A = \pi(R^2 - r^2)$ for *R*

   Ans. *a*) $t = \frac{\sqrt{S}}{4}$,   *b*) $v = \sqrt{\frac{2K}{m}}$,   *c*) $r = \frac{1}{2}\sqrt{\frac{S}{\pi}}$,   *d*) $v = \sqrt{\frac{Fr}{m}}$,   *e*) $b = \sqrt{c^2 - a^2}$,   *f*) $R = \sqrt{\frac{A + \pi r^2}{\pi}}$

12. Complete each perfect binomial square and state its binomial squared: **(4.1)**

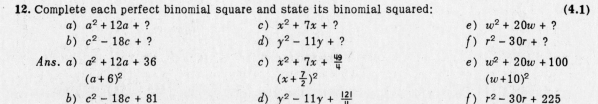

a) $a^2 + 12a + ?$ c) $x^2 + 7x + ?$ e) $w^2 + 20w + ?$

b) $c^2 - 18c + ?$ d) $y^2 - 11y + ?$ f) $r^2 - 30r + ?$

Ans. a) $a^2 + 12a + 36$ c) $x^2 + 7x + \frac{49}{4}$ e) $w^2 + 20w + 100$

$\quad\quad (a+6)^2$ $\quad\quad (x + \frac{7}{2})^2$ $\quad\quad (w+10)^2$

b) $c^2 - 18c + 81$ d) $y^2 - 11y + \frac{121}{4}$ f) $r^2 - 30r + 225$

$\quad\quad (c-9)^2$ $\quad\quad (y - \frac{11}{2})^2$ $\quad\quad (r-15)^2$

13. Solve by completing the square (*use the answers in* **12** *above to help you*):   **(4.2, 4.3)**

a) $a^2 + 12a = 45$ c) $x^2 + 7x = 8$ e) $w^2 + 20w = -19$

b) $c^2 - 18c = -65$ d) $y^2 - 11y = -28$ f) $r^2 - 30r = 99$

Each answer is underlined:

a) $\underline{a = 3 \text{ or } -15}$ c) $\underline{x = 1 \text{ or } -8}$ e) $\underline{w = -1 \text{ or } -19}$

$\quad$ from $(a+6)^2 = 81$ from $(x+\frac{7}{2})^2 = \frac{81}{4}$ from $(w+10)^2 = \pm 9$

b) $\underline{c = 5 \text{ or } 13}$ d) $\underline{y = 4 \text{ or } 7}$ f) $\underline{r = -3 \text{ or } 33}$

$\quad$ from $(c-9)^2 = 16$ from $(y-\frac{11}{2})^2 = \frac{9}{4}$ from $(r-15)^2 = 324$

14. For each equation, state the values of a, b and c. Then find the value of $b^2 - 4ac$.   **(5.1)**

a) $2x^2 + 5x + 1 = 0$ c) $3x^2 - 2 = 4x$ e) $5x^2 = 10x - 4$ g) $x^2 = 10 - 6x$

b) $x^2 + 7x = -5$ d) $2x^2 - 5x = 4$ f) $6x^2 = 10x - 3$ h) $9x^2 = 2 - x$

Ans. a) $a=2$, $b=5$, $c=1$ c) $a=3$, $b=-4$, $c=-2$ e) $a=5$, $b=-10$, $c=4$ g) $a=1$, $b=6$, $c=-10$

$\quad\quad b^2 - 4ac = 17$ $b^2 - 4ac = 40$ $b^2 - 4ac = 20$ $b^2 - 4ac = 76$

b) $a=1$, $b=7$, $c=5$ d) $a=2$, $b=-5$, $c=-4$ f) $a=6$, $b=-10$, $c=3$ h) $a=9$, $b=1$, $c=-2$

$\quad\quad b^2 - 4ac = 29$ $b^2 - 4ac = 57$ $b^2 - 4ac = 28$ $b^2 - 4ac = 73$

15. Express the roots of each equation in simplified radical form, using the value of $b^2 - 4ac$ found in Problem **14**:   **(5.2)**

a) $2x^2 + 5x + 1 = 0$ c) $3x^2 - 2 = 4x$ e) $5x^2 = 10x - 4$ g) $x^2 = 10 - 6x$

b) $x^2 + 7x = -5$ d) $2x^2 - 5x = 4$ f) $6x^2 = 10x - 3$ h) $9x^2 = 2 - x$

Ans. a) $x = \dfrac{-5 \pm \sqrt{17}}{4}$ c) $x = \dfrac{4 \pm \sqrt{40}}{6}$ e) $x = \dfrac{10 \pm \sqrt{20}}{10}$ g) $x = \dfrac{-6 \pm \sqrt{76}}{2}$

b) $x = \dfrac{-7 \pm \sqrt{29}}{2}$ d) $x = \dfrac{5 \pm \sqrt{57}}{4}$ f) $x = \dfrac{10 \pm \sqrt{28}}{12}$ h) $x = \dfrac{-1 \pm \sqrt{73}}{18}$

16. Solve for x, correct to the nearest tenth, using the simplified radical form found in Problem **15**:   **(5.3)**

a) $2x^2 + 5x + 1 = 0$ c) $3x^2 - 2 = 4x$ e) $5x^2 = 10x - 4$ g) $x^2 = 10 - 6x$

b) $x^2 + 7x = -5$ d) $2x^2 - 5x = 4$ f) $6x^2 = 10x - 3$ h) $9x^2 = 2 - x$

Ans. a) $x = -2.3$ or $-.2$ c) $x = 1.7$ or $-.4$ e) $x = 1.4$ or $.6$ g) $x = 1.4$ or -7.4

b) $x = -6.2$ or $-.8$ d) $x = 3.1$ or $-.6$ f) $x = 1.3$ or $.4$ h) $x = .4$ or $-.5$

17. Solve, correct to the nearest tenth: **(5.3)**

a) $2y^2 = -3y + 1$ c) $2w^2 = 3w + 5$ e) $x + 5 = \dfrac{5}{x}$

b) $x(x-4) = -2$ d) $6v^2 + 1 = 5v$ f) $\dfrac{x^2}{2} = 4x - 1$

Ans. a) $y = .3$ or -1.8;   c) $w = 2.5$ or -1;   e) $x = .9$ or -5.9;

$\quad\quad \{.3, -1.8\}$ $\quad\quad \{2.5, -1\}$ $\quad\quad \{.9, -5.9\}$

b) $x = 3.4$ or $.6$;   d) $v = .5$ or $.3$;   f) $x = 7.7$ or $.3$;

$\quad\quad \{.6, 3.4\}$ $\quad\quad \{.3, .5\}$ $\quad\quad \{7.7, .3\}$

18. Solve graphically (*see sketches after Problem* **19.**): **(6.1 to 6.3)**

 a) Graph $y = x^2 - 9$ from $x = -4$ to $x = 4$ and solve $x^2 - 9 = 0$ graphically.

 b) Graph $y = x^2 + 3x - 4$ from $x = -5$ to $x = 2$ and solve $x^2 + 3x = 4$ graphically.

 c) Graph $y = x^2 - 6x + 9$ from $x = 1$ to $x = 5$ and solve $x^2 = 6x - 9$ graphically.

 d) Graph $y = x^2 + 8x + 16$ from $x = -6$ to $x = -2$ and solve $x^2 + 8x = -16$ graphically.

 e) Graph $y = x^2 - 2x + 4$ from $x = -1$ to $x = 3$ and show that $x^2 - 2x + 4 = 0$ has no real roots.

 Ans. *a*) $x = 3$ or -3 *b*) $x = -4$ or 1

  c) $x = 3$ Equal roots since the parabola touches x-axis at one point.

  d) $x = -4$ Equal roots since the parabola touches x-axis at one point.

  e) Roots are not real (imaginary) since the parabola does not meet x-axis.

19. Solve graphically (*see sketches below*): **(6.1 to 6.3)**

a) $x^2 - 1 = 0$	*c*) $x^2 - 4x = 0$	*e*) $x^2 - 2x = 8$
b) $4x^2 - 9 = 0$	*d*) $2x^2 + 7x = 0$	*f*) $4x^2 = 12x - 9$

 Ans. *a*) $x = -1$ or 1 *c*) $x = 0$ or 4 *e*) $x = 4$ or -2

  b) $x = 1\frac{1}{2}$ or $-1\frac{1}{2}$ *d*) $x = 0$ or $-3\frac{1}{2}$ *f*) $x = 1\frac{1}{2}, 1\frac{1}{2}$

Sketches of graphs needed in Problems **18** and **19**, showing relationship of parabola and x-axis:

 18*a*, 18*b*, 19*a* to 19*e*   **18*c*, 18*d*, 19*f***   **18*e***

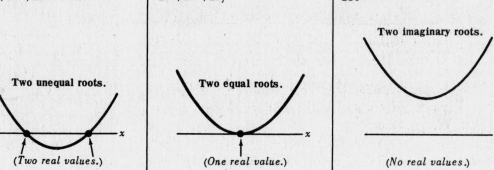

Two unequal roots.   Two equal roots.   Two imaginary roots.

(*Two real values.*)   (*One real value.*)   (*No real values.*)

Chapter 14

Indirect Measurement

1. INDIRECT MEASUREMENT: USING TRIANGLES DRAWN TO SCALE

By indirect measurement, the measure of a quantity is obtained by measuring another quantity instead.

Thus, we can find the distance between two towns, A and B, by measuring $\overline{AB}$ in Fig. 1. Since $AB = 4$ units and the scale is 20 miles per unit, then the actual distance between the towns is 4(20) or 80 miles.

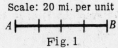

Scale: 20 mi. per unit

Fig. 1

(A scale of 20 miles per unit indicates that each unit on the map represents 20 miles.)

When the situation indicates that measurement of a line or an angle is involved, the term "angle" should be taken to mean the "measure of the angle" and the term "line" to mean the "measure of the line segment".

Using a Scale Triangle to Measure Lines and Angles Indirectly

1. The **actual distance**, D, represented by a line equals the product of the scale, S, and the number, N, of the units in the line: $D = SN$.

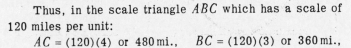

Scale: 120 mi. per unit

(See Section 2 for an extended treatment of $D = SN$.)

Thus, in the scale triangle ABC which has a scale of 120 miles per unit:

$$AC = (120)(4) \text{ or } 480\,\text{mi.,} \quad BC = (120)(3) \text{ or } 360\,\text{mi.,} \quad AB = (120)(5) \text{ or } 600\,\text{mi.}$$

(The length of $\overline{AB}$ can be found by placing the ends of a compass on A and B and then laying off this opening along a line of the graph.)

2. The **actual angle** represented by an angle equals the number of degrees in the angle.

Thus, since $\angle A$ in the scale triangle $= 37°$, the actual $\angle A = 37°$.

(Use a protractor to measure $\angle A$ in the scale triangle.)

1.1. Measuring Indirectly, Using Triangles Drawn to Scale

An aviator flew 480 miles due east from A to C. Then he flew 360 miles due north from C to B. To fly straight back to A,

(1) what distance must be flown and

(2) what angle of turn must be made, to the nearest degree?

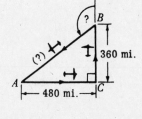

360 mi.

480 mi.

Solution:

Construct scale triangle ABC **as follows:**

1. Choose a convenient scale, say 60 mi. per unit.
2. Lay off 8 units for $AC = 480$ mi.
3. Lay off 6 units for $BC = 360$ mi.
4. Draw AB.

Find distance from A **to** B**:**

By measurement, $AB = 10$ units.

Since scale $= 60$ mi. per unit, distance $AB = 600$ mi.

Find angle of turn at B**:**

Using protractor, angle of turn at $B = 127°$.

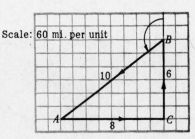

Scale: 60 mi. per unit

Ans. (1) Distance from A to $B = 600$ mi.

(2) Angle of turn at $B = 127°$.

2.   **D = SN: A FORMULA OF INDIRECT MEASUREMENT**

FOR FIGURES DRAWN TO SCALE ON MAPS, GRAPHS, MODELS AND BLUEPRINTS

Rule. A line on a scaled figure such as a map represents a distance, D, equal to the product of the scale, S, and the number of units, N, in the line.

$$\text{Formula}: \quad D = SN \qquad\qquad \text{Other forms}: \quad N = \frac{D}{S}, \quad S = \frac{D}{N}$$

Note. To use this formula, $D = SN$, S must be in distance units per map unit or graph unit, such as miles per inch, or feet per graph unit.

Thus, for a distance of 100 miles represented by a 5 inch line, the scale is 20 **miles per inch.**

2.1. Finding Distance Being Represented: $D = SN$

Find the distance, D, represented by a line $\overline{AB}$ on a map or graph

a) if $AB = 5$ in. and the scale of the map is 20 mi. per in.

b) if $AB = 8$ cm. and the scale of the map is 12 mi. per cm.

c) if $AB = 20$ units and the scale of the graph is $2\frac{1}{2}$ ft. per unit.

d) if $AB = 4\frac{1}{2}$ units and the scale of the graph is 6 yd. per unit.

Solutions: (Using $D = SN$)

     a) $D = (20)(5) = 100$ *Ans.* 100 mi.   *c)* $D = (2\frac{1}{2})(20) = 50$ *Ans.* 50 ft.

     b) $D = (12)(8) = 96$ *Ans.* 96 mi.   *d)* $D = (6)(4\frac{1}{2}) = 27$ *Ans.* 27 yd.

2.2. Finding Number of Units Needed: $N = \dfrac{D}{S}$

On a map or graph, a distance of 60 mi. is to be represented by a line $\overline{CD}$. Find the length needed for $\overline{CD}$, if the scale of the

     a) map is 20 mi. per inch.   *c)* graph is 4 mi. per graph unit.

     b) map is 30 mi. per cm.   *d)* graph is $\frac{1}{2}$ mi. per graph unit.

Solutions: (Using $N = \dfrac{D}{S}$)

     a) $N = \frac{60}{20} = 3$ *Ans.* 3 in.   *c)* $N = \frac{60}{4} = 15$ *Ans.* 15 units

     b) $N = \frac{60}{30} = 2$ *Ans.* 2 cm.   *d)* $N = 60 \div \frac{1}{2} = 120$ *Ans.* 120 units

2.3. Finding Scale: $S = \dfrac{D}{N}$

On a map or graph, a distance of 30 mi. is represented by $\overline{EF}$. Find the scale being used if $\overline{EF}$ equals *a)* 3 in., *b)* 3 yd., *c)* 8 graph units, *d)* $\frac{2}{3}$ graph unit.

Solutions: (Using $S = \dfrac{D}{N}$)

     a) $S = \frac{30}{3} = 10$ *Ans.* 10 mi. per in.   *c)* $S = \frac{30}{8} = 3\frac{3}{4}$ *Ans.* $3\frac{3}{4}$ mi. per unit

     b) $S = \frac{30}{3} = 10$ *Ans.* 10 mi. per yd.   *d)* $S = 30 \div \frac{2}{3} = 45$ *Ans.* 45 mi. per unit

2.4. Finding Distance and Direction

The scale triangle shown was drawn by a navigator to find the distance between two cities, A and B, and the angle of turn at B. He knew that the actual distance from A to C and from C to B was 100 mi. and that $\overline{BC}$ was at right angles to AC. What is the distance AB and the angle of turn shown at B?

Solution:

The scale $S = \dfrac{D}{N} = \dfrac{100}{10} = 10$. The scale is **10 mi. per unit.**

By measurement, $AB = 14$ units. Hence the distance $AB = (14)(10)$ or 140 mi. Using protractor, angle of turn at $B = 135°$.

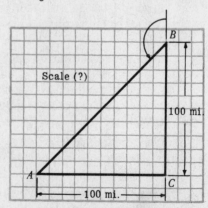

Scale (?)   100 mi.

100 mi.

Ans. $AB = 140$ mi., angle of turn at $B = 135°$.

SUPPLEMENTARY PROBLEMS

1. Solve the following, using triangles drawn to scales of 15 and 30 mi. per unit: **(1.1)**
An aviator flew 240 mi. due south from G to H. Then he
flew 450 mi. due west from H to J. To fly straight back to G,
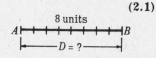
    (*1*) what distance must be flown and
    (*2*) what angle of turn must be made, to the nearest degree?

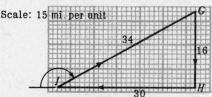
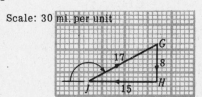

Ans. (*1*) 510 mi.   (*2*) 152°

2. On a graph, a line AB is 8 units long. Find the distance AB **(2.1)**
represents, using a scale of
    a) 30 mi. per unit, *b*) 8 rd. per unit, *c*) $4\frac{1}{2}$ ft. per unit, *d*) 5.1 yd. per unit.
    Ans. a) 240 mi.   *b*) 64 rd.   *c*) 36 ft.   *d*) 40.8 yd.

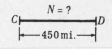

3. On a map, a distance of 450 mi. is to be represented by CD.   **(2.2)**
Find the length of CD, using a scale of
    a) 50 mi. per in., *b*) 150 mi. per ft., *c*) 200 mi. per ft., *d*) 900 mi. per yd.
Ans. a) $\frac{450}{50}$ or 9 in. *b*) $\frac{450}{150}$ or 3 ft.   *c*) $\frac{450}{200}$ or $2\frac{1}{4}$ ft.   *d*) $\frac{450}{900}$ or $\frac{1}{2}$ yd.

4. In a house plan, find the number of units needed to represent   **(2.2)**
    a) a length of 40 ft., using a scale of 5 ft. per unit.   *Ans.* $\frac{40}{5} = 8$
    b) a length of 40 ft., using a scale of 6 in. per unit.   *Ans.* $40 \div \frac{1}{2} = 80$
    c) a length of 10 ft., using a scale of $\frac{1}{4}$ ft. per unit.   *Ans.* $10 \div \frac{1}{4} = 40$
    d) a length of 24 ft., using a scale of $\frac{3}{4}$ ft. per unit.   *Ans.* $24 \div \frac{3}{4} = 32$

5. On a graph, find the number of units required to represent a distance of 200 mi. if the scale used is
    a) 400 mi. per unit, *b*) 150 mi. per unit, *c*) 80 mi. per unit, *d*) $33\frac{1}{3}$ mi. per unit.   **(2.2)**
    Ans. a) $\frac{1}{2}$ *b*) $1\frac{1}{3}$ *c*) $2\frac{1}{2}$ *d*) 6

6. Find the scale being used on a graph   **(2.3)**
    a) if a distance of 12 yd. is represented by a line of 8 units.   *Ans.* $\frac{12}{8}$ or $1\frac{1}{2}$ yd. per unit
    b) if a line of 10 units represents a distance of 75 ft.   *Ans.* $\frac{75}{10}$ or $7\frac{1}{2}$ ft. per unit
    c) if a line of $3\frac{1}{4}$ units represents a distance of 39 in.   *Ans.* $39 \div \frac{13}{4}$ or 12 in. per unit

7. To determine the distance from G to M, a navigator draws the   **(2.4)**
scale triangle shown and finds GM to be 13 units. Find the
distance GM
    a) if the scale used is $3\frac{1}{2}$ mi. per unit.   *Ans.* $45\frac{1}{2}$ mi.
    b) if GK represents 36 mi.   *Ans.* 39 mi.
    c) if MK represents 55 mi..   *Ans.* 143 mi.

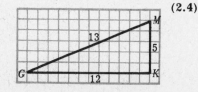

8. To find the distance from P to S, a navigator used the scale   **(2.4)**
triangle shown.
    a) Find the scale used.
    b) Find PS to the nearest number of units.
    c) Using the answer in (*b*), find the distance PS.
    Ans. a) 3 mi. per unit, *b*) 19 units, *c*) 57 mi.

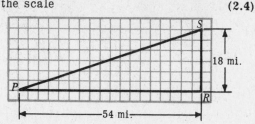

Chapter 15

Law of Pythagoras, Proportions, and Similar Triangles

1. LAW OF PYTHAGORAS

The square of the hypotenuse:

In right triangle ABC, if C is a right angle,

$$c^2 = a^2 + b^2$$

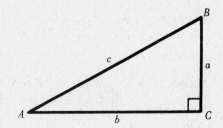

Note. In a triangle, the small letter for a side should agree with the capital letter for the vertex of the angle opposite that side. Thus, side a is opposite angle A, etc.

In this chapter, when measures are involved, the terms hypotenuse, arm, leg, side, and angle should be taken to mean their respective measures, for the sake of simplicity.

Law of Pythagoras: In a right triangle, the **square** of the hypotenuse equals the **sum of the squares** of the two legs or arms.

Pythagoras, a famous Greek mathematician and philosopher, lived about 500 B.C.

The square of either leg:

By transposition, $a^2 = c^2 - b^2$ and $b^2 = c^2 - a^2$

Transformed Law of Pythagoras: In a right triangle, the **square** of either leg equals the **difference of the squares** of the hypotenuse and the other leg.

To test for a right triangle, use the following rule:

Test Rule For a Right Triangle: If $c^2 = a^2 + b^2$ applies to the three sides of a triangle, then the triangle is a right triangle; but if $c^2 \neq a^2 + b^2$, then the triangle is not a right triangle.

Distance Between Two Points on a Graph

If d is the distance between $P_1(x_1, y_1)$ and $P_2(x_2, y_2)$:

$$d^2 = (x_2 - x_1)^2 + (y_2 - y_1)^2$$

Thus, the distance from the point (2,5) to the point (6,8) equals 5, as follows:

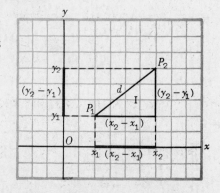

	(x, y)		
P_2	$(6, 8) \longrightarrow$	$x_2 = 6,$	$y_2 = 8$
P_1	$(2, 5) \longrightarrow$	$x_1 = 2,$	$y_1 = 5$

$$d^2 = (x_2 - x_1)^2 + (y_2 - y_1)^2$$
$$d^2 = (6 - 2)^2 + (8 - 5)^2$$
$$d^2 = 4^2 + 3^2 = 25$$
$$d = 5$$

In the following exercises, express each irrational answer in simplest radical form, unless otherwise indicated.

1.1. Finding the Hypotenuse of a Right Triangle: $c^2 = a^2 + b^2$

Find hypotenuse c in the right triangle shown when

a) $a=12$, $b=9$ $\qquad$ b) $a=3$, $b=7$ $\qquad$ c) $a=3$, $b=6$ $\qquad$ d) $a=3$, $b=3\sqrt{3}$

Solutions:

$c^2 = a^2 + b^2$	$c^2 = a^2 + b^2$	$c^2 = a^2 + b^2$	$c^2 = a^2 + b^2$
$c^2 = 12^2 + 9^2$	$c^2 = 3^2 + 7^2$	$c^2 = 3^2 + 6^2$	$c^2 = 3^2 + (3\sqrt{3})^2$
$c^2 = 144 + 81$	$c^2 = 9 + 49$	$c^2 = 9 + 36$	$c^2 = 9 + 27$
$c^2 = 225$	$c^2 = 58$	$c^2 = 45$	$c^2 = 36$
$c = \sqrt{225}$	$c = \sqrt{58}$ *Ans.*	$c = \sqrt{45}$	$c = \sqrt{36}$
$c = 15$ *Ans.*		$c = 3\sqrt{5}$ *Ans.*	$c = 6$ *Ans.*

Note. Since the hypotenuse is to be considered as positive only, reject the negative answer obtainable in each case. Thus, if $c^2 = 225$, c may equal 15 or -15. Reject the negative, -15.

1.2. Finding an Arm of a Right Triangle: $a^2 = c^2 - b^2$ or $b^2 = c^2 - a^2$

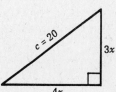

In the right triangle shown, find each missing arm when

a) $b=5$, $c=13$ $\qquad$ b) $a=24$, $c=25$ $\qquad$ c) $b=6$, $c=8$ $\qquad$ d) $a=4\sqrt{3}$, $c=8$

Solutions:

$a^2 = c^2 - b^2$	$b^2 = c^2 - a^2$	$a^2 = c^2 - b^2$	$b^2 = c^2 - a^2$
$a^2 = 13^2 - 5^2$	$b^2 = 25^2 - 24^2$	$a^2 = 8^2 - 6^2$	$b^2 = 8^2 - (4\sqrt{3})^2$
$a^2 = 169 - 25$	$b^2 = 625 - 576$	$a^2 = 64 - 36$	$b^2 = 64 - 48$
$a^2 = 144$	$b^2 = 49$	$a^2 = 28$	$b^2 = 16$
$a = \sqrt{144}$	$b = \sqrt{49}$	$a = \sqrt{28}$	$b = \sqrt{16}$
$a = 12$ *Ans.*	$b = 7$ *Ans.*	$a = 2\sqrt{7}$ *Ans.*	$b = 4$ *Ans.*

1.3. Ratios in a Right Triangle

In a right triangle whose hypotenuse is 20, the ratio of the two arms is $3:4$. Find each arm.

Solution:

Let $3x$ and $4x$ represent the two arms of the right triangle.

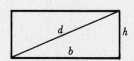

$$(3x)^2 + (4x)^2 = 20^2 \qquad \text{If } x = 4,$$
$$9x^2 + 16x^2 = 400 \qquad 3x = 12$$
$$25x^2 = 400 \qquad 4x = 16$$
$$x^2 = 16$$
$$x = 4 \qquad \textit{Ans.} \text{ Arms are 12 and 16.}$$

1.4. Applying Law of Pythagoras to a Rectangle

In a rectangle, find a) the diagonal if its sides are 9 and 40,

b) one side if the diagonal is 30 and the other side is 24.

Solution:

The diagonal of the rectangle is the hypotenuse of a right triangle.

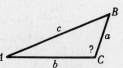

a) $d^2 = 9^2 + 40^2$, $\quad d^2 = 1681$, $\quad d = 41$ $\quad$ *Ans.* 41

b) $h^2 = 30^2 - 24^2$, $\quad h^2 = 324$, $\quad h = 18$ $\quad$ *Ans.* 18

1.5. Testing for Right Triangles, Using the Test Rule

Using the three sides given, which triangles are right triangles?

ΔI: $8, 15, 17$; $\quad \Delta$II: $6, 9, 11$; $\quad \Delta$III: $1\frac{1}{2}, 2, 2\frac{1}{2}$.

Solutions: Rule. If $c^2 = a^2 + b^2$, ΔABC is a right triangle; but if $c^2 \neq a^2 + b^2$, ΔABC is not.

ΔI: $8^2 + 15^2 \overset{?}{=} 17^2$	ΔII: $6^2 + 9^2 \overset{?}{=} 11^2$	ΔIII: $(1\frac{1}{2})^2 + 2^2 \overset{?}{=} (2\frac{1}{2})^2$
$64 + 225 \overset{?}{=} 289$	$36 + 81 \overset{?}{=} 121$	$2\frac{1}{4} + 4 \overset{?}{=} 6\frac{1}{4}$
$289 = 289$	$117 \neq 121$	$6\frac{1}{4} = 6\frac{1}{4}$
ΔI is a rt.Δ	ΔII is not a rt.Δ	ΔIII is a rt.Δ

1.6. Finding Distance Between Two Points on a Graph

Find the distance between each of the following pairs of points:

a) from (3,4) to (6,8)   b) from (3,4) to (6,10)   c) from (−3,2) to (9,−3)

Solutions:

	(x,y)
P_2	$(6,8) \rightarrow x_2 = 6,\ y_2 = 8$
P_1	$(3,4) \rightarrow x_1 = 3,\ y_1 = 4$

$d^2 = (x_2 - x_1)^2 + (y_2 - y_1)^2$
$d^2 = (6-3)^2 + (8-4)^2$
$d^2 = 3^2 + 4^2 = 25$

$d = 5$ *Ans.*

	(x,y)
P_2	$(6,10) \rightarrow x_2 = 6,\ y_2 = 10$
P_1	$(3,4) \rightarrow x_1 = 3,\ y_1 = 4$

$d^2 = (x_2 - x_1)^2 + (y_2 - y_1)^2$
$d^2 = (6-3)^2 + (10-4)^2$
$d^2 = 3^2 + 6^2 = 45$

$d = 3\sqrt{5}$ *Ans.*

	(x,y)
P_2	$(9,-3) \rightarrow x_2 = 9,\ y_2 = -3$
P_1	$(-3,2) \rightarrow x_1 = -3,\ y_1 = 2$

$d^2 = (x_2 - x_1)^2 + (y_2 - y_1)^2$
$d^2 = [9 - (-3)]^2 + (-3-2)^2$
$d^2 = 12^2 + (-5)^2 = 169$

$d = 13$ *Ans.*

Note. Since the distance is considered to be positive only, the negative answer obtainable in each case is to be rejected.

1.7. Using Law of Pythagoras to Derive Formulas

a) Derive a formula for the diagonal d of a square in terms of any side s.

Solutions:

$$d^2 = s^2 + s^2$$
$$d^2 = 2s^2$$
$$d = s\sqrt{2}\ \ Ans.$$

b) Derive a formula for the altitude h of any equilateral triangle in terms of any side s.

The altitude h of the equilateral triangle bisects the base s.

$$h^2 = s^2 - \left(\frac{s}{2}\right)^2$$
$$h^2 = s^2 - \frac{s^2}{4} = \frac{3s^2}{4}$$
$$h = \frac{s}{2}\sqrt{3}\ \ Ans.$$

1.8. Applying Law of Pythagoras to an Inscribed Square

The largest possible square is to be cut from a circular piece of cardboard having a diameter of 10 inches. Find the side of the square to the nearest inch.

Solution:

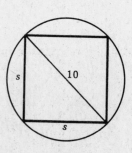

The diameter of the circle will be the diagonal of the square.

Hence, $s^2 + s^2 = 100,\ \ 2s^2 = 100$
$s^2 = 50,\ \ s = 5\sqrt{2} = 7.07$ *Ans.* 7 in.

1.9. Applying Law of Pythagoras to an Isosceles Triangle

Find the altitude of the isosceles triangle shown if
a) $a = 25$ and $b = 30$, b) $a = 12$ and $b = 8$.

Solution:

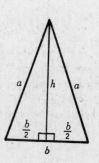

The altitude h of the isosceles triangle bisects the base b.
Hence, $h^2 = a^2 - \left(\frac{b}{2}\right)^2$.

a) $h^2 = 25^2 - 15^2$, $h^2 = 400$, $h = 20$ *Ans.* 20
b) $h^2 = 12^2 - 4^2$, $h^2 = 128$, $h = 8\sqrt{2}$ *Ans.* $8\sqrt{2}$

2. PROPORTIONS: EQUAL RATIOS

Understanding Proportions

A **proportion** is an equality of two ratios.

Thus, $2:5 = 4:10$ or $\frac{2}{5} = \frac{4}{10}$ is a proportion.

The fourth term of a proportion is the **fourth proportional** to the other three taken in order.

Thus, in $2:3 = 4:x$, x is the fourth proportional to 2, 3 and 4.

The **means** of a proportion are its middle terms; that is, its second and third terms.

The **extremes** of a proportion are its outside terms; that is, its first and fourth terms.

Thus, in $a:b = c:d$, the means are b and c, and the extremes are a and d.

> **Proportion Rule**: If $a:b = c:d$, $ad = bc$.

Proof: If $\frac{a}{b} = \frac{c}{d}$, then $\frac{1}{\cancel{b}}d(\frac{a}{\cancel{b}}) = b\frac{1}{\cancel{d}}(\frac{c}{\cancel{d}})$. Hence $ad = bc$.

Stating the Proportion Rule in Two Forms

Fraction Form	Colon Form
In any proportion, the cross-products are equal.	**In any proportion**, the product of the means equals the product of the extremes.

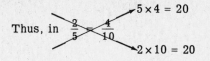

Thus, in $\frac{2}{5} \times \frac{4}{10}$ $\begin{array}{l} 5 \times 4 = 20 \\ 2 \times 10 = 20 \end{array}$

$5 \times 4 = 20$

Thus, in $2:5 = 4:10$

$2 \times 10 = 20$

2.1. Finding a Variable in a Proportion Using Cross-Products

Solve for x:

a) $\frac{x}{20} = \frac{3}{5}$ b) $\frac{3}{x} = \frac{2}{5}$ c) $\frac{x}{2x-3} = \frac{3}{5}$ d) $\frac{32}{x} = \frac{x}{2}$ e) $\frac{b}{a} = \frac{c}{x}$

Solutions:

$5x = 60$	$2x = 15$	$5x = 6x - 9$	$x^2 = 64$	$bx = ac$
$x = 12$ *Ans.*	$x = 7\frac{1}{2}$ *Ans.*	$9 = x$ *Ans.*	$x = \pm 8$ *Ans.*	$x = \frac{ac}{b}$ *Ans.*

2.2. Finding a Variable in a Proportion Using Means and Extremes

Solve for x:

Proportions	Product of Means	Product of Extremes	Product of Means = Product of Extremes	Answers
a) $x:4 = 6:8$	$4(6) = 24$	$8x$	$8x = 24$	$x = 3$
b) $3:5 = x:12$	$5x$	$3(12) = 36$	$5x = 36$	$x = 7\frac{1}{5}$
c) $3:x = x:27$	$x \cdot x = x^2$	$3(27) = 81$	$x^2 = 81$	$x = \pm 9$
d) $x:5 = 2x:x+3$	$5(2x) = 10x$	$x(x+3) = x^2 + 3x$	$x^2 + 3x = 10x$	$x = 0, 7$
e) $x-2:4 = 7:x+2$	$4(7) = 28$	$(x-2)(x+2) = x^2 - 4$	$x^2 - 4 = 28$	$x = \pm 4\sqrt{2}$

2.3. Finding Fourth Proportionals to Three Given Numbers

Find the fourth proportional to each set of numbers:

a) 2, 4, 6   b) 4, 2, 6   c) $\frac{1}{2}$, 3, 4   d) 3, $\frac{1}{2}$, 4   e) b, d, c

Solutions: (*Equate products of the means and extremes.*)

$2:4 = 6:x$	$4:2 = 6:x$	$\frac{1}{2}:3 = 4:x$	$3:\frac{1}{2} = 4:x$	$b:d = c:x$
$2x = 24$	$4x = 12$	$\frac{1}{2}x = 12$	$3x = 2$	$bx = cd$
$x = 12$ *Ans.*	$x = 3$ *Ans.*	$x = 24$ *Ans.*	$x = \frac{2}{3}$ *Ans.*	$x = \frac{cd}{b}$ *Ans.*

2.4. Solving a Verbal Problem Involving a Fraction and a Proportion

The denominator of a fraction is twice the numerator. If each is increased 4, the value of the new fraction is $\frac{2}{3}$. Find the original fraction.

Solution:

Let x = the numerator of the original fraction.

Then $2x$ = the denominator of the original fraction.

If the value of the new fraction is $\frac{2}{3}$ after each of the terms is increased 4, then $\frac{x+4}{2x+4} = \frac{2}{3}$.

Cross-multiplying,

$$3(x+4) = 2(2x+4)$$
$$3x + 12 = 4x + 8$$
$$4 = x, \ 2x = 8. \ \text{ Hence, the original fraction is } \frac{4}{8}.$$

The new fraction $= \frac{4+4}{8+4} = \frac{8}{12} = \frac{2}{3}$.   *Ans.* $\frac{4}{8}$

3. SIMILAR TRIANGLES

Similar Polygons Have the Same Shape

Thus, if $\triangle I$ and $\triangle I'$ are similar, then they have the same shape although they need not have the same size.

Notation: "$\triangle I \sim \triangle I'$" is to be read as "triangle I is similar to triangle I-prime". In the diagram, note how the sides and angles having the same relative position are designated by using the same letters and primes. **Corresponding sides** or angles are those having the same relative position.

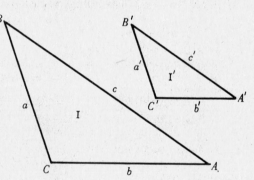

Two Basic Properties of Similar Triangles

Rule 1: If two triangles are similar

a) **their corresponding angles are equal.**

Thus, if $\triangle I \sim \triangle I'$,
then $\angle C' = \angle C = 90°$
$\angle A' = \angle A = 40°$
$\angle B' = \angle B = 50°$.

b) **the ratios of their corresponding sides are equal.**

Thus, if $\triangle I \sim \triangle I'$,

then $c = 15$ since $\frac{c}{5} = \frac{9}{3}$

and $b = 12$ since $\frac{b}{4} = \frac{9}{3}$.

Three Basic Methods of Determining Similar Triangles

Rule 2: Two triangles are similar

a) **if two angles of one equal two angles of the other.**

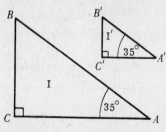

Thus, $\triangle I \sim \triangle I'$ since

$\angle C = \angle C'$ and $\angle A = \angle A'$

b) **if the three ratios of the corresponding sides are equal.**

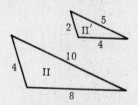

Thus, $\triangle II \sim \triangle II'$ since

$\frac{10}{5} = \frac{8}{4} = \frac{4}{2}$

c) **if two ratios of corresponding sides are equal and the angles between the sides are equal.**

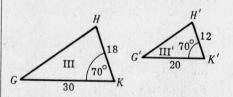

Thus, $\triangle III \sim \triangle III'$ since

$\frac{30}{20} = \frac{18}{12}$ and $\angle K = \angle K'$

Rule 3 : A triangle is similar to any one of its scale triangles.

Thus, if $\triangle$I and $\triangle$I′ are drawn to scale to represent $\triangle ABC$, then they are similar to $\triangle ABC$ and also to each other; that is $\triangle ABC \sim \triangle$I $\sim \triangle$I′

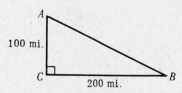

Note. Use **Rule** 2c to show that the triangles are similar. For example, $\triangle$I$\sim \triangle ABC$ since

$$\frac{100}{2} = \frac{200}{4}$$

and the right angles which are between these sides are equal. For this reason a scale triangle may be constructed using only two sides and the included angle.

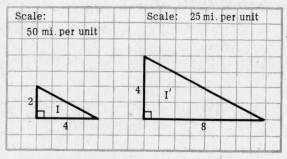

3.1. Rule 1a. Corresponding Angles of Similar Triangles are Equal

If $\triangle$I′$\sim \triangle$I find $\angle C′$
a) if $\angle A = 60°$ and $\angle B = 45°$,
b) if $\angle A + \angle B = 110°$.

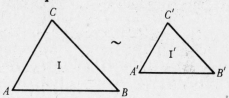

Solutions:

Using **Rule 1**, if $\triangle$I′$\sim \triangle$I then $\angle C′ = \angle C$.
a) Since the sum of the angles of a triangle equals 180°,
   $\angle C = 180° - 60° - 45° = 75°$. Hence, $\angle C′ = 75°$.
b) Since the sum of the angles of a triangle equals 180°,
   $\angle C = 180° - 110° = 70°$. Hence, $\angle C′ = 70°$.

3.2. Rule 1b. Ratios of Corresponding Sides of Similar Triangles are Equal

If $\triangle$II′$\sim \triangle$II, find x and y using the data indicated.

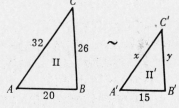

Solutions:

Since $\triangle$II′$\sim \triangle$II,

$$\frac{x}{32} = \frac{15}{20} \qquad\qquad \frac{y}{26} = \frac{15}{20}$$

$$x = \frac{15}{20}(32) \qquad\qquad y = \frac{15}{20}(26)$$

$$x = 24 \qquad\qquad\qquad y = 19\tfrac{1}{2}$$

$Ans.$ $24, 19\tfrac{1}{2}$

3.3. Rule 2. Determining Similar Triangles

a)

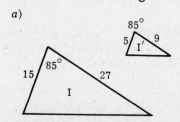

b)

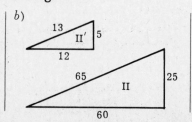

c)

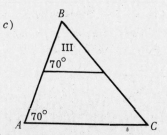

Which rule is needed in each case to show that both triangles are similar?

Solutions:

By **Rule** 2c, $\triangle$I′$\sim \triangle$I
since each has an 85° angle and there are two equal ratios for the sides of these equal angles; i.e., $\frac{27}{9} = \frac{15}{5}$.

By **Rule** 2b, $\triangle$II′$\sim \triangle$II
since $\frac{65}{13} = \frac{25}{5} = \frac{60}{12}$.
Thus, there are three equal ratios of the corresponding sides.

By **Rule** 2a, $\triangle$III$\sim \triangle ABC$
since there are two pairs of equal angles. Each triangle has $\angle B$ and a 70° angle.

3.4. Finding Heights Using Ground Shadows

A tree casts a 15 ft. shadow at a time when a nearby upright pole of 6 ft. casts a shadow of 2 ft. Find the height h of the tree if both tree and pole make right angles with the ground.

Solution:

At the same time in localities near each other, the rays of the sun strike the ground at equal angles; hence $\angle B = \angle B'$. Since the tree and pole make right angles with the ground, $\angle C = \angle C'$. Since there are two pairs of equal angles, $\triangle I' \sim \triangle I$. Hence, $\dfrac{h}{6} = \dfrac{15}{2}$, $h = \dfrac{15}{2}(6) = 45$.

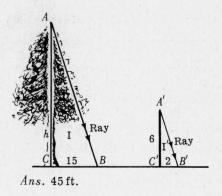

Ans. 45 ft.

3.5. Using a Scale to Find Parts of a Triangle

If $\triangle I'$ is a scale triangle of $\triangle I$:

a) Find a and c when $b = 45$.   *b*) Show that $\triangle ABC$ is a right triangle.

Solution:

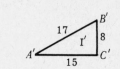

a) Using **Rule 3**, $\triangle I \sim \triangle I'$; hence

$$\frac{a}{8} = \frac{45}{15} \qquad \text{and} \qquad \frac{c}{17} = \frac{45}{15}$$

$$a = 3(8) = 24 \qquad\qquad c = 3(17) = 51 \qquad Ans.\ 24, 51$$

b) Since $8^2 + 15^2 = 17^2$, $\triangle I'$ is a right triangle.

Since $\triangle I \sim \triangle I'$, $\triangle I$ is a right triangle.

3.6. Using a Scale Triangle to Find a Distance

An aviator traveled east a distance of 150 mi. from A to C. He then traveled north for 50 mi. to B. Using a scale of 50 mi. per unit, find his distance from A, to the nearest mile.

Solution:

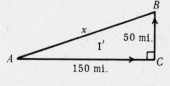

By **Rule 3**, a triangle is similar to any one of its scale triangles.

Let $x = $ length of AB in mi.

In $\triangle I$, the scale triangle of $\triangle I'$, $c^2 = 3^2 + 1^2 = 10$. Hence, $c = \sqrt{10}$.

Since $\triangle I' \sim \triangle I$, $\dfrac{x}{c} = \dfrac{50}{1}$

$$x = 50c$$

$$x = 50\sqrt{10} = 50(3.162) = 158.1 \quad Ans.\ 158 \text{ mi.}$$

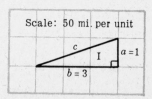

3.7. Applying a Scale to a Square

A baseball diamond is a square 90 ft. on each side. Using a scale of 90 ft. per unit, find the distance from home plate to second base to the nearest foot.

Solution: Using a scale of 90 ft. per unit, each side of the new square will be 1 unit.

Let $x = $ distance from home plate to second base in ft.

In $\triangle I$, the scale triangle of $\triangle I'$, $c^2 = 1^2 + 1^2 = 2$. Hence, $c = \sqrt{2}$.

Since $\triangle I' \sim \triangle I$, $\dfrac{x}{c} = \dfrac{90}{1}$

$$x = 90c$$

$$x = 90\sqrt{2} = 90(1.414) = 127.26 \quad Ans.\ 127 \text{ ft.}$$

SUPPLEMENTARY PROBLEMS

1. In a right triangle whose arms are a and b, find the hypotenuse c when: **(1.1)**
   a) $a=15$, $b=20$ *Ans.* 25   *c)* $a=5$, $b=4$ *Ans.* $\sqrt{41}$ *e)* $a=7$, $b=7$ *Ans.* $7\sqrt{2}$
   b) $a=15$, $b=36$ *Ans.* 39   *d)* $a=5$, $b=5\sqrt{3}$ *Ans.* 10   *f)* $a=8$, $b=4$ *Ans.* $4\sqrt{5}$

2. In the right triangle shown, find each missing arm when   **(1.2)**
   a) $a=12$, $c=20$ *c)* $b=15$, $c=17$ *e)* $a=5\sqrt{2}$, $c=10$
   b) $b=6$, $c=8$ *d)* $a=2$, $c=4$ *f)* $a=\sqrt{5}$, $c=2\sqrt{2}$
   Ans. a) $b=16$, *b)* $a=2\sqrt{7}$, *c)* $a=8$, *d)* $b=2\sqrt{3}$, *e)* $b=5\sqrt{2}$, *f)* $b=\sqrt{3}$

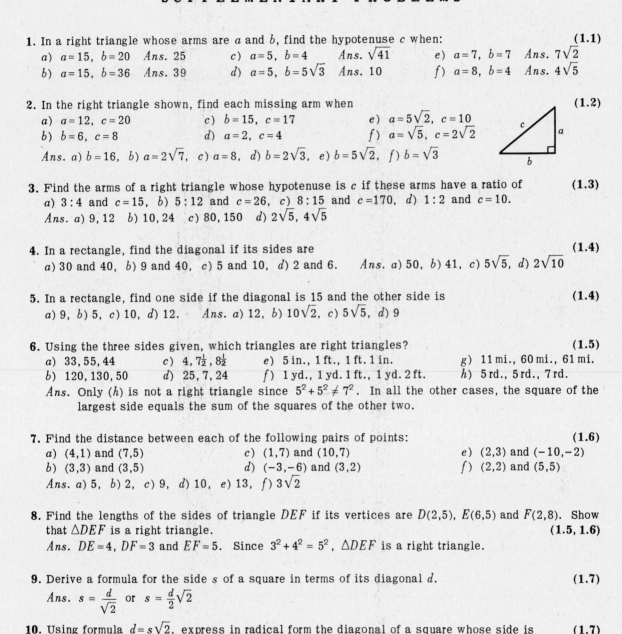

3. Find the arms of a right triangle whose hypotenuse is c if these arms have a ratio of   **(1.3)**
   a) 3:4 and $c=15$, *b)* 5:12 and $c=26$, *c)* 8:15 and $c=170$, *d)* 1:2 and $c=10$.
   Ans. a) 9, 12   *b)* 10, 24   *c)* 80, 150   *d)* $2\sqrt{5}$, $4\sqrt{5}$

4. In a rectangle, find the diagonal if its sides are   **(1.4)**
   a) 30 and 40, *b)* 9 and 40, *c)* 5 and 10, *d)* 2 and 6.   *Ans. a)* 50, *b)* 41, *c)* $5\sqrt{5}$, *d)* $2\sqrt{10}$

5. In a rectangle, find one side if the diagonal is 15 and the other side is   **(1.4)**
   a) 9, *b)* 5, *c)* 10, *d)* 12.   *Ans. a)* 12, *b)* $10\sqrt{2}$, *c)* $5\sqrt{5}$, *d)* 9

6. Using the three sides given, which triangles are right triangles?   **(1.5)**
   a) 33, 55, 44   *c)* 4, $7\frac{1}{2}$, $8\frac{1}{2}$ *e)* 5 in., 1 ft., 1 ft. 1 in.   *g)* 11 mi., 60 mi., 61 mi.
   b) 120, 130, 50   *d)* 25, 7, 24   *f)* 1 yd., 1 yd. 1 ft., 1 yd. 2 ft.   *h)* 5 rd., 5 rd., 7 rd.
   Ans. Only *(h)* is not a right triangle since $5^2+5^2 \neq 7^2$. In all the other cases, the square of the largest side equals the sum of the squares of the other two.

7. Find the distance between each of the following pairs of points: **(1.6)**
   a) (4,1) and (7,5)   *c)* (1,7) and (10,7)   *e)* (2,3) and (−10,−2)
   b) (3,3) and (3,5)   *d)* (−3,−6) and (3,2)   *f)* (2,2) and (5,5)
   Ans. a) 5, *b)* 2, *c)* 9, *d)* 10, *e)* 13, *f)* $3\sqrt{2}$

8. Find the lengths of the sides of triangle DEF if its vertices are $D(2,5)$, $E(6,5)$ and $F(2,8)$. Show that $\triangle DEF$ is a right triangle.   **(1.5, 1.6)**
   Ans. $DE=4$, $DF=3$ and $EF=5$. Since $3^2+4^2 = 5^2$, $\triangle DEF$ is a right triangle.

9. Derive a formula for the side s of a square in terms of its diagonal d.   **(1.7)**
   Ans. $s = \dfrac{d}{\sqrt{2}}$ or $s = \dfrac{d}{2}\sqrt{2}$

10. Using formula $d=s\sqrt{2}$, express in radical form the diagonal of a square whose side is   **(1.7)**
    a) 5, *b)* 7.2, *c)* $\sqrt{3}$, *d)* 90 ft., *e)* 3.47 yd.
    Ans. a) $5\sqrt{2}$, *b)* $7.2\sqrt{2}$, *c)* $\sqrt{6}$, *d)* $90\sqrt{2}$ ft., *e)* $3.47\sqrt{2}$ yd.

11. Using formula $h = \frac{s}{2}\sqrt{3}$, express in radical form the altitude of an equilateral triangle whose side is *a)* 6, *b)* 20, *c)* 11, *d)* 90 in., *e)* 4.6 yd.   **(1.7)**
    Ans. a) $3\sqrt{3}$, *b)* $10\sqrt{3}$, *c)* $\frac{11}{2}\sqrt{3}$, *d)* $45\sqrt{3}$ in., *e)* $2.3\sqrt{3}$ yd.

12. The largest possible square is to be cut from a circular piece of wood. Find the side of the square, to the nearest inch, if the diameter of the circle is *a)* 30 in., *b)* 14 in., *c)* 17 in.   **(1.8)**
    Ans. a) 21 in., *b)* 10 in., *c)* 12 in.

13. Find the altitude of an isosceles triangle if one of its two equal sides is 10 and its base is   **(1.9)**
    a) 12,   *b*) 16,   *c*) 18,   *d*) 10.   *Ans.* *a*) 8,   *b*) 6,   *c*) $\sqrt{19}$,   *d*) $5\sqrt{3}$

14. Solve for x: **(2.1)**

    a) $\frac{5}{7} = \frac{15}{x}$ *c*) $\frac{3}{x} = \frac{x}{12}$ *e*) $\frac{x+2}{5} = \frac{6}{3}$ *g*) $\frac{2x}{x+7} = \frac{3}{5}$

    b) $\frac{7}{x} = \frac{3}{2}$ *d*) $\frac{x}{5} = \frac{15}{x}$ *f*) $\frac{x-1}{3} = \frac{5}{x+1}$ *h*) $\frac{a}{x} = \frac{x}{b}$

    Ans. *a*) 21,   *b*) $4\frac{2}{3}$,   *c*) ±6,   *d*) $\pm5\sqrt{3}$,   *e*) 8,   *f*) ±4,   *g*) 3,   *h*) $\pm\sqrt{ab}$

15. Solve for x: *a*) $x:6 = 8:3$ *d*) $x:2 = 10:x$ *g*) $a:b = c:x$ **(2.2)**
                b) $5:4 = 20:x$ *e*) $(x+4):3 = 3:(x-4)$ *h*) $x:2y = 18y:x$
                c) $9:x = x:4$ *f*) $(2x+8):(x+2) = (2x+5):(x+1)$

    Ans. *a*) 16,   *b*) 16,   *c*) ±6,   *d*) $\pm2\sqrt{5}$,   *e*) ±5,   *f*) 2,   *g*) $\frac{bc}{a}$,   *h*) ±6*y*

16. Find the fourth proportional to each set of numbers: **(2.3)**
    a) 1, 3, 5   *c*) 2, 3, 4   *e*) 3, 2, 5   *g*) 2, 8, 8
    b) 8, 6, 4   *d*) 3, 4, 2   *f*) $\frac{1}{3}$, 2, 5   *h*) $b, 2a, 3b$
    Ans. *a*) 15,   *b*) 3,   *c*) 6,   *d*) $2\frac{2}{3}$,   *e*) $3\frac{1}{3}$,   *f*) 30,   *g*) 32,   *h*) 6*a*

17. Find the original fraction in each problem: **(2.4)**
    a) The denominator of a certain fraction is three times the numerator. If the numerator is decreased 1 and the denominator is increased 3, the value of the new fraction is $\frac{1}{6}$.

    b) The numerator of a certain fraction is 5 less than the denominator. If the denominator is increased 7 and the numerator is unchanged, the value of the new fraction is $\frac{1}{5}$.

    c) The denominator of a certain fraction is 3 more than twice the numerator. If the numerator is doubled and the denominator is unchanged, the value of the new fraction equals $\frac{4}{5}$.

    Ans. *a*) $\frac{3}{9}$ $\left(\text{Equation: } \frac{x-1}{3x+3} = \frac{1}{6}\right)$,   *b*) $\frac{3}{8}$ $\left(\text{Equation: } \frac{x-5}{x+7} = \frac{1}{5}\right)$,   *c*) $\frac{6}{15}$ $\left(\text{Equation: } \frac{2x}{2x+3} = \frac{4}{5}\right)$.

18. If $\triangle\text{I} \sim \triangle\text{I}'$, find $\angle B$ **(3.1)**
           a) if $\angle A' = 120°$ and $\angle C' = 25°$,
           b) if $\angle A' + \angle C' = 127°$.

    Ans. *a*) 35°,   *b*) 53°

19. If $\triangle\text{I} \sim \triangle\text{I}'$, using the data shown   **(3.2)**
    a) find *a* if *c* = 24.   *Ans.* $\frac{a}{4} = \frac{24}{6}$,   *a* = 16

    b) find *b* if *a* = 20.   *Ans.* $\frac{b}{3} = \frac{20}{4}$,   *b* = 15

    c) find *c* if *b* = 63.   *Ans.* $\frac{c}{6} = \frac{63}{3}$,   *c* = 126

20. Which rule is needed in each case to show both triangles are similar?   **(3.3)**
    a) Show $\triangle\text{I} \sim \triangle ABC$.   *b*) Show $\triangle\text{II} \sim \triangle PQR$.   *c*) Show $\triangle\text{III} \sim \triangle FGH$

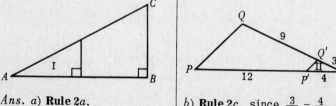
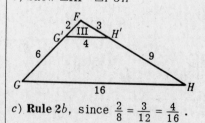

    Ans. *a*) **Rule 2a.**   *b*) **Rule 2c,** since $\frac{3}{12} = \frac{4}{16}$ and   *c*) **Rule 2b,** since $\frac{2}{8} = \frac{3}{12} = \frac{4}{16}$.
                                      each triangle has $\angle R$.

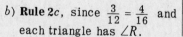

21. A 7 ft. upright pole near a vertical tree casts a 6 ft. shadow. At that time,   **(3.4)**
    a) find the height of the tree if its shadow is 36 ft.   *Ans.* 42 ft.
    b) find the shadow of the tree if its height is 77 ft.   *Ans.* 66 ft.

22. If $\triangle \mathrm{I}'$ is a scale triangle of $\triangle \mathrm{I}$,   **(3.5)**
        a) find *a* and *b* when $c = 125$,
        b) show that $\triangle \mathrm{I}$ is a right triangle.

   Ans. a) 35, 120
        b) $\triangle \mathrm{I}$ is a right triangle since $7^2 + 24^2 = 25^2$ and $\triangle \mathrm{I} \sim \triangle \mathrm{I}'$.

23. Two planes leave an airport at the same time, one going due east at 250 mph and the other due
    north at 150 mph. Using a scale of 200 mi. per unit, find the distance between them at the end of
    4 hr., to the nearest mile.   *Ans.* 1166 mi.   **(3.6)**

24. A square lot, 50 ft. on each side, has a diagonal path. Using a square drawn to a scale of 50 ft.
    per unit, find the length of the path to the nearest foot.   *Ans.* 71 ft.   **(3.7)**

Chapter 16

Trigonometry

1. UNDERSTANDING TRIGONOMETRIC RATIOS

Trigonometry means "measurement of triangles". Consider its parts: "tri" means **three**, "gon" means "angle", and "metry" means "measure". Thus, in trigonometry we study the measurement of triangles.

In trigonometry the following ratios are used in a right triangle to relate the sides and either acute angle:

1. tangent ratio, abbreviated "tan".
2. sine ratio, abbreviated "sin".
3. cosine ratio, abbreviated "cos".

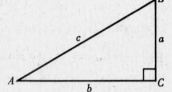

Trigonometry Rules and Formulas

Rules	Formulas
1. The tangent of an acute angle equals the leg opposite the angle divided by the leg adjacent to the angle.	$\tan A = \dfrac{\text{leg opp. } A}{\text{leg adj. } A} = \dfrac{a}{b}$ $\tan B = \dfrac{\text{leg opp. } B}{\text{leg adj. } B} = \dfrac{b}{a}$
2. The sine of an acute angle equals the leg opposite the angle divided by the hypotenuse.	$\sin A = \dfrac{\text{leg opp. } A}{\text{hyp.}} = \dfrac{a}{c}$ $\sin B = \dfrac{\text{leg opp. } B}{\text{hyp.}} = \dfrac{b}{c}$
3. The cosine of an acute angle equals the leg adjacent to the angle divided by the hypotenuse.	$\cos A = \dfrac{\text{leg adj. } A}{\text{hyp.}} = \dfrac{b}{c}$ $\cos B = \dfrac{\text{leg adj. } B}{\text{hyp.}} = \dfrac{a}{c}$

Rules: If A and B are the acute angles of a right triangle:

$$\sin A = \cos B \qquad \cos A = \sin B \qquad \tan A = \frac{1}{\tan B}$$

$$\sin B = \cos A \qquad \cos B = \sin A \qquad \tan B = \frac{1}{\tan A}$$

To Find the Measure of an Angle, or Simply an Angle, to the Nearest Degree

Procedure:

Find x, to the nearest degree, if $\sin x = .6350$.

Solution:

1. Find nearest tabular values:

1. $\sin x = .6350$ is between
   $\sin 40° = .6428$ and $\sin 39° = .6293$

2. Find differences as shown:

2.
$$\sin 40° = .6428$$
$$\sin x\ \ = .6350$$
$$\sin 39° = .6293$$

Differences
.0078
.0057

3. Find angle to the nearest degree:

3. Since $\sin x$ is nearer to $\sin 39°$, $x = 39°$ to the nearest degree. *Ans.* 39°

1.1. Using Table of Sines, Cosines and Tangents

The following values are taken from the **Table of Sines, Cosines and Tangents** (page 372). State each indicated value in proper trigonometric form and complete the last line:

		Sine	Cosine	Tangent
(1)	1°	.0175	.9998	.0175
(2)	30°	.5000	.8660	.5774
(3)	60°	.8660	.5000	1.7321
(4)	(?)	(?)	.3420	(?)

Solution:

(1) Since .0175 is aligned with "Sine" and "1°", sin 1° = .0175.
  Similarly, cos 1° = .9998 and tan 1° = .0175.

(2) From the 30° row, sin 30° = .5000, cos 30° = .8660 and tan 30° = .5774.

(3) From the 60° row, sin 60° = .8660, cos 60° = .5000 and tan 60° = 1.7321.

(4) Since .3420 = cos 70°, the angle is 70°. The other values in this row are
  sin 70° = .9397 and tan 70° = 2.7475.

1.2. Finding Angles to the Nearest Degree

Using the table of sines, cosines and tangents, find x to the nearest degree if

a) sin x = .9235

b) cos $x = \dfrac{21}{25}$

c) tan $x = \dfrac{\sqrt{5}}{10}$

Solutions:

Since $\dfrac{21}{25}$ = .8400, cos x = .8400

Since $\dfrac{\sqrt{5}}{10}$ = .2236, tan x = .2236

Using table:

	Differences
sin 68° = .9272	
sin x = .9235	.0037
sin 67° = .9205	.0030

Since sin x is nearer to sin 67°, x = 67° to the nearest degree. *Ans.* 67°

Using table:

	Differences
cos 32° = .8480	
cos x = .8400	.0080
cos 33° = .8387	.0013

Since cos x is nearer to cos 33°, x = 33° to the nearest degree. *Ans.* 33°

Using table:

	Differences
tan 13° = .2309	
tan x = .2236	.0073
tan 12° = .2126	.0110

Since tan x is nearer to tan 13°, x = 13° to the nearest degree. *Ans.* 13°

1.3. Finding Trigonometric Ratios

In each right triangle, state trigonometric ratios for each acute angle:

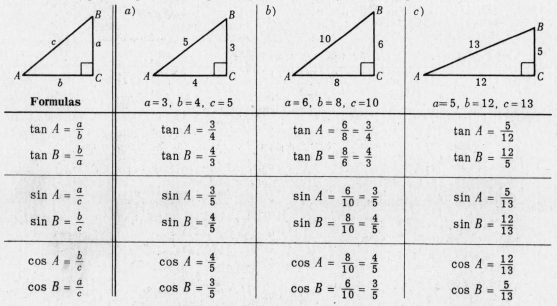

Formulas	*a)* $a=3$, $b=4$, $c=5$	*b)* $a=6$, $b=8$, $c=10$	*c)* $a=5$, $b=12$, $c=13$
$\tan A = \dfrac{a}{b}$	$\tan A = \dfrac{3}{4}$	$\tan A = \dfrac{6}{8} = \dfrac{3}{4}$	$\tan A = \dfrac{5}{12}$
$\tan B = \dfrac{b}{a}$	$\tan B = \dfrac{4}{3}$	$\tan B = \dfrac{8}{6} = \dfrac{4}{3}$	$\tan B = \dfrac{12}{5}$
$\sin A = \dfrac{a}{c}$	$\sin A = \dfrac{3}{5}$	$\sin A = \dfrac{6}{10} = \dfrac{3}{5}$	$\sin A = \dfrac{5}{13}$
$\sin B = \dfrac{b}{c}$	$\sin B = \dfrac{4}{5}$	$\sin B = \dfrac{8}{10} = \dfrac{4}{5}$	$\sin B = \dfrac{12}{13}$
$\cos A = \dfrac{b}{c}$	$\cos A = \dfrac{4}{5}$	$\cos A = \dfrac{8}{10} = \dfrac{4}{5}$	$\cos A = \dfrac{12}{13}$
$\cos B = \dfrac{a}{c}$	$\cos B = \dfrac{3}{5}$	$\cos B = \dfrac{6}{10} = \dfrac{3}{5}$	$\cos B = \dfrac{5}{13}$

1.4. Finding Angles by Trigonometric Ratios

Find A, to the nearest degree, in each:

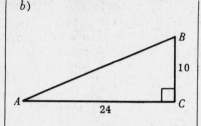

a)   *b)*   *c)*

Solutions:

$\sin A = \dfrac{60}{100} = .6000$ $\tan A = \dfrac{10}{24} = \dfrac{5}{12} = .4167$ $\cos A = \dfrac{1500}{1700} = \dfrac{15}{17} = .8824$

Since $\sin 37° = .6018$ is nearest sine value,

$A = 37°$ *Ans.*

Since $\tan 23° = .4245$ is nearest tangent value,

$A = 23°$ *Ans.*

Since $\cos 28° = .8829$ is nearest cosine value,

$A = 28°$ *Ans.*

1.5. Deriving Trigonometric Values for 30° and 60° Ratios

Show *a)* $\tan 30° = .577$ *d)* $\tan 60° = 1.732$
      b) $\sin 30° = .5$ *e)* $\sin 60° = .866$
      c) $\cos 30° = .866$ *f)* $\cos 60° = .5$

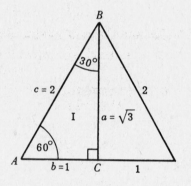

Solutions:

The trigonometric ratios for 30° and 60° may be obtained by using an equilateral triangle. Draw the altitude from the midpoint of the base to the opposite vertex. Consider each side equal to 2 units.

In right triangle I, $c = 2$ and $b = 1$.

By Law of Pythagoras, $a^2 = 2^2 - 1^2 = 3$. Hence, $a = \sqrt{3}$.

Using $\triangle$ I:

a) $\tan 30° = \dfrac{1}{\sqrt{3}} = \dfrac{1}{\sqrt{3}} \cdot \dfrac{\sqrt{3}}{\sqrt{3}} = \dfrac{\sqrt{3}}{3} = .577$ *d)* $\tan 60° = \dfrac{\sqrt{3}}{1} = 1.732$

b) $\sin 30° = \dfrac{1}{2} = .5$ *e)* $\sin 60° = \dfrac{\sqrt{3}}{2} = .866$

c) $\cos 30° = \dfrac{\sqrt{3}}{2} = \dfrac{1.732}{2} = .866$ *f)* $\cos 60° = \dfrac{1}{2} = .5$

1.6. Finding Acute Angles of a Right Triangle Whose Sides Have a Given Ratio

To the nearest degree, find each acute angle of any right triangle whose sides are in the ratio of $3:4:5$.

Solution:

Let $3x$, $4x$ and $5x$ represent the three sides of $\triangle$I as shown in the adjoining figure.

Now, $\tan A = \dfrac{3x}{4x} = \dfrac{3}{4} = .7500$.

Since $\tan 37° = .7536$ is nearest tangent value, $A = 37°$.

$B = 90° - 37° = 53°$.   *Ans.* 37° and 53°

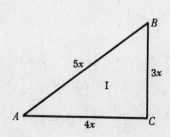

2. SOLVING TRIGONOMETRY PROBLEMS

To Solve Problems by Using Trigonometry

Problem: An aviator flew 70 mi. east from A to C. From C, he flew 100 mi. north to B. Find the angle of turn, to the nearest degree, that must be made at B to return to A.

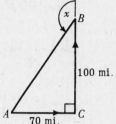

Procedure:	**Solution:**
1. Indicate the values given and the variable on a labeled diagram. *(A diagram should be drawn to scale.)*	1. Let x = angle of turn at B.
2. Write a trigonometric equation involving the given values.	2. $\tan B = \frac{70}{100} = .7000$.
3. Find the variable.	3. Since $B = 35°$ to nearest degree, angle of turn $= 180° - 35° = \underline{145°}$ *Ans.*

2.1. Obtaining Trigonometric Equations Given an Acute Angle and a Side

In each triangle, state the trigonometric equation needed to solve for x and y:

(Avoid division where possible.)

a) **Given acute angle and adjacent leg**	*b*) **Given acute angle and opposite leg**	*c*) **Given acute angle and hypotenuse**
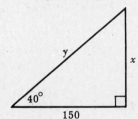	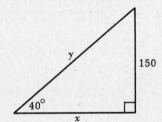	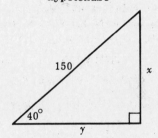

Solution:

a)

(1) **To find x:**

Since $\tan 40° = \frac{x}{150}$,

$x = 150 \tan 40°$

(2) **To find y:**

Since $\cos 40° = \frac{150}{y}$,

$y \cos 40° = 150$

** Hence, $y = \frac{150}{\cos 40°}$

b)

(1) **To find x**, use 50° angle, the other acute angle:

Since $\tan 50° = \frac{x}{150}$,

$x = 150 \tan 50°$

(2) **To find y:**

Since $\sin 40° = \frac{150}{y}$,

$y \sin 40° = 150$

** Hence, $y = \frac{150}{\sin 40°}$

c)

(1) **To find x:**

Since $\sin 40° = \frac{x}{150}$,

$x = 150 \sin 40°$

(2) **To find y:**

Since $\cos 40° = \frac{y}{150}$,

$y = 150 \cos 40°$

Note 1. To find x in (*b*), if $\tan 40°$ were used, division would be needed:

Since $\tan 40° = \frac{150}{x}$, $x \tan 40° = 150$, $x = \frac{150}{\tan 40°}$.

Note 2. To find y in either (*a*) or (*b*), division cannot be avoided, using sine or cosine.

2.2. Solving Trigonometric Equations Derived in 2.1

Solve each trigonometric equation. Find the variable to the nearest integer:

(Equations were obtained in **2.1**.*)*

a) *(1)* $x = 150 \tan 40°$

  (2) $y = \dfrac{150}{\cos 40°}$

b) *(1)* $x = 150 \tan 50°$

  (2) $y = \dfrac{150}{\sin 40°}$

c) *(1)* $x = 150 \sin 40°$

  (2) $y = 150 \cos 40°$

Solutions:

(1) $x = 150 \tan 40°$

$x = 150(.8391)$

$x = 125.87$

$x = 126$ *Ans.*

(1) $x = 150 \tan 50°$

$x = 150(1.1918)$

$x = 178.77$

$x = 179$ *Ans.*

(1) $x = 150 \sin 40°$

$x = 150(.6428)$

$x = 96.42$

$x = 96$ *Ans.*

(2) $y = \dfrac{150}{\cos 40°}$

$y = \dfrac{150}{.7660}$

$y = 195.8$

$y = 196$ *Ans.*

(2) $y = \dfrac{150}{\sin 40°}$

$y = \dfrac{150}{.6428}$

$y = 233.4$

$y = 233$ *Ans.*

(2) $y = 150 \cos 40°$

$y = 150(.7660)$

$y = 114.9$

$y = 115$ *Ans.*

2.3. Finding Legs of a Right Triangle

An aviator takes off at A and ascends at a fixed angle of 22° with level or horizontal ground. After he flies 3000 yd., find, to the nearest 10 yd.,

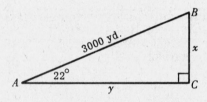

a) the altitude of the plane.

b) the distance from A to C which is on a level with A and directly under the plane.

Solutions:

Let x = altitude of plane in yd.

Since $\sin 22° = \dfrac{x}{3000}$,

$\qquad x = 3000(.3746) = 1123.8$

Ans. 1120 yd., to nearest 10 yd.

Let y = required distance in yd.

Since $\cos 22° = \dfrac{y}{3000}$,

$\qquad y = 3000(.9272) = 2781.6$

Ans. 2780 yd., to nearest 10 yd.

2.4. Finding an Angle and then the Hypotenuse of a Right Triangle

A road is to be constructed so that it will rise 105 ft. for each 1000 ft. of horizontal distance. Find

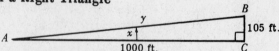

a) its angle of rise, x, to the nearest degree.

b) the length of road, y, to the nearest ft., for each 1000 ft. of horizontal distance, using the value of x found in *(a)*.

Solutions:

Since $\tan x = \dfrac{105}{1000} = .1050$,

$\qquad x = 6°$, to nearest degree. *Ans.*

Since $\cos x = \dfrac{1000}{y}$, $\cos 6° = \dfrac{1000}{y}$.

Hence, $y = \dfrac{1000}{\cos 6°} = \dfrac{1000}{.9945}$ or 1005.5.

Ans. 1006 ft., to nearest ft.

3. ANGLES OF ELEVATION AND DEPRESSION

The line of sight is the line from the eye of the observer to the object sighted.

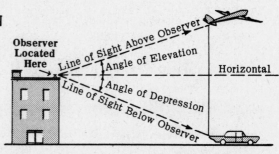

A horizontal line is a line level with the surface of water, or a line at right angles to a vertical line.

Thus, by centering a bubble of air in a water chamber, the table of a transit or sextant may be horizontally leveled.

An angle of elevation (or depression) is an angle formed by a horizontal line and a line of sight above (or below) the horizontal line and in the same vertical plane.

Thus, in the figure above, the observer is sighting an airplane above the horizontal. **The angle of elevation** is found by **elevating** or tilting upward the sighting tube of the transit or sextant above the horizontal position.

Also, in the diagram above, the observer is sighting an automobile below the horizontal. The **angle of depression** is found by **depressing** or tilting downward the sighting tube of the transit or sextant below the horizontal position.

3.1. Using a Transit to Find a Distance

Sighting the top of a building, Henry found the angle of elevation to be 21°. The ground is level. The transit is 5 ft. above the ground and 200 ft. from the building. Find the height of the building, to the nearest ft.

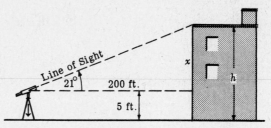

Solution:

Let x = the height, in ft., of the top of the building above the transit.

Then, $\tan 21° = \dfrac{x}{200}$

$.3839 = \dfrac{x}{200}$

$200(.3839) = x$

$x = 77$, to nearest ft.

To find the height h in ft. of the building, add 5 to x:

$h = x + 5$

$h = 77 + 5 = 82$

Ans. 82 ft., to the nearest ft.

3.2. Using Angle of Elevation of Sun

If the angle of elevation of the sun at a certain time is 42°, find, to the nearest foot,
a) the height h of a tree whose shadow s is 25 ft. long.
b) the shadow s of a tree along level ground if its height h is 35 ft.

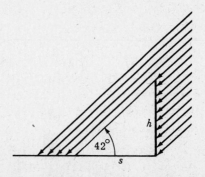

Solutions:

a) $\tan 42° = \dfrac{h}{s}$

$h = s \tan 42°$

$h = 25(.9004)$

$h = 23$, to nearest unit

Ans. 23 ft.

b) $\tan 48° = \dfrac{s}{h}$

$s = h \tan 48°$

$s = 35(1.1106)$

$s = 39$, to nearest unit

Ans. 39 ft.

3.3. Using Both an Angle of Elevation and an Angle of Depression

At the top of a lighthouse 200 ft. high, a lighthouse keeper sighted an airplane, and a ship directly beneath the plane. Sighting the plane, the angle of elevation was 25°. Sighting the ship, the angle of depression was 32°. Find

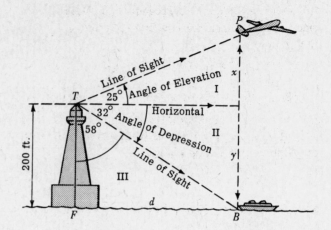

a) the distance *d*, to the nearest 10 ft., of the boat from the foot of the lighthouse.

b) the height *h*, to the nearest 10 ft., of the plane above the water.

Solutions:

a) $\tan 58° = \dfrac{d}{200}$

$1.6003 = \dfrac{d}{200}$

$200(1.6003) = d$

$320.06 = d$

Ans. 320 ft., to nearest 10 ft.

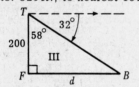

b) Using $d = 320$:

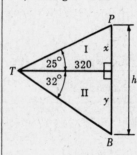

In △I, $\tan 25° = \dfrac{x}{320}$ In △II, $\tan 32° = \dfrac{y}{320}$

$.4663 = \dfrac{x}{320}$ $.6249 = \dfrac{y}{320}$

$320(.4663) = x$ $320(.6249) = y$

$149.216 = x$ $199.968 = y$

Since $h = x + y$

$h = 149 + 200 = 349$

Ans. 350 ft., to nearest 10 ft.

3.4. Using Two Angles of Depression

An observer on the top of a hill 250 ft. above the level of a lake sighted two boats directly in line. Find, to the nearest ft., the distance between the boats if the angles of depression noted by the observer were 11° and 16°.

$CB' = 250 \tan 79°$
$CB = 250 \tan 74°$

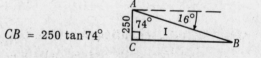

Solution: (*Separate* △I *and* △II *as shown.*)

$BB' = CB' - CB$

$= 250 \tan 79° - 250 \tan 74°$

$= 250(\tan 79° - \tan 74°)$

$= 250(5.1446 - 3.4874)$

$= 250(1.6572)$

$= 414.3$

$CB = 250 \tan 74°$

$CB' = 250 \tan 79°$

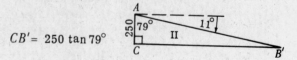

Ans. 414 ft., to nearest ft.

4. INCLINATION OF A LINE AND ITS SLOPE

In the coordinate plane, the **inclination of a line** is the angle which it makes with the positive direction of the *x*-axis.

Thus, in Fig. 1, i represents the angle made by $\overleftrightarrow{P_1 P_2}$ with the positive direction of the x-axis.

Note in Fig. 1 that $\tan i = \dfrac{\Delta y}{\Delta x}$.

Since the slope of a line $= \dfrac{\Delta y}{\Delta x}$, then

slope of a line $= \tan i$

Also, slope of a line $= m$ if the equation of a line is in the form $y = mx + b$.

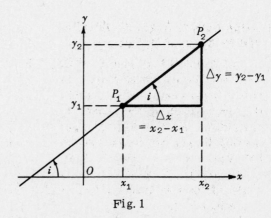

Fig. 1

Rule. If the equation of a line is in the form $y = mx + b$ and i is its inclination, then **slope of the line** $= m = \tan i$.

To Find the Inclination of a Line in the Coordinate Plane

Graph each line and find its inclination, to the nearest degree:

a) $y = 2x + 3$ *b)* $y = \frac{1}{2}x - 1$

Procedure:

Solutions:

1. Graph line:

1.
y	3	5
x	0	1

1.
y	−1	0
x	0	2

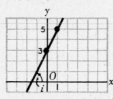 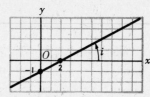

2. Find the slope of line, using $m =$ slope of $y = mx + b$:

2. Slope $= 2$

2. Slope $= \frac{1}{2}$

3. Find inclination i, using $\tan i =$ slope of line:

3. $\tan i = 2.0000$
To nearest degree,
$i = 63°$.   *Ans.* $63°$

3. $\tan i = \frac{1}{2} = .5000$
To nearest degree,
$i = 27°$.   *Ans.* $27°$

4.1. Determining the Inclination of a Line from Its Equation

Find the inclination, to the nearest degree, of each line:

a) $y = x + 1$,   *b)* $y = \frac{1}{2}x - 4$,   *c)* $2y = 4x + 10$,   *d)* $4y - x = 20$.

Solutions:

a) Since $y = x + 1$ is of the form $y = mx + b$, then its slope, $m = 1$.
Hence, $\tan i = 1$. From the table, $i = 45°$.   *Ans.* $45°$

b) Since $y = \frac{1}{2}x - 4$ is of the form $y = mx + b$, then its slope, $m = \frac{1}{2} = .5000$.
Hence, $\tan i = .5000$. To nearest degree, $i = 27°$.   *Ans.* $27°$

c) Divide each side by 2 to obtain an equation of the form $y = mx + b$:
$$2y = 4x + 10 \longrightarrow y = 2x + 5.$$
Hence, its slope, $m = 2 = \tan i$. Since $\tan i = 2$, then $i = 63°$, to nearest degree.   *Ans.* $63°$

d) By transforming $4y - x = 20$ into $4y = x + 20$, then dividing each side by 4, we obtain $y = \frac{1}{4}x + 5$, an equation of the form $y = mx + b$.
Hence, its slope, $m = \frac{1}{4} = \tan i$. Since $\tan i = .2500$, then $i = 76°$, to nearest degree.   *Ans.* $76°$

SUPPLEMENTARY PROBLEMS

1. Using the table of sines, cosines and tangents, find   **(1.1)**
   a) sin 25°, sin 48°, sin 59°, sin 89°   *Ans.* .4226, .7431, .8572, .9998
   b) cos 15°, cos 52°, cos 74°, cos 88°   *Ans.* .9659, .6157, .2756, .0349
   c) tan 4° , tan 34°, tan 55°, tan 87°   *Ans.* .0699, .6745, 1.4281, 19.0811
   d) which sets of values increase as the angle increases from 0° to 90°.   *Ans.* sine and tangent
   e) which set of values decreases as the angle increases from 0° to 90°.   *Ans.* cosine
   f) which set has values greater than 1.   *Ans.* tangent

2. Using the table, find the angle in each :   **(1.1)**
   a) sin x = .3420 *Ans.* x = 20°   *d*) cos A' = .9336 *Ans.* A' = 21°   *g*) tan W = .3443   *Ans.* W = 19°
   b) sin A = .4848 *Ans.* A = 29°   *e*) cos y = .7071 *Ans.* y = 45°   *h*) tan B' = 2.3559 *Ans.* B' = 67°
   c) sin B = .9455 *Ans.* B = 71°   *f*) cos Q = .3584 *Ans.* Q = 69°   *i*) tan R = 28.6363 *Ans.* R = 88°

3. Using the table, find x, to the nearest degree if   **(1.2)**
   a) sin x = .4400   *e*) cos x = .7650   *i*) tan x = 5.5745   *m*) cos x = $\frac{3}{8}$

   b) sin x = .7280   *f*) cos x = .2675   *j*) sin x = $\frac{11}{50}$ *n*) cos x = $\frac{\sqrt{3}}{2}$

   c) sin x = .9365   *g*) tan x = .1245   *k*) sin x = $\frac{\sqrt{2}}{2}$ *o*) tan x = $\frac{2}{7}$

   d) cos x = .9900   *h*) tan x = .5200   *l*) cos x = $\frac{13}{25}$ *p*) tan x = $\frac{\sqrt{3}}{10}$

   Ans. a) 26°, *b*) 47°, *c*) 69°, *d*) 8°, *e*) 40°, *f*) 74°, *g*) 7°, *h*) 27°, *i*) 80°, *j*) 13° since sin x = .2200,
      k) 45° since sin x = .707,   *m*) 68° since cos x = .3750,   *o*) 16° since tan x = .2857,
      l) 59° since cos x = .5200,   *n*) 30° since cos x = .866,   *p*) 10° since tan x = .1732.

4. In each right triangle, find sin A, cos A and tan A (*leave answer in radical form*):   **(1.3)**

   a)   *b*)   *c*)

 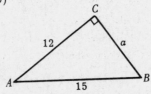 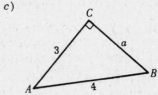

   Ans.
   a) sin $A = \frac{4}{5}$, cos $A = \frac{3}{5}$,   *b*) sin $A = \frac{3}{5}$, cos $A = \frac{4}{5}$,   *c*) sin $A = \frac{\sqrt{7}}{4}$, cos $A = \frac{3}{4}$,
      tan $A = \frac{4}{3}$ tan $A = \frac{3}{4}$ tan $A = \frac{\sqrt{7}}{3}$

5. Find A, to the nearest degree, in each: **(1.4)**

   a)   *b*)   *c*)

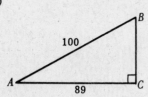

   Ans.
   a) A = 27° since cos A = .8900   *b*) A = 58° since sin A = .8500   *c*) A = 52° since tan A = 1.2800

6. Find B to the nearest degree,   **(1.4)**
   a) if b = 67 and c = 100.   *Ans.* B = 42° since sin B = .6700
   b) if a = 14 and c = 50.   *Ans.* B = 74° since cos B = .2800
   c) if a = 22 and b = 55.   *Ans.* B = 68° since tan B = 2.500
   d) if a = 3 and $b = \sqrt{3}$ *Ans.* B = 30° since tan B = .577

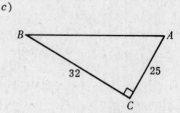

7. Using a square with a side of 1 unit, show that   **(1.5)**
   a) diagonal $c = \sqrt{2}$,
   b) $\tan 45° = 1$,
   c) $\sin 45° = \cos 45° = .707$.

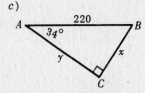

8. To the nearest degree, find each acute angle of any right triangle whose sides are in the ratio of
   a) $5:12:13$ b) $8:15:17$ c) $7:24:25$ d) $11:60:61$ **(1.6)**
   Ans. a) $23°, 67°$ b) $28°, 62°$ c) $16°, 74°$ d) $10°, 80°$

9. In each triangle, state the trigonometric equation needed to solve for x and y: **(2.1)**
   (*Avoid division where possible.*)

   a)   b)   c)

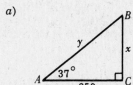   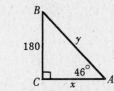   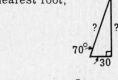

   Ans. a) (*1*) $x = 250 \tan 37°$ | b) (*1*) $x = 180 \tan 44°$, using $B = 44°$ | c) (*1*) $x = 220 \sin 34°$
          (*2*) $y = \dfrac{250}{\cos 37°}$ | (*2*) $y = \dfrac{180}{\sin 46°}$ | (*2*) $y = 220 \cos 34°$

10. Solve each equation. Find the unknown, to the nearest integer.   **(2.2)**
    a) (*1*) $x = 250 \tan 37°$ b) (*1*) $x = 180 \tan 44°$ c) (*1*) $x = 220 \sin 34°$
       (*2*) $y = \dfrac{250}{\cos 37°}$ (*2*) $y = \dfrac{180}{\sin 46°}$ (*2*) $y = 220 \cos 34°$
    Ans. a) $x = 188, \ y = 313$ b) $x = 174, \ y = 250$ c) $x = 123, \ y = 182$

(*In Problems* **11-23**, *the trigonometric expression used to obtain the answer is shown in parentheses.*)

11. A ladder leans against the side of a building and makes an angle of $70°$ with the ground. **(2.1a, 2.2a)**
    The foot of the ladder is 30 feet from the building. Find, to the nearest foot,
    a) how high up on the building the ladder reaches,
    b) the length of the ladder.

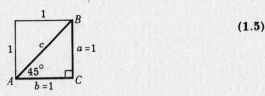

    Ans. a) 82 ft., $(30 \tan 70°)$ b) 88 ft., $\left(\dfrac{30}{\cos 70°}\right)$

12. To find the distance across a swamp, a surveyor took   **(2.1a, 2.2a)**
    measurements as shown. AC is at right angles to BC.
       If $A = 24°$ and $AC = 350$ ft., find the distance BC across
    the swamp.
    Ans. 156 ft., $(350 \tan 24°)$

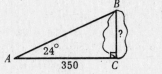

13. A plane rises from a take-off and flies at a fixed angle of   **(2.1b, 2.2b)**
    $9°$ with the horizontal ground. When it has gained 400 ft.
    in altitude, find, to the nearest 10 ft., a) the horizontal
    distance flown, b) the distance the plane has actually flown.
    Ans. a) 2530 ft., $(AC = 400 \tan 81°)$

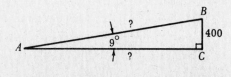

          b) 2560 ft., $\left(AB = \dfrac{400}{\sin 9°}\right)$

14. If the base angle of an isosceles triangle is $28°$ and each   **(2.1c, 2.2c)**
    leg is 45 in., find, to the nearest inch,
    a) the altitude drawn to the base,
    b) the base.

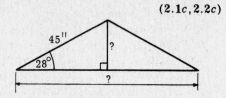

    Ans. a) 21 in., $(45 \sin 28°)$
           b) 79 in., $[2(45 \cos 28°) = 90 \cos 28°]$

15. A road is inclined uniformly at an angle of 6° with the horizontal. After   **(2.3)**
driving 10,000 ft. along this road, find, to the nearest 10 ft., the
a) increase in the altitude of the driver,
b) horizontal distance that has been driven.
Ans. a) 1050 ft., (10,000 sin 6°)   *b*) 9950 ft., (10,000 cos 6°)

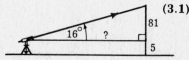

16. An airplane travels 15,000 ft. through the air at a uniform angle of climb, thereby gaining 1900 ft.,
in altitude. Find its angle of climb.   **(2.4)**

Ans. 7° ($\sin x = \frac{1900}{15,000}$ where x is the angle of climb)

17. The angle of elevation of the top of a building from a point 500 ft. from the   **(3.1)**
top is 21°. Disregarding the height of the transit, find to the nearest foot,
a) the height of the building,
b) the distance along level ground from the observer to the foot of the building.
Ans. a) 179 ft., (500 sin 21°)   *b*) 467 ft., (500 cos 21°)

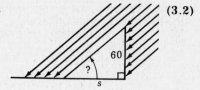

18. Sighting the top of a monument, William found the angle of ele-   **(3.1)**
vation to be 16°. The ground is level and the transit is 5 ft. above
the ground. If the monument is 86 ft. high, find to the nearest
foot the distance from William to the foot of the monument.
Ans. 282 ft., (81 tan 74°)

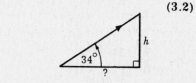

19. Find to the nearest degree the angle of elevation of the sun when   **(3.2)**
a tree 60 ft. high casts a shadow of
a) 10 ft.,   *b*) 20 ft.,   *c*) 40 ft.,   *d*) 60 ft.
Ans. a) 81°, (tan *x* = 6)   *c*) 56°, (tan *x* = 1.5)
     b) 72°, (tan *x* = 3)   *d*) 45°, (tan *x* = 1)

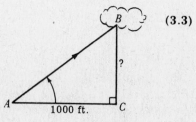

20. At a certain time of day, the angle of elevation of the sun is 34°.   **(3.2)**
Find to the nearest foot the shadow cast by
a) a 15 ft. vertical pole.   *Ans.* 22 ft., (*x* = 15 tan 56°)
b) a building 70 ft. high.   *Ans.* 104 ft., (*x* = 70 tan 56°)
c) a monument 450 ft. high.   *Ans.* 667 ft., (*x* = 450 tan 56°)

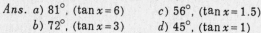

21. A light at *C* is projected vertically to a cloud at *B*. An observer   **(3.3)**
at *A*, 1000 ft. from *C*, notes the angle of elevation of *B*. Find
the height of the cloud, to the nearest foot, if
a) *A* = 20°.   *Ans.* 364 ft., (1000 tan 20°)
b) *A* = 37°.   *Ans.* 754 ft., (1000 tan 37°)
c) *A* = 49°.   *Ans.* 1150 ft., (1000 tan 49°)

22. A lighthouse built at sea level is 180 ft. high. From its top, the   **(3.3)**
angle of depression of a buoy is 24°. Find, to the nearest foot
the distance from the buoy to the foot of the lighthouse.
Ans. 404 ft., (180 tan 66°)

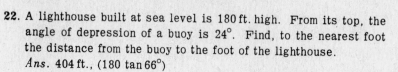

23. An observer on the top of a hill 300 ft. above the level of a lake, sighted two ships directly in
line. Find, to the nearest ft., the distance between the boats if the angles of depression noted by
the observer were
          (3.4)
a) 20° and 15°.   *Ans.* 295 ft., [300 (tan 75° – tan 70°)]
b) 35° and 24°.   *Ans.* 245 ft., [300 (tan 66° – tan 55°)]
c) 9° and 6°.   *Ans.* 960 ft., [300 (tan 84° – tan 81°)]

24. Find the inclination, to the nearest degree, of each line: **(4.1)**

    a) $y = 3x - 1$ *c)* $y = \frac{5}{2}x + 5$ *e)* $5y = 5x - 3$

    b) $y = \frac{1}{3}x - 1$ *d)* $y = \frac{2}{5}x + 5$ *f)* $y = -3$

    a) $\tan i = 3$ *Ans.* 72°   *c)* $\tan i = 2.5$ *Ans.* 68°   *e)* $\tan i = 1$ *Ans.* 45°

    b) $\tan i = .3333$ *Ans.* 18°   *d)* $\tan i = .4$ *Ans.* 22°   *f)* $\tan i = 0$ *Ans.* 0°

Chapter 17

The Variable:
Direct, Inverse, Joint and Power Variation

1. UNDERSTANDING THE VARIABLE

A **variable** is·a letter or other symbol which may represent any number in a specified set of numbers under discussion.

Thus, if $y = 2x$: when $x = 1$, then $y = 2$
                    when $x = 2$, then $y = 4$
                    when $x = 6$, then $y = 12$

$(x,\ y)$
$(1,\ 2)$
$(2,\ 4)$
$(6, 12)$

	(1)	(2)	(3)
y	2	4	12
x	1	2	6

Fig. 1

These three pairs of corresponding values may be shown as ordered pairs or tabulated, Fig. 1. If no replacement set is indicated, assume that the set under discussion is the set of real numbers.

A **constant** is a letter or other symbol which represents a fixed value under discussion.

Thus, 5 and π are constants. Throughout this chapter, the letter k, called the **constant of variation**, shall be used as the constant under discussion.

Measuring the Change in a Variable

As a variable changes in value from one number x_1 to a second number x_2, the change may be measured (1) by subtracting to find the difference, $x_2 - x_1$, or (2) by dividing to find the ratio, $\frac{x_2}{x_1}$.

Thus, the change in the speed of an auto from 20 mph to 60 mph may be expressed as follows:

(*1*) the second speed is $(60 - 20)$ or **40 mph faster** than the first speed.
(*2*) the second speed is $\frac{60}{20}$ or **three times as fast** as the first speed.

Any formula may be considered as a relationship of its variables. Mathematics and science abound in formulas which have exactly the same general structure, $z = xy$. To illustrate, study the following:

	Formula	Rule		
1.	$D = RT$	Distance	= Rate	× Time
2.	$A = LW$	Area	= Length	× Width
3.	$I = PR$	Interest	= Price	× Rate of Interest
4.	$C = NP$	Cost	= Number	× Price
5.	$F = PA$	Force	= Pressure	× Area
6.	$M = DV$	Mass	= Density	× Volume

Note, in each formula which has the form $z = xy$, that there are three variables. Furthermore, one of the variables is the product of the other two. In this chapter, we shall study the relation of these formulas to the three basic types of variation. These types of variation are

      1. Direct Variation
      2. Inverse Variation
      3. Joint Variation

1.1. Using Division to Measure the Change in a Variable

Using division, find the ratio which indicates the change in each variable and express this ratio in a sentence.

a) The price of a suit changes from $40 to $60.
b) The speed of an auto changes from 10 mph to 40 mph.
c) A salary changes from $30 per week to $40 per week.
d) Length of a line changes from 12 ft. to 4 ft.

Solutions:

a) $\dfrac{\$60}{\$40} = \dfrac{3}{2}$.   Hence, second price is **three-halves** of first price.

b) $\dfrac{40\,\text{mph}}{10\,\text{mph}} = 4$.   Hence, second rate is **four times (quadruple)** first rate.

c) $\dfrac{\$40 \text{ per week}}{\$30 \text{ per week}} = \dfrac{4}{3}$.   Hence, second salary is **four-thirds** of first salary.

d) $\dfrac{4 \text{ ft.}}{12 \text{ ft.}} = \dfrac{1}{3}$.   Hence, second length is **one-third** of first length.

1.2. Multiplying or Dividing Variables

Complete each:

a) If x is doubled, it will change from 13 to (   ) or from (   ) to 90.
b) If y is tripled, it will change from 17 to (   ) or from (   ) to 87.
c) If z is halved, it will change from 7 to (   ) or from (   ) to 110.
d) If s is multiplied by $\frac{5}{4}$, it will change from 16 to (   ) or from (   ) to 55.

Ans. a) 26, 45   *b*) 51, 29   *c*) $3\frac{1}{2}$, 220   *d*) 20, 44

2. UNDERSTANDING DIRECT VARIATION: $y = kx$ or $\frac{y}{x} = k$

Direct Variation Formula With Constant Ratio k

$$y = kx \quad \text{or} \quad \frac{y}{x} = k$$

Direct Variation Formula Without Constant

If x varies from x_1 to x_2 while y varies from y_1 to y_2, then

$$\frac{x_2}{x_1} = \frac{y_2}{y_1}$$

Rule 1. If $y = kx$ or $\frac{y}{x} = k$, and k is a constant ratio, then

(*1*) x and y **vary directly** as each other; that is, x varies directly as y and y varies directly as x.

(*2*) x and y are **directly proportional** to each other; that is, $\frac{x_2}{x_1} = \frac{y_2}{y_1}$ as x varies from x_1 to x_2 and y varies from y_1 to y_2 .

Thus:

1. If $y = 4x$, y and x vary directly as each other.

2. If $l = .06P$, l and P vary directly as each other.

3. The perimeter of a square equals four times its side; that is, $P = 4S$. For a square, P and S vary directly as each other.

Multiplication and Division in Direct Variation

Rule 2. If x and y vary directly as each other and a value of either x or y is **multiplied** by a number, then the corresponding value of the other is **multiplied** by the same number.

Thus, if $y = 5x$ and x is tripled, then y is tripled, as shown in the table.

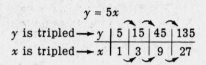

Rule 3. If x and y vary directly as each other and a value of either x or y is **divided** by a number, then the corresponding value of the other is **divided** by the same number.

Thus, if $y = 10x$ and x is halved (divided by 2), then y is halved, as shown in the table.

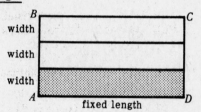

Direct Variation Applied to a Rectangle

To understand direct variation more fully, note how it applies to a rectangle:

If the length of a rectangle is fixed and the width is tripled, then the area is tripled. As a result, the new area $ABCD$ is three times the area of the old (shaded) rectangle, as shown in the adjoining figure.

2.1. Rule 1. Direct Variation in Formulas

(1) Express each equation in the form $y = kx$.
(2) State the variables that vary directly as each other.

a) $120R = P$ c) $.05 = \dfrac{I}{P}$ e) $A = \frac{1}{2}bh$ when b is constant

b) $\dfrac{C}{D} = \pi$ d) $f = \dfrac{n}{d}$ when $f = \dfrac{2}{3}$ f) $V = \pi R^2 H$ when $R = 8$

Ans. a) (1) $P = 120R$, (2) P and R d) (1) $n = \frac{2}{3}d$, (2) n and d
        b) (1) $C = \pi D$, (2) C and D e) (1) $A = kh$, (2) A and h
        c) (1) $I = .05P$, (2) I and P f) (1) $V = 64\pi H$, (2) V and H

2.2. Rules 2 and 3. Multiplication and Division in Direct Variation

Complete each:

a) If $y = 8x$ and x is tripled, then ( ).   *Ans.* a) y is tripled.
b) If $C = \pi D$ and D is quadrupled, then ( ).   *Ans.* b) C is quadrupled.
c) If $C = \pi D$ and C is halved, then ( ).   *Ans.* c) D is halved.
d) If $D = RT$, $T = 12$ and R is divided by 4, then ( ).   *Ans.* d) D is divided by 4.
e) If $A = LW$, L is constant and W is doubled, then ( ).   *Ans.* e) A is doubled.

2.3. Applying Direct Variation to Statements

(1) Complete each statement and (2) state the formula to which direct variation applies.

a) At a uniform speed, doubling time will ( ).
b) If the time of travel is constant, tripling rate will ( ).
c) If a rectangle has a fixed width, to multiply its area by 5 ( ).
d) If the value of a fraction is constant and the numerator is halved, ( ).

Ans. a) (1) double distance, (2) $D = kT$ since $D = RT$ and R is constant.
       b) (1) triple distance, (2) $D = kR$ since $D = RT$ and T is constant.
       c) (1) multiply its length by 5, (2) $A = kL$ since $A = LW$ and W is constant.
       d) (1) the denominator is halved, (2) $n = kd$ since $f = \dfrac{n}{d}$ and f is constant.

2.4. Finding Values for Directly Varying Variables

a) If y and x vary directly as each other and $y = 36$ when $x = 9$, find y when $x = 27$.

Solution: **Proportion Method**

If y and x vary directly,

$$\frac{y_2}{y_1} = \frac{x_2}{x_1}$$

$$\frac{y}{36} = \frac{27}{9}$$

$$y = \frac{27}{9}(36) = 108 \qquad Ans.\ 108$$

	x	y
2nd values	27	y
1st values	9	36

Ratio Method

(Note the equal ratios in the table.)

	x	y
2nd values	27 $\rfloor 3$	y $\rfloor 3$
1st values	9 $\rfloor 1$	36 $\rfloor 1$

If *2nd x-value* is **three times** *1st x-value*, then *2nd y-value* is **three times** *1st y-value*.
Hence, $y = 3(36) = 108$.   *Ans.* 108

Equation Method

If y and x vary directly, $kx = y$.
Since $y = 36$ when $x = 9$, $9k = 36$, $k = 4$.
Since $k = 4$, $y = 4x$.
When $x = 27$, $y = 4(27) = 108$.   *Ans.* 108

---

b) If y and x vary directly as each other and $y = 25$ when $x = 10$, find x when $y = 5$.

Solution: **Proportion Method**

If y and x vary directly,

$$\frac{x_2}{x_1} = \frac{y_2}{y_1}$$

$$\frac{x}{10} = \frac{5}{25}$$

$$x = \frac{5}{25}(10) = 2 \qquad Ans.\ 2$$

	x	y
2nd values	x	5
1st values	10	25

Ratio Method

(Note the equal ratios in the table.)

	x	y
2nd values	x $\rfloor \frac{1}{5}$	5 $\rfloor \frac{1}{5}$
1st values	10	25

If *2nd y-value* is **one-fifth** of *1st y-value*, then *2nd x-value* is **one-fifth** of *1st x-value*.
Hence, $x = \frac{1}{5}(10) = 2$.   *Ans.* 2

Equation Method

If y and x vary directly, $kx = y$.
Since $y = 25$ when $x = 10$, $10k = 25$, $k = 2\frac{1}{2}$.
Since $k = 2\frac{1}{2}$, $y = 2\frac{1}{2}x$.
When $y = 5$, $5 = 2\frac{1}{2}x$, $x = 2$.   *Ans.* 2

2.5. Applying Direct Variation to a Motion Problem

Henry traveled a distance of 124 miles at 40 mph. If he had taken the same amount of time, how far would he have traveled at 50 mph?

Solution:

	(mph) Rate	(mi.) Distance
2nd trip	50 $\rfloor \frac{5}{4}$	D $\rfloor \frac{5}{4}$
1st trip	40	124

Proportion Method

Since $D = RT$ and the time (T) is constant, then D and R vary directly as each other.

Hence, $\dfrac{D_2}{D_1} = \dfrac{R_2}{R_1}$, $\dfrac{D}{124} = \dfrac{50}{40}$, $\dfrac{D}{124} = \dfrac{5}{4}$,

$$D = \frac{5}{4}(124) = 155 \qquad Ans.\ 155\ \text{mi.}$$

Ratio Method (*Note use of the equal ratios in the table.*)

If the second rate is **five-fourths** of the first rate, then the second distance is **five-fourths** of the first distance. Hence, $D = \frac{5}{4}(124) = 155$.   *Ans.* 155 mi.

2.6. Applying Direct Variation to an Interest Problem

In a bank, the annual interest on $4500 is $180. At the same rate, what is the annual interest on $7500.

Solution:

	($) Principal	($) Annual Interest
2nd principal	7500 $\rfloor \frac{5}{3}$	I $\rfloor \frac{5}{3}$
1st principal	4500	180

Proportion Method

Since $I = PR$ and the rate (R) is constant, then I and P vary directly as each other.

Hence, $\dfrac{I_2}{I_1} = \dfrac{P_2}{P_1}$, $\dfrac{I}{180} = \dfrac{7500}{4500}$, $\dfrac{I}{180} = \dfrac{5}{3}$,

$$I = \frac{5}{3}(180) = 300 \qquad Ans.\ \$300$$

Ratio Method (*Note use of the equal ratios in the table.*)

If the second principal is **five-thirds** of the first principal, then the second interest is **five-thirds** of the first interest. Hence, $I = \frac{5}{3}(180) = 300$.   *Ans.* $300

3. UNDERSTANDING INVERSE VARIATION: $xy = k$

Inverse Variation Formula With Constant Product k

$$xy = k$$

Inverse Variation Formula Without Constant

If x varies from x_1 to x_2 while y varies from y_1 to y_2, then

$$\frac{x_2}{x_1} = \frac{y_1}{y_2} \quad \text{or} \quad \frac{y_2}{y_1} = \frac{x_1}{x_2}$$

Rule 1. If $xy = k$ and k is a constant product, then

(1) x and y **vary inversely** as each other; that is, x varies inversely as y and y varies inversely as x.

(2) x and y are **inversely proportional** to each other; that is, $\frac{x_2}{x_1} = \frac{y_1}{y_2}$ or $\frac{y_2}{y_1} = \frac{x_1}{x_2}$ as x varies from x_1 to x_2 and y varies from y_1 to y_2.

Thus:

1. If $xy = 12$, y and x vary inversely as each other.
2. If $PR = 150$, P and R vary inversely as each other.
3. For a fixed distance of 120 miles to be traveled, the motion formula $D = RT$ becomes $120 = RT$. In such a case, R and T vary inversely as each other.

Multiplication and Division in Inverse Variation

Rule 2. If x and y vary inversely as each other and a value of either x or y is **multiplied** by a number, then the corresponding value of the other is **divided** by the same number.

Thus, if $xy = 24$ and y is doubled, then x is halved, as shown in the table.

$$xy = 24$$

y is doubled $\longrightarrow$

y	2	4	8	16
x	12	6	3	$\frac{3}{2}$

x is halved $\longrightarrow$

Rule 3. If x and y vary inversely as each other and either x or y is **divided** by a number, then the other is **multiplied** by the same number.

Thus, if $xy = 250$ and y is divided by 5, then x is multiplied by 5, as shown in the table.

$$xy = 250$$

y is divided by 5 $\longrightarrow$

y	250	50	10	2
x	1	5	25	125

x is multiplied by 5 $\longrightarrow$

Inverse Variation Applied to a Rectangle

To understand inverse variation more fully, note how it applies to a rectangle:

If the length of a rectangle is doubled and the width is halved, its area remains constant. As a result, the new area $ABCD$ equals the old (shaded) area.

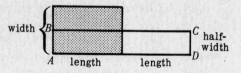

3.1. Rule 1. Inverse Variation in Formulas

(1) Express each equation in the form, $xy = k$.
(2) State the variables that vary inversely as each other.

a) $5RT = 500$

b) $\frac{1}{2}PV = 7$

c) $f = \frac{n}{d}$ when $n = 3$

d) $A = \frac{1}{2}bh$ when A is constant.

Ans. a) (1) $RT = 100$, (2) R and T

Ans. b) (1) $PV = 14$, (2) P and V

Ans. c) (1) $fd = 3$, (2) f and d

Ans. d) (1) $bh = k$, (2) b and h

3.2. Rules 2 and 3. Multiplication and Division in Inverse Variation

Complete each:

a) If $xy = 25$ and x is tripled, then (   ).

b) If $50 = RT$ and R is divided by 10, then (   ).

c) If $BH = 5$ and B is multiplied by $\frac{3}{2}$, then (   ).

d) If $A = LW$, A is constant and L is doubled, then (   ).

e) If $PV = k$ and V is quadrupled, then (   ).

Ans. a) y is divided by 3.

Ans. b) T is multiplied by 10.

Ans. c) H is divided by $\frac{3}{2}$.

Ans. d) W is halved.

Ans. e) P is divided by 4.

3.3. Applying Inverse Variation to Statements

(1) Complete each statement.

(2) State the formula to which inverse variation applies.

a) Over the same distance, doubling the speed (   ).

b) For a fixed area, multiplying the length of a rectangle by 5, (   ).

c) For an enclosed gas at a constant temperature, dividing the pressure by 7 (   ).

d) If the total cost is the same, tripling the price of an article (   ).

Ans. a) (1) halves the time   (2) $RT = k$ since $RT = D$ and D is constant

  b) (1) divides the width by 5   (2) $LW = k$ since $LW = A$ and A is constant

  c) (1) multiplies the volume by 7   (2) $PV = k$ (Boyle's Law)

  d) (1) divides the number of these articles purchased by 3

     (2) $NP = k$ since $NP = C$ and C is constant

3.4. Finding Values for Inversely Varying Variables

a) If y and x vary inversely as each other and $y = 10$ when $x = 6$, find y when $x = 15$.

Solution:

Proportion Method

If y and x vary inversely,

$$\frac{y_2}{y_1} = \frac{x_1}{x_2}$$

$$\frac{y}{10} = \frac{6}{15}$$

$$y = \frac{6}{15}(10) = 4 \qquad Ans.\ 4$$

	x	y
2nd values	15	y
1st values	6	10

Ratio Method

(Note the inverse ratios in the table.)

	x	y
2nd values	15 $\frac{5}{2}$	y $\frac{2}{5}$
1st values	6	10

If *2nd x-value* is **five-halves** of *1st x-value*, then *2nd y-value* is **two-fifths** of *1st y-value*.

Hence, $y = \frac{2}{5}(10) = 4$.   *Ans.* 4

Equation Method

If x and y vary inversely, $k = xy$.

Since $y = 10$ when $x = 6$, $k = (6)(10) = 60$.

Since $k = 60$, $xy = 60$.

When $x = 15$, $15y = 60$, $y = 4$.   *Ans.* 4

b) If y and x vary inversely as each other and $y = 12$ when $x = 4$, find x when $y = 8$.

Solution:

Proportion Method

If y and x vary inversely,

$$\frac{x_2}{x_1} = \frac{y_1}{y_2}$$

$$\frac{x}{4} = \frac{12}{8}$$

$$x = \frac{12}{8}(4) = 6 \qquad Ans.\ 6$$

	x	y
2nd values	x	8
1st values	4	12

Ratio Method

(Note the inverse ratios in the table.)

	x	y
2nd values	x $\frac{3}{2}$	8 $\frac{2}{3}$
1st values	4	12

If *2nd y-value* is **two-thirds** of *1st y-value*, then *2nd x-value* is **three-halves** of *1st x-value*.

Hence, $x = \frac{3}{2}(4) = 6$.   *Ans.* 6

Equation Method

If x and y vary inversely, $k = xy$.

Since $y = 12$ when $x = 4$, $k = (4)(12) = 48$.

Since $k = 48$, $xy = 48$.

When $y = 8$, $8x = 48$, $x = 6$.   *Ans.* 6

3.5. Inverse Variation in a Balanced Lever Problem

Two weights of 35 lb. and 25 lb. are in balance on a lever bar. If the 35 lb. weight is 20 in. from the fulcrum or turning point, how far is the 25 lb. weight from the fulcrum? Consider the weight of the bar as negligible.

Solution:

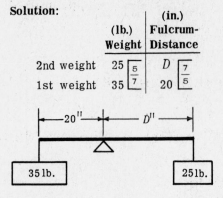

	(lb.) Weight	(in.) Fulcrum- Distance
2nd weight	25 ⌐5/7	D ⌐7/5
1st weight	35 ⌐7	20 ⌐5

Proportion Method

Since weight and fulcrum-distance on a balanced lever vary inversely,

$$\frac{D_2}{D_1} = \frac{W_1}{W_2}, \quad \frac{D}{20} = \frac{35}{25},$$

$$D = \frac{35}{25}(20) = 28 \qquad Ans.\ 28\ \text{in.}$$

Ratio Method (*Note inverse ratios included in table.*)

If the second weight is **five-sevenths** of the first weight, then the second distance is **seven-fifths** of the first distance. Hence, $D = \frac{7}{5}(20) = 28$.   *Ans.* 28 in.

3.6. Inverse Variation in a Meshed Gear Problem

A gear having 36 teeth drives another which has 48 teeth. If the first gear makes 100 revolutions, how many revolutions does the second gear make?

Solution:

	No. of Teeth (T)	No. of Revolutions (R)
2nd gear	48 ⌐4/3	R ⌐3/4
1st gear	36 ⌐3	100 ⌐4

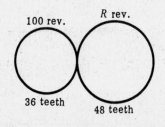

100 rev.   R rev.

36 teeth   48 teeth

Proportion Method

For meshed gears, the number of teeth and the number of revolutions vary inversely.

Hence, $\frac{R_2}{R_1} = \frac{T_1}{T_2}, \quad \frac{R}{100} = \frac{36}{48}$

$$R = \frac{36}{48}(100) = 75 \qquad Ans.\ 75\ \text{rev.}$$

Ratio Method (*Note inverse ratios included in table.*)

If second gear has **four-thirds** as many teeth as first gear, then second gear makes **three-fourths** as many revolutions as first gear.
Hence, $R = \frac{3}{4}(100) = 75$.   *Ans.* 75 rev.

3.7. Inverse Variation in Connected Pulleys

Two pulleys connected by the same belt, have diameters of 10 in. and 14 in. If the smaller pulley turns at 560 rpm (revolutions per minute), what is the turning speed of the larger pulley?

Solution:

	(in.) Diameter (D)	(rpm) Revolutions (R)
2nd pulley	14 ⌐7/5	R ⌐5/7
1st pulley	10 ⌐	560 ⌐

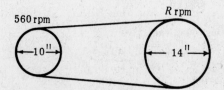

560 rpm   R rpm

10″   14″

Proportion Method

For pulleys connected by the same belt, diameters and revolutions vary inversely.

Hence, $\frac{R_2}{R_1} = \frac{D_1}{D_2}, \quad \frac{R}{560} = \frac{10}{14},$

$$R = \frac{10}{14}(560) = 400 \qquad Ans.\ 400\ \text{rpm}$$

Ratio Method (*Note inverse ratios included in table.*)

If second pulley has **seven-fifths** the diameter of first pulley, then second pulley turns **five-sevenths** as fast as first pulley.
Hence, $R = \frac{5}{7}(560) = 400$.   *Ans.* 400 rpm

4. UNDERSTANDING JOINT VARIATION: $z = kxy$

Joint Variation Formula With Constant Ratio k

$$z = kxy \quad \text{or} \quad \frac{z}{xy} = k$$

Note. When $k=1$, we obtain $z=xy$, the formula structure of $D=RT$, $A=LW$, $I=PR$, etc.

Joint Variation Formula Without Constant

$$\frac{z_2}{z_1} = \frac{x_2 y_2}{x_1 y_1}$$

Rule 1. If $z = kxy$ and k is a constant ratio, then z **varies jointly as x and y.**

Thus:

      (*1*) If $z=5xy$, z varies jointly as x and y.

      (*2*) If $D=RT$, D varies jointly as R and T. Hence, in a motion problem, distance varies jointly as rate and time.

Multiplication in Joint Variation

Rule 2. If z varies jointly as x and y and a value of x is multiplied by a while a value of y is multiplied by b, then the corresponding value of z is multiplied by their product ab, as shown in the table.

      Thus, if $z = 2xy$ and x is doubled while y is tripled, then z is multiplied by 6, as shown in the table.

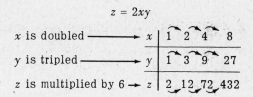

Applying Joint Variation to a Triangle

      To understand joint variation more fully, note how it applies to a triangle:

      If the base and altitude of a triangle are tripled, the area becomes nine times as large. As a result, the new triangle ABC is nine times the old (shaded) triangle.

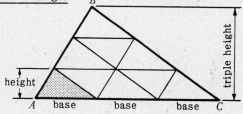

4.1. Rule 1. Joint Variation in Formulas

      (*1*) Express each equation in the form $z = kxy$.
      (*2*) State how the variables vary jointly.

a) $V = \dfrac{Bh}{3}$ *Ans.* (*1*) $V = \frac{1}{3}Bh$,   (*2*) V varies jointly as B and h.

b) $PV = 5T$ *Ans.* (*1*) $T = \frac{1}{5}PV$,   (*2*) T varies jointly as P and V.

c) $V = LWH$ when W is constant.   *Ans.* (*1*) $V = kLH$,   (*2*) V varies jointly as L and H.

d) $P = \dfrac{FS}{t}$ when $t=2$.   *Ans.* (*1*) $P = \frac{1}{2}FS$,   (*2*) P varies jointly as F and S.

4.2. Rule 2. Multiplication in Joint Variation

      Complete each:

a) If $z=5xy$ and x and y are each doubled, then (   ).
b) If $A=\frac{1}{2}bh$ and b and h are each halved, then (   ).
c) If $D=RT$, R is tripled while T is doubled, then (   ).
d) If $V=\frac{1}{3}Bh$, B is multiplied by 10 while h is multiplied by $\frac{1}{5}$, then (   ).

Ans. a) z is multiplied by $2 \cdot 2$ or 4.   *c*) D is multiplied by $3 \cdot 2$ or 6.

      b) A is multiplied by $\frac{1}{2}(\frac{1}{2})$ or $\frac{1}{4}$.   *d*) V is multiplied by $10(\frac{1}{5})$ or 2.

4.3. Finding Values for Jointly Varying Variables

If z varies jointly as x and y, and $z=100$ when $x=4$ and $y=5$, find z when $x=12$ and $y=10$.

Solution:

Proportion Method

	x	y	z
2nd values	12	10	z
1st values	4	5	100

If z varies jointly as x and y,

$$\frac{z_2}{z_1} = \frac{x_2 y_2}{x_1 y_1}, \quad \frac{z}{100} = \frac{(12)(10)}{(4)(5)}$$

$$z = 100(6) = 600 \qquad Ans. \ 600$$

Ratio Method (*Note the ratios included in the table.*)

	x	y	z
2nd values	12	10	z
1st values	4	5	100

If x is tripled and y is doubled, then z is multiplied by 6.

Hence, $z = 6(100) = 600$.   *Ans.* 600

Equation Method

If z varies jointly as x and y, $kxy = z$.

Since $z=100$ when $x=4$ and $y=5$, $(4)(5)k = 100$, $20k = 100$, $k = 5$.

Since $k = 5$. $z = 5xy$.

When $x = 12$ and $y = 10$, $z = 5(12)(10) = 600$.   *Ans.* 600

5. UNDERSTANDING POWER VARIATION

(In each of the following formulas and rules, k is the constant of variation.)

> **1. Direct Square Variation:** $y = kx^2$, $\dfrac{y_2}{y_1} = \left(\dfrac{x_2}{x_1}\right)^2$

Rule 1. If $y = kx^2$, then y varies directly as the square of x. Here, if a value of x is multiplied by a number, then the corresponding value of y is multiplied by the square of that number.

Thus: The surface of a cube equals six times the square of its edge; that is, $S = 6e^2$. For a cube, S varies directly as the square of e. If e is doubled, S is quadrupled.

> **2. Inverse Square Variation:** $y = \dfrac{k}{x^2}$, $\dfrac{y_2}{y_1} = \left(\dfrac{x_1}{x_2}\right)^2$

Rule 2. If $y = \dfrac{k}{x^2}$, then y varies inversely as the square of x. Here, if a value of x is multiplied by a number, then the corresponding value of y is divided by the square of that number.

Thus: If $I = \dfrac{5}{d^2}$, I varies inversely as the square of d. If d is tripled, I is divided by 9.

> **3. Direct Cube Variation:** $y = kx^3$, $\dfrac{y_2}{y_1} = \left(\dfrac{x_2}{x_1}\right)^3$

Rule 3. If $y = kx^3$, then y varies directly as the cube of x. Here, if a value of x is multiplied by a number, then the corresponding value of y is multiplied by the cube of that number.

Thus: The volume of a sphere equals $\frac{4}{3}\pi$ times the cube of its radius; that is, $V = \frac{4}{3}\pi R^3$. For a sphere, the volume varies as the cube of its radius. If R is multiplied by 3, V is multiplied by 27.

5.1. Multiplication and Division in Power Variation

Complete each:

a) If $A = \pi R^2$ and R is multiplied by 5, then (   ).
b) If $V = \frac{4}{3}\pi R^3$ and R is divided by 2, then (   ).
c) If $F = \frac{k}{d^2}$ and d is doubled, then (   ).

Solutions:

    a) Using **Rule 1**, A is multiplied by 5^2 or 25.
    b) Using **Rule 3**, V is divided by 2^3 or 8.
    c) Using **Rule 2**, F is divided by 4 or multiplied by $\frac{1}{4}$.

5.2. Direct Square Variation in Problem Solving

After the brakes have been applied, the distance an automobile goes before stopping varies directly as the square of its speed. For an auto going 30 mph, the stopping distance is 27 ft. What is the stopping distance of an auto going 50 mph?

Solution:

	(ft.) Stopping Distance (D)	(mph) Speed (R)
2nd stop	D $\boxed{\frac{25}{9}}$	50 $\boxed{\frac{5}{3}}$
1st stop	27	30

Proportion Method

Since distance varies directly as the square of speed,

$$\frac{D_2}{D_1} = \left(\frac{R_2}{R_1}\right)^2, \quad \frac{D}{27} = \left(\frac{50}{30}\right)^2 = \frac{25}{9}$$

$$D = \frac{25}{9}(27) = 75 \quad Ans.\ 75\,\text{ft.}$$

Ratio Method (*Note how the ratios are included in the table.*)

If the second speed is $\frac{5}{3}$ of the first speed, then the second distance is $\frac{25}{9}$ of the first. Hence, $D = \frac{25}{9}(27) = 75.$ *Ans.* 75 ft.

5.3. Applying Inverse Square Variation to Illumination

The intensity of light on a surface varies inversely as the square of the distance from a pin-point source. If the distance from the source changes from $2\frac{1}{2}$ ft. to $7\frac{1}{2}$ ft., how many times as bright will the intensity become?

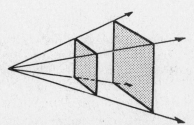

Solution:

	(ft.) Distance (D)	(light units) Intensity (I)
2nd	$D_2 = 7\frac{1}{2}$ $\boxed{\frac{3}{1}}$	I_2 $\boxed{\frac{1}{9}}$
1st	$D_1 = 2\frac{1}{2}$	I_1

Since intensity (I) varies inversely as the square of the distance (D), then if D is multiplied by 3, I is divided by 9; that is, the intensity becomes one-ninth as bright.

Otherwise: $\dfrac{I_2}{I_1} = \left(\dfrac{D_1}{D_2}\right)^2 = \left(\dfrac{2\frac{1}{2}}{7\frac{1}{2}}\right)^2 = \dfrac{1}{9}$ or $I_2 = \dfrac{1}{9}I_1$

Ans. one-ninth

5.4. Finding Values of Variables in Direct Square Variation

If y varies directly as the square of x and $y = 9$ when $x = 5$, find y when $x = 20$.

Solution:

	x	y
2nd values	20 $\boxed{\frac{4}{1}}$	y $\boxed{\frac{16}{1}}$
1st values	5	9

Proportion Method

Since y varies directly as the square of x, $\dfrac{y_2}{y_1} = \left(\dfrac{x_2}{x_1}\right)^2.$

Hence, $\dfrac{y}{9} = \left(\dfrac{20}{5}\right)^2,$ $\dfrac{y}{9} = 16,$ $y = 144.$ *Ans.* 144

Ratio Method (*Note ratios included in the table.*)

If x is multiplied by 4, then y is multiplied by 16.
Hence, $y = 16(9) = 144.$ *Ans.* 144

5.5. Finding Values of Variables in Inverse Square Variation

If y varies inversely as the square of x and $x = 8$ when $y = 48$, find y when $x = 32$.

Solution:

	x	y
2nd values	32	y
1st values	8	48

(ratios shown: x: $\frac{4}{1}$, y: $\frac{1}{16}$)

Proportion Method

Since y varies inversely as the square of x, $\frac{y_2}{y_1} = (\frac{x_1}{x_2})^2$.

Hence, $\frac{y}{48} = (\frac{8}{32})^2$, $\frac{y}{48} = \frac{1}{16}$, $y = 3$.   *Ans.* 3

Ratio Method (*Note ratios included in the table.*)

If x is multiplied by 4, y is divided by 16.   Hence, $y = \frac{48}{16} = 3$.   *Ans.* 3

6. USING A SYMBOL TO SIMPLIFY VARIATION

The following is designed to further an understanding of the principles introduced in Sections 1 – 5. For this purpose a new symbol is introduced.

A New Ratio Symbol: $\overparen{+}x)$

If x varies from a value x_1 to a new value x_2, the ratio of the second value to the first may be symbolized as $\overparen{+}x)$; that is

$$\overparen{+}x) = \frac{x_2}{x_1} \qquad \text{Read } \overparen{+}x) \text{ as ``}x\text{-ratio''.}$$

Similarly, the symbol may be used for any variable-ratio. Thus, $\overparen{+}y) = \frac{y_2}{y_1}$; read $\overparen{+}y)$ as "y-ratio".

Understanding the New Symbol

$\overparen{+}x) = 2$ means that x is doubling in value. Compare this with $x = 2$ which means that x has a value of 2. Similarly, $\overparen{+}y) = 3$ means that y is tripling in value. In a motion problem, $\overparen{+}R) = 3$ and $\overparen{+}T) = 4$ mean that a speed is being tripled and a time of travel quadrupled. In such a case, $\overparen{+}D) = 12$; that is, the distance traveled is 12 times as far.

The Ratio of Any Two Values of a Constant Equals 1: $\overparen{+}k) = 1$

Since a constant remains fixed in value, the ratio of any two of its values must be 1.

Comparing the Meanings of $\overparen{+}x)$ and $\triangle x$: $\overparen{+}x) = \frac{x_2}{x_1}$ vs. $\triangle x = x_2 - x_1$

If x changes in value from 3 to 9, $\triangle x = 9 - 3 = 6$; that is, x becomes 6 more. In this case, $\overparen{+}x) = \frac{9}{3} = 3$; that is, x becomes three times as much.

Using the Ratio Symbol to Replace Factors

> In an equation or formula containing only factors,
> (1) replace each variable factor by its ratio, and
> (2) replace each constant factor by 1.

Thus, if $z = kxy$ and k is constant, then $\overparen{+}z) = \overparen{+}x)\overparen{+}y)$; that is, $\frac{z_2}{z_1} = \frac{x_2 y_2}{x_1 y_1}$.

If $V = \frac{4}{3}\pi R^3$, then $\overparen{+}V) = \overparen{+}R)^3$. Hence, if the radius of a sphere is made three times as large, its volume will be twenty-seven times as great.

347

SUMMARY OF THE VARIATION FORMULAS

Type of Variation	Formula of Variation	Formula Using Ratio Symbol	Formula Using Subscripts
Direct	$y = kx$	$(\to y) = (\to x)$	$\dfrac{y_2}{y_1} = \dfrac{x_2}{x_1}$
Inverse	$xy = k$	$(\to x)(\to y) = 1$	$\dfrac{x_2 y_2}{x_1 y_1} = 1$ (See note)
Joint	$z = kxy$	$(\to z) = (\to x)(\to y)$	$\dfrac{z_2}{z_1} = \dfrac{x_2 y_2}{x_1 y_1}$
Direct square	$y = kx^2$	$(\to y) = (\to x)^2$	$\dfrac{y_2}{y_1} = \left(\dfrac{x_2}{x_1}\right)^2$
Inverse square	$y = \dfrac{k}{x^2}$	$(\to y) = \dfrac{1}{(\to x)^2}$	$\dfrac{y_2}{y_1} = \dfrac{1}{\left(\dfrac{x_2}{x_1}\right)^2} = \left(\dfrac{x_1}{x_2}\right)^2$
Direct cube	$y = kx^3$	$(\to y) = (\to x)^3$	$\dfrac{y_2}{y_1} = \left(\dfrac{x_2}{x_1}\right)^3$

Note: When $\dfrac{x_2 y_2}{x_1 y_1} = 1$, we can readily obtain $\dfrac{x_2}{x_1} = \dfrac{y_1}{y_2}$ or $\dfrac{y_2}{y_1} = \dfrac{x_1}{x_2}$. From this it can be understood that in **inverse variation**, the ratios are **inversely equal**. On the other hand, in **direct variation**, the ratios are **directly equal**.

6.1. Expressing Formulas in Ratio Form. Express each formula in ratio form:

a) $A = \frac{1}{2}bh$ c) $V = LWH$ e) $E = \frac{1}{2}mv^2$ and m is constant

b) $A = 6e^2$ d) $V = \frac{4}{3}\pi R^3$ f) $F = \dfrac{kmm'}{d^2}$ and k, m and m' are constant

Solutions:

a) $(\to A) = (\to b)(\to h)$ c) $(\to V) = (\to L)(\to W)(\to H)$ e) $(\to E) = (\to v)^2$

b) $(\to A) = (\to e)^2$ d) $(\to V) = (\to R)^3$ f) $(\to F) = \dfrac{1}{(\to d)^2}$

6.2. Using the Ratio Symbol in Problem Solving

Complete each of the following:

a) If a man triples his speed and doubles his time, he will go (   ).

b) Quadrupling the radius of a circle multiplies the circumference by (   ) and the area by (   ).

c) Tripling the radius of a sphere multiplies the area by (   ) and the volume by (   ).

d) Applying $PV = k$, if pressure, P, is two-thirds as much, then volume, V, is (   ).

e) Applying $V = \frac{1}{3}\pi R^2 H$, if radius, R, is doubled and volume, V, is fixed, then height, H, is (   ).

f) Applying $V = \pi R^2 H$, if volume, V, is multiplied by 8 and height, H, is doubled, then radius is (   ).

Solutions:

	Formulas	Formulas in Ratio Form	Procedure
a)	$D = RT$	$(\downarrow D) = (\downarrow R)(\downarrow T)$	Given: $(\downarrow R) = 3$ and $(\downarrow T) = 2$ Hence, $(\downarrow D) = 3(2) = 6$ *Ans.* 6 times as far.
b)	$C = 2\pi R$ $A = \pi R^2$	$(\downarrow C) = (\downarrow R)$ $(\downarrow A) = (\downarrow R)^2$	Given: $(\downarrow R) = 4$ Hence, $(\downarrow C) = 4$ and $(\downarrow A) = 4^2 = 16$. *Ans.* Multiplies the circumference by 4 and the area by 16.
c)	$A = \pi R^2$ $V = \frac{4}{3}\pi R^3$	$(\downarrow A) = (\downarrow R)^2$ $(\downarrow V) = (\downarrow R)^3$	Given: $(\downarrow R) = 3$ Hence, $(\downarrow A) = 3^2 = 9$ and $(\downarrow V) = 3^3 = 27$. *Ans.* Multiplies the area by 9 and the volume by 27.
d)	$PV = k$	$(\downarrow P)(\downarrow V) = 1$	Given: $(\downarrow V) = \frac{2}{3}$ Hence, $\frac{2}{3}(\downarrow P) = 1$, $(\downarrow P) = \frac{3}{2}$. *Ans.* Three-halves as much.
e)	$V = \frac{1}{3}\pi R^2 H$	$(\downarrow V) = (\downarrow R)^2(\downarrow H)$	Given: $(\downarrow V) = 1$ and $(\downarrow R) = 2$ Hence, $4(\downarrow H) = 1$, $(\downarrow H) = \frac{1}{4}$. *Ans.* One-fourth as long.
f)	$V = \pi R^2 H$	$(\downarrow V) = (\downarrow R)^2(\downarrow H)$	Given: $(\downarrow V) = 8$ and $(\downarrow H) = 2$ Hence, $2(\downarrow R)^2 = 8$, $(\downarrow R)^2 = 4$, $(\downarrow R) = \sqrt{4} = 2$. *Ans.* 2.

SUPPLEMENTARY PROBLEMS

1. Using division, find the ratio which indicates the change in each variable and express this ratio in a sentence. **(1.1)**

    a) The speed of a plane changes from 200 mph to 100 mph.

    b) A salary changes from $50 per week to $60 per week.

    c) The length of a line changes from 2 ft. to 1 ft. 6 in.

    d) The price of a radio set changes from $100 to $175.

    e) John's monthly income remains at $275 per month.

    f) The bus fare changes from 25¢ to 40¢.

Ans. a) $\frac{1}{2}$; second speed is **one-half** of first.   *d)* $\frac{7}{4}$; second price is **seven-fourths** of first.

    b) $\frac{6}{5}$; second salary is **six-fifths** of first.   *e)* 1; second income **is equal to** first.

    c) $\frac{3}{4}$; second length is **three-quarters** of first.   *f)* $\frac{8}{5}$; second fare is **eight-fifths** of first.

2. Complete each: **(1.2)**
   a) If x is tripled, it will change from 7 to (   ) or from (   ) to 72.   *Ans.* 21, 24
   b) If y is multiplied by $\frac{3}{2}$, it will change from 12 to (   ) or from (   ) to 48.   *Ans.* 18, 32
   c) If z is divided by 5, it will change from 35 to (   ) or from (   ) to 75.   *Ans.* 7, 375
   d) If k which equals 5.7 remains constant, the new value is (   ).   *Ans.* 5.7
   e) If r is divided by $\frac{2}{5}$, it will change from 40 to (   ) or from (   ) to 30.   *Ans.* 100, 12

3. *(1)* Express each equation in the form, $y = kx$.   **(2.1)**
   (2) State the variables that vary directly as each other.

   a) $\frac{C}{R} = 2\pi$ c) $24 = \frac{P}{T}$ e) $V = \frac{1}{3}Bh$ when $h = 60$

   b) $8s = p$ d) $f = \frac{n}{d}$ when $d = 5$ f) $I = PRT$ when R and T are constant

   Ans. a) *(1)* $C = 2\pi R$, *(2)* C and R c) *(1)* $P = 24T$, *(2)* P and T e) *(1)* $V = 20B$, *(2)* V and B
          b) *(1)* $p = 8s$, *(2)* p and s d) *(1)* $f = \frac{1}{5}n$, *(2)* f and n f) *(1)* $I = kP$, *(2)* I and P

4. Complete each: **(2.2)**
   a) If $b = 5c$ and c is doubled, then (   ).   *Ans.* b is doubled.
   b) If $\frac{c}{d} = 1.5$ and d is halved, then (   ).   *Ans.* c is halved.
   c) If $h = \frac{7}{5}p$ and p is divided by 5, then (   ).   *Ans.* h is divided by 5.
   d) If $LW = A$, L is constant and W is multiplied by 7, then (   ).   *Ans.* A is multiplied by 7.
   e) If $NP = C$, $P = 150$ and C is multiplied by $3\frac{1}{2}$, then (   ).   *Ans.* N is multiplied by $3\frac{1}{2}$.

5. *(1)* Complete each statement. *(2)* State the formula to which direct variation applies.   **(2.3)**
   a) If the time of travel remains fixed, halving rate will (   ).
   b) Doubling the length of a rectangle which has a constant width will (   ).
   c) If one-third as many articles are purchased at the same price per article, then the cost is (   ).
   d) At the same rate of interest, to obtain three times as much annual interest, (   ).
   e) If the circumference of a circle is quadrupled, then its radius (   ).

   Ans. a) *(1)* halve distance. *(2)* $D = kR$ since $D = RT$ and T is constant.
          b) *(1)* double area. *(2)* $A = kL$ since $A = LW$ and W is constant.
          c) *(1)* one-third as much. *(2)* $C = kN$ since $C = NP$ and P is constant.
          d) *(1)* triple principal. *(2)* $I = kP$ since $I = PR$ and R is constant.
          e) *(1)* is quadrupled. *(2)* $C = 2\pi R$.

6. Find each missing value: **(2.4)**
   a) If y varies directly as x and $y = 10$ when $x = 5$, find y when $x = 15$.   *Ans.* 30
   b) If r varies directly as s and $r = 80$ when $s = 8$, find r when $s = 6$.   *Ans.* 60
   c) If L varies directly as A and $L = 6$ when $A = 21$, find L when $A = 28$.   *Ans.* 8
   d) If D varies directly as T and $D = 100$ when $T = 2$, find T when $D = 300$.   *Ans.* 6
   e) If N varies directly as C and $C = 25$ when $N = 10$, find C when $N = 16$.   *Ans.* 40

7. A pilot flew 800 mi. at 120 mph. In the same time   **(2.5)**
   a) how many miles would he have traveled at 150 mph?   *Ans.* 1000 mi.
   b) how fast must he go to fly 1200 mi.?   *Ans.* 180 mph

8. A motorist finds in traveling 100 mi. that he is consuming gas at the rate of 15 mi. per gal. If he
   uses the same number of gallons, find   **(2.5)**
   a) how far he could travel if gas were consumed at the rate of 12 mi. per gal.   *Ans.* 80 mi.
   b) the rate of consumption if he covers 120 mi.
                                                 Ans. 18 mi. per gal.

9. A salesman earned \$25 in commission when he sold \$500 worth of tools. If his rate of commission
   remains fixed,   **(2.6)**
   a) how much would his commission be if he sold \$700 worth of tools?   *Ans.* \$35
   b) how much must he sell to earn \$45 in commission?
                                              Ans. \$900

10. The annual dividends on $6000 worth of stock is $360. At the same dividend rate, what is the annual dividends on $4500?   *Ans.* $270   **(2.6)**

11. (*1*) Express each equation in the form, $xy = k$.   **(3.1)**
(*2*) State the variables that vary inversely as each other.

     a) $3LW = 27$ *d*) $f = \frac{n}{d}$ when $n = 25$

     b) $\frac{PV}{10} = 7$ *e*) $A = \frac{1}{2}Dd$ when A is constant

     c) $\frac{1}{y} = x$ *f*) $A = \pi ab$ when $A = 30$

  Ans. a) (*1*) $LW = 9$, (*2*) L and W *d*) (*1*) $fd = 25$, (*2*) f and d
         b) (*1*) $PV = 70$, (*2*) P and V *e*) (*1*) $Dd = k$, (*2*) D and d
         c) (*1*) $xy = 1$, (*2*) x and y *f*) (*1*) $ab = \frac{30}{\pi}$, (*2*) a and b

12. Complete each: **(3.2)**
  a) If $pv = 20$ and p is doubled, then (   ). *Ans.* v is halved.
  b) If $RT = 176$ and R is tripled, then (   ). *Ans.* T is divided by 3 or multiplied by $\frac{1}{3}$,
  c) If $240 = RP$ and P is multiplied by $\frac{4}{3}$, then (   ). *Ans.* R is divided by $\frac{4}{3}$ or multiplied by $\frac{3}{4}$.
  d) If $IR = E$, E is constant and I is divided by 15, then (   ). *Ans.* R is multiplied by 15.

13. (*1*) Complete each statement.   **(3.3)**
(*2*) State the formula to which inverse variation applies.

  a) For a fixed area, tripling the width of a rectangle (   ).
  b) Taking twice as long to cover the same distance requires (   ).
  c) If the pressure of an enclosed gas at constant temperature is reduced to one-half, then its volume (   ).
  d) Quadrupling the length of a triangle with a fixed area (   ).
  e) If the numerator remains the same, halving the denominator will (   ).

  Ans. a) (*1*) divides the length by 3. (*2*) $LW = k$ since $A = LW$ and A is constant.
         b) (*1*) half the rate.   (*2*) $RT = k$ since $D = RT$ and D is constant.
         c) (*1*) is doubled.   (*2*) $PV = k$ (*Boyle's Law*).
         d) (*1*) divides the height by 4. (*2*) $bh = k$ since $A = \frac{1}{2}bh$ and A is constant.
         e) (*1*) double the fraction.   (*2*) $fd = k$ since $f = \frac{n}{d}$ and n is constant.

14. Find each missing value: **(3.4)**
  a) If y varies inversely as x, and $y = 15$ when $x = 2$, find y when $x = 6$.   *Ans.* 5
  b) If t varies inversely as r, and $t = 15$ when $r = 8$, find t when $r = 24$.   *Ans.* 5
  c) If b varies inversely as h, and $b = 21$ when $h = 3$, find b when $h = 9$.   *Ans.* 7
  d) If R varies inversely as T, and $R = 36$ when $T = 2\frac{1}{2}$, find R when $T = 2$.   *Ans.* 45
  e) If P varies inversely as V, and $P = 12$ when $V = 40$, find V when $P = 10$.   *Ans.* 48

15. Two weights of 40 lb. and 48 lb. are in balance on a lever bar. If the 40 lb. weight is 15 in. from the fulcrum, how far is the 48 lb. from the fulcrum? Consider the weight of the bar as negligible. *Ans.* $12\frac{1}{2}$ in.   **(3.5)**

16. On a lever, a weight of 42 lb. is 20 in. from the fulcrum. Consider the weight of the bar as negligible.   **(3.5)**
  a) What weight could be balanced three times as far from the fulcrum? *Ans.* 14 lb.
  b) What weight could be balanced 5 in. nearer the fulcrum? *Ans.* 56 lb.
  c) At what distance from the fulcrum should a weight which is two-thirds as heavy be placed for balance? *Ans.* 30 in.

17. A gear having 60 teeth is meshed with one having 48 teeth.   **(3.6)**
    a) When the larger makes 28 revolutions, how many revolutions does the smaller make? *Ans.* **35**
    b) When the smaller makes 40 revolutions, how many revolutions does the larger make? *Ans.* **32**

18. Two pulleys are connected by the same belt. One pulley has a diameter of 16 in. and a speed of 450 rpm.   **(3.7)**
    a) If the diameter of the other pulley is 10 in., what is its speed? *Ans.* **720 rpm**
    b) If the speed of the other pulley is 360 rpm, what is its diameter? *Ans.* **20 in.**

19. (*1*) Express each equation in the form $z = kxy$.   **(4.1)**
    (*2*) State how the variables vary jointly.

    a) $3PT = 100I$ *Ans. a*) (*1*) $I = .03PT$, (*2*) I varies jointly as P and T.
    b) $2A = dD$ *Ans. b*) (*1*) $A = \frac{1}{2}dD$, (*2*) A varies jointly as d and D.
    c) $V = LWH$ and L is constant   *Ans. c*) (*1*) $V = kWH$, (*2*) V varies jointly as W and H.

20. Complete each: **(4.2)**
    a) If $A = \frac{1}{2}dd'$ and d and d' are each multiplied by 5, then (   ).   *Ans.* A is multiplied by 25.
    b) If $I = .03PR$, P is multiplied by 6 and R by $\frac{1}{2}$, then (   ).   *Ans.* I is tripled.
    c) If $V = 10WH$ and W and H are each halved, then (   ).   *Ans.* V is divided by 4.
    d) If $A = \pi ab$, a is quadrupled and b is divided by 4, then A is (   ). *Ans.* A remains constant.

21. Applying the rule, distance equals the product of rate and time, complete each of the following: **(4.2)**
    a) Take four times as long and double rate, then (   ).   *Ans.* distance is eight times as far
    b) Double time and triple rate, then (   ).   *Ans.* distance is six times as far
    c) Halve time and double rate, then (   ).   *Ans.* distance remains constant
    d) Double time and (   ), then distance remains constant.   *Ans.* halve rate
    e) (   ) and quadruple rate, then distance is twice as far.   *Ans.* halve time

22. Find each missing value: **(4.3)**
    a) If z varies jointly as x and y, and $z = 48$ when $x = 4$ and $y = 3$, find y when $z = 96$ and $x = 2$.
    b) If A varies jointly as b and h, and $A = 24$ when $b = 4$ and $h = 12$, find h when $A = 48$ and $b = 6$.
    c) If V varies jointly as B and h, and $V = 75$ when $B = 25$ and $h = 9$, find V when $B = 15$ and $h = 18$.
    Ans. a) 12, *b*) 16, *c*) 90

23. For each of the following, indicate the type of variation that applies: **(2.1, 3.1, 4.1)**

    a) $D = 45T$ *Ans.* direct   *e*) $S = 2\pi Rl$ *Ans.* joint   *i*) $y = \frac{2}{3}x$ *Ans.* direct

    b) $15 = RT$ *Ans.* inverse   *f*) $\frac{C}{D} = \pi$ *Ans.* direct   *j*) $\frac{x}{y} = 10$ *Ans.* direct

    c) $2\frac{1}{2}R = D$ *Ans.* direct   *g*) $15 = 2\pi rh$ *Ans.* inverse   *k*) $\frac{10}{y} = x$ *Ans.* inverse

    d) $RD = 7$ *Ans.* inverse   *h*) $A = \frac{1}{2}bh$ *Ans.* joint   *l*) $PV = kT$ *Ans.* joint

24. For each of the following, indicate the type of variation that applies: **(2.1, 3.1, 4.1)**
    a) $A = LW$ *Ans.* joint   *e*) $V = LWH$ when L is constant   *Ans.* joint
    b) $A = LW$ when L is constant   *Ans.* direct   *f*) $V = LWH$ when L and W are constant   *Ans.* direct
    c) $A = LW$ when W is constant   *Ans.* direct   *g*) $V = LWH$ when V and L are constant   *Ans.* inverse
    d) $A = LW$ when A is constant   *Ans.* inverse   *h*) $V = LWH$ when V and H are constant   *Ans.* inverse

25. Complete each: **(5.1)**
    a) If $A = 4\pi R^2$ and R is doubled, then (   ).   *Ans.* A is quadrupled
    b) If $V = 10\pi h^2$ and h is divided by 5, then (   ).   *Ans.* V is divided by 25
    c) If $S = 4e^3$ and e is quadrupled, then (   ).   *Ans.* S is multiplied by 64
    d) If $I = \frac{k}{d^2}$ and d is divided by 10, then (   ).   *Ans.* I is multiplied by 100

26. After the brakes have been applied, the distance an automobile goes before stopping varies directly as the square of the speed of the car. For a car going 20 mph, the stopping distance is 15 ft. **(5.2)**
 a) What is the stopping distance of the same car going 60 mph? *Ans.* 135 ft.
 b) What is the speed of the car when its stopping distance is 240 ft.? *Ans.* 80 mph

27. The energy of a moving body varies directly as the square of its speed. If a body has an energy of 50 units at a speed of 5 ft. per sec., **(5.2)**
 a) What is its energy at a speed of 10 ft. per sec.? *Ans.* 200 units
 b) What is its speed when its energy is 5000 units? *Ans.* 50 ft. per sec.

28. The amount of heat received by a body varies inversely as the square of its distance from a **(5.3)** source. How many times as much heat will be received if the body is moved to a point
 a) twice as far, b) one-third as far, c) four-thirds as far ?
 Ans. a) one-fourth as much, b) nine times as much, c) nine-sixteenths as much.

29. If y varies directly as the square of x, and $y=9$ when $x=6$, a) find y when $x=18$, b) find x when $y=36$. *Ans.* a) $y=81$, b) $x=12$ **(5.4)**

30. If y varies inversely as the square of x, and $y=36$ when $x=15$, a) find y when $x=30$, b) find x when $y=4$. *Ans.* a) $y=9$, b) $x=45$ **(5.5)**

31. Express each formula in ratio form: **(6.1)**

 a) $A = \frac{1}{2}bh$

 b) $A = \frac{1}{2}bh$ when b is constant

 c) $A = \frac{1}{2}bh$ when A is constant

 d) $V = LWH$

 e) $V = LWH$ when W is constant

 f) $V = LWH$ when V and L are constant

 g) $A = 4\pi R^2$

 h) $V = \frac{4}{3}\pi R^3$

 i) $V = \pi R^2 H$

 j) $V = \pi R^2 H$ when H is constant

 k) $E = \frac{1}{2}mv^2$

 l) $F = \dfrac{kmm'}{d^2}$ when k, m, and m' are constant

 Ans.

 a) $(A) = (b)(h)$

 b) $(A) = (h)$

 c) $(b)(h) = 1$

 d) $(V) = (L)(W)(H)$

 e) $(V) = (L)(H)$

 f) $(W)(H) = 1$

 g) $(A) = (R)^2$

 h) $(V) = (R)^3$

 i) $(V) = (R)^2(H)$

 j) $(V) = (R)^2$

 k) $(E) = (m)(v)^2$

 l) $(F) = \dfrac{1}{(d)^2}$

32. Complete each of the following: **(6.2)**
 a) If a man doubles his speed and triples his time, then he will go ( ).
 b) Tripling the radius multiplies the circumference by ( ) and the area by ( ).
 c) Applying Boyle's Law, $PV = k$, if the pressure of an enclosed gas becomes four-thirds as large, then the volume becomes ( ).
 d) Applying Newton's Law of Gravitation, $F = \dfrac{kmm'}{d^2}$, if the distance between two constant masses is doubled, then the force of attraction is ( ).
 e) If the stopping distance of a car varies directly as the square of its speed, then one who goes four times as fast will require a stopping distance ( ).

 Solutions:
 a) Since $D = RT$, $(D) = (R)(T)$. Hence, if $(R) = 2$ and $(T) = 3$, $(D) = (2)(3) = 6$.
  Ans. Six times as far.
 b) Since $C = 2\pi R$ and $A = \pi R^2$, then $(C) = (R)$ and $(A) = (R)^2$. Hence, if $(R) = 3$, then $(C) = 3$ and $(A) = 3^2 = 9$. *Ans.* Multiplies the circumference by 3 and the area by 9.

c) Since $PV = k$, $(\div P)(\div V) = 1$. Hence, if $(\div P) = \frac{4}{3}$, $(\div V) = \frac{3}{4}$.   *Ans.* Three-fourths as large.

d) Here, $(\div F) = \dfrac{1}{(\div d)^2}$. Hence, if $(\div d) = 2$, then $(\div F) = \dfrac{1}{2^2} = \dfrac{1}{4}$.   *Ans.* One-fourth as much.

e) Here, $(\div D) = (\div R)^2$ where D represents the stopping distance of the car and R its rate of speed. Hence, if $(\div R) = 4$, $(\div D) = 4^2 = 16$.   *Ans.* Sixteen times as long.

Chapter 18

Functions and Relations

1. UNDERSTANDING RELATIONS

A relation is a set of ordered pairs

Thus, the set $\{(2, 0), (1, 1), (0, 2)\}$ and the set $\{(a, 1), (e, 2), (i, 3), (o, 4), (u, 5)\}$ are relations.

Methods of Defining a Relation

A relation may be defined by (1) a rule, (2) a formula, (3) a table, and (4) a graph.

Thus, if a selection of three pens are made from a collection of red and black pens, the set $\{(3, 0), (2, 1), (1, 2), (0, 3)\}$ indicates the various ways in which a selection could be made, letting the first number of each ordered pair represent the number of red pencils selected and the second number, the number of black pencils selected. The defining of the relation between the red pens and the black pens can be done as follows:

1. **By a rule**: The sum of the number of red pens selected and the number of black pens selected is 3 and the numbers of such pens are whole numbers. (*A selection of a part of a pen must be ruled out.*)

2. **By a formula**: If x represents the number of red pens and y represents the number of black pens, then $x + y = 3$ and $x, y \in W$ where W is the set of whole numbers. In setbuilder notation, the formula is written as $\{(x, y): x + y = 3, x, y \in W\}$.

3. **By a table of values**:

Table of Values

(x, y)

(3, 0)
(2, 1)
(1, 2)
(0, 3)

4. **By a graph**: Since x and y are whole numbers, the graph of the relation, Fig. 1, consists of four points, each one of the points being the graph of one of the ordered pairs of the relation. A graph of this kind is a **lattice**.

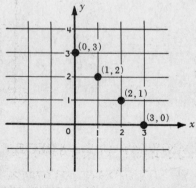

Fig. 1

If x and y are real numbers, the graph of $x + y = 3$ is the straight line in Fig. 2. In this case, the set (x, y) can include ordered pairs such as $(2\frac{1}{2}, \frac{1}{2})$, $(-\frac{1}{4}, 3\frac{1}{4})$, and $(\sqrt{2}, 3 - \sqrt{2})$.

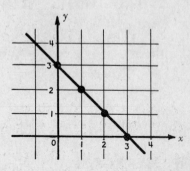

Fig. 2

Domain and Range of a Relation

The **domain of a relation** is the set of the first elements of its ordered pairs while the **range of a relation** is the

354

set of the second elements of the same ordered pairs.

Thus, with respect to the relation $\{(3, 0), (2, -1), (1, -2), (0, -3)\}$, the domain of the relation is the set $\{3, 2, 1, 0\}$ while the range of the relation is the set $\{0, -1, -2, -3\}$.

1.1. Stating the Domain and Range of a Relation

State the domain and the range of each of the following:

a) $\{(0, 0), (1, 1), (1, -1), (4, 2), (4, -2)\}$ b) $\{(0, 0), (1, 3), (2, 6), (3, 9)\}$
c) $\{(5, \sqrt{5}), (6, \sqrt{6}), (7, \sqrt{7})\}$ d) $\{(1, 75), (1, 80), (2, 80), (3, 85)\}$

Ans. a) Domain: $\{0, 1, 4\}$; Range: $\{0, 1, -1, 2, -2\}$ b) Domain: $\{0, 1, 2, 3\}$; Range: $\{0, 3, 6, 9\}$
c) Domain: $\{5, 6, 7\}$; Range: $\{\sqrt{5}, \sqrt{6}, \sqrt{7}\}$ d) Domain: $\{1, 2\}$; Range: $\{75, 80, 85\}$.

1.2. Listing the Ordered Pairs of a Relation Defined by a Formula

Using the replacement set $\{1, 2, 3, 4, 5\}$ for both x and y, list the set of ordered pairs (x, y) of the relation defined by each of the following:

a) $y = x + 1$,   b) $y = 4 - x$,   c) $y = 2(x - 3)$,   d) $y = x^2 + 1$

Ans. a) $\{(1, 2), (2, 3), (3, 4), (4, 5)\}$ b) $\{(1, 3), (2, 2), (3, 1)\}$
c) $\{(4, 2), (5, 4)\}$ d) $\{(1, 2), (2, 5)\}$

1.3. Listing the Ordered Pairs of a Relation Defined in Set-Builder Notation

Using the replacement set $\{-4, -2, 0, 2, 4\}$ for both x and y, list the set of the ordered pairs defined by each of the following:

a) $\{(x, y): x = -y\}$,   b) $\{(x, y): y = 2x\}$,   c) $\{(x, y): y = |x| - 2\}$,   d) $\{(x, y): y = x + 1\}$

Ans. a) $\{(-4, 4), (-2, 2), (0, 0), (2, -2), (4, -4)\}$,   b) $\{(-2, -4), (0, 0), (2, 4)\}$,
c) $\{(-4, 2), (-2, 0), (0, -2), (2, 0), (4, 2)\}$,   d) $\emptyset$, the empty set.

1.4. Defining a Relation by a Graph

If W represents the set of whole numbers, define each of the following relations by a graph:

a) $\{(x, y): x + y = 4, x, y \in W\}$,   b) $\{(x, y): y = 9 - 2x, x, y \in W\}$

Ans. a) **Table of Values**

(x, y)
$(0, 4)$
$(1, 3)$
$(2, 2)$
$(3, 1)$
$(4, 0)$

b) **Table of Values**

(x, y)
$(1, 7)$
$(2, 5)$
$(3, 3)$
$(4, 1)$

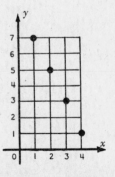

2. UNDERSTANDING FUNCTIONS

In accordance with the following definition, a function is a special kind of relation:

A function is a relation in which each first element of an ordered pair has one and only one second element.

Thus, $\{(1, 2), (1, 3)\}$ is a relation that is not a function while $\{(1, 2), (-1, 3)\}$ is a relation that is a function. Note in the relation $\{(1, 2), (1, 3)\}$ that the first element 1 has two different second elements.

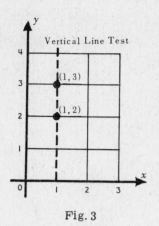

Fig. 3

Vertical Line Test of a Relation

In the case of a numerical relation that is not a function, a vertical line will pass through the graphs of two ordered pairs (Fig. 3), which will not occur in the case of a relation that is a function (Fig. 4).

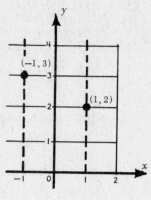

Fig. 4

In the following four graphs of sets of real numbers, the graphs in Fig. 5 and Fig. 6 are graphs of functions while the graphs in Fig. 7 and Fig. 8 are the graphs of relations that are not functions. Note in the case of the graphs of functions that no vertical line can cut the graph in more than one point.

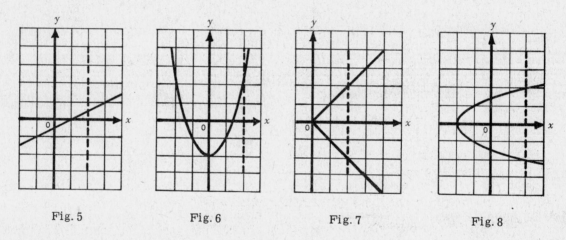

Fig. 5   Fig. 6   Fig. 7   Fig. 8

2.1. Selecting Relations That Are Functions

Which of the following relations are functions?

$a)$ $\{(3, 4), (-3, 5), (4, 5)\}$ $b)$ $\{(4, 3), (5, -3), (5, 4)\}$

$c)$ $\{(1, 2), (1, -2), (-2, 1)\}$ $d)$ $\{(2, 1), (-2, 1), (1, -2)\}$

Ans. $a)$ Function: The first number of every pair is associated with one and only one number.

     $b)$ Not a function: The first number 5 is associated with -3 and also with 4.

     $c)$ Not a function: The first number 1 is associated with 2 and also with -2.

     $d)$ Function: The first number of every pair is associated with one and only one number.

2.2. Determining the Relation Defined by a Graph, Its Domain and Its Range

For each of the following graphs, state the relation, and the domain and range of the relation:

$a)$

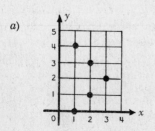

$b)$

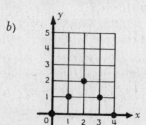

Ans. a) Relation: $\{(1, 0), (2, 1), (3, 2), (2, 3), (1, 4)\}$
    Domain: $\{1, 2, 3\}$ Range: $\{0, 1, 2, 3, 4\}$
  b) Relation: $\{(0, 0), (1, 1), (2, 2), (3, 1), (4, 0)\}$
    Domain: $\{0, 1, 2, 3, 4\}$ Range: $\{0, 1, 2\}$

2.3. Determining if a Relation Defined by a Graph Is a Function

Which of the following graphs defines a relation that is a function?
(How is the vertical line test used to provide an answer?)

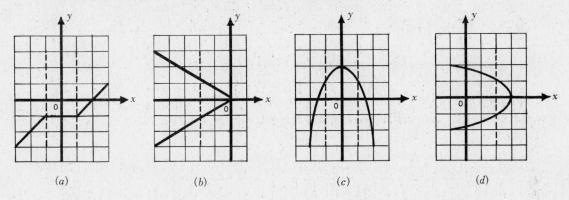

(*a*)   (*b*)   (*c*)   (*d*)

Ans. (*a*) and (*c*) Function: No vertical line meets the graph in more than one point.
    (*b*) and (*d*) Relation is not a function: Note the vertical line that intersects the graph in
each case in more than one point.

3. FUNCTION NOTATION

Arguments and Values of a Function

An **argument of a function** is a member of its domain while a **value of a function** is a member
of its range.

Thus, for the function $F = \{(2, 4), (3, 9), (4, 16), (5, 25)\}$ the arguments of F are 2, 3, 4, and
5; the values of F are 4, 9, 16, and 25.

Function Notation

The fact that any value of set F is the square of the corresponding argument of F can be
expressed in the following **function notation**:

$$f(x) = x^2, \text{ read, ``} f \text{ of } x \text{ equals } x\text{-squared''}.$$

Keep in mind that $f(x)$ is a notation, not a product of f and x.

In $f(x) = x^2$, an argument of F may replace x in order to obtain the corresponding value of F.
For example, if $x = 2$, then $f(2) = 2^2 = 4$ while if $x = 5$, then $f(5) = 5^2 = 25$. In this way, we obtain two ordered pairs of F, (2, 4) and (5, 25).

If set F is defined by $f(x) = 3x + 1$, we may determine the argument of F that corresponds
to a given value of F. For example, if 25 is a value of F, then since $f(x) = 3x + 1$, $3x + 1 = 25$.
Hence, $3x = 24$ and $x = 8$.

  Note. If the domain is not stated, the domain is understood to be the set of real numbers for
    which expressions in the rule are meaningful.

Thus, if $f(x) = \dfrac{3x + 1}{x - 2}$, then x may be any real number except 2.

3.1. Evaluating Given Functions

Find $f(10)$ if   a) $f(x) = x^2 + 3x + 4$,   b) $f(x) = x^3 - 250$,   c) $f(x) = \dfrac{x^2 + 5x}{3x - 20}$

Ans. a) 134. ($10^2 + 3(10) + 4 = 134$),   b) 750. ($10^3 - 250 = 750$),   c) 15. ($\dfrac{10^2 + 5(10)}{3(10) - 20} = 15$).

3.2. Evaluating a Given Function

If $f(x) = x^2 + 5$, find a) $f(2.5)$, b) $f(\sqrt{15})$, c) $f(x + 2)$.

Ans. a) 11.25. ($2.5^2 + 5 = 6.25 + 5 = 11.25$), b) 20. $[(\sqrt{15})^2 + 5 = 15 + 5 = 20]$
   c) $x^2 + 4x + 9$. $[(x + 2)^2 + 5 = x^2 + 4x + 4 + 5 = x^2 + 4x + 9]$.

3.3. Finding an Argument of a Given Function for a Given Value of the Function

a) Given $f(x) = 5x + 3$ and $f(x) = -2$. Find x.

b) Given $f(x) = x^2 + 4$ and $f(x) = 53$. Find x.

c) Given $f(x) = 20 + x - x^2$ and $f(x) = 8$. Find x.

Ans. a) -1 (Since $5x + 3 = -2$, then $5x = -5$ and $x = -1$)

   b) 7 or -7 (Since $x^2 + 4 = 53$, then $x^2 = 49$ and $x = \pm 7$)

   c) 8 or -4 (Since $20 + x - x^2 = 8$, then $x^2 - x - 12 = 0$. Hence, $(x - 8)(x + 4) = 0$ and $x = 8$ or -4.

4. CARTESIAN PRODUCT SETS

A **Cartesian product set** is a set consisting of ordered pairs of numbers obtained by selecting the first number of each ordered pair from one of two given sets and the second number from the other of the given sets. For example, if $A = \{1, 3\}$ and $B = \{2, 4, 6\}$ then the following Cartesian product sets are obtainable:

$$A \times B = \{(1, 2), (1, 4), (1, 6), (3, 2), (3, 4), (3, 6)\}$$
$$B \times A = \{(2, 1), (4, 1), (6, 1), (2, 3), (4, 3), (6, 3)\}$$

In the case of set $A \times B$, the first number is chosen from set A and the second from set B whereas in the case of $B \times A$, the first number is chosen from set B and the second from set A. $A \times B$ is read, "A cross B".

Cartesian product sets can be obtained by choosing both numbers of each ordered pair from a single set. Thus, if $A = \{2, 5, 8\}$, then

$$A \times A = \{(2, 2), (2, 5), (2, 8), (5, 2), (5, 5), (5, 8), (8, 2), (8, 5), (8, 8)\}$$

The number of ordered pairs in a Cartesian product set is the product of the numbers of members in each of the sets from which the numbers were chosen.

Thus, if A is a set of 5 members and B is a set of 3 members, then $A \times B$ has 15 members, $A \times A$ has 25 members, and $B \times B$ has 9 members.

Domain and Range of a Cartesian Product Set

In accordance with the definition of a Cartesian product set, the domain of $A \times B$ is set A and the range of $A \times B$ is set B.

Forming a Cartesian Product Set Using a Tree Diagram

The following diagram, called a "tree diagram" is useful in obtaining the ordered pairs of $A \times B$ from (for example) $A = \{1, 3, 5\}$ and $B = \{2, 4, 6\}$:

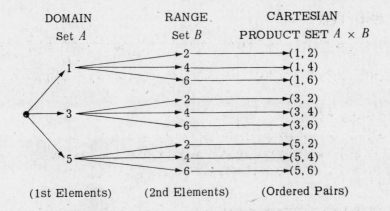

| DOMAIN | RANGE | CARTESIAN |
| Set A | Set B | PRODUCT SET $A \times B$ |

(1st Elements)   (2nd Elements)   (Ordered Pairs)

Graphs of Cartesian Products Sets

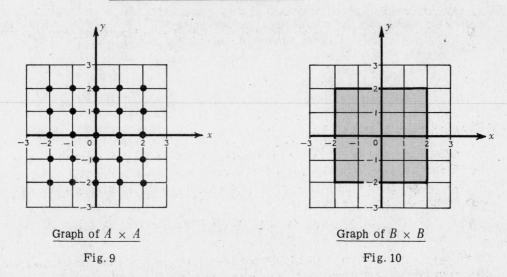

Graph of $A \times A$ Graph of $B \times B$

Fig. 9   Fig. 10

The graph in Fig. 9 is a lattice graph of $A \times A$ when $A = -2, -1, 0, 1, 2$. The graph consists of 25 points, each of which is the graph of an ordered pair in $A \times A$.

The shaded region in Fig. 10 is the graph of $B \times B$ when R represents the set of real numbers and $B = \{x: -2 \leq x \leq 2, \ x \in R\}$. Here, x is any real number between -2 and 2 and also including -2 and 2. Hence, the graph consists of the sides of the shaded square as well as its interior.

4.1. Forming Cartesian Product Sets

If $A = \{-2, 1, 4\}$ and $B = \{10, 20\}$, list the ordered pairs of each of the following:
 a) $A \times B$,   b) $B \times A$,   c) $A \times A$,   d) $B \times B$

Ans. a) $A \times B = \{(-2, 10), (-2, 20), (1, 10), (1, 20), (4, 10), (4, 20)\}$
 b) $B \times A = \{(10, -2), (10, 1), (10, 4), (20, -2), (20, 1), (20, 4)\}$
 c) $A \times A = \{(-2, -2), (-2, 1), (-2, 4), (1, -2), (1, 1), (1, 4), (4, -2), (4, 1), (4, 4)\}$
 d) $B \times B = \{(10, 10), (10, 20), (20, 10), (20, 20)\}$

4.2. Graphing Cartesian Product Sets

If $A = \{-3, -2, 1, 0, 1\}$ and B is the set of all real numbers between -3 and 1, including -3 but not including 1, graph $a)$ $A \times A$, $b)$ $B \times B$

Ans. $a)$ Lattice Graph of $A \times A$ $b)$ Graph of $B \times B$

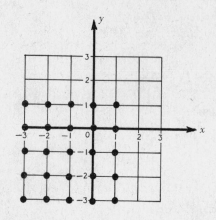
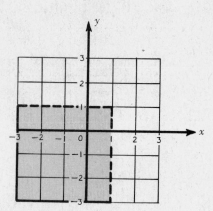

$a)$ The lattice graph of $A \times A$ consists of 25 points.

$b)$ The graph of $B \times B$ is the shaded interior of the square and the two full sides. Since $x \neq 1$, the sides in dashed line segments are not included in the required graph.

SUPPLEMENTARY PROBLEMS

1. State the domain and range of each of the following: **(1.1)**
    $a)$ $\{(1, 80), (2, 80), (3, 65)\}$,
    $b)$ $\{(5, \sqrt{5}), (9, 3), (13, \sqrt{13})\}$,
    $c)$ $\{(3, 3), (3, -3), (4, 4), (4, -4)\}$,
    $d)$ $\{(-1, 1), (-2, 1), (-3, 1), (-4, 1)\}$

Ans. $a)$ Domain: $\{1, 2, 3\}$; Range: $\{65, 80\}$, $b)$ Domain: $\{5, 9, 13\}$; Range: $\{\sqrt{5}, 3, \sqrt{13}\}$,
    $c)$ Domain: $\{3, 4\}$; Range: $\{-4, -3, 3, 4\}$, $d)$ Domain: $\{-1, -2, -3, -4\}$; Range: $\{1\}$

2. Using the replacement set $\{-1, 1, 3, 5\}$ for both x and y, list the set of ordered pairs (x, y) of the relation defined by each of the following: **(1.2)**
    $a)$ $y = x - 2$, $b)$ $y = |x| + 2$, $c)$ $y = \frac{1}{2}(x - 1)$, $d)$ $y = x^2 + 2$

Ans. $a)$ $\{(1, -1), (3, 1), (5, 3)\}$ $b)$ $\{(-1, 3), (1, 3), (3, 5)\}$ $c)$ $\{(3, 1), (-1, -1)\}$ $d)$ $\{(-1, 3), (1, 3)\}$

3. Using the replacement set $\{-3, -1, 1, 3, 5\}$ for both x and y, list the ordered pairs defined by each of the following: **(1.3)**
    $a)$ $\{(x, y): y > x + 4\}$, $b)$ $\{(x, y): y = 3x + 2\}$, $c)$ $\{(x, y): x + 2y = 3\}$, $d)$ $\{(x, y): y - x = 3\}$.

Ans. $a)$ $(-3, 3), (-3, 5), (-1, 5)$; $b)$ $(-1, -1), (1, 5)$; $c)$ $(5, -1), (1, 1), (-3, 3)$; $d)$ $\emptyset$

4. If E represents the set of positive even integers, define each of the following by a graph: **(1.4)**

   a) $\{(x, y): x + y = 10, \ x, y \in E\}$,   b) $\{(x, y): x + 2y < 14, \ x, y \in E\}$.

Ans. **Table of Values**   **Table of Values**

a)

(x, y)
$(2, 8)$
$(4, 6)$
$(6, 4)$
$(8, 2)$

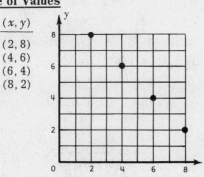

(x, y)
$(2, 2)$
$(2, 4)$
$(4, 2)$
$(4, 4)$
$(6, 2)$

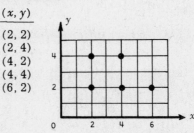

5. Which of the following relations are functions?   **(2.1)**

   a) $\{(0, 1), (0, 2)\}$ b) $\{(1, 0), (2, 0)\}$ c) $\{(-3, 1), (-3, 2), (-3, 3)\}$ d) $\{(1, -3), (2, -3), (3, -3)\}$

   e) $\{(1, 1), (\frac{1}{2}, 1), (\frac{1}{4}, 1), (-\frac{1}{4}, 1)\}$ f) $\{(-1, 1), (-2, 2), (-3, 3), (2, -1), (3, -3), (1, -1)\}$

   Ans. (b), (d), (e), and (f) are functions.

6. For each of the following graphs, state the relation, the domain and range of the relation, and whether the relation is a function: **(2.2), (2.3)**

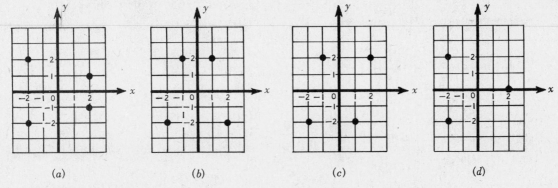

      (a)   (b)   (c)   (d)

Ans. a) Relation: $\{(-2, 2), (-2, -2), (2, -1), (2, 1)\}$; Domain: $\{-2, 2\}$; Range: $\{-2, -1, 1, 2\}$
      Relation is not a function.

    b) Relation: $\{(-2, -2), (-1, 2), (1, 2), (2, -2)\}$; Domain: $\{-2, -1, 1, 2\}$; Range: $\{-2, 2\}$
      Relation is a function.

    c) Relation: $\{(-2, -2\}, (-1, 2), (1, -2), (2, 2)\}$; Domain: $\{-2, -1, 1, 2\}$; Range: $\{-2, 2\}$
      Relation is a function.

    d) Relation: $\{(-2, -2), (-2, 2), (2, 0)\}$; Domain: $\{-2, 2\}$; Range: $\{-2, 0, 2\}$
      Relation is not a function.

7. Find $f(-1)$, $f(\frac{1}{2})$, and $f(10)$ if: **(3.1)**

      a) $f(x) = 2x^2$,   b) $f(x) = 2x + 2$,   c) $f(x) = 12 + x - x^2$

   Ans. a) $f(-1) = 2$, $f(\frac{1}{2}) = \frac{1}{2}$, $f(10) = 50$;   b) $f(-1) = 0$, $f(\frac{1}{2}) = 3$, $f(10) = 22$;   c) $f(-1) = 10$,
       $f(\frac{1}{2}) = 12\frac{1}{4}$, $f(10) = -78$.

8. If $f(x) = \dfrac{2\sqrt{x}}{3(x - 2)}$, find   a) $f(25)$,   b) $f(\frac{9}{4})$,   c) $f(y^2)$,   d) $f(x^2 + 2)$ **(3.2)**

   Ans. a) $\dfrac{10}{69}$,   b) 4,   c) $\dfrac{2y}{3(y^2 - 2)}$,   d) $\dfrac{2\sqrt{x^2 + 2}}{3x^2}$.

9. Find x if a) $f(x) = 3x - 5$ and $f(x) = 10$, b) $f(x) = x^2 + 3$ and $f(x) = 4$, c) $f(x) = x^2 - x$ and $f(x) = 30$, d) $f(x) = \frac{1}{2}x^2 + 3x$ and $f(x) = 8$. **(3.3)**

Ans. a) 5, b) 1 or –1, c) –5 or 6, d) –8 or 2.

10. If $R = \{1, 3, 5\}$ and $S = \{-\frac{1}{2}, 1\frac{1}{2}\}$, list the ordered pairs of each of the following: **(4.1)**

   a) $R \times S$, b) $R \times R$, c) $S \times S$, d) $S \times R$

Ans. a) $R \times S = \{(1, -\frac{1}{2}), (1, 1\frac{1}{2}), (3, -\frac{1}{2}), (3, 1\frac{1}{2}), (5, -\frac{1}{2}), (5, 1\frac{1}{2})\}$

   b) $R \times R = \{(1, 1), (1, 3), (1, 5), (3, 1), (3, 3), (3, 5), (5, 1), (5, 3), (5, 5)\}$

   c) $S \times S = \{(-\frac{1}{2}, -\frac{1}{2}), (-\frac{1}{2}, 1\frac{1}{2}), (1\frac{1}{2}, -\frac{1}{2}), (1\frac{1}{2}, 1\frac{1}{2})\}$

   d) $S \times R = \{(-\frac{1}{2}, 1), (-\frac{1}{2}, 3), (-\frac{1}{2}, 5), (1\frac{1}{2}, 1), (1\frac{1}{2}, 3), (1\frac{1}{2}, 5)\}$

11. If $S = \{-4, -2, 0, 2, 4\}$ and T is the set of all real numbers between –4 and 4, including 4 but not including –4, graph a) $S \times S$, b) $T \times T$. **(4.2)**

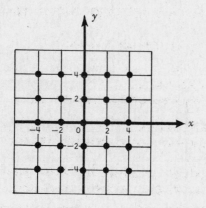

Lattice graph: 25 points.

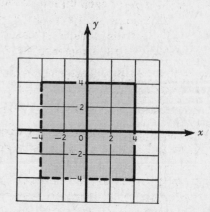

Graph consists of the interior of the square and the two sides that are full lines.

Chapter 19

Reviewing Arithmetic

1. REVIEWING WHOLE NUMBERS

A. Understanding Whole Numbers

(1) Whole numbers are the numbers used in counting and also zero.
Thus 3, 35 and 357 are whole numbers.

(2) Place-value of each digit of a whole number:
Depending on its **place in the whole number**, each digit of the number **represents** a number of units, tens, hundreds, thousands, and so on.
Thus in 35, 3 represents 3 tens; while in 357, 3 represents 3 hundreds.

(3) Reading whole numbers using place-value.
In reading a whole number, give place-value to its digits.
Thus, read 4444 as "four **thousand**, four **hundred**, forty (four **tens**) and four".

(4) Rounding off a whole number: approximate value of a number.
In rounding off a whole number to the nearest ten, replace the number by the multiple of 10 to which it is closest.
Thus, 37 to the nearest ten becomes 40. Here, 37 is between 30 and 40. However, 37 is closer to 40. Similarly round off a number to the nearest hundred, nearest thousand, etc.

Note. When a whole number is exactly halfway between two possible answers, round it off to the larger. Thus, round off 235 to the nearest ten as 240, not 230.

(5) An approximate value of a whole number is a value obtained by rounding off the whole number. Thus, 40 is an approximate value of 37.

(6) Estimating answers by using approximate values of whole numbers.

Estimate: a) 38×72 b) $\dfrac{4485}{503}$ c) $7495 - 2043$

Procedure:

	a)	b)	c)
1. **Round off** each number to a suitable multiple of 10, 100, etc.:	1. Round off 38 to 40, 72 to 70	1. Round off 4485 to 4500, 503 to 500	1. Round off 7495 to 7500, 2043 to 2000
2. **Perform** the indicated operation on the resulting **approximations**:	2. $40 \times 70 = 2800$	2. $\dfrac{4500}{500} = 9$	2. $\begin{array}{r} 7500 \\ -2000 \\ \hline 5500 \end{array}$
	Ans. 2800	*Ans.* 9	*Ans.* 5500

(7) Roman numbers.
Roman numbers: $M = 1000$, $D = 500$, $C = 100$, $L = 50$, $X = 10$, $V = 5$, $I = 1$. In calculating a Roman number, **add** if a smaller digit follows a larger one but **subtract** if a smaller digit precedes a larger.
Thus, $XI = 11$ but $IX = 9$; $MC = 1100$ but $CM = 900$.
Hence, $MCMLIX = M + CM + L + IX = 1000 + 900 + 50 + 9 = 1959$.

B. Terms Used in the Fundamental Operations

Addition, subtraction, multiplication and division are the four fundamental operations performed on numbers. The names used in each operation must be memorized. Note them in each of the following.

(1) Addition : Add 77 and 20.

<table>
<tr><td colspan="2" align="center">Terms Used in Addition</td><td></td><td></td></tr>
<tr><td>Addends are the numbers that are added.</td><td></td><td>Addend</td><td>77</td></tr>
<tr><td></td><td></td><td>Addend</td><td>+ 20</td></tr>
<tr><td>Sum is the answer obtained in addition.</td><td></td><td>Sum</td><td>97</td></tr>
</table>

(2) Subtraction : Subtract 20 from 77.

<table>
<tr><td colspan="2" align="center">Terms Used in Subtraction</td><td></td><td></td></tr>
<tr><td>Minuend is the number from which we subtract.</td><td></td><td>Minuend</td><td>77</td></tr>
<tr><td>Subtrahend is the number being subtracted.</td><td></td><td>Subtrahend</td><td>− 20</td></tr>
<tr><td>Difference is the answer obtained in subtraction.</td><td></td><td>Difference</td><td>57</td></tr>
</table>

(*The answer in subtraction may be called* **remainder**.)

(3) Multiplication : Multiply 77 by 20.

<table>
<tr><td colspan="2" align="center">Terms Used in Multiplication</td><td></td><td></td></tr>
<tr><td>Multiplicand is the number being multiplied.</td><td></td><td>Multiplicand</td><td>77</td></tr>
<tr><td>Multiplier is the number by which we multiply.</td><td></td><td>Multiplier</td><td>× 20</td></tr>
<tr><td>Product is the answer obtained in multiplication.</td><td></td><td>Product</td><td>1540</td></tr>
</table>

(*Numbers being multiplied are also* **factors** *of their product*.)

(4) Division : Divide 77 by 20.

<table>
<tr><td colspan="2" align="center">Terms Used in Division</td><td></td><td></td></tr>
<tr><td>Dividend is the number being divided.</td><td></td><td>Dividend</td><td>77</td></tr>
<tr><td>Divisor is the number by which we divide.</td><td></td><td>Divisor</td><td>20</td></tr>
<tr><td>Quotient is the answer obtained in division.</td><td></td><td>Quotient =</td><td>$3\frac{17}{20}$</td></tr>
</table>

(*Call the quotient a complete quotient to distinguish it from* 3, *the partial quotient*.)

Rule: Complete quotient = partial quotient + $\dfrac{\text{remainder}}{\text{divisor}}$

Thus, in $3\frac{17}{20}$ above, 3 is the partial quotient and 17 is the remainder.
Keep in mind, $3\frac{17}{20} = 3 + \frac{17}{20}$.

C. Checking the Fundamental Operations

(1) Add 25, 32 and 81. **Check** the addition.

Add either down the column or up the column. **To check addition, add** the col- in the reverse direction.

$$\text{Add down} \downarrow \begin{array}{r} 25 \\ 32 \\ 81 \\ \hline 138 \end{array} \uparrow \text{Check up}$$

(2) Subtract 32 from 85. **Check** the subtraction.

To check subtraction, add the difference and subtrahend. The answer thus obtained should be the minuend.

$$\begin{array}{r} 85 \\ -32 \\ \hline 53 \end{array} \qquad \begin{array}{r} \text{Check: } 53 \\ +32 \\ \hline 85 \end{array}$$

(3) Multiply 85 by 32. **Check** the multiplication.

To check multiplication, multiply the numbers after interchanging them.

$$\begin{array}{r} 85 \\ \times 32 \\ \hline 170 \\ 255 \\ \hline 2720 \end{array} \qquad \begin{array}{r} \text{Check: } 32 \\ \times 85 \\ \hline 160 \\ 256 \\ \hline 2720 \end{array}$$

(4) **Divide** 85 by 32. **Check** the division.

To check division, multiply the divisor by the partial quotient. To the result obtained, **add** the remainder. The final answer should be the dividend.

$$32 \overline{)85} \quad \begin{array}{r} 2 \text{ (Partial Quotient)} \\ 85 \\ 64 \\ \hline 21 \text{ (Remainder)} \end{array}$$

Check : 32
$\times 2$
64
$+ 21$
85

Ans. $2\frac{21}{32}$

2. REVIEWING FRACTIONS

A. Understanding Fractions

Proper and Improper Fractions

(1) A **proper fraction** is a fraction whose value is less than 1. In a proper fraction, the numerator is less than the denominator.

Thus, $\frac{5}{8}$ and $\frac{69}{70}$ are proper fractions. Each has a value less than 1.

(2) An **improper fraction** is a fraction whose value is equal to or greater than 1. In an improper fraction, the numerator is equal to or greater than the denominator.

Thus, $\frac{8}{5}$ and $\frac{15}{15}$ are improper fractions; $\frac{8}{5}$ is greater than 1, and $\frac{15}{15}$ equals 1.

(3) The **terms of a fraction** are its numerator and denominator.

Thus, the terms of $\frac{25}{30}$ are 25 and 30.

(4) **Equivalent fractions** are fractions having the same value.

Thus, $\frac{1}{5}$, $\frac{2}{10}$, $\frac{5}{25}$ and $\frac{20}{100}$ are equivalent fractions; that is, $\frac{1}{5} = \frac{2}{10} = \frac{5}{25} = \frac{20}{100}$.

B. Changing Forms of Mixed Numbers and Improper Fractions

(1) A **mixed number** equals a whole number plus a fraction. Thus, $17\frac{2}{5} = 17 + \frac{2}{5}$.

(2) **Changing a mixed number to an improper fraction.**

Change to an improper fraction: a) $17\frac{2}{5}$ b) $101\frac{2}{9}$

Procedure:

1. **Multiply** whole number by denominator:
2. **Add** numerator to product:

3. **Form fraction** by placing result over denominator:

Solutions:

1. $17 \times 5 = 85$
2. $\frac{+2}{87}$

3. *Ans.* $\frac{87}{5}$

1. $101 \times 9 = 909$
2. $\frac{+2}{911}$

3. *Ans.* $\frac{911}{9}$

(3) **To change an improper fraction to a mixed number,** divide the numerator by the denominator.

Thus, $\frac{87}{5} = 87 \div 5 = 17\frac{2}{5}$.

C. Changing a Fraction to an Equivalent Fraction

(1) **Fundamental Law of Fractions:**

To change a fraction to an equivalent fraction, multiply or divide both the numerator and denominator by the same number.

Thus, $\frac{2}{5} = \frac{2 \times 10}{5 \times 10} = \frac{20}{50}$.   In turn, $\frac{20}{50} = \frac{20 \div 10}{50 \div 10} = \frac{2}{5}$.

(2) **To raise a fraction to higher terms,** multiply its terms by the same whole number. Thus, when $\frac{2}{5}$ is changed to $\frac{20}{50}$, it has been changed to higher terms.

(3) **To reduce a fraction to lower terms,** divide its terms by the same whole number. Thus, when $\frac{20}{50}$ is changed to $\frac{2}{5}$, it has been changed to lower terms.

(4) **To reduce a fraction to lowest terms,** divide both numerator and denominator by the greatest common factor.

Thus, $\frac{20}{50}$ can be reduced to $\frac{10}{25}$, $\frac{4}{10}$ or $\frac{2}{5}$; but to reduce it to lowest terms, use $\frac{2}{5}$. To obtain $\frac{2}{5}$, divide terms by 10, the greatest common factor of 20 and 50.

(5) To change a fraction to a new specified fraction.

Change to new fraction: $a)\ \frac{3}{5} = \frac{?}{45}$ $\bigm|$ $b)\ \frac{3}{5} = \frac{45}{?}$

Procedure:

Solutions:

1. **Divide** new denominator by old denominator, or divide new numerator by old numerator:

    1. $45 \div 5 = 9$ 1. $45 \div 3 = 15$

2. **Multiply** the result by old numerator or old denominator:

    2. $\dfrac{\times 3}{27}$ 2. $\dfrac{\times 5}{75}$

3. **Form fraction** needed:

    3. $Ans.\ \frac{27}{45}$ 3. $Ans.\ \frac{45}{75}$

(6) To compare the size of fractions.

Compare $\frac{5}{9}$ and $\frac{7}{12}$

Procedure:

Solution:

1. **Change to equivalent fractions** having the same denominator. Use the least common denominator (**L.C.D.**). See page 261.

    1. **Change:** $\frac{5}{9} = \frac{?}{36}$ and $\frac{7}{12} = \frac{?}{36}$.

        Here, $\frac{5}{9} = \frac{20}{36}$ and $\frac{7}{12} = \frac{21}{36}$.

2. **Compare** new fractions:

    2. Since $\frac{20}{36}$ is less than $\frac{21}{36}$,

        then $\frac{5}{9}$ is less than $\frac{7}{12}$.

D. Multiplying and Dividing Mixed Numbers and Fractions

Multiply and divide as indicated: $a)\ 1\frac{1}{6} \div 1\frac{5}{9}$ $\bigm|$ $b)\ 1\frac{1}{7} \times 2\frac{11}{12} \div \frac{8}{9}$

Procedure:

Solutions:

1. **Change** mixed numbers to fractions:

    1. $\frac{7}{6} \div \frac{14}{9}$ 1. $\frac{8}{7} \times \frac{35}{12} \div \frac{8}{9}$

2. **Multiply** by each inverted divisor:

    2. $\frac{7}{6} \times \frac{9}{14}$ 2. $\frac{8}{7} \times \frac{35}{12} \times \frac{9}{8}$

3. **Divide** a numerator and a denominator by a common factor of both:

    3. $\dfrac{\overset{1}{\cancel{7}}}{\underset{2}{\cancel{6}}} \times \dfrac{\overset{3}{\cancel{9}}}{\underset{2}{\cancel{14}}}$ 3. $\dfrac{\overset{1}{\cancel{8}}}{\underset{1}{\cancel{7}}} \times \dfrac{\overset{5}{\cancel{35}}}{\underset{4}{\cancel{12}}} \times \dfrac{\overset{3}{\cancel{9}}}{\underset{1}{\cancel{8}}}$

4. **Multiply** the remaing factors in the numerator and denominator separately:

    4. $\frac{3}{2 \times 2} = \frac{3}{4}\ Ans.$ 4. $\frac{5 \times 3}{4} = \frac{15}{4}$ or $3\frac{3}{4}\ Ans.$

E. Adding and Subtracting Fractions

(1) Combining fractions having same denominator.

Combine: $a)\ \frac{5}{12} + \frac{11}{12} - \frac{7}{12}$ $\bigm|$ $b)\ \frac{15}{7} - \frac{3}{7} + \frac{2}{7}$

Procedure:

Solutions:

1. **Keep** the common denominator and add or subtract the numerator as indicated:

    1. $\frac{5 + 11 - 7}{12}$ 1. $\frac{15 - 3 + 2}{7}$

2. **Reduce** result to the lowest terms:

    2. $\frac{9}{12} = \frac{3}{4}\ Ans.$ 2. $\frac{14}{7} = 2\ Ans.$

(2) Combining fractions having different denominators.

Combine: $\frac{5}{6} - \frac{7}{12} + \frac{23}{36}$

Procedure:

Solution:

1. **Change** the fractions to equivalent fractions having the same denominator, using the **L.C.D.**:

    1. **L.C.D.** $= 36$

        $\frac{30}{36} - \frac{21}{36} + \frac{23}{36}$

2. **Combine** the resulting fractions:

    2. $\frac{30 - 21 + 23}{36}$

3. **Reduce** to lowest terms:

    3. $\frac{32}{36} = \frac{8}{9}\ Ans.$

F. Adding and Subtracting Mixed Numbers

Add or subtract as indicated: $a)\ 15\frac{7}{8} + 9\frac{1}{4}$ $b)\ 15\frac{7}{8} - 9\frac{1}{4}$

Procedure: **Solutions:**

1. **Add** the fractions or **subtract** the fractions as indicated:

$$1.\quad 15\tfrac{7}{8} \rightarrow \tfrac{7}{8}$$
$$+\,9\tfrac{1}{4} \rightarrow \tfrac{2}{8}$$
$$\overline{1\tfrac{1}{8}}$$

$$1.\quad 15\tfrac{7}{8} \rightarrow \tfrac{7}{8}$$
$$-\,9\tfrac{1}{4} \rightarrow \tfrac{2}{8}$$
$$\overline{\tfrac{5}{8}}$$

2. **Add** the whole numbers or **subtract** the whole numbers as indicated:

$$2.\quad 15$$
$$+\,9$$

$$2.\quad 15$$
$$-\,9$$

3. **Add** both results:

$$3.\quad 24 + 1\tfrac{1}{8}$$
$$25\tfrac{1}{8}\ Ans.$$

$$3.\quad 6 + \tfrac{5}{8}$$
$$6\tfrac{5}{8}\ Ans.$$

Here are the complete solutions of (*a*) and (*b*) above!

$$a)\ 15\tfrac{7}{8} \rightarrow \tfrac{7}{8}$$
$$+\,9\tfrac{1}{4} \rightarrow \tfrac{2}{8}$$
$$\overline{24 + 1\tfrac{1}{8}}$$
$$25\tfrac{1}{8}\ Ans.$$

$$b)\ 15\tfrac{7}{8} \rightarrow \tfrac{7}{8}$$
$$-\,9\tfrac{1}{4} \rightarrow \tfrac{2}{8}$$
$$\overline{6 + \tfrac{5}{8}}$$
$$6\tfrac{5}{8}\ Ans.$$

Note: When the fraction of the minuend is smaller than the fraction of the fraction of the subtrahend, borrow one unit from the minuend to increase the smaller fraction.

Thus, $5\frac{2}{7} - 1\frac{5}{7} = 4\frac{9}{7} - 1\frac{5}{7} = 3\frac{4}{7}$.

$$5\tfrac{2}{7} = 4\tfrac{9}{7}$$
$$-\,1\tfrac{5}{7} = -1\tfrac{5}{7}$$
$$\overline{3\tfrac{4}{7}}$$

3. REVIEWING DECIMALS

A. Understanding Decimals

(1) **A decimal or decimal fraction** is a fraction whose denominator is 10, 100, 1000 or some other power of 10.

Thus, $\frac{3}{100}$ may be written in decimal form as .03 .

(2) **Rounding off a decimal: approximate value of a decimal** .

In rounding off a decimal to the nearest tenth, replace the decimal by the tenth to which it is closest. Thus, .37 to the nearest tenth becomes .4. Here, .37 is between .30 and .40. However, .37 is closer to .40 or .4.

Similarly, round off a decimal to the nearest hundredth, nearest thousandth, and so on.

Note. When a decimal is exactly halfway between two possible answers, round it off to the larger. Thus, round off .25 to the nearest tenth as .3, not .2.

(3) **An approximate value of a decimal** is a value obtained by rounding off the decimal.

Thus, .4 is an approximate value of .37.

(4) **To estimate answers** of exercises or problems involving decimals, use rounded off values of these decimals.

Thus, to estimate $.38 \times .72$, round off to $.4 \times .7$ and use .28 as the estimated answer.

B. Changing Forms of Fractions and Decimals

(1) **To change a common fraction to a decimal fraction**, divide the numerator by the denominator. Carry the answer to the desired number of places if a remainder exists.

Thus, $\frac{3}{8} = \frac{3.000}{8} = .375$, $\frac{5}{16} = \frac{5.0000}{16} = .3125$.

Equivalent Fractions and Decimals

$\frac{1}{2} = .5$	$\frac{1}{3} = .33\frac{1}{3}$	$\frac{1}{8} = .125$	$\frac{1}{5} = .2$	$\frac{1}{7} = .14\frac{2}{7}$
$\frac{1}{4} = .25$	$\frac{2}{3} = .66\frac{2}{3}$	$\frac{3}{8} = .375$	$\frac{2}{5} = .4$	$\frac{1}{9} = .11\frac{1}{9}$
$\frac{3}{4} = .75$	$\frac{1}{6} = .16\frac{2}{3}$	$\frac{5}{8} = .625$	$\frac{3}{5} = .6$	$\frac{1}{12} = .08\frac{1}{3}$
$\frac{1}{10} = .1$	$\frac{5}{6} = .83\frac{1}{3}$	$\frac{7}{8} = .875$	$\frac{4}{5} = .8$	$\frac{1}{16} = .06\frac{1}{4}$

(2) **To change a decimal fraction to a common fraction,** change the decimal to a common fraction and reduce to lowest terms.
Thus, $.65 = \frac{65}{100} = \frac{13}{20}$.

C. Adding and Subtracting Decimals

Procedure:

1. Arrange the decimals vertically with decimal points directly under each other:

2. **Add or subtract** as in whole numbers, placing the decimal point in the result directly under the other decimal points:

a) Add 1.35 and .952
Solutions:

1. $\begin{array}{r} 1.35 \\ +\ .952 \end{array}$

2. 2.302

Ans. 2.302

b) Subtract .952 from 1.35

1. $\begin{array}{r} 1.350 \\ -\ .952 \end{array}$

2. .398

Ans. .398

D. Multiplying and Dividing Decimals

(1) Multiplying and dividing numbers by 10, 100, 1000 or some power of 10.

To multiply a decimal by a power of 10, move the decimal point as many places to the right as there are zeros in the power.

Thus, to multiply 5.75 by **1000**, move decimal point **three** places to the right.
Ans. 5750.

To divide a decimal by a power of 10, move the decimal point as many places to the left as there are zeros in the power.

Thus, to divide 5.75 by **1000**, move decimal point **three** places to the left.
Ans. .00575

(2) Multiplying Decimals

Procedure:

1. **Multiply** as in whole numbers:

2. **Mark off** decimal places in the product equal to the sum of the decimal places in the numbers multiplied:

Multiply: *a*) 1.1 by .05
Solutions:

1. $\begin{array}{r} \textbf{1.1}\ (\textit{one place}) \\ \times .05\ (\textit{two places}) \end{array}$

2. .055 (*three places*)

Ans. .055

b) 3.71 × .014

1. $\begin{array}{r} \textbf{3.71}\ (\textit{2 places}) \\ \times .014\ (\textit{3 places}) \\ \hline 1484 \\ 371 \end{array}$

2. .05194 (*5 places*)

Ans. .05194

(3) Dividing Decimals

Procedure:

1. **Move** the decimal point of the divisor to the right to make the divisor a whole number:

2. **Move** the decimal point of the dividend the same number of places to the right:

3. **Divide** as in whole numbers and mark off decimal places in the quotient equal to new number of places in the dividend:

Divide: *a*) .824 by .04
Solutions:

1. $\dfrac{.824}{.04}$

2. $\dfrac{.82\overset{\frown}{4}}{.04}$

3. $\dfrac{82.4}{4}$
= 20.6

b) 5.194 by 1.4

b) **Vertically Arranged**

$$\begin{array}{r} 3.7\ 1 \\ 1.4\ )\overline{5.1\ 9\ 4} \\ 4\ 2 \\ \hline 9\ 9 \\ 9\ 8 \\ \hline 1\ 4 \\ 1\ 4 \end{array}$$

Note. If a remainder exists, the quotient may be carried to additional decimal places by adding zeros to the dividend.

Thus, $\dfrac{1}{7} = \dfrac{1.0000000000000}{7} = .142857142857\frac{1}{7}$

4. REVIEWING PER CENTS AND PERCENTAGE

A. Understanding Per Cents and Percentage

Per cent means hundredths. The per cent symbol, %, is a combination of a 1 and two zeros. Thus, 7% of a number means .07 or $\frac{7}{100}$ of the number.

Rule. Percentage = Rate × Base

The **percentage** is the answer obtained when a per cent is taken of a number.
The **rate** is the per cent taken of a number.
The **base** is the number of which a per cent is being taken.
Thus, since 2% of 400 = 8, 8 is the percentage, 2% is the rate and 400 is the base.

B. Interchanging Forms of Per Cents, Decimals and Fractions

(1) Interchanging forms of per cents and fractions.

To Change a Per Cent to a Fraction

1. **Omit** the % sign.
2. **Divide** the number by 100.
3. **Reduce** to lowest terms.

Thus, $150\% = \frac{150}{100} = \frac{3}{2}$.

Also, $2\frac{1}{2}\% = \frac{5}{2} \times \frac{1}{100} = \frac{1}{40}$.

To Change a Fraction to Per Cent

1. **Add** the % sign.
2. **Multiply** the number by 100.

Thus, $\frac{3}{2} = (\frac{3}{2} \times 100)\% = 150\%$.

Also, $\frac{1}{40} = (\frac{1}{40} \times 100)\% = 2\frac{1}{2}\%$.

Equivalent Per Cents and Fractions

$\frac{1}{2} = 50\%$	$\frac{1}{3} = 33\frac{1}{3}\%$	$\frac{1}{8} = 12\frac{1}{2}\%$	$\frac{1}{5} = 20\%$	$\frac{1}{7} = 14\frac{2}{7}\%$
$\frac{1}{4} = 25\%$	$\frac{2}{3} = 66\frac{2}{3}\%$	$\frac{3}{8} = 37\frac{1}{2}\%$	$\frac{2}{5} = 40\%$	$\frac{1}{9} = 11\frac{1}{9}\%$
$\frac{3}{4} = 75\%$	$\frac{1}{6} = 16\frac{2}{3}\%$	$\frac{5}{8} = 62\frac{1}{2}\%$	$\frac{3}{5} = 60\%$	$\frac{1}{12} = 8\frac{1}{3}\%$
$\frac{1}{10} = 10\%$	$\frac{5}{6} = 83\frac{1}{3}\%$	$\frac{7}{8} = 87\frac{1}{2}\%$	$\frac{4}{5} = 80\%$	$\frac{1}{16} = 6\frac{1}{4}\%$

(2) Interchanging forms of per cents and decimals.

To Change a Per Cent to a Decimal

1. **Omit** the % sign.
2. **Move** the decimal point two places to the left.

Thus, $175\% = 1.75$.
Also, $12.5\% = .125$.

To Change a Decimal to a Per Cent

1. **Add** the % sign.
2. **Move** the decimal point two places to the right.

Thus, $1.75 = 175\%$.
Also, $.125 = 12.5\%$.

C. Percentage Problems (*See algebraic solution of these types on pages 33 to 36*)

Three Types of Percentage Problems

Types and Their Rules	Problems and Their Solutions	Problems and Their Solutions
(1) Finding Percentage **Rule. Rate × Base = Percentage**	*a*) Find 5% of 400. $.05 \times 400 = 20$	*d*) Find 30% of 80. $.30 \times 80 = 24$
(2) Finding Base **Rule. Base = $\frac{\text{Percentage}}{\text{Rate}}$**	*b*) 5% of what no. is 20 ? $\frac{20}{.05} = \frac{2000}{5} = 400$	*e*) 30% of what no. is 24 ? $\frac{24}{.30} = \frac{240}{3} = 80$
(3) Finding Rate **Rule. Rate = $\frac{\text{Percentage}}{\text{Base}}$**	*c*) 20 is what % of 400 ? $\frac{20}{400} = \frac{1}{20} = .05 = 5\%$	*f*) 24 is what % of 80 ? $\frac{24}{80} = \frac{3}{10} = .3 = 30\%$

Table of Approximate Square Roots

N	√N	N	√N	N	√N	N	√N	N	√N
1	1.000	51	7.141	101	10.05	151	12.29	201	14.18
2	1.414	52	7.211	102	10.10	152	12.33	202	14.21
3	1.732	53	7.280	103	10.15	153	12.37	203	14.25
4	2.000	54	7.348	104	10.20	154	12.41	204	14.28
5	2.236	55	7.416	105	10.25	155	12.45	205	14.32
6	2.449	56	7.483	106	10.30	156	12.49	206	14.35
7	2.646	57	7.550	107	10.34	157	12.53	207	14.39
8	2.828	58	7.616	108	10.39	158	12.57	208	14.42
9	3.000	59	7.681	109	10.44	159	12.61	209	14.46
10	3.162	60	7.746	110	10.49	160	12.65	210	14.49
11	3.317	61	7.810	111	10.54	161	12.69	211	14.53
12	3.464	62	7.874	112	10.58	162	12.73	212	14.56
13	3.606	63	7.937	113	10.63	163	12.77	213	14.59
14	3.742	64	8.000	114	10.68	164	12.81	214	14.63
15	3.873	65	8.062	115	10.72	165	12.85	215	14.66
16	4.000	66	8.124	116	10.77	166	12.88	216	14.70
17	4.123	67	8.185	117	10.82	167	12.92	217	14.73
18	4.243	68	8.246	118	10.86	168	12.96	218	14.76
19	4.359	69	8.307	119	10.91	169	13.00	219	14.80
20	4.472	70	8.367	120	10.95	170	13.04	220	14.83
21	4.583	71	8.426	121	11.00	171	13.08	221	14.87
22	4.690	72	8.485	122	11.05	172	13.11	222	14.90
23	4.796	73	8.544	123	11.09	173	13.15	223	14.93
24	4.899	74	8.602	124	11.14	174	13.19	224	14.97
25	5.000	75	8.660	125	11.18	175	13.23	225	15.00
26	5.099	76	8.718	126	11.22	176	13.27	226	15.03
27	5.196	77	8.775	127	11.27	177	13.30	227	15.07
28	5.292	78	8.832	128	11.31	178	13.34	228	15.10
29	5.385	79	8.888	129	11.36	179	13.38	229	15.13
30	5.477	80	8.944	130	11.40	180	13.42	230	15.17
31	5.568	81	9.000	131	11.45	181	13.45	231	15.20
32	5.657	82	9.055	132	11.49	182	13.49	232	15.23
33	5.745	83	9.110	133	11.53	183	13.53	233	15.26
34	5.831	84	9.165	134	11.58	184	13.56	234	15.30
35	5.916	85	9.220	135	11.62	185	13.60	235	15.33
36	6.000	86	9.274	136	11.66	186	13.64	236	15.36
37	6.083	87	9.327	137	11.70	187	13.67	237	15.39
38	6.164	88	9.381	138	11.75	188	13.71	238	15.43
39	6.245	89	9.434	139	11.79	189	13.75	239	15.46
40	6.325	90	9.487	140	11.83	190	13.78	240	15.49
41	6.403	91	9.539	141	11.87	191	13.82	241	15.52
42	6.481	92	9.592	142	11.92	192	13.86	242	15.56
43	6.557	93	9.644	143	11.96	193	13.89	243	15.59
44	6.633	94	9.695	144	12.00	194	13.93	244	15.62
45	6.708	95	9.747	145	12.04	195	13.96	245	15.65
46	6.782	96	9.798	146	12.08	196	14.00	246	15.68
47	6.856	97	9.849	147	12.12	197	14.04	247	15.72
48	6.928	98	9.899	148	12.17	198	14.07	248	15.75
49	7.000	99	9.950	149	12.21	199	14.11	249	15.78
50	7.071	100	10.00	150	12.25	200	14.14	250	15.81

N	√N	N	√N	N	√N	N	√N	N	√N
251	15.84	301	17.35	351	18.73	401	20.02	451	21.24
252	15.87	302	17.38	352	18.76	402	20.05	452	21.26
253	15.91	303	17.41	353	18.79	403	20.07	453	21.28
254	15.94	304	17.44	354	18.81	404	20.10	454	21.31
255	15.97	305	17.46	355	18.84	405	20.12	455	21.33
256	16.00	306	17.49	356	18.87	406	20.15	456	21.35
257	16.03	307	17.52	357	18.89	407	20.17	457	21.38
258	16.06	308	17.55	358	18.92	408	20.20	458	21.40
259	16.09	309	17.58	359	18.95	409	20.22	459	21.42
260	16.12	310	17.61	360	18.97	410	20.25	460	21.45
261	16.16	311	17.64	361	19.00	411	20.27	461	21.47
262	16.19	312	17.66	362	19.03	412	20.30	462	21.49
263	16.22	313	17.69	363	19.05	413	20.32	463	21.52
264	16.25	314	17.72	364	19.08	414	20.35	464	21.54
265	16.28	315	17.75	365	19.10	415	20.37	465	21.56
266	16.31	316	17.78	366	19.13	416	20.40	466	21.59
267	16.34	317	17.80	367	19.16	417	20.42	467	21.61
268	16.37	318	17.83	368	19.18	418	20.45	468	21.63
269	16.40	319	17.86	369	19.21	419	20.47	469	21.66
270	16.43	320	17.89	370	19.24	420	20.49	470	21.68
271	16.46	321	17.92	371	19.26	421	20.52	471	21.70
272	16.49	322	17.94	372	19.29	422	20.54	472	21.73
273	16.52	323	17.97	373	19.31	423	20.57	473	21.75
274	16.55	324	18.00	374	19.34	424	20.59	474	21.77
275	16.58	325	18.03	375	19.36	425	20.62	475	21.79
276	16.61	326	18.06	376	19.39	426	20.64	476	21.82
277	16.64	327	18.08	377	19.42	427	20.66	477	21.84
278	16.67	328	18.11	378	19.44	428	20.69	478	21.86
279	16.70	329	18.14	379	19.47	429	20.71	479	21.89
280	16.73	330	18.17	380	19.49	430	20.74	480	21.91
281	16.76	331	18.19	381	19.52	431	20.76	481	21.93
282	16.79	332	18.22	382	19.54	432	20.78	482	21.95
283	16.82	333	18.25	383	19.57	433	20.81	483	21.98
284	16.85	334	18.28	384	19.60	434	20.83	484	22.00
285	16.88	335	18.30	385	19.62	435	20.86	485	22.02
286	16.91	336	18.33	386	19.65	436	20.88	486	22.05
287	16.94	337	18.36	387	19.67	437	20.90	487	22.07
288	16.97	338	18.38	388	19.70	438	20.93	488	22.09
289	17.00	339	18.41	389	19.72	439	20.95	489	22.11
290	17.03	340	18.44	390	19.75	440	20.98	490	22.14
291	17.06	341	18.47	391	19.77	441	21.00	491	22.16
292	17.09	342	18.49	392	19.80	442	21.02	492	22.18
293	17.12	343	18.52	393	19.82	443	21.05	493	22.20
294	17.15	344	18.55	394	19.85	444	21.07	494	22.23
295	17.18	345	18.57	395	19.87	445	21.10	495	22.25
296	17.20	346	18.60	396	19.90	446	21.12	496	22.27
297	17.23	347	18.63	397	19.92	447	21.14	497	22.29
298	17.26	348	18.65	398	19.95	448	21.17	498	22.32
299	17.29	349	18.68	399	19.97	449	21.19	499	22.34
300	17.32	350	18.71	400	20.00	450	21.21	500	22.36

Table of Approximate Square Roots

N	$\sqrt{N}$	N	$\sqrt{N}$
501	22.38	751	27.40
502	22.41	752	27.42
503	22.43	753	27.44
504	22.45	754	27.46
505	22.47	755	27.48
506	22.49	756	27.50
507	22.52	757	27.51
508	22.54	758	27.53
509	22.56	759	27.55
510	22.58	760	27.57
511	22.61	761	27.59
512	22.63	762	27.60
513	22.65	763	27.62
514	22.67	764	27.64
515	22.69	765	27.66
516	22.72	766	27.68
517	22.74	767	27.69
518	22.76	768	27.71
519	22.78	769	27.73
520	22.80	770	27.75
521	22.83	771	27.77
522	22.85	772	27.78
523	22.87	773	27.80
524	22.89	774	27.82
525	22.91	775	27.84
526	22.93	776	27.86
527	22.96	777	27.87
528	22.98	778	27.89
529	23.00	779	27.91
530	23.02	780	27.93
531	23.04	781	27.95
532	23.07	782	27.96
533	23.09	783	27.98
534	23.11	784	28.00
535	23.13	785	28.02
536	23.15	786	28.04
537	23.17	787	28.05
538	23.19	788	28.07
539	23.22	789	28.09
540	23.24	790	28.11
541	23.26	791	28.12
542	23.28	792	28.14
543	23.30	793	28.16
544	23.32	794	28.18
545	23.35	795	28.20
546	23.37	796	28.21
547	23.39	797	28.23
548	23.41	798	28.25
549	23.43	799	28.27
550	23.45	800	28.28
551	23.47	801	28.30
552	23.49	802	28.32
553	23.52	803	28.34
554	23.54	804	28.35
555	23.56	805	28.37
556	23.58	806	28.39
557	23.60	807	28.41
558	23.62	808	28.43
559	23.64	809	28.44
560	23.66	810	28.46
561	23.69	811	28.48
562	23.71	812	28.50
563	23.73	813	28.51
564	23.75	814	28.53
565	23.77	815	28.55
566	23.79	816	28.57
567	23.81	817	28.58
568	23.83	818	28.60
569	23.85	819	28.62
570	23.87	820	28.64
571	23.90	821	28.65
572	23.92	822	28.67
573	23.94	823	28.69
574	23.96	824	28.71
575	23.98	825	28.72
576	24.00	826	28.74
577	24.02	827	28.76
578	24.04	828	28.77
579	24.06	829	28.79
580	24.08	830	28.81
581	24.10	831	28.83
582	24.12	832	28.84
583	24.15	833	28.86
584	24.17	834	28.88
585	24.19	835	28.90
586	24.21	836	28.91
587	24.23	837	28.93
588	24.25	838	28.95
589	24.27	839	28.97
590	24.29	840	28.98
591	24.31	841	29.00
592	24.33	842	29.02
593	24.35	843	29.03
594	24.37	844	29.05
595	24.39	845	29.07
596	24.41	846	29.09
597	24.43	847	29.10
598	24.45	848	29.12
599	24.47	849	29.14
600	24.49	850	29.15
601	24.52	851	29.17
602	24.54	852	29.19
603	24.56	853	29.21
604	24.58	854	29.22
605	24.60	855	29.24
606	24.62	856	29.26
607	24.64	857	29.27
608	24.66	858	29.29
609	24.68	859	29.31
610	24.70	860	29.33
611	24.72	861	29.34
612	24.74	862	29.36
613	24.76	863	29.38
614	24.78	864	29.39
615	24.80	865	29.41
616	24.82	866	29.43
617	24.84	867	29.44
618	24.86	868	29.46
619	24.88	869	29.48
620	24.90	870	29.50
621	24.92	871	29.51
622	24.94	872	29.53
623	24.96	873	29.55
624	24.98	874	29.56
625	25.00	875	29.58
626	25.02	876	29.60
627	25.04	877	29.61
628	25.06	878	29.63
629	25.08	879	29.65
630	25.10	880	29.66
631	25.12	881	29.68
632	25.14	882	29.70
633	25.16	883	29.72
634	25.18	884	29.73
635	25.20	885	29.75
636	25.22	886	29.77
637	25.24	887	29.78
638	25.26	888	29.80
639	25.28	889	29.82
640	25.30	890	29.83
641	25.32	891	29.85
642	25.34	892	29.87
643	25.36	893	29.88
644	25.38	894	29.90
645	25.40	895	29.92
646	25.42	896	29.93
647	25.44	897	29.95
648	25.46	898	29.97
649	25.48	899	29.98
650	25.50	900	30.00
651	25.51	901	30.02
652	25.53	902	30.03
653	25.55	903	30.05
654	25.57	904	30.07
655	25.59	905	30.08
656	25.61	906	30.10
657	25.63	907	30.12
658	25.65	908	30.13
659	25.67	909	30.15
660	25.69	910	30.17
661	25.71	911	30.18
662	25.73	912	30.20
663	25.75	913	30.22
664	25.77	914	30.23
665	25.79	915	30.25
666	25.81	916	30.27
667	25.83	917	30.28
668	25.85	918	30.30
669	25.87	919	30.32
670	25.88	920	30.33
671	25.90	921	30.35
672	25.92	922	30.36
673	25.94	923	30.38
674	25.96	924	30.40
675	25.98	925	30.41
676	26.00	926	30.43
677	26.02	927	30.45
678	26.04	928	30.46
679	26.06	929	30.48
680	26.08	930	30.50
681	26.10	931	30.51
682	26.12	932	30.53
683	26.13	933	30.55
684	26.15	934	30.56
685	26.17	935	30.58
686	26.19	936	30.59
687	26.21	937	30.61
688	26.23	938	30.63
689	26.25	939	30.64
690	26.27	940	30.66
691	26.29	941	30.68
692	26.31	942	30.69
693	26.32	943	30.71
694	26.34	944	30.72
695	26.36	945	30.74
696	26.38	946	30.76
697	26.40	947	30.77
698	26.42	948	30.79
699	26.44	949	30.81
700	26.46	950	30.82
701	26.48	951	30.84
702	26.50	952	30.85
703	26.51	953	30.87
704	26.53	954	30.89
705	26.55	955	30.90
706	26.57	956	30.92
707	26.59	957	30.94
708	26.61	958	30.95
709	26.63	959	30.97
710	26.65	960	30.98
711	26.66	961	31.00
712	26.68	962	31.02
713	26.70	963	31.03
714	26.72	964	31.05
715	26.74	965	31.06
716	26.76	966	31.08
717	26.78	967	31.10
718	26.80	968	31.11
719	26.81	969	31.13
720	26.83	970	31.14
721	26.85	971	31.16
722	26.87	972	31.18
723	26.89	973	31.19
724	26.91	974	31.21
725	26.93	975	31.22
726	26.94	976	31.24
727	26.96	977	31.26
728	26.98	978	31.27
729	27.00	979	31.29
730	27.02	980	31.30
731	27.04	981	31.32
732	27.06	982	31.34
733	27.07	983	31.35
734	27.09	984	31.37
735	27.11	985	31.38
736	27.13	986	31.40
737	27.15	987	31.42
738	27.17	988	31.43
739	27.18	989	31.45
740	27.20	990	31.46
741	27.22	991	31.48
742	27.24	992	31.50
743	27.26	993	31.51
744	27.28	994	31.53
745	27.29	995	31.54
746	27.31	996	31.56
747	27.33	997	31.58
748	27.35	998	31.59
749	27.37	999	31.61
750	27.39	1000	31.62

Table of Natural Trigonometric Functions

Angle	Sine	Cosine	Tangent	Angle	Sine	Cosine	Tangent
1°	.0175	.9998	.0175	46°	.7193	.6947	1.0355
2°	.0349	.9994	.0349	47°	.7314	.6820	1.0724
3°	.0523	.9986	.0524	48°	.7431	.6691	1.1106
4°	.0698	.9976	.0699	49°	.7547	.6561	1.1504
5°	.0872	.9962	.0875	50°	.7660	.6428	1.1918
6°	.1045	.9945	.1051	51°	.7771	.6293	1.2349
7°	.1219	.9925	.1228	52°	.7880	.6157	1.2799
8°	.1392	.9903	.1405	53°	.7986	.6018	1.3270
9°	.1564	.9877	.1584	54°	.8090	.5878	1.3764
10°	.1736	.9848	.1763	55°	.8192	.5736	1.4281
11°	.1908	.9816	.1944	56°	.8290	.5592	1.4826
12°	.2097	.9781	.2126	57°	.8387	.5446	1.5399
13°	.2250	.9744	.2309	58°	.8480	.5299	1.6003
14°	.2419	.9703	.2493	59°	.8572	.5150	1.6643
15°	.2588	.9659	.2679	60°	.8660	.5000	1.7321
16°	.2756	.9613	.2867	61°	.8746	.4848	1.8040
17°	.2924	.9563	.3057	62°	.8829	.4695	1.8807
18°	.3090	.9511	.3249	63°	.8910	.4540	1.9626
19°	.3256	.9455	.3443	64°	.8988	.4384	2.0503
20°	.3420	.9397	.3640	65°	.9063	.4226	2.1445
21°	.3584	.9336	.3839	66°	.9135	.4067	2.2460
22°	.3746	.9272	.4040	67°	.9205	.3907	2.3559
23°	.3907	.9205	.4245	68°	.9272	.3746	2.4751
24°	.4067	.9135	.4452	69°	.9336	.3584	2.6051
25°	.4226	.9063	.4663	70°	.9397	.3420	2.7475
26°	.4384	.8988	.4877	71°	.9455	.3256	2.9042
27°	.4540	.8910	.5095	72°	.9511	.3090	3.0777
28°	.4695	.8829	.5317	73°	.9563	.2924	3.2709
29°	.4848	.8746	.5543	74°	.9613	.2756	3.4874
30°	.5000	.8660	.5774	75°	.9659	.2588	3.7321
31°	.5150	.8572	.6009	76°	.9703	.2419	4.0108
32°	.5299	.8480	.6249	77°	.9744	.2250	4.3315
33°	.5446	.8387	.6494	78°	.9781	.2079	4.7046
34°	.5592	.8290	.6745	79°	.9816	.1908	5.1446
35°	.5736	.8192	.7002	80°	.9848	.1736	5.6713
36°	.5878	.8090	.7265	81°	.9877	.1564	6.3138
37°	.6018	.7986	.7536	82°	.9903	.1392	7.1154
38°	.6157	.7880	.7813	83°	.9925	.1219	8.1443
39°	.6293	.7771	.8098	84°	.9945	.1045	9.5144
40°	.6428	.7660	.8391	85°	.9962	.0872	11.4301
41°	.6561	.7547	.8693	86°	.9976	.0698	14.3007
42°	.6691	.7431	.9004	87°	.9986	.0523	19.0811
43°	.6820	.7314	.9325	88°	.9994	.0349	28.6363
44°	.6947	.7193	.9657	89°	.9998	.0175	57.2900
45°	.7071	.7071	1.0000	90°	1.0000	.0000	

INDEX

Abscissa, 145
Absolute value, 46, 48; in equations, 177, 179-180; graphing equations involving, 179-180
Addends, 7, 364; literal, 7; numerical, 7
Addition, 1, 364; associative law of, 12; checking, 7, 364; commutative law of, 7; of decimals, 368; equality rule of, 30-1, 37-8; in equation solving, 37-8; of fractions, 260-2; inequality rule of, 104; as inverse of subtraction, 29; of monomials, 74; in order of operation, 14-15; of polynomials, 74-5; of radicals, 284-5; of signed numbers, 54-7; of square roots, 284-5; words denoting, 10
Additive identity, 4
Additive inverses, 54
Adjacent angles, 197-9
Age problems, 192-3
Algebraic representation of verbal statements, 4, 6, 10-2
Angle(s), 118-120; acute, 119; adjacent, 197-9; complementary, 197-9; of depression or elevation, 329-30; equal, 118; finding an, in trigonometry, 324-5; kinds of, 119; measure of, 118-20; obtuse, 119; pairs of, 197-9; reflex, 119; right, 119; straight, 119; sum of, of any triangle, 198-9; supplementary, 197-9
Approximation(s), 363-367
Arc(s), 121, 125
Area(s), 126-9
Argument, 357-8
Arithmetic, 363-9; checking operations in, 364-5; of decimals, 367-8; of fractions and mixed numbers, 365-7; of percents and percentage, 369; of whole numbers, 363-5
Arithmetic mean, 215-6
Ascending order, 74
Associative laws, 12-3
Average, 215-6
Axes of a graph, 144
Axis of symmetry of a parabola, 305

Bar, 77-9
Base(s), 17-18; in percentage, 369; of powers, 17-8
Binomial(s), 70: difference of two squares, 238; factors of trinomial, 240-4; product of, 237-9; square of, 241-2
Braces, 2, 77-8; as a group symbol, 77-8; for sets, 2
Bracket, 77-8

Cartesian plane, 144
Cartesian product set, 358-60; domain of, 358-9; range of, 358-9
Changing forms, of fractions and

decimals, 365-8; of mixed numbers and improper fractions, 365; of per cents, decimals, and fractions, 369
Checking, addition, 7, 364; addition of polynomials, 75; division, 365; division of polynomials, 83-4; equations, 27, 32-9; identities, 27; multiplication, 8, 364; multiplication of polynomials, 81-2; subtraction, 364; subtraction of polynomials, 76-7; verbal problems, 33, 37-8, 40-1, 187-189
Chord, 121
Circle, 121, 123-5, 128
Circumference, 121, 124-6
Closure, law of, 19
Coefficients, 16, 32-3; in quadratic equations, 297, 303; in trinomial, 240-1
Coin problems, 201-2
Combination problems, 213-4
Combining: areas, 129; like terms, 72-7; monomials, 72-7; signed numbers, 54-9; volumes, 132
Common denominator(s), 261-3
Common factor(s), 234-5
Commutative law(s), 7-9
Complementary angles, 197-9
Complete factoring, 243-4
Completing the square, 301-3
Complex fractions, 262-3
Complex numbers, 271
Composite number, 231
Compound sentence(s), 176-8
Cone(s), 116, 123; circular, 123; of revolution, 123
Conjunction(s), 2, 176-7
Consecutive integers, 190-2
Consistent equations, 170-1
Constant, 3, 336; of variation, 337-346
Coordinate(s), 48-9, 117
Coordinate geometry, 144-169
Cosine, 324
Cost problems, 203-4
Cross-products, 317-8
Cube, 17, 116, 122; perfect, 273
Cube root, 271
Cubic measure, 130-2; unit of, 130
Cylinder(s), 116, 123; circular, 123; of revolution, 123

Decagon, 120
Decimal(s), 367-8; as rational numbers, 273-7; repeating or terminating, 273-7
Degree, 118; of an equation, 93; of monomial, 70; of polynomial, 71
Delta form of slope rule, 155
Denominator, 250, 365; least common, 261-2; rationalizing the, 288
Dependent equations, 170-2
Descending order, 74

Diagonal, 316
Diameter, 121
Difference(s), 364; of two squares, 238; used to derive equations, 158-9; used to determine distances, 314, 316; used to find slope, 154-8
Digit(s), 3
Digit problems, 214-6
Direct variation, 337-9; cube, square, 344-5
Directed distance, 144
Directly proportional quantities, 337-9
Disjunction, 2, 176-7
Distance between two points, 314, 316; indirect measurement of, 311-3; by trigonometry, 328-330
Distributive law, 72-3, 81, 84
Dividend, 364
Divisibility, 232
Division, 1, 364; of decimals, 368; in fraction form, 250; of fractions, 259-60; as inverse of multiplication, 29; of polynomials, 84-6; of powers of same base, 82-3; of radicals, 286-7; rule of equality, 31-3; rule of inequality, 105-6; of signed numbers, 62-3; in solving equations, 32-3; in solving inequalities, 105-7; symbols of, 9; words denoting, 11; impossibility of, by zero, 9, 51-2, 272-3
Divisor, 231, 364
Dodecagon, 120
Domain, 3, 103, 354

English into algebra, changing verbal statements into algebraic expressions, 4, 6, 10-12; changing verbal statements into equations, 4, 6, 28; expressing addition and subtraction, 10; expressing multiplication and division, 11; in problem solving, 187-230; representing quantities by signed numbers, 46, 48, 60
Equation(s), 26; conditional, 26; consistent 170-1; containing absolute values, 179-80; containing parentheses, 97-8; dependent, 170-2; deriving from tables, 158-9; equivalent, 30; first degree in one variable, 93-101; first degree in two variables, 170-6; graphs of linear, 147-158, 170-2; graphs of quadratic, 304-6; inconsistent, 170, 172; literal, 102-3; quadratic, 297-310; radical, 289-90; roots of, 27; simple, 26-45; solving by equality rules, 29-41; systems of, 170-186; trigonometric, 324-330
Equilateral: polygon, 120; triangle, 121

Catalog

If you are interested in a list of SCHAUM'S OUTLINE SERIES send your name and address, requesting your free catalog, to:

SCHAUM'S OUTLINE SERIES, Dept. C
McGRAW-HILL BOOK COMPANY
1221 Avenue of Americas
New York, N.Y. 10020